Ceramic and Specialty Electrolytes for Energy Storage Devices

Volume II

Ceramic and Specialty Electrolytes for Energy Storage Devices

Volume II

Edited by
Prasanth Raghavan and Jabeen Fatima M. J.

CRC Press is an imprint of the
Taylor & Francis Group, an **informa** business

First edition published 2021
by CRC Press
6000 Broken Sound Parkway NW, Suite 300, Boca Raton, FL 33487-2742

and by CRC Press
2 Park Square, Milton Park, Abingdon, Oxon, OX14 4RN

© 2021 Taylor & Francis Group, LLC

CRC Press is an imprint of Taylor & Francis Group, LLC

Reasonable efforts have been made to publish reliable data and information, but the author and publisher cannot assume responsibility for the validity of all materials or the consequences of their use. The authors and publishers have attempted to trace the copyright holders of all material reproduced in this publication and apologize to copyright holders if permission to publish in this form has not been obtained. If any copyright material has not been acknowledged please write and let us know so we may rectify in any future reprint.

Except as permitted under U.S. Copyright Law, no part of this book may be reprinted, reproduced, transmitted, or utilized in any form by any electronic, mechanical, or other means, now known or hereafter invented, including photocopying, microfilming, and recording, or in any information storage or retrieval system, without written permission from the publishers.

For permission to photocopy or use material electronically from this work, access www.copyright.com or contact the Copyright Clearance Center, Inc. (CCC), 222 Rosewood Drive, Danvers, MA 01923, 978-750-8400. For works that are not available on CCC please contact mpkbookspermissions@tandf.co.uk

Trademark notice: Product or corporate names may be trademarks or registered trademarks and are used only for identification and explanation without intent to infringe.

Library of Congress Cataloging-in-Publication Data

Names: Raghavan, Prasanth, editor. | J, Jabeen Fatima M., editor.
Title: Ceramic and specialty electrolytes for energy storage devices / edited by Prasanth Raghavan and Jabeen Fatima M.J.
Description: First edition. | Boca Raton : CRC Press, 2021. | Includes bibliographical references and index.
Identifiers: LCCN 2020053547 (print) | LCCN 2020053548 (ebook) | ISBN 9780367701444 (hbk) | ISBN 9781003144816 (ebk)
Subjects: LCSH: Storage batteries--Materials. | Solid state batteries--Materials. | Electronic ceramics. | Electrolytes.
Classification: LCC TK2945.C47 C47 2021 (print) | LCC TK2945.C47 (ebook) | DDC 621.31/24240284--dc23
LC record available at https://lccn.loc.gov/2020053547
LC ebook record available at https://lccn.loc.gov/2020053548

ISBN: 9780367701444 (hbk)
ISBN: 9780367701567 (pbk)
ISBN: 9781003144816 (ebk)

Typeset in Times
by Deanta Global Publishing Services Chennai India

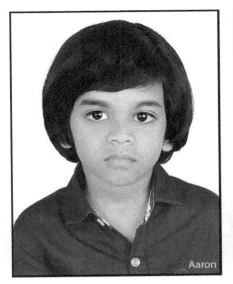

dedicated to
Aaron *and* **Ayaan**,
who are never going to read this book

Contents

Preface ix

Editors xi

Contributors xiii

Abbreviations xv

Chapter 1   Solid-State Electrolytes for Lithium-Ion Batteries: Performance
Requirements and Ion Transportation Mechanism in Solid
Polymer Electrolytes 1

*Jabeen Fatima M. J., Abhijith P. P., Jishnu N. S., Akhila Das,
Neethu T.M. Balakrishnan, Jou-Hyeon Ahn, and Prasanth Raghavan*

Chapter 2   Solid-State Electrolytes for Lithium-Ion Batteries: Novel
Lithium-Ion Conducting Ceramic Materials: Oxides
(Perovskite, Anti-Perovskite) and Sulfide-Type Ion Conductors 19

*Prasanth Raghavan, Abhijith P. P., Jishnu N. S., Neethu T. M.
Balakrishnan, Akhila Das, Jabeen Fatima M. J., and Jou-Hyeon Ahn*

Chapter 3   Solid-State Electrolytes for Lithium-Ion Batteries: Novel
Lithium-Ion Conducting Ceramic Materials: NASICON- and
Garnet-Type Ionic Conductors 51

*Prasanth Raghavan, Abhijith P. P., Jishnu N. S.,
Neethu T. M. Balakrishnan, Anjumole P. Thomas,
Jabeen Fatima M. J., and Jou-Hyeon Ahn*

Chapter 4   Polymer and Ceramic-Based Quasi-Solid Electrolytes for
High Temperature Rechargeable Energy Storage Devices 73

*Sajan Chinnan, Nikhil Medhavi, Akhila Das,
Neethu T. M. Balakrishnan, Leya Rose Raphael, Jishnu N. S.,
Jabeen Fatima M. J., Prasanth Raghavan*

Chapter 5   Quasi-Solid-State Electrolytes for Lithium-Ion Batteries 113

Hiren K. Machhi, Keval K. Sonigara, Saurabh S. Soni

vii

viii   Contents

Chapter 6   Electrolytes for High Temperature Lithium-Ion Batteries:
                 Electric Vehicles and Heavy-Duty Applications 139

                 *Leya Rose Raphael, Neethu T.M. Balakrishnan, Akhila Das,
                 Nikhil Medhavi, Jabeen Fatima M. J., Jou-Hyeon Ahn,
                 Prasanth Raghavan*

Chapter 7   Electrolytes for Low-Temperature Lithium-Ion Batteries
                 Operating in Freezing Weather 161

                 *Neethu T. M. Balakrishnan, Leya Rose Raphael,
                 Akhila Das, Jishnu N. S., Jou-Hyeon Ahn, Jabeen Fatima M. J.,
                 Prasanth Raghavan*

Chapter 8   Electrolytes for Magnesium-Ion Batteries: Next Generation
                 Energy Storage Solutions for Powering Electric Vehicles 177

                 *Akhila Das, Anjumole P. Thomas, Neethu T.M. Balakrishnan,
                 Jishnu N.S., Jabeen Fatima M. J., Jou-Hyeon Ahn,
                 Prasanth Raghavan*

Chapter 9   Aqueous Electrolytes for Lithium- and Sodium-Ion Batteries 193

                 Saurabh S. Soni and Jyoti Prasad

Chapter 10   Transparent Electrolytes: A Promising Pathway for Transparent
                 Energy Storage Devices in Next Generation Optoelectronics 217

                 *Anjumole P. Thomas, Akhila Das, Neethu T.M. Balakrishnan,
                 Sajan Chinnan, Jou-Hyeon Ahn, Jabeen Fatima M. J.,
                 Prasanth Raghavan*

Chapter 11   Recent Advances in Non-Platinum-Based Cathode
                 Electrocatalysts for Direct Methanol Fuel Cells 237

                 Bhagyalakhi Baruah and Ashok Kumar

Chapter 12   Platinum-Free Anode Electrocatalysts for Methanol
                 Oxidation in Direct Methanol Fuel Cells 261

                 Bhagyalakhi Baruah and Ashok Kumar

Chapter 13   Ionic Liquid-Based Electrolytes for Supercapacitor Applications 285

                 Bhuvaneshwari Balasubramaniam, Ankit Tyagi, Raju Kumar Gupta

Index 307

Preface

Since the commercialization of batteries began, energy storage systems have an ineluctable role in day to day life. In 1991, Sony introduced the first commercial lithium-ion battery, which was considered to be a milestone that led to the revolution of portable electronic gadgets such as cellular phones, laptops, tablets, etc. Today, a renewable source of electrical energy is being sought to replace fossil fuels, which has led to pollution and climate change. This initiative has forced the global market to focus more on electric vehicles. Energy storage devices are mainly comprised of lithium-ion batteries (LIBs), supercapacitors, and fuel cells. The performance of these storage devices is estimated using two main parameters: energy density and power density. The first parameter defines the amount of energy that can be stored in a given volume or weight, while the second parameter describes the speed at which energy is stored or discharged from the device. An ideal storage device should simultaneously deliver high energy density and high power density. The commercially available LIBs are capable of releasing high energy density, whereas supercapacitors release higher power density. The present research and development of new and innovative component materials are progressing to address the requirements of super gadgets. The ideal energy storage devices for long-range applications are still in their infancy, so there are still many materials left to explore.

Even though LIBs have already been widely used in different areas, they are still facing a lot of issues, including poor safety, short performance life, and relatively low specific energy. To address those issues, new battery formats, namely solid-state LIBs, have been developed. Mainly improving the efficiency of any storage device directly depends on the performance of its components, especially the behavior of electrodes and electrolytes on charging and discharging. Material selection is the primary concern in developing advanced energy storage applications. The electrolyte is considered to be the heart of the energy storage device, and its properties greatly affect the energy capacity, rate performance, cyclability, and safety of these devices. Because device portability is a major requirement, safety is a key concern, therefore, requiring the use of special electrolytic systems capable of replacing conventional liquid electrolyte systems. The organic chemicals used in the liquid electrolyte initiated the solid electrolyte interface formation at the anode of the LIBs, which, on continuous cycling, formed dendritic projections extending toward the cathode causing the devices to catch fire or explode.

The present book offers a detailed explanation of recent signs of progress and challenges in ceramic and specialty electrolytes for energy storage devices. The influences of electrolyte properties on the performances of different energy storage devices are discussed in detail. The detailed explanation has been classified under four major categories, which include a general introduction to energy storage devices and a history of lithium-ion batteries followed by a thorough investigation on ceramic solid and quasi-solid electrolytes and specialty electrolytes for energy storage devices. The book is organized into 13 chapters. Chapter 1 discusses solid-state electrolytes for LIBs. A detailed outlook on the performance requirements and ion transportation mechanism in solid polymer electrolytes is investigated. This is followed by a detailed review of solid-state electrolytes for LIBs. Chapter 2 covers solid-state electrolytes based on oxides (perovskite, antiperovskite) and sulfide-type ion conductor electrolytes for LIBs. Chapter 3 reviews solid-state electrolytes based on NASICON and garnet-type ionic conductors. The following two chapters discuss specialized energy storage devices and LIBs. The subsequent eight chapters are focused on specialty electrolytes, including electrolytes for high-temperature LIBs, low-temperature LIBs, and magnesium-ion batteries, which are investigated in detail. Apart from these, electrolytes for sodium-ion batteries, transparent electrolytes for energy storage devices, nonplatinum-based cathode electrocatalyst for direct methanol fuel cells, nonplatinum-based anode electrocatalyst for direct methanol fuel cells, and ionic liquid-based electrolytes for supercapacitor applications are investigated and described in detail in these chapters.

This book covers a wide range of ceramic and specialty-based electrolytes and includes useful information for the development of various electrolytes. We truly believe that this book will be very useful not only for researchers but also for engineers developing next-generation energy storage devices. As the battery industry has grown so much over the past 10 years, there have been a lot of new people coming into the battery world from other industries. So, whether you are looking to learn something about one aspect of energy storage devices to bolster your knowledge or are entirely new and are looking to learn all about the basics, this book will be an informative guide to add to your reference collection.

Prof. (Dr.) Rachid Yazami
Draper Prize winner 2014 for the development of LIBs

Editors

Prasanth Raghavan, PhD, is a Professor in the Department of Polymer Science and Rubber Technology at Cochin University of Science and Technology (CUSAT), India, and Visiting Professor in the Department of Materials Engineering and Convergence Technology at Gyeongsang National University, Republic of Korea, as well as Associate Faculty at Inter University Centre for Nanomaterials and Devices (IUCND), CUSAT, India. He earned his PhD in engineering in 2009, under the guidance of Prof. Jou-Hyeon Ahn, from the Department of Chemical and Biological Engineering at Geyongsang National University, Republic of Korea, under the prestigious Brain Korea (BK21) Fellowship. He completed his BTech and MTech from CUSAT, India. After a couple of years as a Project Scientist at the Indian Institute of Technology (IIT-D), New Delhi, he moved abroad for his PhD studies in 2007. His PhD research was focused on fabrication and investigation of nanoscale fibrous electrolytes for high performance energy storage devices. He completed his engineering doctoral degree in less than 3 years, a record that is still unbroken in the Republic of Korea. After earning his PhD, Dr. Raghavan joined Nanyang Technological University (NTU), Singapore, as a Research Scientist, in collaboration with Energy Research Institute at NTU (ERI@N) and Germany's Technische Universität München (TUM) CREATE, a joint electromobility research center between NTU and TUM, where he worked with Prof. (Dr.) Rachid Yazami, who successfully introduced graphitic carbon as an anode for commercial lithium-ion batteries and received the Draper Prize, along with Nobel laureates, Prof. (Dr.) John B. Goodenough and Prof. (Dr.) Akira Yoshino. After four years in Singapore, Dr. Raghavan worked as a Research Scientist at Rice University, Texas, USA, where he worked with Prof. Pulickal M. Ajayan, the co-inventor of carbon nanotubes, and 2019 Chemistry Nobel laureate Prof. J. B. Goodenough. Dr. Raghavan was selected for the Brain Korea Fellowship (2007); SAGE Research Foundation Fellowship, Brazil (2009); Estonian Science Foundation Fellowship, European Science Foundation Fellowship (2010); and Faculty Recharge, UGC (2015). He received many international awards including the Young Scientist Award, Korean Electrochemical Society (2009), and Bharat Vikas Yuva Ratna Award, (2016). He has developed many products, such as a high performance breaking parachute for Indian Defense, flex wheels for space shuttles, high performance lithium-ion batteries for leading portable electronic device and automobile industries, etc. He has a general research interest in polymer synthesis and processing, nanomaterials, green/nanocomposites, and electrospinning. His current research focuses on nanoscale materials and polymer composites for printed and lightweight charge storage solutions, including high temperature supercapacitors and batteries, recycling and waste management. He has published many research papers in high-impact factor journals and a number of books/book chapters and has more than 5000 citations and an h-index of 45 plus. Apart from science and technology, Dr. Raghavan is a poet, social activist, and a columnist in online portals and printed media.

Jabeen Fatima M. J., PhD, is a Research Scientist at the Materials Science and NanoEngineering Lab (MSNE Lab) in the Department of Polymer Science and Rubber Technology (PSRT) at Cochin University of Science and Technology (CUSAT), India. Before joining MSNE Lab, she worked as a guest Assistant Professor in the Department of NanoScience and Technology at University of Calicut, India. She earned her PhD in Nanoscience and Technology from the University of Calicut, India, in 2016, with a prestigious National Fellowship JRF/SRF from the Council of Scientific and Industrial Research (CSIR), under the Ministry of Science and Technology, Government of India. Her research area focuses on synthesis of nanostructures for photoelectrodes for photovoltaic applications, energy storage devices, photoelectrochemical water splitting, catalysis, etc. She earned her MS degree in Applied Chemistry (University First Rank) after completing her BSc degree in Chemistry from Mahatma Gandhi University (MGU), Kottayam, India. She received many prestigious fellowships, including Junior/Senior Research fellowship (JRF/SRF) from the Centre for Science and Research, Department of Science and Technology, Ministry of India; Post-doctoral/research scientist fellowship from Kerala State Council for Science, Technology and Environment (KSCSTE); and InSc research excellence award. She has published many full-length research articles in peer-reviewed, international journals and book chapters with international publishers. She serves as reviewer for many STEM journals published by Wiley International, Elsevier, Springer Nature, etc. Her current areas of interest include the development of flexible and free-standing electrodes for printable and stretchable energy storage solutions and development of novel nanostructured materials and ternary composite electrodes and electrolytes for sustainable energy applications such as supercapacitors, fuel cells, and lithium-ion batteries.

Contributors

Jou-Hyeon Ahn
Department of Materials Engineering
and Convergence Technology
Gyeongsang National University
Republic of Korea

and

Department of Chemical Engineering
Gyeongsang National University
Republic of Korea

Neethu T. M. Balakrishnan
Department of Polymer Science and
Rubber Technology (PSRT)
Cochin University of Science and
Technology (CUSAT)
Kerala, India

Bhagyalakhi Baruah
Department of Physics
Tezpur University
Tezpur, Assam, India

B. Bhuvaneshwari
Department of Chemical Engineering
Indian Institute of Technology Kanpur
Kanpur, India

Sajan Chinnan
Department of Chemistry
Indian Institute of Science Education
and Research (IISER)
Mohali, Punjab, India

and

Department of Polymer Science and
Rubber Technology (PSRT)
Cochin University of Science and
Technology (CUSAT)
Kerala, India

Akhila Das
Department of Polymer Science and
Rubber Technology (PSRT)
Cochin University of Science and
Technology (CUSAT)
Kerala, India

Raju Kumar Gupta
Department of Chemical Engineering
Indian Institute of Technology Kanpur
Kanpur, India

Jabeen Fatima M. J.
Department of Polymer Science and
Rubber Technology (PSRT)
Cochin University of Science and
Technology (CUSAT)
Kerala, India

Ashok Kumar
Department of Physics
Tezpur University
Tezpur, Assam, India

Hiren K. Machhi
Department of Chemistry
Sardar Patel University
Vallabh Vidyanagar, Gujarat, India

Nikhil Medhavi
Department of Polymer Science and
Rubber Technology (PSRT)
Cochin University of Science and
Technology (CUSAT)
Kerala, India

Abhijith P. P.
Department of Polymer Science and
  Rubber Technology (PSRT)
Cochin University of Science and
  Technology (CUSAT)
Kerala, India

and

Department of Nanoscience and
  Technology
University of Calicut
Kerala, India

Jyoti Prasad
Department of Chemistry
Sardar Patel University
Vallabh Vidyanagar, Gujarat, India

Prasanth Raghavan
Department of Polymer Science and
  Rubber Technology (PSRT)
Cochin University of Science and
  Technology (CUSAT)
Kerala, India

and

Department of Materials Engineering
  and Convergence Technology
Gyeongsang National University
Jinju, South Korea

and

Department of Materials Science and
  Nano Engineering
Rice University
Houston, Texas, USA

Leya Rose Raphael
Department of Polymer Science and
  Rubber Technology (PSRT)
Cochin University of Science and
  Technology (CUSAT)
Kerala, India

Jishnu N. S.
Rubber Technology Centre
Indian Institute of Technology (IIT-KGP)
Kharagpur, West Bengal, India

and

Leibniz Institute of Polymer Research
  Dresden e. V.
Dresden, Germany

and

Department of Polymer Science and
  Rubber Technology (PSRT)
Cochin University of Science and
  Technology (CUSAT)
Kerala, India

Saurabh S. Soni
Department of Chemistry
Sardar Patel University
Vallabh Vidyanagar, Gujarat, India

Keval K. Sonigara
Department of Chemistry
Sardar Patel University
Vallabh Vidyanagar, Gujarat, India

Anjumole P. Thomas
Department of Polymer Science and
  Rubber Technology (PSRT)
Cochin University of Science and
  Technology (CUSAT)
Kerala, India

Ankit Tyagi
Department of Chemical Engineering
Indian Institute of Technology Kanpur
Kanpur, India

Abbreviations

[BMI] [BF$_4$]	1-butyl-3-methylimidazolium tetrafluoroborate
[BMI][TFSI]	1-butyl-3-methylimidazolium bis(trifluoromethylsulphonylimide)
[BMIM][Cl]	1-butyl-3-methylimidazolium chloride
[BPy] [TFSI]	Butylpyridinium bis(triflouromethylsulphonylimide)
[Py14]FSI	1-butyl-1-methylpyrrolidinium bis(fluorosulfonyl)imide
0D	Zero-dimensional
1D	One-dimensional
2D	Two-dimensional
3D	Three-dimensional
3D-N-RGO/MnO	Three-dimensional nitrogen-doped graphene/MnO
AC	Applied current
AFC	Alkaline fuel cells
AIMD	Ab initio molecular dynamics
Al-BTC	Aluminum benzenetricarboxylate
AN	Acrylonitrile
AQ	Anthraquinone
ATRP	Atom transfer radical polymerization
Au	Gold
BDC	1,4-benzenedicarboxylate
BEV	Full-battery electric vehicles
BMIMBF$_4$	1-butyl-3-methylimidazolium tetrafluoroborate
BMITFSI	1-Butyl-3-methyl bis(trifluoromethylsulfonyl)imide
BMMIM-TFSI	1-butyl-2,3-dimethylimidazolium bis(trifluoromethanesulfonyl)imide
BOB	Bis(oxolato)borate
BPEG	Triboron-based PEG
BPO	Benzoyl peroxide
CA	Chronoamperometry
CAB	Cellulose acetate butyrate
CAGR	Compound annual growth rate
CECRI	Central Electro Chemical Research Institute
CH$_3$OH	Methanol
CMC	Carboxymethylcellulose
CN	Cyanide
CNT	Carbon nanotube
CO	Carbon monoxide
CO$_2$	Carbon dioxide
CP	Composite polymer
CPE	Composite polymer electrolytes
CR	Coin-round
Cu(OH)$_2$	Copper hydroxide

CuO/Ni	Self-supported CuO grown on Ni foam
CV	Cyclic voltammetry
DBP	Dibutyl phthalate
DC	Direct current
DFT	Density functional theory
DMC	Dimethyl carbonate
DMF	Dimethylformamide
DMFC	Direct methanol fuel cells
DMP	Dimethyl phthalate
DMS	Dimethyl sulfite
DOP	Dioctyl phthalate
DSC	Differential scanning calorimetry
DVIMBr	1,4-di(vinylimidazolium)butane bisbromide
EC	Ethylene carbonate
ED	Electrodeposition
EDLC	Electrochemical double-layer capacitor
EDOT	3,4-ethylene dioxythiophene
EGDMA	Ethylene glycol dimethacrylate
EMIMFSI	1-ethyl-3-methylimidazolium bis(fluorosulfonyl)imide
EMIM-TFSI	1-ethyl-3-methyl imidazolium bis(trifluoromethanesulfonylimide)
EMITf	1-ethyl 3-methy-l-imidazolium trifluoromethanesulfonate
EMI-TFSA	1-ethyl-3-methylimidazolium bis(trifluoromethylsulfonyl)amide
EMITFSI	1-ethyl-3-methylimidazolium triluoromethanesufonate
ETPTA	Trimethylolpropane ethoxylate triacrylate
ePPO	Elastomer poly(propylene oxide)
ESR	Equivalent series resistance
et al.	Et alia
FA	Formic acid
FCs	Fuel cells
FEC	Fluoroethylene carbonate
FePc/N-GP	FePc immobilized on nitrogen-doped electrochemically exfoliated graphene
FESEM	Field emission scanning electron microscopy
FSI	Fluorosulphonylamide
FT-IR	Fourier transform infrared spectroscopy
FTO	Fluorine doped tin oxide
GCD	Galvanostatic charge discharge
GCE	Glassy carbon electrode
GDL	Gas diffusion layer
GPE	Gel polymer electrolytes
h-BN	Hexagonal boron nitride
HCHO	Formaldehyde
HCOOH	Formic acid
HEA	Hydroxyethyl acrylate
HEC	Hydroxyethyl cellulose

Abbreviations xvii

HEMA	2-hydroxyethylmethacrylate
HFP	Hexafluoropropylene
HIP	Hot iso-static pressing
HMPP	2-Hydroxy-2-methylpropiophenone
HQ	Hydroquinone
HT	High temperature
ICSD	Crystal structure database
ILPE	Ionic liquid polymer electrolyte
ILs	Ionic liquids
IM(2o2)11TFSI	1,2-dimethyl-3-ethoxyethyl imidazolium bis(trifluoromethanesulfonyl)imide
ITO	Indium tin oxide
KOH	Potassium hydroxide
LAGP	Lithium aluminum germanium phosphate
LATP	Lithium aluminum titanium phosphate
LCP	Lithium cobalt phosphate
LED	Light emitting diode
LFP	Lithium iron phosphate
LGPS	$Li_{10}GeP_2S_{12}$
Li	Lithium
LiBOB	Lithium bis oxalate borate
LIBs	Lithium ion batteries
LiFSI	Lithium bis(flourosulphonyl) imide
Li-ion	Lithium-ion
LiDFOB	Lithium diflouro oxalate borate
LiPAAOB	Lithium polyacrylic acid oxalate borate
LiPON	Lithium phosphorous oxynitride
LiPSTFSI	Lithium poly[(4-styrenesulfonyl) (trifluoromethanesulfonyl)imide]
LiPVAOB	Lithium polyvinyl alcohol oxalate borate
LiRAP	Li-rich antiperovskites
LISICON	Lithium superionic conductor
LiSnZr(PO$_4$)	Li-tin-zirconium phosphate
LiTFSI	Lithium bis(trifluoromethanesulfonyl)imide
LLT	Lithium lanthanum titanate
LLTaO	Lithium lanthanum tantalum oxide
LSV	Linear sweep voltammetry
LTC	Lithium-thionyl chloride
LTO	Lithium titanate
MAH	Maleic anhydride
MCFC	Molten carbonate fuel cell
MCMB	Mesocarbon microbead
MD	Molecular dynamics
MEEP	Poly[bis-(methoxyethoxyethoxide)phosphazene]
Meso NiPO	Mesoporous nickel phosphate
MFC	Microbial fuel cell

MFNC	Metal free nanocarbon
MIB	Magnesium ion batteries
MIL-53	1,4-benzenedicarboxylate
MIL-53(Al)	Al, 1,4-benzenedicarboxylate
MMA	Methyl methacrylate
MMPIBF$_4$	1-n-propyl-2,3-dimethylimidazolium tetrafluoroborate
MMPIPF$_6$	1-n-propyl-2,3-dimethylimidazolium hexafluorophosphate
MnO$_2$	Manganese dioxide
MnO$_2$/N-HGSs	MnO$_2$ nanofilms directly grown over nitrogen-doped
MnPc	Manganese Phthalocyanine
M–N$_x$	Transition metal-nitrogen macrocycle
MOFs	Metal organic frameworks
MOR	Methanol oxidation reaction
MoS$_2$/P-ICPC	MoS$_2$ encapsulated interconnected porous carbon
MPc	Metal phthalocyanine
MPEGA	Methoxy-polyethylene glycol acrylate
MPL	Microporous layer
MWCNT	Multiwalled carbon nanotube
N, S@C	Nitrogen and sulphur co-doped honeycomb like porous
N$_2$H$_4$.H$_2$O	Hydrazine hydrate
Na-MMT	Na-montmorillonite
NASICON	Sodium SuperIonic CONductor
NC	Networked cellulose
NCL	The National Chemical Laboratory
Ni	Nickel
Ni NPs/TNTs/Ti	Nickel/TiO$_2$ nanotube modified on titanium substrate
NiCd	Nickel-cadmium
Ni-Cu-P/C	Ni-P and Ni-Cu-P alloys supported on carbon electrodes
NiMH	Nickel–metallic hydride
NiO NS@NW/NF	Nickel oxide nanosheet@nanowire arrays modified on nickel foam
NiOOH	Nickel oxyhydroxide
NMC	Lithium nickel manganese cobalt oxide
NMR	Nuclear magnetic resonance spectroscopy
NNRs	Ni/NiO nanorods
NPs	Nanoparticles
NWs	Nanowires
O$_2$	Oxygen
OH	Hydroxyl
OMMT	Organic montmorillonite
ORR	Oxygen reduction reaction
P(BMA-St)	Poly(butyl methacrylate-styrene)
P(VC-*co*-VAc)	Poly (vinyl chloride-co-vinyl acetate)
P12FSI	*N*-ethyl-*N*-methylpyrrolidinium bis(fluorosulfonyl)imide
PAFC	Phosphoric acid fuel cell

Abbreviations

PAN	Polyacrylonitrile
PBE	Poly(bisphenyl A-co-epichlorohydrin)
PBMA	Polybenzyl methacrylate
PC	Propylene carbonate
PCF-HCP	Porous carbon framework obtained from N-rich hyper crosslinked polymer
Pd	Palladium
PDADMA	Poly(diallyldimethylammonium)
PDAD-MATFSI	Poly[diallyldimethylammonium bis(trifluoromethane) sulfonimide]
PDMS	Poly-dimethyl siloxane
PDMS-A	Poly[dimethylsiloxane-co-(siloxane-g-acrylate)]
PDMS-P	Poly(dimethylsiloxane-co-phenylsiloxane)
PE	Polyethene
PEDOT	Poly(3,4-ethylenedioxythiophene)
PEDOT:PSS	Poly(3,4-ethylenedioxythiophene) polystyrene sulphonate
PEFCs	Polymer electrolyte fuel cells
PEG	Poly(ethylene glycol)
PEG800	Poly(ethylene glycol)
PEGDA	Poly(ethylene glycol) diacrylate
PEGDA-co-VC	Poly(ethylene glycol) diacrylate-co-vinylene carbonate
PEGDM	Poly(ethylene glycol) dimethacrylate
PEGDME	Polyethylene glycol dimethyl ether
PEGM	Poly(ethylene glycol)methyl ether methacrylate
PEI	Polyethylenimine
PEM	Proton exchange membrane
PEMFC	Proton exchange membrane fuel cell
PEMFCs	Polymeric electrolyte membrane fuel cells
PEO	Poly(ethylene oxide)
PEO/PVdF	Polyethylene oxide/polyvinylidene diflouride
PES	Poly(oligo[oxyethylene]oxysebacoyl)
PFPE	Perfluoropolyether
PFPE-diol	Hydroxy-terminated perfluoropolyether
PHEMO	Poly (3-{2-[2-(2-hydroxyethoxy) ethoxy] ethoxy} methyl-3'- methyloxetane)
PHL	PVdF-co-HFP-LSO
PHP	PVdF-co-HFP-PPCl
PIL	Polymer ionic liquid
PILGE	Polymer ionic liquid gel electrolyte
Pip$_{14}$TFSI	1-butyl-1-methylpiperidinium bis(triflourosulphonyk)imide
PLL	PEO-LiTFSI-LLZTO
PLS	Polyurethane lithium salt
PMA	Polymethyl acrelate
PMMA	Polymethyl methacrylate
PNIPAM/AM	Poly(N-isopropylacrylamide-co-acrylamide)

PNSE	Polymer nanocomposite-based solid-state electrolyte
POEM-*g*-PDMS	Poly(oxyethylene) methacrylate-g-poly(dimethyl siloxane)
POSS	Polyhedraloligomeric silsesquioxane
PP	Polypropylene
PP13TFSI	N-methyl-N-propylpiperidinium bis(trifluoromethanesulfony)limide
PPC	Poly(propylene carbonate)
PPCl	1-methyl-1-propylpiperidinium chloride
PPTA	Poly(para phenylene terephthalamide) (PPTA)
PPy	Polypyrrole
PS	Polystyrene
PS–PEO–PS	Polystyrene–poly(ethylene oxide)–polystyrene
Pt	Platinum
PTFE	Polytetraflouroethylene
PUA	Polyurethane acrylate
PVA	Poly(vinyl alcohol)
PVAc	Polyvinyl acetate
PVA-β-CN	Cyanoethyl-β-polyvinyl alcohol
PVC	Poly(vinyl chloride)
PVdF	Polyvinylidene difluoride
PVdF	Polyvinylidene fluoride
PVdF-*co*-HFP	Poly (vinylidene fluoride)-*co*-hexafluoro propylene
PVF	Polyvinylformal
PVIM-*co*-PPEGMA	Poly(N-vinlyimidazole)-co-poly(poly(ethylene glycol) methyl ether methacrylate
PVIMTFSI-*co*-PPEGMA	Poly(N-(1-vinylimidazolium-3-butyl)-ammonium bis(trifluoro methanesulfonyl)imide)-co-poly(poly (ethylene glycol) methyl ether methacrylate)
PVP	Polyvinylpyrrolidone
PVP-PEG-PVP	Poly(vinyl pyridine)-PEG-poly(vinyl pyridine)
Py14-TFSI	Lithium bis(trifluoromethane sulphonyl)imide
Py13Br	N-methyl-N-propyl pyrrolidinium bromide
Py13TFSI	1-methyl-3-propylpyrrolidinium bis(trifluoromethanesulfonyl)imide
QSEs	Quasi-solid electrolytes
QSSEs	Quasi-solid-state electrolytes
RAM	Random-access memory
rGO	Reduced graphene oxide
Rh	Rhodium
RHE	Reversible hydrogen electrode
Rh-NSs/RGO	Rh nanosheets-reduced graphene oxide
RT	Room temperature
RTILs	Room temperature ionic liquids
SC	Supercapacitor
SCE	Saturated calomel electrode

Abbreviations

SCEs	Solid ceramic electrolytes
SCN	Succinonitrile
SC-PMO	Porous MnO_2 by sonochemical method
SCs	Supercapacitors
SEM	Scanning electron microscopy
SEs	Solid electrolytes
SIBs	Sodium ion batteries
SICPN	Semi-interpenetrating cross-linked polymer network
SiO₂	Silicon dioxide
SiO₂PPTFSI	1-methyl-1-propylpiperidinium bis(trifluoromethanesulfonyl) imide
SLIC	Single lithium ion conducting
SN	Succinonitrile
Sol	Solution
SPE	Solid polymer electrolytes
SSBs	Solid-state batteries
SSEs	Solid state electrolytes
SWCNT	Single-wall carbon nanotube
SWCNT@NPC	SWCNT embedded in nitrogen and phosphorus co-doped carbon
Ta	Tantalum
TBT	Tetrabutyl titanate
TEG	Tetraethylene glycol
TEGDA-BA	Triethylene glycol diacetate2-propenoic acid butyl ester
TEM	Transmission electron microscopy
TFSI	Bis(trifluromethanesulfonyl) imide
T$_g$	Glass transition temperature
TGA	Thermogravimetric analysis
THF	Tetrahydrofuran
Ti NPs/ITO	Ti nanoparticle-implanted ITO electrode
TiO₂	Titanium dioxide
TMC	Transition metal chalcogenides
TMOS	Tetramethoxysilane
TMP	Trimethyl phosphate
TPU	Thermoplastic polyurethane
TSE	Transparent solid electrolyte
TSSE	Transparent solid state electrolyte
UV	Ultraviolet
VC	Vinylene carbonate
VIPS	3-(1-vinyl-3-imidazolic) propanesulfonate
vs.	Versus
w/w	Weight by weight
WCA	Water contact angle
wt.%	Weight percentage
XRD	X-ray diffraction
ZIBs	Zinc ion batteries
ϒ-BL	ϒ-Butyrolactone

SYMBOLS

α	Alpha
A	Area of the electrode
β	Beta
E_{cell}	Cell terminal voltage
I	Current density
δ	Delta
S	Deterioration rate
F	Faraday constant
γ	Gamma
$\geq$	Greater than or equal to
$:$	Is to
$\leq$	Less than or equal to
n	Number of electrons transferred
Ω	Ohm
I_p	Peak current density
ΔE_p	Peak to peak separation voltage
$\%$	Percentage
$\%$	Percentage
I_F/I_R	Ratio of forward to backward current
J_f/J_b	Ratio of forward to backward current density
$^\circledR$	Registered trademark
ν	Scan rate
E°_{anode}	Standard anode potential
$E^\circ_{cathode}$	Standard cathode potential
Γ^*	Surface concentration
T	Temperature
t	Time
R	Universal gas constant

UNITS

$A\ g^{-1}$	Ampere per gram
cm	Centimeter
$^\circ C$	Degree celcius/Degree centigrade
$F\ g^{-1}$	Farad per gram
$F\ cm^{-3}$	Faraday per centimetre cube
GHz	Gigahertz
GPa	Gigapascal
g	Gram
h	Hour
ions cm^{-2}	Ions per centimetre square
K	Kelvin
keV	Kilo electron volts

Abbreviations

xxiii

kV	Kilo Volt
KW kg^{-1}	Kilowatt per kilogram
kWh L^{-1}	Kilowatt hour per litre
MHz	Megahertz
MPa	Megapascal
MPa	Megapascal
m^{2}g^{-1}	Meter square per gram
μWh cm^{-2}	Micro watt hour per centimetre square
μm	Micrometer
mA mg^{-1}	Milliampere per milligram
mAh g^{-1}	Milliampere hour per gram
mW cm^{-2}	Milliwatt per centimetre square
mF cm^{-2}	Millifarad per centimetre square
mS cm^{-1}	MilliSiemens per centimetre
mA	Milliampere
mA h	Milliampere hour
mV	Millivolt
mV s^{-1}	Millivolt per second
M	Molar
nm	Nanometer
%	Percentage
S	Siemens
S cm^{-1}	Siemens per centimetre
V	Voltage

1 Solid-State Electrolytes for Lithium-Ion Batteries

Performance Requirements and Ion Transportation Mechanism in Solid Polymer Electrolytes

Jabeen Fatima M. J., Abhijith P. P.,
Jishnu N. S., Akhila Das, Neethu T.M. Balakrishnan,
Jou-Hyeon Ahn, and Prasanth Raghavan

CONTENTS

1.1 Introduction 1
1.2 Theory of Polymers in Solid Polymer Electrolytes 4
1.3 Ionic Conductivity and Ion Transfer Mechanism in Solid Polymer
Electrolytes 7
1.4 Effect of Polymer Properties on Ionic Conductivity and Ion
Transference Number 11
    1.4.1 Glass Transition Temperature 12
    1.4.2 Degree of Crystallinity 12
    1.4.3 Crystal Growth from the Melt 13
    1.4.4 Crystal Growth from Solution 13
1.5 Conclusion 14
Acknowledgment 14
References 14

1.1 INTRODUCTION

Lithium-ion batteries (LIBs) are the most popular among electrochemical energy storage devices and have a monopoly on powering the electronic gadgets and zero-emission automobile market due to their relatively high energy density, higher output voltage, negligible self-discharge, and lack of a memory effect [1–4]. A conventional lithium-ion battery comprises two electrodes, an anode and a cathode, and an

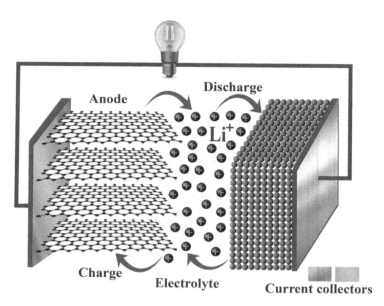

FIGURE 1.1 Schematic representation of the structure and working principle of lithium-ion batteries including the movement of ions between electrodes during charge (forward arrow) and discharge (backward arrow) states.

electrolyte system, as shown in Figure 1.1. The electrolyte is one of the key components and is known as the heart of the battery, acting as the ion transport pathway between the positive and negative electrode. The cell capacity, working temperature range, safety, electrochemical performance, and cyclability of lithium-ion batteries are enhanced by adopting the electrolyte system. According to their physical state, electrolytes can be broadly classified into liquid electrolytes, quasi-solid electrolytes, gel electrolytes, and solid electrolytes (SEs).

Traditionally, to fabricate LIBs, a lithium salt (e.g., $LiPF_6$, $LiClO_4$, and LiTFSI) dissolved in carbonate solvent (ethylene carbonate [EC], dimethyl carbonate [DMC], propylene carbonate [PC], ethyl methyl carbonate [EMC], etc.) is used as the electrolyte (organic liquid electrolyte [OLE]). Even though these organic liquid electrolytes possess high ionic conductivity and a lithium-ion transference number, they suffer from some inherent drawbacks, such as flammability, leakage, and environmental toxicity, which hinder their application in electric vehicles (EVs) and airplanes that need energy storage devices with high energy densities and, more importantly, high safety [5–8]. In this regard, replacing OLEs with safer solid electrolytes seems to be a reliable solution for the aforementioned safety issues [9,10]. In comparison with OLEs, SEs have outstanding advantages in terms of mechanical strength, dimensional stability, thermal stability, and electrochemical stability. Furthermore, SEs can also act as a separator between the anode and cathode to prevent internal electrical short circuits by preventing the transportation of electrons during the charging and discharging cycles of the battery, which greatly simplifies the battery fabrication.

Solid-State Electrolytes for Lithium-Ion Batteries

Also, thermally and mechanically stable SEs raise the possibility of using lithium-metal as an anode for high energy density LIBs [11,12], called lithium-ion metal batteries. In LIBs, to attain a high and reversible specific energy from a lithium-metal polymer battery (LMPB), the repetitive deposition and stripping of lithium must remain highly reversible during the electrochemical process. The cycling of lithium-metal is known to result in the deposition of lithium dendrites that can decrease the life cycle of the cell and cause safety concerns. It was reported that the use of solid electrolytes can suppress dendrite growth and improve plating morphology [13]. SEs generally have no practical use in room temperature applications due to their low ionic conductivity and a lithium transference number below 50°C. However, the Bolloré Company has attempted to commercialize SE-based lithium-ion batteries, and Cui's group at the Qingdao Institute of Bioenergy and Bioprocess Technology has proposed a new generation of solid polymer electrolytes (SPEs) in recent years. The major advantages of SEs in LIBs can be bulleted as follows [14–17]:

- The safety of LIBs has been greatly improved due to the absence of an organic liquid electrolyte which has low vapor pressure and boiling point.
- The high thermal stability of SEs simplifies the casing module and cooling system, which can reduce the weight of the battery, thereby increasing the energy density, lowering the production cost, saving space, and simplifying the battery fabrication.
- A plurality of electrodes can be stacked in a series as a single unit due to the solid-state characteristics and dimensional stability of SEs, which makes it possible to fabricate batteries with a high output voltage as a single unit rather than stacking a number of batteries as a module.
- The wide electrochemical window (≥ 5 V) of SEs due to the absence of an organic solvent makes it possible to use high-voltage electrode materials, thereby improving the operating voltage and compacting the battery especially for powering electric vehicles.
- SEs can compensate for the volume changes of electrodes by elastic and plastic deformation during the continuous charge and discharge cycling.
- The manufacturing and material costs of LIBs can be significantly reduced by replacing the liquid electrolyte with SEs (the fabrication cost of polymer electrolytes (PEs) is much lower than that of conventional liquid electrolyte-Celgard® separator systems); the use of positive temperature coefficient resistors, fuses, and solid packages with superior mechanical strength is not required (the volume expansion of the battery with temperature is much lower due to the absence of organic solvents having lower melting and boiling points, which in turn reduces the internal pressure of the battery build-up by the vaporization of the carbonate solvents) in SE-based LIBs, which leads to high temperature tolerance and dimensional stability, thereby saving on production costs.

Based on the matrix used for the preparation of SEs, they are classified as ceramic (inorganic solid electrolytes) and organic (solid polymer electrolytes). Inorganic solid electrolytes (such as a sodium superionic conductor [NASICON] Li–Al–Ti–PO$_4$) possess high ionic conductivity (can reach more than 10^{-4} S cm^{-1} at 25°C) and a Li$^+$ transference number at room temperature [18,19], but they show large grain boundary resistance, poor interface compatibility between an inorganic solid electrolyte and an electrode, a relatively cumbersome fabrication process, and a large energy barrier for lithium-ion electrolyte migration at the electrode interface. These features cause a series of problems, especially the growth of lithium dendrites during the charging–discharging process and an inferior plating morphology [20–22]. Moreover, inorganic solid electrolytes are too hard and brittle for flexible battery applications and have poor processability. Recently, a number of inorganic oxide electrolytes have been investigated, such as NASICON-type phosphates [23], garnet oxides Li$_x$La$_3$M$_2$O$_{12}$ (M = Ta, Nb, Zr) [24], and perovskite-type Li$_{3x}$La$_{2/3-x1/3-2x}$TiO$_3$ [25]. Sulfide electrolytes Li$_{10}$GeP$_2$S$_{12}$ [26] and Li$_2$S-P$_2$S$_5$ [25] glass-ceramics with unprecedented conductivities of 1.2×10^{-2} and 3.2×10^{-3} S cm^{-1}, respectively, have been reported. Unfortunately, they have low thermodynamic stability, can be easily reduced by lithium-metal, and are oxidized by high-voltage active cathode materials. Also, these sulfides produce toxic H$_2$S on contact with moisture. In contrast with inorganic solid electrolytes, organic solid electrolytes, commonly known as solid polymer electrolytes, exhibit excellent interfacial compatibility with both electrodes and favorable mechanical properties. In addition, the energy density of LIBs can be greatly improved by using SPEs which have a much lower density than that of inorganic solid electrolytes [27,28]. Also, they have excellent processibility, exceptional toughness, and are lightweight and flexible. Solid polymer electrolytes are categorized as dry solid polymer electrolytes, rubbery electrolytes, and single-ion conducting polymer electrolytes. This chapter systematically discusses the performance requirements and ion transfer mechanisms of SPEs, the theory of polymers in solid polymer electrolytes, lithium-ion conducting materials in the preparation of SPEs, and the unique class of SPEs called single-ion conductors.

1.2 THEORY OF POLYMERS IN SOLID POLYMER ELECTROLYTES

In a lithium-ion battery, the polymer electrolyte is sandwiched between the anode (lithium-metal, carbon, lithium titanate [LTO], etc.) and the composite cathode (LiFePO$_4$, LiMnO$_4$, LiCoO$_2$, etc.), acting as an electrolyte cum separator, which plays a crucial role in the electrochemical performance of lithium-ion batteries. Typically, SPEs are prepared by mixing or dissolving lithium salts in a high molecular weight polymer matrix such as polyethylene oxide (PEO), polyvinylidene difluoride (PVdF), or its co-polymer polyvinylidene fluoride-co-hexafluoropropylene (PVdF-co-HFP), polyacrylonitrile (PAN), etc. The polymer acts as the host matrix for the transmission of lithium-ions and the mechanical substrate to separate the electrode. The performance of SPEs greatly depends on the selection of materials such as the polymeric matrix, ion-conducting promoters, type of lithium salts, etc. The dielectric properties, the functional group present in the monomer unit of the polymer, the glass transition temperature, the degree of crystallinity, the affinity of the polymer to the lithium salt, etc., significantly influence the electrolyte properties

Solid-State Electrolytes for Lithium-Ion Batteries

and thus the battery performance. For practical application, a polymer electrolyte for lithium-ion batteries should inherently possess the following properties [29,30]:

- **High ionic conductivity:** It should be a good ionic conductor ($\geq 10^{-3}$ S cm^{-1} at room temperature) and electronic insulator, facilitating lithium-ion transport between the electrodes during the charge–discharge cycle, minimizing self-discharge, and avoiding an internal short circuit. Ionic conductivity significantly affects the internal impedance and electrochemical behavior of the battery, especially at higher C-rates [31].
- **Dissolution ability:** For solid polymer electrolytes, the host polymer matrix should have the ability to dissolve or manufacture complexes with lithium-ions. Certain polymers such as PEO, PVdF, and PAN have polar functional groups, which facilitate easy dissociation of lithium salts, thereby improving the ionic transportation and producing a host polymer with a relatively high dielectric constant [29]. A series of polymers have sequential polar groups such as the ether group (–O–), the ester group (=O), the carbonyl group (C=O), the fluoride group (–F), the thiol group (—S—), the nitrogen in the imide group (—NH—), and the acrylonitrile group (C≡N) to dissolve/dissociate lithium salts and form polymer–salt complexes.
- **High lithium-ion transference number:** Ideally, the Li$^+$-ion transference number should be close to unity in any electrolyte system. Restricting the mobility of anions in an electrolyte can greatly increase the Li$^+$-ion transference number. To reduce the mobility of anions, two main approaches have been reported: (i) anchoring the anions by means of physical or chemical bonds to the backbone of the polymer chain (common method to prepare single-ion conducting polymer electrolytes); and (ii) introducing anion receptors [32,33] such as tri(methyl)borate (1), tris(tri-fluoromethyl)borate (2), tris(hepta-fluorobutyl)borate (3), tris(hexa-fluoroisopropyl)borate (4), tris(perfluoro-*tert*-butyl)borate (5), tris(triphenyl)borate (6), tris(hexa-fluorocumyl)borate (7), tris(penta-fluorophenyl) borate (8), and tris(penta-fluorophenyl)borane (TPFPB; 9) (Figure 1.2), which could selectively complex with anions in electrolytes [34,35]. A large Li$^+$-ion transference number can reduce the concentration polarization of electrolytes during the charge/discharge process, thereby producing a higher power density [36].
- **Wide electrochemical stability window:** The electrochemical window of an electrolyte is defined as the voltage range in which the materials in the electrolyte are neither oxidized nor reduced. In other words, it is the difference in voltage between the potentials of the oxidation and reduction reaction. Hence, the polymer matrix, lithium salts, and any additives used in the battery electrolyte should have an oxidation potential higher than the embedding potential of a Li$^+$-ion in the composite cathode and a lower reduction potential than that of lithium-metal or graphitic carbon in the anode. Typically, all polymer electrolytes have an electrochemical window of ≥ 4 V vs. Li/Li$^+$ which is sufficient for even high-voltage battery electrodes.

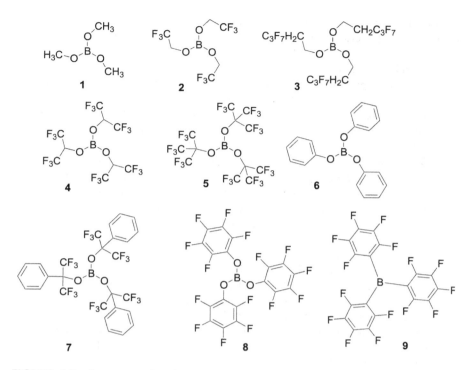

FIGURE 1.2 Structures of various trialkyl/triaryl borates and TPFPB anion receptors. Adapted and reproduced with permission from Reference [32]. Copyright 2000 Elsevier.

- **Good compatibility and adhesion with battery electrodes:** Ideally, the battery electrolyte should be chemically inert to both electrodes and should have good compatibility with the electrodes. This is very important for a good interface between the electrodes which, in turn, significantly contributes to the electrochemical performance and rate capability of the battery. An electrolyte that has good compatibility with an electrode can form a good interface with the electrode, thereby reducing the interfacial resistance and facilitating a higher rate of charge–discharge cycling stability to the battery.
- **Excellent chemical and thermal stability:** The battery electrolytes should be inert to any battery components such as electrodes, current collectors, battery additives if any, and cell packaging materials, which could minimize dendrite formation and avoid any unwanted chemical reactions or corrosion. Also, the electrolytes should have excellent thermal stability, which ensures the safe operation of lithium-ion batteries even at temperatures above room temperature, and avoids electrical (shorting, overcharge) as well as a thermal runaway or battery explosion. This is easily achieved by the selection of thermally stable or flame-retardant polymers with a

high dielectric constant such as PVdF, PVdF-*co*-HFP, PAN, etc., as the host matrix for SPEs.

- **Good mechanical strength and dimensional stability:** The mechanical strength and dimensional stability of a polymer electrolyte are two of the most important factors in the design of solid polymer electrolytes for large-scale manufacture of lithium-ion batteries. Polymer electrolytes are not hard or brittle like inorganic or glass-ceramic solid electrolytes, and have excellent dimensional stability. Because of their viscoelastic properties and semi-crystalline nature, solid polymer electrolytes are able to elastically relax when stress arises during the manufacturing process, cell assembly, packaging, storage, and use. Some feasible approaches to improve the mechanical and dimensional stability of SPEs are incorporating inorganic micro-nano-sized fillers [37], chemical cross-linking of the polymer to make 3D network structures [38], and sandwiching between the mechanically strong polymeric layers [30,39] physically supported by polyolefin membrane.
- **Sustainability:** The materials used in the fabrication of solid polymer electrolytes should be abundant with a low impact synthesis. Also, the constituent materials should be environmentally friendly or have a negligible impact on pollution or environmental hazards.

1.3 IONIC CONDUCTIVITY AND ION TRANSFER MECHANISM IN SOLID POLYMER ELECTROLYTES

Typically in SPEs, the Li$^+$-ions are dissolved in a polymer matrix and Li$^+$-ion transport occurs only in the amorphous phase of the polymer above their glass transition temperature where polymer chain motion creates a dynamic, disordered environment that plays a critical role in facilitating ion transport [40–44]. However, in SPEs with high lithium-ion conductivity, the polymer not only dissolves the lithium salt, but it is also able to couple with lithium-ions. Hence, the local relaxation and segmental motion of amorphous regions within the polymer chain at or above the glass transition temperature (T_g) plays a significant role in the ionic conductivity of SPEs [40,45]. In addition, the number of free Li$^+$-cations also significantly affects the Li$^+$-transportability within the SPE. Hence, ionic conductivity of SPEs is greatly influenced by the effective number of mobile ions (free ions), the elementary electric charge, and the ion mobility. The effective number of mobile ions greatly depends on the degree of salt dissociation in the polymer host, which is significantly affected by the chemical nature of the host polymer matrix. As previously mentioned, the polar groups in the polymer, such as –O–, =O, C=O), –F, —S—, C≡N, —NH—, etc., are effective building blocks for dissolving and dissociating lithium salts. In polyethylene oxide, for example, the lone pair of oxygens (ether linkages) on the PEO segment is coordinated with the lithium-ion by Coulombic interaction, helping to improve the segmental motion and the dissociation of lithium salts into the respective anion and cation. In the process, PEO acts as a solvent, and the lithium salt dissolves into the PEO matrix. Similarly, other atoms such as =O, —C=O, –F, —S—, —NH—, —C≡N also play a similar role. Hence, Li$^+$-ions are located at suitable coordination sites (e.g., –O– in polyethylene oxide, –F in PVdF or PVdF-co-HFP, —C≡N in PAN, and –NR in polyamide) in the polar chains of the polymer. The polymer chains undergo constant local segmental motion, which results in the appearance of free volumes [46,47]. The challenges and perspectives of lithium-ion transport in a solid-state electrolyte [48] are depicted in Figure 1.3. In SPEs, under the electric field, the migration movement of Li$^+$-cations is from one coordination point to another along the polymer segment, or they jump from one segment to another through these free volumes. Hence, the mechanism of ion motion may involve the formation of time-dependent pathways in the polymer matrix, the short-range transport of ions temporarily attached to the polymer chain, and ion hopping between an ionic cluster or coordination center. The Li$^+$-ion transport mechanism of solid polymer electrolytes based on PEO [46,47] is shown in Figure 1.4. In 2001, this concept of ionic conduction in SPEs was overturned by Bruce et al. [49]. In their study, they showed that the ionic conductivity (Li$^+$-ion conductivity) in the static, ordered environment of the crystalline phase can be greater than that in the equivalent amorphous material above T_g. The study also demonstrated that ion transport in crystalline polymer electrolytes can be dominated by cations, whereas both ions are generally mobile in the amorphous phase [50].

Based on experimental studies of ionic conductivity in PEO-based crystalline complexes formed with six ether oxygens per cation, Stoeva et al. [51] proposed that in the crystalline phase of P(EO)$_6$:LiX (X = PF$_6$, AsF$_6$, SbF$_6$, all these compounds are iso-structural), pairs of PEO chains fold to form cylindrical tunnels, within which the Li$^+$ cations are located and coordinated with ether oxygens, while the anions are located outside these tunnels in the inter-chain space and do not coordinate with cations. The structure of a PEO$_6$:LiAsF$_6$ crystalline complex suggests that Li$^+$-ion transport along the tunnels may be possible in the crystalline 6:1 complex. These Li$^+$-ions

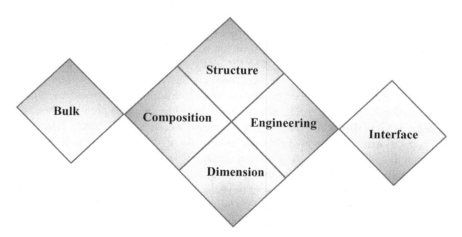

FIGURE 1.3 Challenges and perspectives of lithium-ion transport in a solid-state electrolyte.

Solid-State Electrolytes for Lithium-Ion Batteries

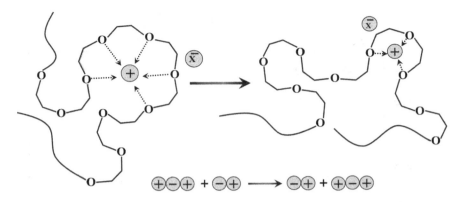

FIGURE 1.4 Schematic illustration of the lithium-ion transport mechanism in polyethylene oxide (PEO)-based solid polymer electrolytes.

can migrate from one site to another along these cylindrical tunnels without the aid of segmental motion [51]. To compare ionic conductivity in the static, ordered environment of a crystalline polymer electrolyte with the dynamic and disordered environment of an amorphous polymer electrolyte above T_g, Stoeva et al. [51] prepared crystalline and amorphous forms of PEO_6:$LiSbF_6$. The variation in ionic conductivity as a function of temperature for the crystalline and amorphous PEO_6:$LiSbF_6$ materials is shown in Figure 1.5. A temperature-dependent ionic conductivity study shows that the ionic conductivity in crystalline PEO_6:$LiSbF_6$ is higher than for the same composition in the amorphous state, even above T_g [51]. The crystalline phase reaches conductivity more than one order of magnitude higher than the amorphous phase at the lowest temperatures. Nuclear magnetic resonance (NMR) studies on these electrolytes demonstrated that PF_6 ions do not move with respect to polymer chains, indicating that the ionic conductivity is dominated by Li^+-ions; that is, the cation transport number $T_{Li}^+ = 1$.

Generally, ion transport in solids involves ions hopping between adjacent sites. In the conventional view of ionic conductivity in polymer electrolytes, ions move in a dynamic environment created by the polymer chain motion in the amorphous phase above T_g. A crankshaft-like motion associated with short segments of the polymer chains randomly creates suitable coordination sites adjacent to the ions, so that these ions may hop from one site to another. Such segmental modes, involving the motion of groups of atoms on the polymer chains, are usually relatively slow, limiting the hopping rate and therefore the maximum conductivity.

By considering the ionic conductivity in crystalline ceramic materials such as $Na\beta Al_2O_3$, $RbAg_4I_5$, the lithium superionic conductor (LISICONs) ($Li_{14}Zn(GeO_4)_4$) [52,53], or $Li_{0.5}La_{0.5}TiO_3$ [54], it can also be claimed that ion transport is favored in crystalline polymer electrolytes. Some of these crystalline ceramic materials display the highest known ionic conductivities in the solid state, exceeding by 1–3 orders of magnitude the maximum conductivity of conventional amorphous polymer electrolytes. For instance, $RbAg_4I_5$ has a conductivity of over 10^{-1} S cm^{-1}, and $Li_{0.5}La_{0.5}TiO_3$

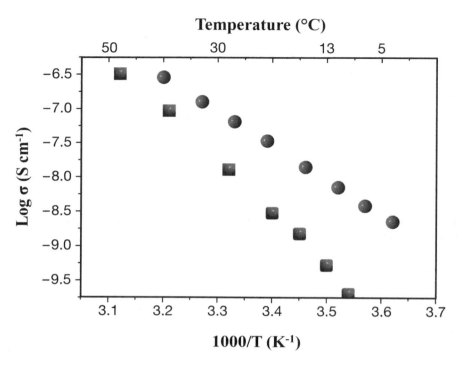

FIGURE 1.5 Ionic conductivity (S cm^{-1}) of amorphous (open circles) and crystalline (filled circles) PEO$_6$:LiSbF$_6$ as a function of temperature. Adapted and reproduced with permission from Reference [51]. Copyright 2003 American Chemical Society.

achieves 10^{-3} S cm^{-1} [53,54] at room temperature. High ionic conductivity can also be obtained in plastic crystals where ion transport is aided by rotational disorder [55]. In their later studies [56–58], Bruce et al. [49] proposed that modifying these stoichiometric crystalline complexes by replacing a few mol.% of XF$_6$ ions with monovalent ions having very different shapes and sizes such as N(SO$_2$CF$_3$)$_2$ or anions with different charges such as SiF$_6^{2-}$ can increase the ionic conductivity by 1.5–2 orders of magnitude. However, the opposite results were reported by Henderson et al. after examining the ionic conductivity of the same crystalline SPEs, P(EO)$_6$–LiX (X = PF$_6$, AsF$_6$, SbF$_6$) [59,60]. Sun et al. [61] have also reported comparable ionic conductivities in amorphous and crystalline di-block copolymers. Even though a large number of studies have reported on the ion transfer mechanism in solid polymer electrolytes, more systematic microscopic studies on ionic conductivity as a function of temperature (temperature-dependent ionic conductivity) would provide more clear information on the ion transfer mechanism. Hence, a comprehensive description of lithium-ion transportation in SPEs is challenging because the systems are complicated and no simple structural–property correlation has yet been derived.

A good understanding of conducting mechanisms is necessary for the design of solid polymer electrolytes with practical application in lithium-ion batteries. Solid

Solid-State Electrolytes for Lithium-Ion Batteries

polymer electrolytes are a complex system that contains materials with multiple conducting species that make a more complex conduction mechanism. As per the equation, $\sigma = F \sum N_i R_i E_i$ (where F, N_i, R_i, and E_i are the Faraday constant, the number of charge carriers, the ionic charge of the charge carriers, and the ionic mobility, respectively), the conductivity (σ) of such a complex system is primarily governed by two parameters: (i) the number of charge carriers and (ii) the mobility of the charge carriers.

The temperature-dependent ionic conductivity of the SPE system often follows two dominant conduction mechanisms: (i) the Arrhenius type or the Vogel–Tammann–Fulcher (VTF) type [29,62,63]. The VTF equation was devised early in the 20th century for describing the diffusion process in glassy and disordered materials [60] from quasi-thermodynamic models with free volume and configurational entropy, and its behavior can be related to ion motion coupled with the long-range motions of the polymer segments. In general, for a polymer electrolyte, the log σ vs. $1/T$ curves are typically nonlinear or slightly curved, so the activation energy for the ionic conduction E_a can be obtained using the Vogel–Tammann–Fulcher model {$\sigma = \sigma_0 T^{1/2} \exp[E_a/R(T - T_0)]$} instead of the simple Arrhenius model ($\sigma = \sigma_0 \exp(E_a/RT)$) used for the treatment of linear Arrhenius plots. This indicates that the conduction mechanism not only involves the increasing dissociation of lithium salt and the lowering of ionic coupling but also an ionic hopping motion coupled with relaxation/breathing and/or the segmental motion of polymeric chains [64–67]. Here, σ_0 is the pre-exponential factor, which is related to the number of charge carriers N_i; E_a is the activation energy for the ionic conductivity which can be calculated from the nonlinear least-squares fitting of the data from plots of log σ vs. $1/T$; and T_0 is the equilibrium glass transition temperature ($T_0 \backsimeq T_g - 50$ K). The materials that obey the linear Arrhenius equation indicate that ion transport occurs in such materials via a simple hopping mechanism decoupled from relaxation, breathing, and the segmental motion of polymeric chains [62]. Based on ionic conductivity studies of PEO and polyphenylene oxide (PPO) salt complexes, the ionic conductivity can be related to frequency and temperature using the William–Landel–Ferry (WLF) equation, considering the relaxation process of polymer molecular chain motion in an amorphous system. The expression is

$$\log \sigma_{(T)} / \sigma_{(T_g)} = C1\left(T - T_g\right) / C2 + \left(T - T_g\right)$$

Here, $\sigma_{(T_g)}$ is the conductivity of the relevant ions at glass transition temperature T_g, and $C1$ and $C2$ are the WLF parameters in the free volume equation of ion migration, respectively.

1.4 EFFECT OF POLYMER PROPERTIES ON IONIC CONDUCTIVITY AND ION TRANSFERENCE NUMBER

The physical and electrochemical properties of solid polymer electrolytes are significantly influenced by the physicochemical properties of the host matrix. The polarity and dielectric constant of the polymers positively contribute to the dissociation of lithium salts, the Li^+-ion transport number, and ionic conductivity. The presence of certain functional groups, the glass transition temperature, crystallinity, microstructure, polymer type such as homopolymer or copolymer, constituent polymers (in the case of polymer blends), molecular weight, etc., greatly influence the ionic conductivity, the transportation mechanism, the transference number, the electrochemical performance, and the rate capability of SPEs. The effect of the functional group present in a polymer chain was discussed in Section 1.2, hence this section discusses the effect of the other two important properties of polymers on ionic conductivity viz. the glass transition temperature (T_g) and the crystallinity of the polymers.

1.4.1 GLASS TRANSITION TEMPERATURE

The glass transition temperature (T_g) is one of the most important properties of polymers. It is the temperature at which the chain segments start to move while the molecular chains remain static. Below their T_g, only vibrations of molecule atoms or groups exist in their respective equilibrium positions. Below T_g, the polymers are rigid and brittle, and the molecules have very little mobility. At T_g, a dramatic change occurs in the physical properties of the polymer host, including the density, specific heat, mechanical modulus, mechanical energy absorption, dielectric and acoustical equivalents, and rate of gas or liquid diffusion through the polymer. Generally, T_g can be determined by differential scanning calorimetry (DSC) measurements. The polymer structure, crystallinity, molecular weight, thermal history, and pressure are considered to influence T_g.

Generally, lowering the T_g can enhance the segmental mobility of the polymer chains, which is the simplest and most efficient way to improve the ionic conductivity. Above T_g, the ions can move in the space provided by the free volume of the polymer host and migrate from one coordination site to a new site along the chains. Alternatively, the ions can hop from one chain to another under the effect of an electric field. Because Li^+-ion conductivity in SPEs at room temperature is low, strategies have been developed to lower the T_g and enhance the conductivity. In particular, the use of branched chains with lower T_g values compared to the host polymer chain and the addition of nano-additives are effective approaches to improve the ion transport capability of SPEs.

1.4.2 DEGREE OF CRYSTALLINITY

Crystallinity is the degree of long-range order in a material and has a significant impact on the material properties. The crystallization of polymers is a process associated with the partial alignment of their molecular chains. Polymers can crystallize upon cooling from the melt or solvent evaporation, corresponding to the different filming technologies used to fabricate polymer electrolytes. The properties of polymers are determined not only by the degree of crystallinity but also by the size and orientation of the molecular chains. The degree of crystallinity can be estimated by different analytical methods including density measurements, DSC,

Solid-State Electrolytes for Lithium-Ion Batteries

X-ray diffraction (XRD), infrared spectroscopy, and nuclear magnetic resonance. In addition, the distribution of crystalline and amorphous regions can be visualized with microscopic techniques, such as polarized light microscopy and transmission electron microscopy [25].

The crystallization process involves nucleation and crystal growth. Nucleation starts with small, nanometer-sized areas where some chains or their segments align. These nucleation seeds can either dissociate or grow further depending on the conditions. Apart from the thermal mechanism, nucleation is strongly affected by impurities, plasticizers, fillers, and other additives in the polymer. For this reason, crystallinity can be reduced by the addition of inorganic particles or plasticizers into the polymer matrix. SPE membranes are generally manufactured using the solvent casting method or a hot-press filming method, and the crystal growth is different between the melt and the solution.

1.4.3 CRYSTAL GROWTH FROM THE MELT

Crystal growth only occurs at temperatures below the melting temperature (T_m) and above T_g. Higher temperatures destroy the molecular arrangement and, below T_g, the movement of molecular chains is frozen. Nevertheless, secondary crystallization can proceed even below T_g on a timescale of months to years. The growth of the crystalline regions preferably occurs in the direction of the largest temperature gradient and is suppressed at the top and bottom of the crystalline lamellae by the amorphous folded parts at those surfaces. In the case of a strong temperature gradient, the growth has a unidirectional, dendritic character. In the preparation process, the working temperature (melt and post-processing temperature), retention time, pressure used in the hot-press method, material composition, and concentration greatly affect the percentage crystallinity of the SEs.

1.4.4 CRYSTAL GROWTH FROM SOLUTION

Polymers can also be crystallized from a solution or upon the evaporation of a solvent. This process depends on the degree of dilution; that is, in dilute solutions, the molecular chains have no connection with each other and exist as separate polymer coils in the solution. Increasing the concentration, which can occur via solvent evaporation, induces interactions between the molecular chains and, possibly, crystallization, as in crystallization from a melt. The crystallinity can be controlled by several factors such as the concentration, solvent, additives, composition, solvent volatilization speed, and temperature. Above all, the degree of crystallinity determines the mechanical and thermal properties, as well as the ionic conductivity, of the polymer. High crystallinity, which reduces ion transportation, decreases the free volume of the crystal because of the more compact packing of parallel polymer chains. In conclusion, favorable ionic conductivity can be obtained by lowering the degree of crystallinity by adding additives such as plasticizers, nanofillers, low crystalline or amorphous polymer, and grafted polymers.

1.5 CONCLUSION

Polymer electrolytes are promising candidates for next-generation energy storage devices. The current generation relies on electronic gadgets that are powered using energy storage devices. Among these energy storage devices, lithium-ion batteries have a key role owing to their enhanced energy density. In the current era, society is being mobilized by lithium-ion batteries, from health trackers to electric vehicles. As a major energy storage device used in our day-to-day life, the safety of lithium-ion batteries is of primary concern, hence major research interest is focused on electrolytes. Gel polymer electrolytes overcome the demerits of conventional liquid electrolytes. The ionic conductivity of the liquid electrolyte is high but safety issues have been raised due to development of thermal energy inside the LIBs during the continuous charge-discharge cycling, the battery lead to firing. The use of polymeric electrolytes overcomes these issues but conductivity is decreased. The improvement in properties such as ionic conductivity, glass transition temperature, and degree of crystallinity will enhance the performance of electrolytes for efficient energy storage devices.

ACKNOWLEDGMENT

Dr. M.J. Jabeen Fatima and Dr. Prasanth Raghavan would like to acknowledge the Kerala State Council for Science, Technology and Environment (KSCSTE), Kerala, for financial assistance.

REFERENCES

1. Balogun MS, Yang H, Luo Y, et al. (2018) Achieving high gravimetric energy density for flexible lithium-ion batteries facilitated by core-double-shell electrodes. *Energy Environ Sci* 11:1859–1869. doi: 10.1039/c8ee00522b
2. Zhou L, Zhang K, Hu Z, et al. (2018) Recent developments on and prospects for electrode materials with hierarchical structures for lithium-ion batteries. *Adv Energy Mater* 8:1–23. doi: 10.1002/aenm.201701415
3. Chen C, Xie X, Anasori B, et al. (2018) MoS_2-on-MXene heterostructures as highly reversible anode materials for lithium-ion batteries. *Angew Chemie - Int Ed* 57:1846–1850. doi: 10.1002/anie.201710616
4. Jiang Y, Zhang Y, Yan X, et al. (2017) A sustainable route from fly ash to silicon nanorods for high performance lithium ion batteries. *Chem Eng J* 330:1052–1059. doi: 10.1016/j.cej.2017.08.061
5. Liu Z, Li H, Zhu M, et al. (2018) Towards wearable electronic devices: A quasi-solid-state aqueous lithium-ion battery with outstanding stability, flexibility, safety and breathability. *Nano Energy* 44:164–173. doi: 10.1016/j.nanoen.2017.12.006
6. Deng J, Bae C, Marcicki J, et al. (2018) Safety modelling and testing of lithium-ion batteries in electrified vehicles. *Nat Energy* 3:261–266. doi: 10.1038/s41560-018-0122-3
7. Jiang L, Wang Q, Li K, et al. (2018) A self-cooling and flame-retardant electrolyte for safer lithium ion batteries. *Sustain Energy Fuels* 2:1323–1331. doi: 10.1039/c8se00111a
8. Chen YM, Hsu ST, Tseng YH, et al. (2018) Minimization of ion–solvent clusters in gel electrolytes containing graphene oxide quantum dots for lithium-ion batteries. *Small* 14:1–11. doi: 10.1002/smll.201703571

Solid-State Electrolytes for Lithium-Ion Batteries

9. Kim SH, Choi KH, Cho SJ, et al. (2018) Flexible/shape-versatile, bipolar all-solid-state lithium-ion batteries prepared by multistage printing. *Energy Environ Sci* 11:321–330. doi: 10.1039/c7ee01630a

10. Li Y, Xu B, Xu H, et al. (2017) Hybrid polymer/garnet electrolyte with a small interfacial resistance for lithium-ion batteries. *Angew Chemie - Int Ed* 56:753–756. doi: 10.1002/anie.201608924

11. Zhang Y, Chen R, Liu T, et al. (2017) High capacity, superior cyclic performances in all-solid-state lithium-ion batteries based on $78Li_2S$-$22P_2S_5$ glass-ceramic electrolytes prepared via simple heat treatment. *ACS Appl Mater Interfaces* 9:28542–28548. doi: 10.1021/acsami.7b06038

12. Kim DH, Oh DY, Park KH, et al. (2017) Infiltration of solution-processable solid electrolytes into conventional Li-ion-battery electrodes for all-solid-state Li-ion batteries. *Nano Lett* 17:3013–3020. doi: 10.1021/acs.nanolett.7b00330

13. Howlett PC, MacFarlane DR, Hollenkamp AF (2004) High lithium metal cycling efficiency in a room-temperature ionic liquid. *Electrochem Solid-State Lett* 7:97–101. doi: 10.1149/1.1664051

14. Kato Y, Hori S, Saito T, et al. (2016) High-power all-solid-state batteries using sulfide superionic conductors. *Nat Energy* 1:1–7. doi: 10.1038/nenergy.2016.30

15. Choi JW, Aurbach D (2016) Promise and reality of post-lithium-ion batteries with high energy densities. *Nat Rev Mater* 1: 16013. doi: 10.1038/natrevmats.2016.13

16. Xu RC, Xia XH, Yao ZJ, et al. (2016) Preparation of Li7P3S11 glass-ceramic electrolyte by dissolution-evaporation method for all-solid-state lithium ion batteries. *Electrochim Acta* 219:235–240. doi: 10.1016/j.electacta.2016.09.155

17. Oh DY, Choi YE, Kim DH, et al. (2016) All-solid-state lithium-ion batteries with TiS2 nanosheets and sulphide solid electrolytes. *J Mater Chem A* 4:10329–10335. doi: 10.1039/c6ta01628f

18. Li Y, Zhou W, Xin S, et al. (2016) Fluorine-doped antiperovskite electrolyte for all-solid-state lithium-ion batteries. *Angew Chemie - Int Ed* 55:9965–9968. doi: 10.1002/anie.201604554

19. Xu H, Wang S, Wilson H, et al. (2017) Y-Doped NASICON-type $LiZr_2(PO_4)_3$ solid electrolytes for lithium-metal batteries. *Chem Mater* 29:7206–7212. doi: 10.1021/acs.chemmater.7b01463

20. Yue L, Ma J, Zhang J, et al. (2016) All solid-state polymer electrolytes for high-performance lithium ion batteries. *Energy Storage Mater* 5:139–164. doi: 10.1016/j.ensm.2016.07.003

21. Zhang H, Li C, Piszcz M, et al. (2017) Single lithium-ion conducting solid polymer electrolytes: Advances and perspectives. *Chem Soc Rev* 46:797–815. doi: 10.1039/c6cs00491a

22. Seidel SM, Jeschke S, Vettikuzha P, Wiemhöfer HD (2015) PVDF-HFP/ether-modified polysiloxane membranes obtained via airbrush spraying as active separators for application in lithium ion batteries. *Chem Commun* 51:12048–12051. doi: 10.1039/c5cc04424c

23. Shimonishi Y, Zhang T, Imanishi N, et al. (2011) A study on lithium/air secondary batteries - Stability of the NASICON-type lithium ion conducting solid electrolyte in alkaline aqueous solutions. *J Power Sources* 196:5128–5132. doi: 10.1016/j.jpowsour.2011.02.023

24. Murugan R, Thangadurai V, Weppner W (2007) Fast lithium ion conduction in garnet-type $Li_7La_3Zr_2O_{12}$. *Angew Chemie - Int Ed* 46:7778–7781. doi: 10.1002/anie.200701144

25. Stramare S, Thangadurai V, Weppner W (2003) Lithium lanthanum titanates: A review. *Chem Mater* 15:3974–3990. doi: 10.1002/chin.200352244

26. Kamaya N, Homma K, Yamakawa Y, et al. (2011) A lithium superionic conductor. *Nat Mater* 10:682–686. doi: 10.1038/nmat3066

27. Kalhoff J, Eshetu GG, Bresser D, Passerini S (2015) Safer electrolytes for lithium-ion batteries: State of the art and perspectives. *ChemSusChem* 8:2154–2175. doi: 10.1002/cssc.201500284
28. Tang Y, Zhang Y, Li W, et al. (2015) Rational material design for ultrafast rechargeable lithium-ion batteries. *Chem Soc Rev* 44:5926–5940. doi: 10.1039/C4CS00442F
29. Agrawal RC, Pandey GP (2008) Solid polymer electrolytes: Materials designing and all-solid-state battery applications: An overview. *J Phys D Appl Phys* 41: 223001. doi: 10.1088/0022-3727/41/22/223001
30. Raghavan P, Lim DH, Ahn JH, et al. (2012) Electrospun polymer nanofibers: The booming cutting edge technology. *React Funct Polym* 72:915–930. doi: 10.1016/j.reactfunctpolym.2012.08.018
31. Kulkarni AR (2002) *Proceedings of the 8th Asian Conference on Solid State Ionics: trends in the new millennium*, Malaysia, 15–19 December 2002,. edited by B. V. R. Chowdari, World Scientific, Asian Society for Solid State Ionics. Singapore; River Edge, pp 273–282.
32. McBreen J, Lee HS, Yang XQ, Sun X (2000) New approaches to the design of polymer and liquid electrolytes for lithium batteries. *J Power Sources* 89:163–167. doi: 10.1016/S0378-7753(00)00425-0
33. Prakash Reddy V, Blanco M, Bugga R (2014) Boron-based anion receptors in lithium-ion and metal-air batteries. *J Power Sources* 247:813–820. doi: 10.1016/j.jpowsour.2013.09.028
34. Lee HS, Yang XQ, McBreen J, et al. (1995) A new family of anion receptors and their effect on ion pair dissociation and conductivity of lithium salts in non-aqueous solutions. *Electrochim Acta* 40:2353–2356. doi: 10.1016/0013-4686(95)00192-H
35. Lee HS, Ma ZF, Yang XQ, et al. (2004) Synthesis of a series of fluorinated boronate compounds and their use as additives in lithium battery electrolytes. *J Electrochem Soc* 151:A1429. doi: 10.1149/1.1779407
36. Song JY, Wang YY, Wan CC (1999) Review of gel-type polymer electrolytes for lithium-ion batteries. *J Power Sources* 77:183–197. doi: 10.1016/S0378-7753(98)00193-1
37. Kane SN, Mishra A, Dutta AK (2016) Preface: International conference on recent trends in physics (ICRTP 2016), 13-14 Feburuary 2016, Indore. In: *Journal of Physics: Conference Series*. 755: 011001, doi:10.1088/1742-6596/755/1/011001
38. Murata K, Izuchi S, Yoshihisa Y (2000) An overview of the research and development of solid polymer electrolyte batteries. *Electrochim Acta* 45:1501–1508. doi: 10.1016/S0013-4686(99)00365-5
39. Lim D-H, Haridas AK, Figerez SP, et al. (2018) Tailor-made electrospun multilayer composite polymer electrolytes for high-performance lithium polymer batteries. *J Nanosci Nanotechnol* 18:6499–6505. doi: 10.1166/jnn.2018.15689
40. MacCallum, JR, Vincent CA (1987) Polymer electrolytes reviews-I. In: JR MacCallum and CA Vincent (Eds.), Elsevier Applied Science Publishers, London, ISBN 1-85166-07 1-2, pp. 173–236. doi.org/10.1002/pi.4980200325
41. Berthier C, Gorecki W, Minier M, et al. (1983) Microscopic investigation of ionic conductivity in alkali metal salts-poly(ethylene oxide) adducts. *Solid State Ion* 11:91–95. doi: 10.1016/0167-2738(83)90068-1
42. Druger SD, Ratner MA, Nitzan A (1983) Polymeric solid electrolytes: Dynamic bond percolation and free volume models for diffusion. *Solid State Ionics* 9–10:1115–1120. doi: 10.1016/0167-2738(83)90139-X
43. Gray FM (1997) *Polymer Electrolytes*. Royal Society of Chemistry. Cambridge, London ISBN 0-85404-557-0, pp. 175. doi.org/10.1002/(SICI)1097-0126(199805)46:1<78::AID-PI16>3.0.CO;2-I

Solid-State Electrolytes for Lithium-Ion Batteries

44. Scrosati B (1993) Applications of electroactive polymers. In: B. Scrosati (Ed.), *Chapman and Hall*. Chapman and Hall, London, Springer, Dordrecht, pp. 354. doi.org/10.1002/pi.1994.210330323
45. Gadjourova Z, Andreev YG, Tunstall DP, Bruce PG (2001) Ionic conductivity in crystalline polymer electrolytes. *Nature* 412:520–523. doi: 10.1038/35087538
46. Xu K (2004) Nonaqueous liquid electrolytes for lithium-based rechargeable batteries. *Chem Rev* 104:4303–4417. doi: 10.1021/cr030203g
47. Florjañczyk Z, Zygado-Monikowska E, Ostrowska J, Frydrych A (2014) Solid polymer electrolytes based on ethylene oxide polymers. *Polimery/Polymers* 59:80–87. doi: 10.14314/polimery.2014.080
48. Zhao W, Yi J, He P, Zhou H (2019) Solid-state electrolytes for lithium-ion batteries: Fundamentals, challenges and perspectives. *Electrochem Energy Rev* 2:574–605. doi: 10.1007/s41918-019-00048-0
49. Gadjourova Z, Andreev YG, Tunstall DP, Bruce PG (2001) Ionic conductivity in crystalline polymer electrolytes. *Nature* 412:520–523. doi: 10.1038/35087538
50. Gorecki W, Donoso P, Berthier C, et al. (1988) NMR, DSC and conductivity study of the polymer solid electrolytes P(EO) $(LiC_{p+1}F_{2p+3}SO3)x$. *Solid State Ion* 28–30:1018–1022. doi: 10.1016/0167-2738(88)90323-2
51. Stoeva Z, Martin-Litas I, Staunton E, et al. (2003) Ionic conductivity in the crystalline polymer electrolytes $PEO_6:LiXF_6$, X = P, As, Sb. *J Am Chem Soc* 125:4619–4626. doi: 10.1021/ja029326t
52. Shriver DF, (1994) Polymer electrolytes I: General principles. In: PG Bruce (Ed.), *Solid State Electrochemistry (Chemistry of Solid State Materials)*, Cambridge, Cambridge University Press, London, pp. 95–118. doi.org/10.1017/CBO9780511524790.006
53. Bruce PG, West AR (1984) Ion trapping and its effect on the conductivity of LISICON and other solid electrolytes. *J Solid State Chem* 53:430–434. doi: 10.1016/0022-4596(84)90122-1
54. Inaguma Y, Liquan C, Itoh M, et al. (1993) High ionic conductivity in lithium lanthanum titanate. *Solid State Commun* 86:689–693. doi: 10.1016/0038-1098(93)90841-A
55. Macfarlane DR, Huang J, Forsyth M (1999) Lithium-doped plastic crystal electrolytes exhibiting fast ion conduction for secondary batteries. *Nature* 402:792–794. doi: 10.1038/45514
56. Stoeva Z, Martin-Litas I, Staunton E, et al. (2003) Ionic conductivity in the crystalline polymer electrolytes $PEO_6:LiXF_6$, X = P, As, Sb. *J Am Chem Soc* 125:4619–4626. doi: 10.1021/ja029326t
57. Lilley SJ, Andreev YG, Bruce PG (2006) Ionic conductivity in crystalline $PEO_6:Li(AsF_6)_{1-x}(SbF_6)_x$. *J Am Chem Soc* 128:12036–12037. doi: 10.1021/ja063091u
58. Zhang C, Staunton E, Andreev YG, Bruce PG (2005) Raising the conductivity of crystalline polymer electrolytes by aliovalent doping. *J Am Chem Soc* 127:18305–18308. doi: 10.1021/ja056129w
59. Henderson WA, Brooks NR, Young VG (2003) Single-crystal structures of polymer electrolytes. *J Am Chem Soc* 125:12098–12099. doi: 10.1021/ja036535k
60. Henderson WA, Passerini S (2003) Ionic conductivity in crystalline-amorphous polymer electrolytes $-P(EO)_6:LiX$ phases. *Electrochem Commun* 5:575–578. doi: 10.1016/S1388-2481(03)00131-0
61. Sun J, Liao X, Minor AM, et al. (2014) Morphology-conductivity relationship in crystalline and amorphous sequence-defined peptoid block copolymer electrolytes. *J Am Chem Soc* 136:14990–14997. doi: 10.1021/ja5080689
62. Ratner MA, Johansson P, Shriver DF (2000) Polymer electrolytes: Ionic transport mechanisms and relaxation coupling. *MRS Bull* 25:31–37. doi: 10.1557/mrs2000.16

63. Quartarone E, Mustarelli P (2011) Electrolytes for solid-state lithium rechargeable batteries: Recent advances and perspectives. *Chem Soc Rev* 40:2525–2540. doi: 10.1039/c0cs00081g

64. Shubha N, Prasanth R, Hng HH, Srinivasan M (2014) Study on effect of poly (ethylene oxide) addition and in-situ porosity generation on poly (vinylidene fluoride)-glass ceramic composite membranes for lithium polymer batteries. *J Power Sources* 267:48–57. doi: 10.1016/j.jpowsour.2014.05.074

65. Cheruvally G, Kim JK, Choi JW, et al. (2007) Electrospun polymer membrane activated with room temperature ionic liquid: Novel polymer electrolytes for lithium batteries. *J Power Sources* 172:863–869. doi: 10.1016/j.jpowsour.2007.07.057

66. Prasanth R, Shubha N, Hoon H, Srinivasan M (2014) Effect of poly (ethylene oxide) on ionic conductivity and electrochemical properties of poly (vinylidene fluoride) based polymer gel electrolytes prepared by electrospinning for lithium ion batteries. *J Power Sources* 245:283–291. doi: 10.1016/j.jpowsour.2013.05.178

67. Shubha N, Prasanth R, Hoon HH, Srinivasan M (2014) Plastic crystalline-semi crystalline polymer composite electrolyte based on non-woven poly(vinylidenefluoride-co-hexafluoropropylene) porous membranes for lithium ion batteries. *Electrochim Acta* 125:362–370. doi: 10.1016/j.electacta.2014.01.024

2 Solid-State Electrolytes for Lithium-Ion Batteries

Novel Lithium-Ion Conducting Ceramic Materials: Oxides (Perovskite, Anti-Perovskite) and Sulfide-Type Ion Conductors

Prasanth Raghavan, Abhijith P. P., Jishnu N. S., Neethu T. M. Balakrishnan, Akhila Das, Jabeen Fatima M. J., and Jou-Hyeon Ahn

CONTENTS

2.1 Introduction 20
2.2 Oxide-Type Lithium-Ion Conductors..23
    2.2.1 Perovskite Conductors 23
    2.2.2 Anti-Perovskite Conductors...26
2.3 Sulfide-Type Lithium-Ion Conductors 30
    2.3.1 LISICON and Thio-LISICONs..30
    2.3.2 LGPS Family 34
    2.3.3 Argyrodites 36
    2.3.4 Other New Thio-Phosphates..38
    2.3.5 Layered Sulfides 41
2.4 Conclusion 43
Acknowledgment 44
References..44

2.1 INTRODUCTION

Portable energy storage devices have had a profound impact on the development of automobiles and electronics which influences all aspects of day-to-day life. The most convenient form of energy storage is portable chemical energy such as batteries and supercapacitors. Among the different sources, fossil fuel has become the dominant chemical energy source due to its ease of storage, access, and transport. However, there are serious environmental issues associated with the use of fossil fuels. It is a well-known fact that carbon dioxide, which is the gas released when fossil fuels are burned, is one of the primary gases responsible for global warming. Such gases cause a rise in the earth's temperature to the point that polar ice caps are melting, low-lying lands are flooding, and sea levels are increasing which threatens the existence of many animals and plants including mankind. Fossil fuels are a non-renewable energy source and are being extracted at an exorbitant rate to meet demand. It is estimated that fossil fuels will be extinct within the next 30–40 years, hence a steep hike in fuel costs is expected in the near future. In this scenario, if an effective alternate to oil is not found or automobiles do not switch from gasoline engines to electrically powered engines, we will no longer be able to drive cars. To make such a switch, it is necessary to have better energy conversion and storage devices. Among the different energy storage devices, rechargeable batteries are the most promising as they are capable of efficiently storing energy from renewable sources. On a fundamental level, the battery cell is composed of three integral components: the anode, the cathode, and the electrolyte/ionic conductor. The major components and structure of a battery are shown in Figure 2.1.

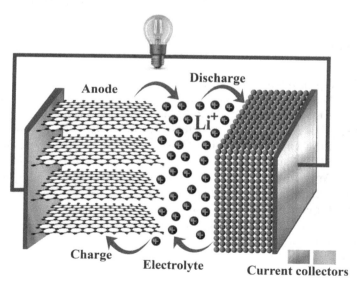

FIGURE 2.1 Schematic representation of the structure and working principle of lithium-ion batteries including the movement of ions between electrodes during charge (forward arrow) and discharge (backward arrow) states.

Solid-State Electrolytes for Lithium-Ion Batteries

Recently, battery research has advanced at a rapid pace, especially in improving safety. Today's portable batteries meet the demands of most portable applications, but a better battery is required for applications such as electric vehicles (EVs). Lithium-ion batteries (LIBs) or lithium-metal batteries are being scrutinized as the most promising electrical energy storage device for electric/hybrid vehicles, and hold great promise for future transportation. The most important property for a battery module powering an electric vehicle is thermal stability. Such heavy-duty batteries should be safe to operate over a wide range of temperatures, where the electrolyte plays a key role. Hence, in general, an electrolyte is specifically designed for a particular battery application. Different types of electrolytes such as organic liquid electrolytes, ionic liquid (room temperature ionic liquids [RTILs]) electrolytes, inorganic liquid electrolytes, organic solid electrolytes (solid polymer electrolytes [SPEs]), and inorganic solid electrolytes are used in lithium-ion batteries.

Inorganic solid-state Li-ion conducting materials have been considered for Li-based electrolytes because they have a wide electrochemical window (0–5 V) and are thermally stable and electronically/electrically insulating; however, their Li-ion conductivity is not as good as organic liquid electrolytes or organic solid electrolytes. Because of their inferior room temperature lithium-ion conductivity, inorganic solid-state electrolytes have been excluded from large-scale battery applications and their practical applications in thin-film batteries are limited.

The state-of-the-art electrolyte used in lithium-ion batteries is the organic liquid electrolyte, which is simply a solution of a suitable lithium salt ($LiPF_6$, lithium bis(trifluoromethanesulfonyl)imide [LiTFSI], $LiClO_4$, etc.) in an aprotic solvent (ethylene carbonate [EC], dimethyl carbonate [DMC], propylene carbonate [PC], ethyl methyl carbonate [EMC], etc.). These liquid electrolytes show good conductivity (in the order of 10^{-2} to 10^{-3} S cm^{-1} at room temperature); however, they suffer from electrochemical stability issues due to the narrow electrochemical window, and thermal stability issues due to their low flashpoint below 30°C. Electrolyte leakage, inferior cycling stability, rate capability, growth of dendrites, and associated thermal runway are some of the other concerns related to organic liquid electrolytes. Accordingly, the development of an electrolyte with a wider electrochemical window and improved thermal safety properties has become one of the most promising avenues for improving the safety and electrochemical properties of Li-ion batteries. Also, the all-solid-state battery, comprising only solid-state electrolytes, provides good safety in heavy-duty lithium-ion batteries and lithium-metal batteries in electric vehicles and stationary power sources. Also, solid electrolytes with sufficient stiffness can suppress the growth of lithium-metal dendrites during cycling [1]. Hence, lithium-ion conducting inorganic solid electrolytes are a promising candidate for the fabrication of all-solid-state batteries; however, even though they have a wide electrochemical window (>5 V) and excellent safety and shelf life, most solid-state electrolytes suffer from low room temperature ionic conductivity which prevents them from being used in practical applications.

In recent years, inorganic solid electrolytes have shown improved performance. A large number of novel solid-state electrolyte lithium-ion conducting ceramic and glass-ceramic materials have been developed with Li-ion conductivity comparable and even exceeding organic liquid electrolytes. Figure 2.2 shows the ionic conductivity of different inorganic solid-state electrolytes in comparison with organic liquid electrolytes, solid polymer electrolytes, ionic liquids, and gel polymer electrolytes [2,3].

Solid-state electrolytes can address the aforementioned concerns on capacity losses, life cycle, operating temperatures, safety, and the reliability of organic liquid as well as gel electrolytes [4,5]. In addition, they present advantages such as the simplicity of design, the absence of leakage and pollution, and better resistance to shocks and vibrations compared with organic liquid electrolytes [6–8]. The search for solid electrolyte materials with improved conductivity has been encouraged by the discovery of lithium nitride (Li_3N) which was discovered in the 1970s (Figure 2.3), and has a very high conductivity of 6×10^{-3} S cm^{-1} at room temperature. Following lithium nitride, different classes of lithium-ion conductors including the lithium superionic conductor (LISICON) and thio-LISICON-type, garnet-type, perovskite-type, and sodium superionic conductor (NASICON)-type lithium-ion conductors have been reported. This chapter discusses ionic conductivity, the electrochemical performance and structure of typical oxide-type electrolytes (perovskites and antiperovskite lithium conductors) and sulfide-type lithium-ion conductors (LISICON and thio-LISICONs, $Li_{10}GeP_2S_{12}$ [LGPS] family, argyrodites, layered sulfides), and

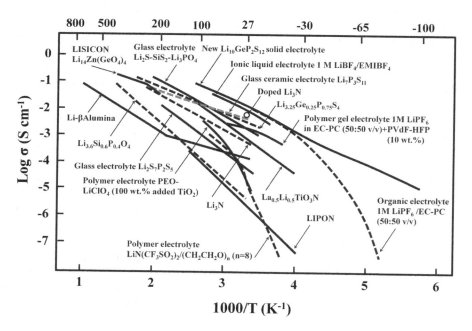

FIGURE 2.2 Thermal evolution of ionic conductivity (Arrhenius plot) of $Li_{10}GeP_2S_{12}$, together with those of other lithium solid electrolytes, organic liquid electrolytes, polymer electrolytes, room temperature ionic liquids, and gel electrolytes. Adapted and reproduced with permission from Ref. [3]. Copyright © 2011 Springer Nature.

Solid-State Electrolytes for Lithium-Ion Batteries

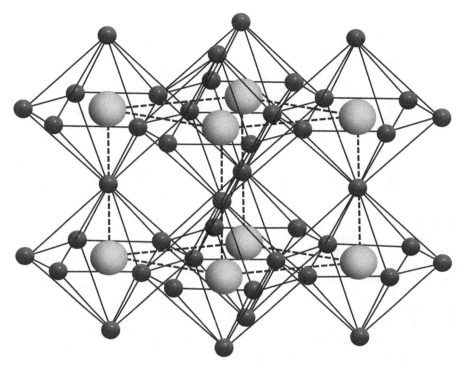

FIGURE 2.3 Crystal structure of lithium nitride (Li$_3$N) solid-state lithium-ion conductor.

demonstrates their thermal stability and applications in all solid-state lithium-metal batteries.

2.2 OXIDE-TYPE LITHIUM-ION CONDUCTORS

2.2.1 Perovskite Conductors

A perovskite is any material with the same type of crystal structure as calcium titanium oxide. The name perovskite comes from the mineral that was first discovered in the Ural Mountains of Russia by Gustav Rose in 1839, and is named after Russian mineralogist L. A. Perovski. The general chemical formula for a perovskite compound is ABX$_3$, where A and B are two cations of very different sizes and X is an anion that bonds to both. The ideal cubic structure has the B cation in 6-fold coordination surrounded by an octahedron of anions, and the A cation in 12-fold cuboctahedral coordination, as shown in Figure 2.4. Recently, perovskite Li$^+$-ion conductors and structurally related variants have attracted extensive attention based on optimal bulk Li$^+$ conductivities among various solid electrolytes. A large number of studies have been reported with varying lithium ionic conductivities through the replacement of A- and B-sites with different cations in which ionic conductivities can reach up to 10^{-3} S cm^{-1}. The lithium-based perovskite has the general formula

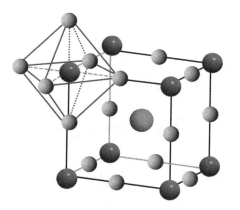 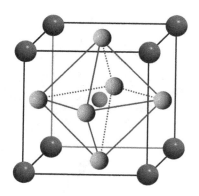

FIGURE 2.4 Idealized crystal structure for solid-state Li-ion conductors, (a) and (b): perovskite general structure.

of (ABO$_3$) type; for example, the structure of perovskite-type lithium lanthanum titanate solid-state electrolytes can be represented as Li$_{3x}$La$_{(2/3)-x}$TiO$_3$ (LLTO) and has a cubic structure with a space group of P4/mmm and C-mmm (Figure 2.5), where the value of x ranges from 0.07 to 0.13 and the activation energy ranges from 0.3 to 0.4 eV [9]. The preparation conditions for LLTO are very strict and show poor ionic conductivity ($\leq 10^{-4}$ S cm^{-1}). In LLTO crystals, the Li$^+$-ion conductivity is as a result of the large concentration of A-site vacancies formed by four adjacent TiO$_6$ octahedra, which facilitate the migration of Li cations through the bottlenecks [10].

Based on the adoption of different synthesis routes, and architected heterogeneous lattice vacancies can result in different perovskite-like compounds with diverse crystal structures, including cubic, hexagonal, orthorhombic, and tetragonal. For the development of solid polymer electrolytes or inorganic solid-state electrolytes, it is important to understand the crystal structure and ionic conduction mechanism in LLTO. Yashima et al. [11] studied the Li$^+$-ion migration path in La$_{0.62}$Li$_{0.16}$TiO$_3$ and Bohnke et al. [10] studied the ionic conduction mechanism in LLTOs. In their study, it was found that Li cations can migrate from the 2c site on the (002) La-deficient layer to the 2c-4f-2c or 2c-2d-2c tie line at 77 K to enhance conductivity [11], and confirmed that the ionic conduction mechanism of LLTOs incorporated the tilting and/or rotation of BO$_6$ octahedra as promoted by either rising temperatures or increasing vacancies in the structure [10]. Recently, a poly(ethylene oxide) (PEO)-based polymer composite electrolyte incorporated with Li$_{0.33}$La$_{0.557}$TiO$_3$ nanowires as filler and LiClO$_4$ as the lithium salt has been reported with a lithium-ion conductivity of 2.4 × 10^{-4} S cm^{-1} at 25°C [12]. Lui et al. [13] compared the effect of LLTO morphology (nanoparticles and nanowires) on the ionic conductivity of polymer electrolytes prepared by electrospinning (Figure 2.6).

The introduction of LLTO nanowire into polyacrylonitrile (PAN) achieved higher ionic conductivity (2.4 × 10^{-4} S cm^{-1} at room temperature) than pristine PAN. The composite electrolyte offers a 3D long-distance Li$^+$-ion transmission network, which

Solid-State Electrolytes for Lithium-Ion Batteries 25

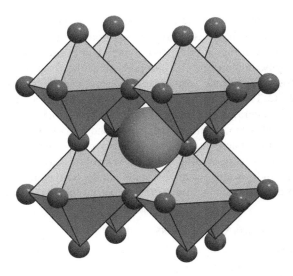

FIGURE 2.5 Idealized schematic visualization of crystal structure for A-site deficient perovskite-type $La_{(2/3)x}Li_{3x}TiO_3$.

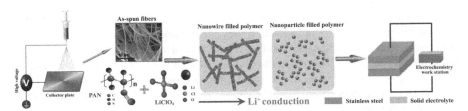

FIGURE 2.6 Schematic illustration for the synthesis of ceramic nanowire-filled polymer-based composite electrolytes. Adapted and reproduced with permission from Ref. [13]. Copyright© 2009, American Chemical Society.

reduces the negative effect of the agglomeration of inorganic ceramics in polymers relative to nanoparticles. This work opened up a new way to develop one-dimensional fast ion-conductive ceramic materials in solid electrolytes for lithium batteries. Goodenough et al. [14] fabricated a 3D-LLTO/PEO composite electrolyte using a hydrogel-derived method in which the LLTO was incorporated into the hydrogel template and then cast with PEO after removing the template. Compared to the traditional simple dispersion process, the use of an artificial 3D infiltration network avoids the agglomeration of nano-sized LLTOs. In addition, the ultra-high specific surface area of uniformly distributed nano-sized LLTOs provides a continuous phase interface network as lithium-ion transport channels. However, the composite electrolyte exhibited an ionic conductivity of 8.8×10^{-5} S cm^{-1} at room temperature.

Similarly, Fu et al. prepared a 3D garnet nanofiber network–polymer nanocomposite electrolyte [15]. In this approach, a continuous network of Li$^+$-ion conduction channels was formed by uniformly distributed porous $Li_7La_3Zr_2O_{12}$ (LLZO) in the interconnected nanofibers. The 3D fibrous network structures of LLZO were fabricated and then the LiTFSI-PEO polymer was poured into the porous 3D LLZO ceramic networks, forming 3D garnet–polymer composite films. The combined LiTFSI-PEO polymer and porous 3D inorganic structure form the 3D LLZO–polymer nanocomposite membrane which exhibits a high ionic conductivity of 2.5 × 10^{-4} S cm^{-1} at 25°C. The highly conducting three-dimensional ion transport network of ceramic or glass-ceramic Li$^+$-ion conductors offers a new option of designing composite electrolytes having improved ionic conductivity, thermal stability, and mechanical properties. These studies show that perovskite-type conductors are considered promising candidates as all-solid-state electrolytes based on their appropriate electrochemical windows and acceptable ionic conductivities; however, the intercalation of Li-ions and limited electrodes greatly restrict their practical application.

2.2.2 ANTI-PEROVSKITE CONDUCTORS

Inspired by the high-temperature superionic conductivity of NaMgF$_3$ and (K, Na)MgF$_3$ perovskites [16–18], Zhao et al. [19] proposed a novel family of "electronically inverted" lithium-rich anti-perovskites (LiRAPs), e.g., Li$_3$OCl and Li$_3$O(Cl, Br), as Li-rich superionic conductors. The atomic structure of Li$_3$OCl [18,20], a typical LiRAP, is shown in Figure 2.7. Even though this new strain of electrolyte shares similar structures with standard perovskite-type electrolytes, the ions of the anti-perovskites in the corresponding lattice sites can undergo electronic inversion, hence they are referred to as anti-perovskites. This class of material can accommodate a large number of mobile Li-ions in the crystal lattice and has a low energy barrier for ionic transport. As discussed in Section 2.2.1, in a typical A$^+$B^{2+}X$^-$$_3$ perovskite structure, A (Na$^+$) is a monovalent metallic cation, B (Mg^{2+}) is a divalent metallic cation, and X (F$^-$) is a strongly electronegative monovalent anion, whereas, A, B, and X in anti-perovskites possess inverted charges. To obtain such a Li$^+$ ionic conductor, Zhao

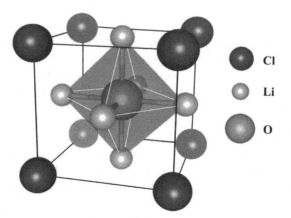

FIGURE 2.7 Atomic structure of Li$_3$OCl in a unit cell. Lithium, oxygen, and chlorine atoms are located at the octahedral vertices, octahedral centers, and cube vertices, respectively.

et al. [19] replaced the electronegative anion element in the traditional perovskite system (e.g., fluorine in $NaMgF_3$) with the electropositive lithium metal, and continued the electronic inversion to $A^-B^{2-}X^+_3$, where A^- is a monovalent anion, B^{2-} is a divalent anion, and X^+ is a strongly electropositive monovalent cation, namely Li^+, located at the octahedral vertices. In the structure, the divalent anion element at the octahedral center (B-site) of a LiRAP is conveniently occupied by chalcogens^{2-} (O^{2-}, S^{2-}), and the monovalent anion element at the dodecahedral center (A-site) can be halogens (F^-, Cl^-, Br^-, I^-) or a mixture of halogens; the notation for anti-perovskites is generally defined as $X^+_3B^{2-}A^-$. The very first lithium-rich anti-perovskite reported was Li_3OCl, exhibiting room temperature ionic conductivity values of 0.85×10^{-3} and 1.94×10^{-3} S cm^{-1} with an activation energy of 0.26 and 0.18 eV for the end member Li_3OCl and a 50/50 mixed phase of $Li_3OCl_{0.5}Br_{0.5}$ anti-perovskites, respectively. The ionic conductivity is quite low even though it has low activation energy values. These ionic conductivity values increase to 4.82×10^{-3} and 6.05×10^{-3} S cm^{-1} as the temperature increases to $T = 250°C$. The mixed-halogen phase $Li_3O(Cl, Br)$ anti-perovskites show higher ionic conductivity than the end member anti-perovskites, likely due to their peculiar topological nature resulting from the different sizes of anions. The end member Li_3OBr has large Br anions that almost fill the dodecahedral A-site of the anti-perovskite, which leaves little room for Li^+-cations to hop into the interstitial space. In the other end member, Li_3OCl has smaller Cl^- anions that are not large enough to fill the dodecahedral space substantially, the perovskite structure distorts via octahedral tilting, which results in (partially) collapsed A-sites (the coordination goes from 12 to 8, correspondingly). This low-symmetry phase still leaves no significant channels for ionic transport. Alternating larger Br^- and smaller Cl^- anions in the dodecahedral A-sites in a 3D topology generates a larger unit cell closer to the end member Li_3OBr [21]. Simultaneously, it straightens the octahedral tilting, which results in a less distorted perovskite structure with larger 12-coordinated dodecahedra for the smaller Cl^- anion to reside. Such a topological setting provides free space in the chlorine-occupied dodecahedra for the Li^+ cations to hop into and pass through via the interstitial Frenkel route [19]. However, in 2003, a similar anti-perovskite system based on the composition $Li_{3-n}(OH)_nX$ (X = Cl, Br; $0.83 < n < 2$) was reported by Schwering et al. [22]. In their study, they reported that structural phase transition to the cubic phase was accompanied by a significant jump in the Li ionic conductivity of $Li_2(OH)Cl$ by three orders of magnitude to reach 10^{-4} S cm^{-1} above room temperature.

In their study, Zhang et al. [23] reported that chemical substitution can easily manipulate Li^+ conduction in anti-perovskites. Using different chemical substitutions, they demonstrated that dodecahedral sites can be supplanted by larger anions (Br^-, I^-) to allow for the replacement of Li with divalent cations (Mg^{2+}, Ca^{2+}, Ba^{2+}) at the Li_6O octahedral center and that the depletion of monovalent lithium rich anti-perovskite. LiA (samples: $Li_{2.95}OCl_{0.95}$, $Li_{2.90}OCl_{0.90}$, $Li_{2.85}OCl_{0.85}$, and $Li_{2.80}OCl_{0.80}$) can optimize superionic conductivity and showed an increase in room temperature ionic conductivity from 1.94×10^{-3} to 6.05×10^{-3} S cm^{-1} for $Li_3OCl_{0.5}Br_{0.5}$. In addition, thermal treatments such as annealing, pressing, and heating/cooling, and the thermal/electrochemical history can also affect conductivity. Zhang et al. [23]

demonstrated a significantly improved room temperature ionic conductivity for the end member Li_3OCl, Li_3OBr, and the 50/50 mixed phase of $Li_3OCl_{0.5}Br_{0.5}$ anti-perovskites. After annealing above 250°C under vacuum for 24 h, their ambient temperature ionic conductivity could be enhanced by two orders of magnitude [23], which is due to the structural changes (e.g., octahedral tilting), the grain boundary changes, and the migration of vacancies. It is important to note that the thermal treatment history, texture formation and evolution, crystallization kinetics, octahedral tilting, and grain boundaries affect the microstructure which, in turn, significantly influences ionic conductivity. An LiRAP has other advantages including (i) low electronic conductivity with minimum self-discharge for a long shelf life (bandgap exceeds 5 eV for Li_3OCl); (ii) stable operation at high temperature up to 275°C; (iii) large electrochemical working windows; and (iv) environmental friendliness [23,24]. Lu et al. [25] prepared an anti-perovskite solid electrolyte film by pulsed laser deposition at temperatures lower than 300°C and studied their ionic properties with temperature and their compatibility and cyclability with Li metal in $Li/Li_3OCl/Li$ symmetric cells. The ionic conductivities of the Li_3OCl films were determined to be 8.9×10^{-6} S cm^{-1} at room temperature and 3.5×10^{-4} S cm^{-1} at 140°C which shows that the room temperature ionic conductivity of this solid electrolyte film is more than an order of magnitude in comparison with its bulk counterpart (5.8×10^{-7} S cm^{-1}). In addition, the temperature-dependent ionic conductivity of the films is well fitted by the Arrhenius equation with an activation energy of 0.36 eV. The enhanced ionic conductivity of the Li_3OCl film is attributed to the Li^+ and/or Cl vacancies and also the preferential orientation of the film. Compatibility and cycling stability studies in a $Li/Li_3OCl/Li$ symmetric cell showed an initial increase in resistance especially up to 20–30 cycles and then self-stabilized [25]. In addition, another novel class of anti-perovskite, $Li_{3-2x}M_xHalO$ (M stands for divalent cations such as Mg^{2+}, Ca^{2+}, or Ba^{2+}, and 'Hal' stands for halides such as Cl$^-$, I$^-$, or a mixture), as glassy electrolytes based on a LiRAP was first reported by Braga et al. [26]. These novel glassy materials exhibit ultra-fast ionic conduction of 25×10^{-3} S cm^{-1} at 25°C and are lightweight, non-flammable, and thermally and electrochemically stable materials. Hence, they show promise in future applications in which higher valence dopants can result in higher conductivities.

Despite the superionic properties of Li-rich anti-perovskites, the lithium-ion conductivity mechanism is still not well understood. Several theoretical studies have focused on investigating their phase stability [23,24,27], Li migration mechanism [23,24,28], charge carrier concentration [28], and compositional optimization [29] using first-principles calculations and lattice dynamics calculations as reported. The mechanism of Li^+ transport in Li_3OCl, Li_3OBr, and their mixed composite $Li_3OCl_{0.5}Br_{0.5}$ has been investigated [23] and in Li_3OCl LiRAP by defect chemistry [30] or, very recently, Li_3OCl LiRAP by first-principles study [31]. To date, there is no consensus on the mechanism of Li transport in Li_3OCl.

Zhang et al. [23] and Mouta et al. [28] reported a high formation energy of 41.5 eV for a lithium Frenkel pair. This finding rules out the possibility that the main mechanism of Li transport involves the formation and recombination of lithium vacancy and interstitial pairs. Zhang et al. [23] and Lu et al. [30] proposed a Li vacancy

Solid-State Electrolytes for Lithium-Ion Batteries

diffusion model, in which Li vacancies are considered to be the main mobile charge carriers, but the migration energy barrier of a Li vacancy (~0.3 eV) was higher than that observed in experiments (0.26 eV) [19]. Zhang et al. [23] proposed the lithium vacancy hopping mechanism and calculated the migration barrier to be 367 meV. Deng et al. [29] further identified a lower barrier of Li vacancy (282 meV) by varying the halide sublattice ordering. In contrast, Emly et al. [24] proposed the Li-interstitial dumbbell model with a three-atoms cooperative hopping mechanism in which the migration mechanism involved Li-interstitial dumbbells with a computed energy barrier 50% lower than that of the vacancy-driven migration. Although the model can be well explained by the activation energy in experiments because of the considerably low migration energy barrier of an interstitial-Li atom (0.17 eV), the higher defect formation energy of the carrier (~1.94 eV) indicates that Li^+ conductivity is quite low [24]. Mouta et al. [28] also showed that Li^+ vacancies are the dominant carrier because of their low defect formation energy, which is approximately 0.48 eV lower than that of interstitial-Li atoms; however, in contrast, the migration energy barrier of a Li vacancy is approximately 0.2 eV higher than that of interstitial lithium. These results show that the origin of the low activation energy and high conductivity of Li_3OCl is not yet well understood. In addition to the mobility in bulk, another important area for Li^+ mobility is at the surface of Li_3OCl. Understanding the surface character of Li_3OCl is essential to systematically control the performance of the materials [28]. Phase diagrams and electronic structure calculations proved that anti-perovskites (Li_3OCl, Li_3OBr, and their mixed composite $Li_3OCl_{0.5}Br_{0.5}$) were thermodynamically metastable but electrochemically stable [23]. Furthermore, ab initio molecular dynamics (AIMD) simulations were conducted and revealed that increased structural disorders and Li vacancies can lead to enhanced Li^+ diffusion.

In their work. Lu et al. [30], investigated the defect chemistry and the associated lithium transport in Li_3OCl, using ab initio density functional theory (DFT) calculations and classical molecular dynamics (MD) simulations. They studied three types of charge neutral defect pairs: (i) LiCl Schottky pair, (ii) Li_2O Schottky pair, and (iii) the Li interstitial with a substitutional defect of O on the Cl site. Among these charge neutral defect pairs, the LiCl Schottky pair has the lowest binding energy and is the most energetically favorable for diffusion as computed by DFT. The computed Li^+-ion diffusion coefficients for LiCl Schottky systems are significantly higher than those for the other two defects considered and were confirmed by classical MD simulations. Also, it was found that the activation energy in LiCl-deficient Li_3OCl is comparable to experimental values. The high ionic conductivity and low activation energies of LiCl Schottky systems can be explained by the low energy pathways of Li between the Cl vacancies; thus, Lu et al. [30] concluded that Li vacancy hopping is the main diffusion mechanism in highly conductive Li_3OCl. Very recently, Wu et al. [31] systematically investigated the stability, geometric structure, electronic properties, and Li^+-ion mobility of a Li_3OCl (100) surface using first-principles density functional theory calculations. In the study, they considered several geometric structure models with different low Miller indices to obtain the most stable surface structure and found that the Li_3OCl (1 0 0) surface with Li– and Cl– termination on both sides was the most stable configuration, which is further verified by calculating the atomic relaxation and electronic properties. To study the lithium motilities on the surface, they calculated the defect formation energies and migration energy barriers showed that interstitial Li with a migration energy barrier of 0.086 eV is the most important carrier at the surface. These results provide fundamental insights into Li$_3$OCl surface properties and Li-ion mobility at the surface [31]. Even though many computational studies have reported Li$^+$ mobility in bulk Li$_3$OCl and have proposed different Li$^+$ diffusion models, there is still no consensus on the Li$^+$ migration mechanism in Li$_3$OCl material, hence the mechanism of Li-rich anti-perovskites remains a much debated topic and further studies are needed to address this issue.

2.3 SULFIDE-TYPE LITHIUM-ION CONDUCTORS

The structurally and chemically related Li thio-phosphate family of materials has recently received attention as promising candidates for inorganic solid electrolytes, where ionic conductivity as large as 10^{-3} S cm^{-1} has been reported. These materials are characterized by the composition Li$_v$PS$_w$. The comparison between the crystalline Li phosphate and the corresponding thio-phosphates has provided further insight into solid electrolyte development.

2.3.1 LISICON AND THIO-LISICONS

Crystalline materials that possess well-defined conduction pathways for lithium-ion transport are expected to have superior conductivity compared to their amorphous counterparts. For instance, Li$_{14}$Zn(GeO$_4$)$_4$ (LISICON) is composed of LiO$_4$, ZnO$_4$, GeO$_4$, and LiO$_6$ tetrahedra arranged in the γ-Li$_3$PO$_4$ structure with conduction pathways in the c-direction [32] (Figure 2.8).

LISICON-type solid electrolytes exhibit relatively low room temperature ionic conductivity (~10^{-7} S cm^{-1}) and an electrochemical window of about 5 V. Li$_{14}$ZnGe$_4$O$_{16}$ is a typical example of a LISICON-type ionic conductor, in which Li$_{14}$ZnGe$_4$O$_{16}$ is

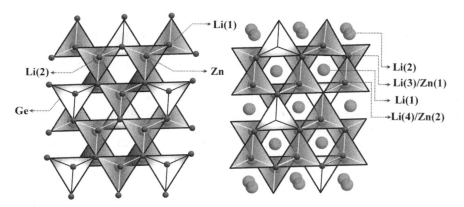

FIGURE 2.8 Schematic visualization of the crystal structure of LISICON member Li$_{14}$ZnGe$_4$O$_{16}$.

Solid-State Electrolytes for Lithium-Ion Batteries 31

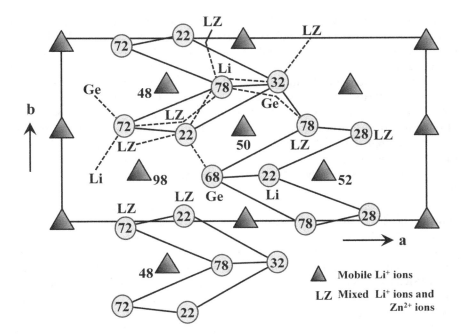

FIGURE 2.9 Projection of the LISICON structure on the *ab* plane. Adapted and reproduced with permission from Ref. [33]. Copyright © 1978 Elsevier.

a member of the $Li_{2+2x}Zn_{1-x}GeO_4$ system and can be viewed as a Li_4GeO_4–Zn_2GeO_4 solid solution. These $Li_{14}ZnGe_4O_{16}$ LISICONs were first proposed by Hong in 1978 [33]. Figure 2.9 shows the 2D projection of the LISICON structure on the *ab* plane; the framework is related to the γ-Li_3PO_4 crystal structure. In their crystals, $Li_{11}ZnGe_4O_{16}$ forms a three-dimensional skeleton structure and lithium ions in the skeleton distribute in 4c and 8d sites (Figure 2.9). These 4c and 8d sites are occupied by four and seven Li^+ ions, respectively. The remaining three Li^+ ions are located in 4c and 4a interstitial sites and their thermal coefficients are exceptionally high, which indicates that they can be mobile. Each 4a site in the framework is connected to two 4c sites and vice versa. The bottlenecks to Li^+ transport between these sites are parallelograms, which have a tilt angle with the *ab* plane. On the basis of calculations, Zheng et al. [34] reported that the average size of the bottlenecks (4.38 Å) is bigger than the minimum size required for Li^+ transport ($2r_{Li} + 2r_o = 4.0$ Å), which promotes the mobility of Li^+ ions.

The $Li_{14}ZnGe_4O_{16}$ shows an ionic conductivity of only 10^{-7} S cm^{-1} at room temperature, reaching 0.13 S cm^{-1} at 300°C, which is quite low for a good solid-state electrolyte. Robertson et al. [35] beautifully explained this inferior lithium-ion conductivity, which results from the trapping of the mobile Li^+ ions by the immobile sublattice at lower temperatures via the formation of defect complexes. Furthermore, Thangadurai et al. [7] reported that $Li_{14}ZnGe_4O_{16}$ is highly reactive with Li metal and atmospheric CO_2, hence conductivity decreases with time, limiting its use as an electrolyte in LIBs. It has been realized that larger and more polarizable anions tend to substantially enhance the mobility of the cationic species. Thus, much effort has been made to improve the ionic conductivity of LISICON-type solid electrolytes by replacing the oxide with sulfur in the framework of the LISICON structure, which has led to the discovery of sulfide-based glassy ceramics with Li conductivities in the range of 10^{-4} to 10^{-3} S cm^{-1} at room temperature, and the resulting LISICONs are referred as thio-LISICONs. In 2001, this novel design principle—the replacement of oxygen with sulfur in tetrahedral anionic sublattices featuring strongly covalent bonding, combined with aliovalent cation substitution to dope the system either with Li vacancies or Li interstitials—was used by Kanno and co-workers [36] to prepare the first crystalline sulfide-based Li-ion conductor with conductivities exceeding 1×10^{-3} S cm^{-1}.

Since the radius of S^{2-} is higher than O^{2-}, this substitution can significantly enhance the size of the Li$^+$ transport bottlenecks. In addition, S^{2-} has better polarization capability than O^{2-}, and thus weakens the interaction between the skeleton and Li$^+$-ions, diminishes interactions between Li$^+$ in the sublattice, and increases the concentration of mobile Li$^+$-ions. Therefore, compared with LISICON systems, the thio-LISICON materials can achieve significantly higher ionic conductivity (over 10^{-4} S cm^{-1} at room temperature). The thio-LISICONs also exhibit enhanced electrochemical performance as compared with LISICON family conductors and can be described through the nominal composition of Li$_{4-x}$M$_{1-y}$M*$_y$S$_4$ (M = Si, Ge, and M* = P, Al, Zn, Ga) [36,37]. The maximum ionic conductivity of the thio-LISICON family is greater than 10^{-3} S cm^{-1} at $x = 0.75$, and $y = x$ in Li$_{4-x}$M$_{1-y}$M*$_y$S$_4$ (M = Si, Ge, and M* = P, Al, Zn, Ga) [37–40]. A variety of thio-LISICON materials, their conductivities, and their conduction mechanisms are shown in Figure 2.10 [37].

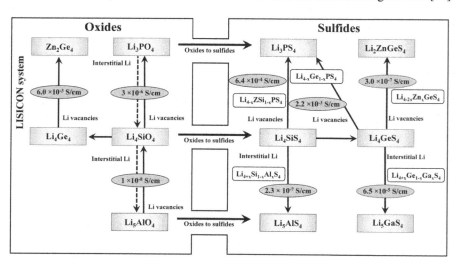

FIGURE 2.10 LISICON and thio-LISICON family tree with listed lithium-ion conduction mechanisms and ionic conductivity values. Adapted and reproduced with permission from Ref. [37]. Copyright © 2001 Electrochemical Society, Inc.

Depending on the valence of the cations and the excess or deficiency of Li from the parent thio-LISICON phase, ionic conduction may occur through either a Li interstitial or a vacancy mechanism, respectively. The LISICON counterparts are also shown in Figure 2.10, with the thio-LISICON materials demonstrating notably higher ionic conductivities. Thio-LISICON solid electrolytes also have advantages, such as easy reduction of grain boundary resistance by conventional cold press of electrolyte powers and preferable application in all-solid-state batteries due to their mechanical property [41]. Among these conductors, the ionic conduction of $Li_{4-x}Ge_{1-x}P_xS_4$ ($Li_{3.25}Ge_{0.25}P_{0.75}S_4$ showed an ionic conductivity of 2.2×10^{-3} S cm^{-1} at 25°C) showed superior performances than any other member. Also it showed negligible electronic conductivity, high electrochemical stability, no phase transition up to 500°C, high apparent kinetic chemical stability (no reaction with Li metal), and a large nominal electrochemical stability window between 0 and 5 V vs Li/Li$^+$ [37]. As discussed earlier, ionic conduction performances are mainly dependent on the radius and polarizability of constituted ions, hence the S-doped LISICONs exhibit higher ionic conductivity compared with their oxide analogues. Furthermore, the best performing thio-LISICON solid solution member ($\sigma = 2.2 \times 10^{-3}$ S cm^{-1} at 25°C) with the composition $Li_{3.25}Ge_{0.25}P_{0.75}S_4$ is a vacancy-doped system; the aliovalent cation substitution of Ge^{4+} with trivalent cations such as Al^{3+} leads to interstitial ion-doped systems such as $Li_{4+x}Si_{1-x}Al_xS_4$ and $Li_{4+x}Ge_{1-x}Ga_xS_4$ with slightly lower conductivities. The solid solution member $x = 0.6$ in $Li_{4-x}Si_{1-x}P_xS_4$ shows an ionic conductivity of 6.4×10^{-4} S cm^{-1} [42].

Most recently, Kamaya et al. [3] also developed a novel crystalline sulfide Li-ion electrolyte ($Li_{10}GeP_2S_{12}$) with outstanding electrochemical properties (exceedingly high conductivity of 12×10^{-3} S cm^{-1} at 27°C and a wide potential window). Its crystal structure was different from typical thio-LISICON structures. The crystal structure of this novel thio-LISICON had a 3D framework structure consisting of $(Ge_{0.5}P_{0.5})S_4$ tetrahedra, PS$_4$ tetrahedra, LiS$_4$ tetrahedra, and LiS$_6$ octahedra. The exceptionally high ionic conductivity benefited from the 3D diffusion pathways both along the c-axis and in the ab plane. Crystallographic studies determined the crystal skeleton of $Li_{10}GeP_2S_{12}$ using X-ray diffraction (XRD) and synchrotron radiation X-ray data associated with the ab initio method to reveal a 3D framework with LiS$_6$ octahedra and $(Ge_{0.5}P_{0.5})S_4$ tetrahedra forming 1D chains connected by a common edge and connected at the corners with PS$_4$ tetrahedra [3]. In addition, neutron Rietveld analysis was used to further confirm Li occupation and the Li content. Du et al. [43] also reported that tetrahedrally coordinated Li1 (16h) and Li3 (8f) sites were responsible for ionic conduction and formed a 1D tetrahedral chain along the c-direction whereas the octahedrally coordinated Li2 sites were not available for Li$^+$ diffusion, suggesting that Li$^+$ diffusion paths along the c-axis were better for Li$^+$ diffusion than that in the ab plane (reflecting only weak anisotropy of Li$^+$ diffusion) with the thermodynamic stability being studied using ab initio methods. LIBs assembled with a LiCoO$_2$ cathode and a Li-In alloy anode using this novel electrolyte showed desirable battery performances. The cell delivered a discharge capacity higher than 120 mAh g^{-1} with excellent Coulombic efficiency of about 100% after the second cycle as well as a high decomposition potential of over

34 Ceramic and Specialty Electrolytes

5 V [3]. The strong Coulombic connection between mobile ions can prompt Li-ion transport in a string-like manner in LGPS with low activation energy barriers and extremely high ionic conductivities [44]. Very recently, Bron et al. [45] reported the synthesis of $Li_{10}SnP_2S_{12}$ by replacing Ge with Sn, whose total conductivity reached 4×10^{-3} S cm^{-1} at room temperature.

2.3.2 LGPS FAMILY

The ionic conductors belonging to the LGPS family are a unique class of compounds that have closed the gap between the liquid electrolyte and thio-LISICONs or Li argyrodites in terms of their conductivity and electrochemical performance. Since this class of material was first proposed by Kamaya et al. [3] in 2011, $Li_{10}GeP_2S_{12}$ has attracted wide interest due to its incredible ionic conductivity on a par with that achieved in common organic liquid electrolytes. The $Li_{10}GeP_2S_{12}$ was the first solid electrolyte reported to have an ionic conductivity greater than that of some liquid electrolytes at room temperature. The tetragonal compound $Li_{10}GeP_2S_{12}$ with $P4_2/$ nmc symmetry was found by Kamaya et al. [3]. The tetragonal unit cell of LGPS consists of $(Ge_{0.5}P_{0.5})S_4$ (50% Ge, 50% P occupancy), PS_4, and LiS_4 tetrahedra and LiS_6 octahedra [46]. $(Ge_{0.5}P_{0.5})S_4$ tetrahedra and LiS_6 octahedra share a common edge and form 1D chains along the c-direction. These chains are connected to one another by PS_4 tetrahedra through a common corner shared with LiS_6 octahedra, forming a 3D framework. LiS_4 tetrahedra form chains along the c-direction within this scaffold and lithium conduction occurs primarily in 1D channels formed by lithium-ion 16h and 8f tetrahedral sites. It is worth noting that the proposed structure is based only on the nominal composition of LGPS and the disordered distribution of GeS_4 and PS_4 tetrahedra can lead to the coexistence of different local microstructures [43]. The presence of microstructural fluctuations is expected to have a small effect on the electrochemical properties of the material. The $Li_{10}GeP_2S_{12}$ shows Li-ion conductivities as high as 1.2×10^{-2} S cm^{-1} at room temperature, which is one order of magnitude larger than those found in thio-LISICONS and exhibit an activation energy of 0.25 eV from 163 to 383 K [3].

The weak conduction pathways formed by corner-sharing LiS_4 tetrahedra in the ab plane significantly contribute to the ionic conductivity of LGPS. The nature of this anisotropy in LGPS crystal has been elucidated by molecular dynamics studies, and the activation energy for the ionic conduction in the c-direction is calculated as 0.17 eV [47] and 0.19 eV [48] (corresponding to $\approx$40 mS cm^{-1}) which is calculated as 0.28 eV [47] and 0.30 eV [48] in the ab plane and is further confirmed by solid-state nuclear magnetic resonance (NMR) studies. Solid-state NMR studies found that the activation energy for ionic conduction in LGPS is 0.16 and 0.26 eV in the c-direction and ab plane, respectively [49].

The overall activation energy for lithium-ion conduction in LGPS is observed to be a weighted average of the anisotropic values, which indicates that the contribution from the ab plane is essential for the high ionic conductivity in LGPS. A 1D ionic conductor typically does not exhibit high ionic conductivity due to thermodynamically favorable structural defects that easily block the transport of the

Solid-State Electrolytes for Lithium-Ion Batteries

ionic species. Conversely, high symmetry structures with a 3D network of ionic transport pathways and a concomitant high density of vacancies would lead to the structural instability of the material. The existence of lithium conduction pathways perpendicular to the 1D channels in LGPS combines the features of 1D and 3D ionic conductors and ensures that conductivity is robust with respect to the high concentration of defects [3].

However, the unstable interface of LGPS [50] as well as the low abundance and high cost of Ge in the electrolyte needs to be addressed. Because of the high cost and low abundance of Ge, new LGPS-type materials have been prepared and are classified as Ge-free and Ge-doped electrolytes ($Li_{10}GeP_2S_{12}$ and Li_7GePS_8), making them an economically viable electrolyte [51]. To address the high cost of Ge, researchers have attempted to replace Ge^{4+} with homologous Si^{4+} or Sn^{4+}, resulting in materials such as $Li_{10}SnP_2S_{12}$ [45], $Li_{10+\delta}(Sn_ySi_{1-y})_{1+\delta}P_{2-\delta}S_{12}$ [52], and $Li_{11}Si_2PS_{12}$ [53]. Unfortunately, the studies observed that these Si- and Sn-doped materials exhibited lower conductivities than the parent LGPS. In their studies, Zeier et al. [54] found that Sn^{4+} substitution can render the bottleneck of Li^+ diffusion along the z-direction, which induces tougher activation barriers and significantly affects the ionic conductivity. However, Kato et al. [55] reported an Si^{4+} substituted LGPS as $Li_{9.5}4Si_{1.74}P_{1.44}S_{11.7}C_{l0.3}$ which exhibited an exceptionally high ionic conductivity of up to 2.5×10^{-3} S cm^{-1} at room temperature. The ionic conductivity of $Li_{9.54}Si_{1.74}P_{1.44}S_{11.7}C_{l0.3}$ is found to be double that of the archetype LGPS, and is the highest ionic conductivity ever reported for Li-ion conductors [55]. In their studies, the researchers used the anisotropic thermal displacement of Li^+-ions and nuclear density distribution to verify 3D Li^+-ion migration channels with 1D channels along the c-axis and 2D channels in the ab plane. These studies suggested that the 3D conduction pathway in the LGPS-type conductor can contribute to optimal ionic conductivity [55]. In addition, these researchers also reported that the LGPS-type ionic conductor has good chemical stability, especially up to 100°C, which is mainly attributed to the lack of elemental diffusion and low interfacial resistance. However, in most of the sulfides, LGPS is also extremely air-sensitive and prone to fast hydrolysis when exposed to humid air, yielding H_2S, a highly toxic volatile, as a decomposition product. Also, LGPS and other sulfide solid electrolytes were found to be thermally stable up to 400–550°C, which indicates that these materials are thermally very stable even beyond the relevant operating temperatures for batteries [56]. Moreover, $Li_{9.6}P_3S_{12}$ also possesses a similar LGPS structure and has been reported to have excellent electrochemical stability and longer life spans under extreme cell operation conditions. In situ X-ray photoelectron spectroscopy (XPS) measurements of Li metal and relevant calculations revealed that lithiation of LGPS starts at 1.71 vs Li/Li^+, with the final equilibrium phases of Li metal being $Li_{15}Ge_4$, Li_3P, and Li_2S [50,57]. The oxidation stability of LGPS is limited to 2.14 V, with the final delithiation products being P_2S_5, GeS_2, and S. Generally, all sulfide solid electrolytes are oxidized between 2 and 2.5 V to form sulfur with relatively high decomposition energies, thus indicating that the observed large electrochemical stability window of more than 5 V is purely kinetic in origin. In fact, most decomposition products at high voltages are electronically insulating and/or are only formed at large overpotentials (especially when the formation of gaseous products is involved), such that the sluggish kinetics of the decomposition reactions may provide a larger thermodynamic electrochemical stability window. Recently, Sun et al. [52] successfully obtained an Sn-Si derivative of LGPS-type conductors $[Li_{10+\delta}(Sn_ySi_{1-y})_{1+\delta}P_{2-\delta}S_{12}]$ in the form of a Li_3PS_4-Li_4SnS_4-Li_4SiS_4 quasi-ternary system. It has also been reported that by adjusting the ratio of Sn/Si and $M^{4+}(Sn^{4+}$ and $Si^{4+})/P^{5+}$ in the [M1/P1] (4d) site, the dual doping of the original LGPS with Sn and Si can significantly improve ionic conduction. By dual doping with Sn and Si, the resulting $Li_{10.35}(Sn_{0.27}Si_{1.08})P_{1.65}S_{12}$ ionic conductors achieved an ionic conductivity of 1.1×10^{-2} S cm^{-1}, which is extremely close to the ionic conductivity of archetype LGPS (1.2×10^{-2} S cm^{-1}).

2.3.3 ARGYRODITES

Argyrodites-type crystalline materials such as Li_6PS_5Cl have been identified as potentially fast chalcogenide-based Li-ion conductors and a promising solid-state electrolyte for all-solid-state lithium-ion batteries due to their high room temperature lithium-ion conductivity, good processability, and excellent electrochemical stability. Lithium argyrodites are generally represented by the formulas Li_7PCh_6 or $Li_{7-x}BCh_{6-x}X_x$ (B = P, As; Ch = S, Se; X = Cl, Br, I; $0 < x \leq 1$), which indicates the large scope of substitutional patterns by both aliovalent and isovalent substitutions on both the cation and anion sublattices [58,59]. Their ionic conductivities are in the range of 10^{-3} to 10^{-2} S cm^{-1} [60,61] and an electrochemical stability of >7 V vs Li$^+$/Li [62]. Together with their observed excellent electrochemical inertness of >7 V vs Li/Li$^+$ and low electronic conductivity of <10^{-10} S cm^{-1} [62], lithium argyrodites show performance parameters roughly on a par with those of the thio-LISICONs. These fast lithium-ion conductors isostructural to the Cu- and Ag-argyrodites crystallize in tetrahedral close-packed structures of the anions with topologies similar to those of the cubic Laves phase $MgCu_2$ with Li randomly distributed across tetrahedral interstitials (cubic unit cell with space group F–43m, space group number 216).

Within the close-packed crystal structure of argyrodites, phosphorus atoms fill tetrahedral interstices, forming a network of isolated PS_4 tetrahedron (similarly to the thio-LISICON structure), while lithium ions are randomly distributed over the remaining tetrahedral interstices (48h and 24g sites) (i.e., PS_4^{3-} anions are located in the middle of 4b sites whereas the remaining sulfur atoms take up 4a and 4c sites) [63]. Here, it is worth noting that, despite the replacement of sulfur with halogens, the sulfur of PS_4^{3-} is not substituted and halogens take up 4a or 4c sites to display a face-centered structure in which the remaining tetrahedral interstices (24g and 48h Wyckoff sites) are occupied by Li-ions. In addition, position 24g can serve as the transition state for jumps between 2 48h sites and 12 48h sites, which can constitute a cage structure by surrounding each 4c site (Figure 2.11).

Lithium-ion diffusion occurs through these partially occupied positions forming hexagonal cages, which are connected to each other by an interstitial site around the halide ions or sulfur anions in the case of Li_6PS_5Cl or Li_6PS_5Br and Li_6PS_5I, respectively [61]. This kind of Li diffusion can be attributed to three different jump processes, including next-neighbor jumps (48h–24g–48h), intra-cage jumps (48h–48h

Solid-State Electrolytes for Lithium-Ion Batteries

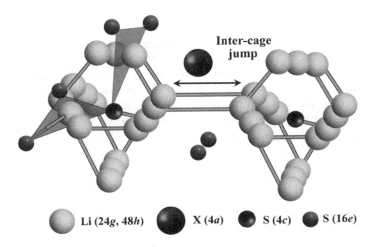

FIGURE 2.11 Li positions and possible jump routes in the crystal structure of Li$_6$PS$_5$X. Adapted and reproduced with permission from Ref. [64] Copyright © 2018 Royal Society of Chemistry.

jumps within the cage), and inter-cage jumps (48h–48h jumps between cages) [63]. Among these processes, inter-cage jumps are considered to play a dominant role in macroscopic long-range ion transport whereas intra-cage jumps with low jump rates can constrain Li$^+$-ion diffusion [65,66]. Due to the ease of diffusion between the hexagons made of partially occupied positions, the activation energy for the ionic movement is significantly low in the argyrodites-type electrolyte, which is typically in the range from 0.2 to 0.3 eV [67]. Deiseroth et al. [60] reported that Li$_6$PS$_5$X can be formed by mixing Li$_2$S, P$_2$S$_5$, and LiX under 550°C. Compared to the Cl or Br analogs Li$_6$PS$_5$Cl or Li$_6$PS$_5$Br, the Li$_6$PS$_5$I has significantly lower ionic conductivity. This may be explained by the difference in the connectivity of the hexagonal cages and the distribution of lithium among the different sites as well as the disorder on the S^{2-}/X$^-$ sublattice which exist in chloride and bromide analogs. The replacement of sulfur with halogen can generate vacancies, which is associated with disorder on the S^{2-}/X$^-$ sublattice and can enhance local Li-ion diffusion. Deiseroth et al. [60] reported that Cl^{-1} and Br^{-1} can take up 4a and 4c sites in Li$_6$PS$_5$X to allow for the significant disordering of halogen ions, resulting in high conductivities for Li$_6$PS$_5$Cl and Li$_6$PS$_5$Br. Alternatively, I^{-1} can barely take up 4a sites and I-containing argyrodites lack the disorder to display higher activation barriers for conduction. In addition, Kraf et al. [63] reported the effect of lattice dynamics on ionic motion and concluded that the migration barrier of moving cations decreases with softer lattices. In comparison with Li$_6$PS$_5$I, the considerable variation in the ionic conductivity of Li$_6$PS$_5$X (with X = Cl, Br) highlights the importance of disorder in promoting high ionic conductivity [67]. It is worth noting that the substitution of sulfur with oxygen leads to a significant decrease in lithium-ion conductivity, a trend similar to that observed in LISICON and thio-LISICON ionic conductors [62].

2.3.4 OTHER NEW THIO-PHOSPHATES

Apart from the thio-phosphates previously discussed, several novel sulfide-based Li-ion conductors with different features have also been recently reported. Li_4PS_4I, $Li_{6+x}P_{1-x}Si_xS_5Br$, $Li_{1+2x}Zn_{1-x}PS_4$ are some of the representative candidates for such new thio-phosphates ionic conductors. In the early 1980s, the $Li_2S/P_2S_5/LiI$ system exhibiting quite high conductivities of around 10^{-3} S cm^{-1} at room temperature was first reported. While those former investigations focused on compositions with a $Li_2S:P_2S_5$ ratio of 2:1 including up to 45 mol.% of LiI [68,69], there have been more recent studies of the system with $Li_2S:P_2S_5$ ratios of 7:3 (with up to 20 mol.% LiI) [70] and 3:1 with 35 mol.% [71] and 33 mol.% of LiI ($=Li_7P_2S_8I$) [72,73], respectively. These exhibited high room temperature ionic conductivities (1.3×10^{-3} S cm^{-1}), excellent electrochemical stabilities up to 10 V against Li metal, and good battery performances [74], making the $Li_2S/P_2S_5/LiI$ system highly promising for robust solid electrolyte materials for all-solid-state lithium-ion batteries. Very recently, it has been reported that the Li_3PS_4 precursor can react with LiI dissolved in either acetonitrile or dimethoxy ethane, followed by heat treatment, to form either $Li_7P_2S_8I$ or Li_4PS_4I [72,75]. Compared to Li_4PS_4I, the $Li_7P_2S_8I$ exhibits a high ionic conductivity and excellent stability against the Li metal. However, it was found that the addition of LiI into Li_3PS_4 glass, using a mechano ball-milling method for 35 h, could also result in an increase in the ionic conductivity up to 10^{-3} S cm^{-1}. The P_2S_5 can react instantly with the LiI solution in ethyl propionate (EP) to form a dissolved product, which then further reacts with Li_2S to form a solid electrolyte precursor $Li_{7-0.08x}P_2S_{8-0.04x}I$. In this simple one-pot synthesis, Li_2S, P_2S_5, and LiI powders were shaken for different times in the solvent. The resulting $Li_7P_2S_8I$ (prepared with $x = 1$ and a shaking time of 45 min) exhibited an ionic conductivity up to 4.6×10^{-4} S cm^{-1} at room temperature. The formation of electrolyte precursors in 30 min is the shortest time ever reported [76].

The Li_4PS_4I superionic conductor synthesized by a solvent-based soft chemistry approach exhibits a new structure type with a layer-like arrangement of isolated PS4^{3-} tetrahedra in which Li$^+$ ions diffuse in a complex 3D migration pathway system. The total lithium-ion conductivity determined for Li_4PS_4I is in the range of 6.4×10^{-5} to 1.2×10^{-4} S cm^{-1} at room temperature with activation energies (E_a) of 0.37 (35 kJ mol^{-1}) to 0.43 eV (41 kJ mol^{-1}) and followed Arrhenius behavior (σT vs T^{-1}). The NMR analyses revealed a hopping rate for the Li$^+$ ions of $\tau^{-1} = 5 \times 10^8$ s^{-1} corresponding to a bulk conductivity of 1.3×10^{-3} S cm^{-1} at 500 K and an activation energy of $E_a = 0.23(1)$ eV [75]. The measured room temperature lithium-ion conductivities are remarkably higher than the other Li_4PS_4I phases is formally composed ofLi_3PS_4 (β: 9×10^{-7} S cm^{-1}, γ: 3×10^{-7} S cm^{-1}) [77,78] and LiI ($\sim 10^{-7}$) [79], but still lower than that of β-Li_3PS_4 that was prepared from the precursor Li_3PS_4:3THF (2×10^{-4} S cm^{-1}) [80].

In order to shed light on the full potential of the Li_4PS_4I superionic conductor reported by Sedlmaier et al. [75], a theoretical study on Li_4PS_4I in the framework of density functional theory was performed by Sicolo et al. [81]. After creating a structural model that accurately accounts for the partial occupancies determined by diffraction experiments, Sicolo et al. [81] performed molecular dynamics simulations, unraveled the diffusion mechanisms, and calculated the diffusion coefficients and the activation barrier for diffusion. Figure 2.12 shows (110) and (220) sections of the lithium distribution during a 180 ps MD run at 600 K on the $1 \times 1 \times 2$ supercell. The color code indicates the residence time of Li-ions at any position (light: short, dark: long). A first, qualitative inspection shows that the Li migration paths are three-dimensional as foreseen by the topological analysis performed by Sedlmaier [75]. The theoretical studies found that these Li_4PS_4I exhibited a new crystal structure that was composed of insular PS43-tetrahedra aligned by layers vertical to the c-axis and Li-ions were dispersed over five partially occupied sites and diffused in a 3D migration pathway. The calculations based on density functional theory in order to predict the ion conductivity of crystalline and amorphous Li_4PS_4I suggest that Li_4PS_4I has the potential to be a truly superionic conductor with a much higher conductivity than what has been previously experimentally measured. According to topo-structural analyses, the Li-ion conductivity of the Li_4PS_4I was ~1.2×10^{-4} S cm^{-1} [75] and based on recent calculations, a higher conductivity of >10^{-1} S cm^{-1} is attainable [81]. Based on the simulations, Sicolo et al. [81] estimate conductivities of 2.28×10^{-1} S cm^{-1} at 300 K and 1.2 S cm^{-1} at 500 K, much higher than the reported conductivities (1.2×10^{-4} to 6.4×10^{-5} S cm^{-1} at 300 K and 1.3×10^{-3} S cm^{-1} at 500 K) [75].

Minafra et al. [82] synthesized superionic Li-argyrodite $Li_{6+x}P_{1-x}Si_xS_5Br$ through aliovalent doping into argyrodites and investigated the influence of aliovalent

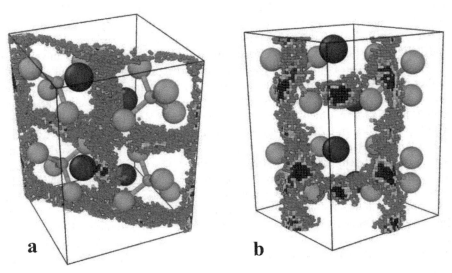

FIGURE 2.12 Representative sections of the lithium distribution in a $1 \times 1 \times 2$ super cell during a 180 ps MD run at 600 K. (a) The (110) section shows three-dimensional diffusion pathways; (b) the (220) section provides a more detailed view of the diffusion mechanism along the z-direction, together with Li1 positions. Adapted and reproduced with permission from Ref. [81]. Copyright © 2018 Elsevier.

substitution in Li_6PS_5Br. Using Rietveld refinements against X-ray and neutron diffraction, coupled with impedance spectroscopy, they monitored the influence of Si^{4+} substitution for P^{5+} in $Li_{6+x}P_{1-x}Si_xS_5Br$ on the structure and ionic transport properties. The study reported that the $Li_{6+x}P_{1-x}Si_xS_5Br$ exhibited both structural changes and a significant enhancement in lithium ionic conductivity as compared with non-doped argyrodites. Also, it was found that stepwise incorporation of Si^{4+} leads to an expansion of the unit cell (increase in polyhedral volumes), as well as the inclusion of additional Li^+ within the structure. The increasing Li content occupies the structural transition state and, in combination with the structural changes, leads to a three-fold improvement in the ionic conductivity and therefore improved transport properties. It was observed that with increasing Si^{4+} content, the amount of Li^+ increases (increases the carrier concentration) and a three-fold increase in the conductivity from 0.7×10^{-3} S cm^{-1} for the unsubstituted sample to 2.4×10^{-3} S cm^{-1} for aliovalent doped (adding more lithium cations into the transition state of hopping) $Li_{6.35}P_{0.65}Si_{0.35}S_5Br$. As the Si^{4+} content is increased further, the conductivity slightly decreases, which is possibly due to the solubility limit of Si^{4+} being surpassed and the associated phase segregations [82].

More recently, theoretical studies have also revealed that $Li_{1+2x}Zn_{1-x}PS_4$ (LZPS) as characterized by a body-centered-cubic structure can provide high Li-ion conductivity. Structural screening of materials in the Inorganic Crystal Structure Database (ICSD) [83] reveals that the crystal structure of LZPS contains a bcc arrangement of sulfur anions and may therefore be expected to have high lithium-ion mobility. The crystal structure of LZPS has previously been characterized [84]. Richards et al. [85] employed computational techniques based on density functional theory and ab initio molecular dynamics simulations to investigate the ionic conductivity, and nudged elastic band simulations to investigate the transport mechanisms and phase stability of LZPS in detail. These researchers reported that $Li_{1+2x}Zn_{1-x}PS_4$ with higher x can exhibit lower Li migration barriers by first-principles calculations. Here, the structure of the parent phase stoichiometric $LiZnPS_4$ is composed of PS_4^{3-} and ZnS_4^{6-} tetrahedra in which Li takes over 2b sites and Zn distributes over 2a sites. The S^{2-} sublattice in LZPS is very close to bcc having an a/c ratio of 0.9 and with sulfur atoms each displaced only 0.29 Å from their ideal positions. As for the crystal structure of $Li_{1+2x}Zn_{1-x}PS_4$ ($x > 0$), these researchers reported that excess Li-ions can share 2a sites with Zn and occupy 2d sites that are charge compensated due to the replacement of Zn^{2+} in the 2a sites with Li^+. Because of the relatively small size of the PS_4 tetrahedron, the P layer is slightly thinner than the Zn layer and these remaining tetrahedral sites are high energy in comparison with the standard Li sites. Each interstitial Li^+ is charge compensated by substitution of a nearby Zn^{2+} atom with Li^+. The phonon calculations show that this occupancy is crucial for improving ionic transport.

Kaup et al. [86] also synthesized a well-crystallized LZPS with a high x value of 0.35 and reported that the resulting $Li_{1.7}Zn_{0.65}PS_4$ can exhibit high conductivities of $>10^{-4}$ S cm^{-1}. The conductivities range from 5.40×10^{-8} S cm^{-1} at $x = 0$ to 8.4×10^{-4} S cm^{-1} at $x = 0.75$. The obtained phases, $Li_{1.7}Zn_{0.65}PS_4$ and $Li_{1.2}Zn_{0.9}PS_4$, respectively, demonstrated ionic conductivities of 1.30×10^{-4} and 1.65×10^{-5} S cm^{-1}.

Solid-State Electrolytes for Lithium-Ion Batteries

These values are more than four orders of magnitude higher compared to that of the parent $LiZnPS_4$ phase, owing to the Li occupation of the 2d interstitial site in the lattice and decreased Li-ion migration barriers [87]. Despite these performances, however, the conductivities of these experimental $Li_{1+2x}Zn_{1-x}PS_4$ samples were all lower than those obtained through theoretical calculations, which may be due to the amorphous content and highly metastable defect composition. In addition, studies have revealed that $Li_{2.5}Zn_{0.25}PS_4$ with a glassy matrix can provide conductivities of up to 8×10^{-4} S cm^{-1}. However, contact with a lithium-metal anode may reduce the Zn^{2+} in LZPS and result in electrical conductivity [85] similar to $Li_{10}GeP_2S_{12}$ and related materials.

2.3.5 LAYERED SULFIDES

Recently, it has been shown that aliovalent substitution in Li_4SnS_4 (i.e., $Li_{4-x}Sn_{1-x}As_xS_4$ where $x = 0$ to 0.25) has yielded an ion conductor with excellent air stability [5], and a series of fast Li-ion conductors based on $Li_{3x}[Li_xSn_{1-x}S_2]$ has been identified in which $Li[Li_{0.33}Sn_{0.67}S_2]$ (Li: Sn = 1:2) and $Li_{0.6}[Li_{0.2}Sn_{0.8}S_2]$ (Li:Sn = 1:4) are two outstanding superionic conductors that exhibit different crystal structures and lithium-ion conductivities. The crystal structure of the layered lithium intercalated tin sulfide $Li[Li_{0.33}Sn_{0.67}S_2]$ shows Li distributed both in and between Li/Sn-ordered honeycomb sulfide layers [88,89]. Both the layered sulfides $Li_2Sn_2S_5$ and Li_2SnS_3 can be synthesized using several approaches such as a facile wet chemistry approach for both [88], a high-temperature solid-state synthesis approach for Li_2SnS_3 ($x=0.33$) [89], and other methods for $Li_2Sn_2S_5$ ($x = 0.2$) [90]. Li_2SnS_3 and $Li_2Sn_2S_5$ are fast Li^+ ion conductors that exhibit high thermal stability (m.p. ~750°C) as well as environmental stability at ambient conditions. In the case of the Li-rich prototype Li_2SnS_3 (space group $C2/c$), Brant et al. [89] reported the crystallization of Li_2SnS_3 in a layered A_2BO_3 structure with an NaCl-like network in which the framework was built up by Li/Sn-ordered sulfide layers with Sn-ions arranged in a honeycomb fashion and Li-ions sandwiched between the layers. According to impedance spectroscopy, Li_2SnS_3 exhibits Li^+ ion conductivity of 1.5×10^{-5} S cm^{-1} at room temperature and 1.6×10^{-3} S cm^{-1} at 100°C, which is among the highest for ternary chalcogenides yet to be reported. It is a vast improvement compared to the closely related polycrystalline, ternary thio-LISICONs: Li_2GeS_3 (ionic conductivity of 9.7×10^{-9} S cm^{-1} at 125°C), Li_5GaS_4 (ionic conductivity of 5.1×10^{-8} S cm^{-1} at 100°C), and Li_4GeS_4 (ionic conductivity of 2.0×10^{-7} S cm^{-1} at 25°C) [36]. The room temperature conductivity of Li_2SnS_3 is two orders of magnitude higher than the related ternary chalcogenide $Li_4Sn_2Se_6$ (ionic conductivity of 2×10^{-7} S cm^{-1} at 25°C) [91]. Based on first-principles calculations, it has been proposed that the origin of the fast ion conductivity in Li_2SnS_3 arises from the mobility of the Li(I) and Li(III) that reside in the lithium sulfide layers between the honeycomb-like $(SnS_3)^{2-}$ layers.

As for the Li-depleted version, Holzmann et al. [90] reported that the structure of $Li_2Sn_2S_5$ (in $C2/m$) was similar to the parent compound Li_2SnS_3, whereas the Li content decreased to 60% in the interlayer gallery (Figure 2.13). They prepared both $Li_{1.0}(Li_{0.33}Sn_{0.67}S_2)$ and $Li_{0.6}(Li_{0.2}Sn_{0.8}S_2)$. Both $Li(Li_{0.33}Sn_{0.67}S_2)$ and $Li_{0.6}(Li_{0.2}Sn_{0.8}S_2)$

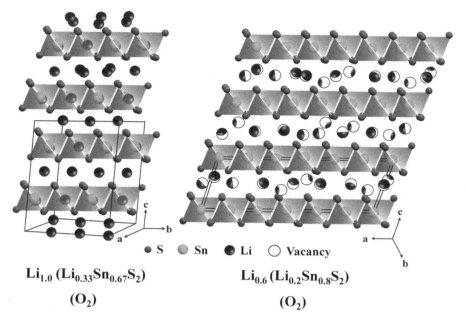

FIGURE 2.13 Left: crystal structure of $Li_{1.0}(Li_{0.33}Sn_{0.67}S_2)$ with a full Sn/Li order. Right: crystal structure of $Li_{0.6}(Li_{0.2}Sn_{0.8}S_2)$ with partially substituted Sn positions and an O1 type stacking. Adapted and reproduced with permission from Ref. [90]. Copyright © 2016 Royal Society of Chemistry.

display O-type stacking of the layers, where the interlayer atoms are octahedrally coordinated by sulfur atoms (Li/SnS$_6$ octahedra), which is similar to many other honeycomb-type compounds [92–97]. In $Li_{0.6}(Li_{0.2}Sn_{0.8}S_2)$, only 77% of the interlayer lithium atoms occupy those octahedral sites and the remaining 23% occupy tetrahedral sites that are closer to the covalent layers [90]. Pulsed field gradient (PFG) NMR studies on powder samples display intragrain (bulk) diffusion coefficients D_{NMR} on the order of 10^{-11} m^2 s^{-1} at room temperature, which corresponds to a conductivity σ_{NMR} of 9.3×10^{-3} S cm^{-1} and is in good agreement with the lithium-ion conductivity of 1.5×10^{-2} S cm^{-1} measured by impedance spectroscopy on powder pellets. Also, the direct current galvanostatic polarization/depolarization measurements on such powder pellet samples show negligible electronic contributions (less than 10^{-9} S cm^{-1}). By assuming the Nernst–Einstein equation, the high lithium-ion conductivity of $Li_{0.6}(Li_{0.2}Sn_{0.8}S_2)$ is on a par with the best Li conducting solid-state electrolytes reported to date. Compared to fully occupied $Li(Li_{0.33}Sn_{0.67}S_2)$, the significantly higher ionic conductivity of Li-depleted $Li_{0.6}(Li_{0.2}Sn_{0.8}S_2)$ is mostly due to their unique crystal structure.

By analyzing the structure–property relationships in $Li_{0.6}(Li_{0.2}Sn_{0.8}S_2)$ and $Li(Li_{0.33}Sn_{0.67}S_2)$ by means of single crystal X-ray diffraction and ssNMR, it was reported that the removal of Li$^+$ ions from the interlayer gallery significantly improved lithium-ion conductivity. It is worth noting that the removal of Li$^+$-ions (i.e., partial occupancy) slightly decreases the number of mobile Li$^+$-ions while at

TABLE 2.1
Summary of Fast Ion-Conductive Ceramics–Polymer Solid Electrolytes

Year	Polymer electrolyte ingredients	Ionic conductivity (S cm^{-1})	References
2003	$Li_5La_3M_2O_{12}$ (M = Nb, Ta)-PEO-LiPF$_6$	10^{-6} (25°C)	[98]
2015	$Li_7La_3Zr_2O_{12}$ (LLZO)-PEO-LiClO$_4$	4.42×10^{-4} (55°C)	[99]
2015	$Li_{0.33}La_{0.557}TiO_3$ (LLTO) random nanowire-PAN-LiClO$_4$	2.4×10^{-4} (25°C)	[100]
2015	$Li_{2.5}Al_{0.5}Ge_{1.5}(PO_4)_3$ (LAGP)-PEO-LiClO$_4$	2.6×10^{-4} (55°C)	[101]
2015	$Li_7La_3Zr_2O_{12}$ (LLZO)-PEO-LiClO$_4$	4.42×10^{-4} (55°C)	[99]
2016	$Li_{6.4}La_3Zr_2Al_{0.2}O_{12}$ (LLZO)-PEO-LiTFSI	2.5×10^{-4} (25°C)	[102]
2016	$Li_{1.5}Al_{0.5}Ge_{1.5}(PO_4)_3$ (LAGP)-PEO-LiTFSI	6.76×10^{-4} (60°C)	[103]
2016	$Li_{10}GeP_2S_{12}$-PEO-LiTFSI	10^{-5} (25°C)	[104]
2017	$Li_{6.20}Ga_{0.30}La_{2.95}Rb_{0.05}Zr_2O_{12}$-PVdF-LiTFSI	1.62×10^{-3} (25°C)	[105]
2017	$Li_{6.75}La_3Zr_{1.73}Ta_{0.23}O_{12}$-PVdF-LiClO$_4$	5×10^{-4} (25°C)	[106]
2017	$Li_{0.33}La_{0.557}TiO_3$ (LLTO) aligned nanowire-PAN-LiClO$_4$	6.05×10^{-5} (30°C)	[107]
2017	$Li_{1.3}Al_{0.3}Ti_{1.7}(PO_4)_3$(LATP)-PEO-BPEG-LiTFSI	2.5×10^{-4} (60°C)	[108]
2018	$Li_7La_3Zr_2O_{12}$ (LLZO)-PEO-LiTFSI	1.12×10^{-4} (25°C)	[109]
2018	$Li_{6.4}La_3Zr_{1.4}Ta_{0.6}O_{12}$ (LLZTO)-PEO-LiTFSI	10^{-4} (55°C)	[110]
2018	$Li_{0.33}La_{0.557}TiO_3$-PEO-LiClO$_4$	2.4×10^{-4} (25°C)	[9]
2018	3D-$Li_{0.35}La_{0.55}TiO_3$ (LLTO)-PEO-LiTFSI	8.8×10^{-5} (25°C)	[111]

the same time facilitating the easy motion of Li$^+$-ions by increasing their mobility. This means that the Li depopulation resulted in an increase in the interlayer distance due to charge compensation by additional Sn in the honeycomb layers as well as the enhancement of Li mobility in the interlayer gallery, which significantly contributed to high ionic conductivities.

Therefore, besides a distinctly different Sn/Li order in the mixed Li/SnS$_2$ layers, the Li$^+$ ions in $Li_{0.6}(Li_{0.2}Sn_{0.8}S_2)$ have more space to move, due not only to the slightly larger layer distance in $Li_{0.6}(Li_{0.2}Sn_{0.8}S_2)$, but also to the lower occupancy of the Li sites located in between the layers. Based on impedance spectroscopy analysis, it was also reported that the activation energy of $Li_2Sn_2S_5$ was 0.17 eV, which was lower than that of Li_2SnS_3 (0.59 eV). This could be attributed to the different Li diffusion pathways in which for $Li_2Sn_2S_5$, there was an additional diffusion pathway of hops between tetrahedral (T) and face-sharing octahedral (O) Li sites as compared with the pure O–O trajectories in $Li_2Sn_2S_5$. Furthermore, the study suggests that for the single crystalline $Li_{0.6}(Li_{0.2}Sn_{0.8}S_2)$ samples, even higher conductivity is possible along the *ab* plane based on structural anisotropy (Table 2.1) [90].

2.4 CONCLUSION

The requirement of the current generation for efficient energy storage devices without compromising on the safety of the system has led to investigations into solid and gel electrolytes. Polymer-based electrolytes are being widely investigated under these categories, but these polymer-based systems decompose at elevated temperatures. Thus, the investigation of electrolytes capable of performing at elevated temperatures without decomposing has led to the development of chalcogenide-based solid-state electrolytes. A detailed analysis of the ionic conductivity, electrochemical performance, thermal stability, and structures of these chalcogenide system was analyzed. Perovskites and anti-perovskite-based lithium conductors were employed as oxide electrolytes, and LISICONs, thio-LISICONs, LGPS and similar compounds, argyrodites, layered sulfides, etc., were investigated under sulfide-type lithium-ion conductors. These inorganic compounds were found to be highly stable at elevated temperatures with enhanced ionic conductivity ($\sim 10^{-3}$ S cm^{-1}), upgrading them to be an excellent candidate for high-temperature lithium-ion batteries.

ACKNOWLEDGMENT

Dr. M.J. Jabeen Fatima and Dr. Prasanth Raghavan would like to acknowledge the Kerala State Council for Science, Technology and Environment (KSCSTE), Kerala, for financial assistance.

REFERENCES

1. Monroe C, Newman J (2005) The impact of elastic deformation on deposition kinetics at lithium/polymer interfaces. *J Electrochem Soc* 152:A396. doi: 10.1149/1.1850854
2. Lin Y, Liu Ke, Wu M, et al. (2020) Enabling solid-state Li metal batteries by in-situ forming ionogel interlayers. *ACS Appl Energy Mater* 3:5712–5721 doi: 10.1021/acsaem.0c00662
3. Kamaya N, Homma K, Yamakawa Y, et al. (2011) A lithium superionic conductor. *Nat Mater* 10:682–686. doi: 10.1038/nmat3066
4. Hayashi A, Noi K, Sakuda A, Tatsumisago M (2012) Superionic glass-ceramic electrolytes for room-temperature rechargeable sodium batteries. *Nat Commun* 3:2–6. doi: 10.1038/ncomms1843
5. Dudney N, Liang C, Sahu G, Lin Z, Li J, Liu Z (2015) Multi-phase semicrystalline microstructures drive exciton dissociation in neat plastic semiconductors. *J Mater Chem C* 3: Sahu, Gayatri, Zhan Lin, Juchuan Li, Zengcai Liu, Nancy Dudney and Chengdu Liang (2014) Air-Stable, High-Conduction Solid Electrolytes of Arsenic-Substituted Li$_4$SnS$_4$. *R Soc Chem* 4:1166–1169. https://doi.org/10.1039/b000000x
6. Fergus JW (2010) Ceramic and polymeric solid electrolytes for lithium-ion batteries. *J Power Sources* 195:4554–4569. doi: 10.1016/j.jpowsour.2010.01.076
7. Thangadurai V, Weppner W (2006) Recent progress in solid oxide and lithium ion conducting electrolytes research. *Ionics (Kiel)* 12:81–92. doi: 10.1007/s11581-006-0013-7
8. Knauth P (2009) Inorganic solid Li ion conductors: An overview. *Solid State Ionics* 180:911–916. doi: 10.1016/j.ssi.2009.03.022
9. Stramare S, Thangadurai V, Weppner W (2003) Lithium lanthanum titanates: A review. *Chem Mater* 15:3974–3990. doi: 10.1002/chin.200352244
10. Bohnke O, Bohnke C, Fourquet JL (1996) Mechanism of ionic conduction and electrochemical intercalation of lithium into the perovskite lanthanum lithium titanate. *Solid State Ionics* 91:21–31. doi: 10.1016/s0167-2738(96)00434-1
11. Yashima M, Itoh M, Inaguma Y, Morii Y (2005) Crystal structure and diffusion path in the fast lithium-ion. *J Am Chem Soc* 127:3491

Solid-State Electrolytes for Lithium-Ion Batteries

12. Zhu P, Yan C, Dirican M, et al. (2018) $Li_{0.33}La_{0.557}TiO_3$ ceramic nanofiber-enhanced polyethylene oxide-based composite polymer electrolytes for all-solid-state lithium batteries. *J Mater Chem A* 6:4279–4285. doi: 10.1039/c7ta10517g

13. Liu W, Liu N, Sun J, et al. (2015) Ionic conductivity enhancement of polymer electrolytes with ceramic nanowire fillers. *Nano Lett* 15:2740–2745. doi: 10.1021/acs.nanolett.5b00600

14. Bae J, Li Y, Zhang J, et al. (2018) A 3D nanostructured hydrogel-framework-derived high-performance composite polymer lithium-ion electrolyte. *Angew Chemie - Int Ed* 57:2096–2100. doi: 10.1002/anie.201710841

15. Fu K, Gong Y, Dai J, et al. (2016) Flexible, solid-state, ion-conducting membrane with 3D garnet nanofiber networks for lithium batteries. *Proc Nat Acad Sci USA* 113:7094–7099.

16. O'Keeffe M, Bovin JO (1979) Solid electrolyte behavior of $NaMgF_3$: Geophysical implications. *Science* 206:599–600. doi: 10.1126/science.206.4418.599

17. Zhao Y (1998) Crystal chemistry and phase transitions of perovskite in P-T-X space: Data for $(K_xNa_{1-x})MgF_3$ perovskites. *J Solid State Chem* 141:121–132. doi: 10.1006/jssc.1998.7927

18. Yoshiasa A, Sakamoto D, Okudera H, et al. (2005) Electrical conductivities and conduction mechanisms of perovskite-type $Na_{1-x}K_xMgF_3$ (x=0, 0.1, 1) and $KZnF_3$. *Zeitschrift fur Anorg und Allg Chemie* 631:502–506. doi: 10.1002/zaac.200400358

19. Zhao Y, Daemen LL (2012) Superionic conductivity in lithium-rich anti-perovskites. *J Am Chem Soc* 134:15042–15047. doi.org/10.1021/ja305709z

20. Lu Z, Chen C, Baiyee ZM, Chen X, Niu C, Ciucci F (2015) Defect chemistry and lithium transport in Li_3OCl anti-perovskite superionic conductors. *Phys Chem* 17:32547–32555. doi.org/10.1039/C5CP05722A

21. Wortmann R, Sitta S, Horst S (1989) $Li7O_2Br_3$ — Eine weitere Strukturvariante der neuen Alkalimetallchalkogenidhalogenid-Perowskite. *Z Naturforsch* 44b:1348–1350. doi.org/10.1515/znb-1989-1103

22. Schwering G, Hönnerscheid A, Van Wüllen L, Jansen M (2003) High lithium ionic conductivity in the lithium halide hydrates $Li_{3-n}(OH_n)Cl$ ($0.83 \leq n \leq 2$) and $Li_{3-n}(OH_n)$ Br ($1 \leq n \leq 2$) at ambient temperatures. *ChemPhysChem* 4:343–348. doi: 10.1002/cphc.200390060

23. Zhang Y, Zhao Y, Chen C (2013) Ab initio study of the stabilities of and mechanism of superionic transport in lithium-rich antiperovskites. *Phys Rev B - Condens Matter Mater Phys* 87:1–8. doi: 10.1103/PhysRevB.87.134303

24. Emly A, Kioupakis E, Van der Ven A (2013) Phase stability and transport mechanisms in antiperovskite Li_3OCl and Li_3OBr superionic conductors. *Chem. Mater* 25: 4663–4670. doi: 10.1002/chin.201405001

25. Lü X, Wu G, Howard JW, et al. (2014) Li-rich anti-perovskite Li_3OCl films with enhanced ionic conductivity. *Chem Commun* 50:11520–11522. doi: 10.1039/C4CC05372A

26. Braga MH, Ferreira JA, Stockhausen V, et al. (2014) Novel Li_3ClO based glasses with superionic properties for lithium batteries. *J Mater Chem A* 2:5470–5480. doi: 10.1039/c3ta15087a

27. Chen MH, Emly A, Van Der Ven A (2015) Anharmonicity and phase stability of anti-perovskite Li_3OCl. *Phys Rev B - Condens Matter Mater Phys* 91:1–8. doi: 10.1103/PhysRevB.91.214306

28. Mouta R, Melo MÁB, Diniz EM, Paschoal CWA (2014) Concentration of charge carriers, migration, and stability in Li_3OCl solid electrolytes. *Chem Mater* 26:7137–7144. doi: 10.1021/cm503717e

29. Deng Z, Radhakrishnan B, Ong SP (2015) Rational composition optimization of the lithium-rich $Li_3OCl_{1-x}Br_x$ anti-perovskite superionic conductors. *Chem Mater* 27:3749–3755. doi: 10.1021/acs.chemmater.5b00988

30. Lu Z, Chen C, Baiyee ZM, et al. (2015) Defect chemistry and lithium transport in Li_3OCl anti-perovskite superionic conductors. *Phys Chem Chem Phys* 17:32547–32555. doi: 10.1039/c5cp05722a
31. Wu M, Xu B, Luo W, et al. (2020) First-principles study on the structural, electronic, and Li-ion mobility properties of anti-perovskite superionic conductor Li_3OCl (1 0 0) surface. *Appl Surf Sci* 510: 145394. doi: 10.1016/j.apsusc.2020.145394
32. Kokal I (2012) Solid state electrolytes for all-solid-state 3D lithium-ion batteries. ISBN 978-90-386-3270-4, Technische Universiteit Eindhoven
33. Hong HYP (1978) Crystal structure and ionic conductivity of $Li_{14}Zn(GeO_4)_4$ and other new Li^+ superionic conductors. *Mater Res Bull* 13:117–124. doi: 10.1016/0025-5408(78)90075-2
34. Zheng ZS, Zhang ZT, Tang ZL (2003) Lithium inorganic solid electrolytes. *Prog Chem* 15:101–106.
35. Robertson AD, West AR, Ritchie AG (1997) Review of crystalline lithium-ion conductors suitable for high temperature battery applications. *Solid State Ionics* 104:1–11.
36. Kanno R, Hata T, Kawamoto Y, Irie M (2000) Synthesis of a new lithium ionic conductor, thio-LISICON-lithium germanium sulfide system. *Solid State Ionics* 130:97–104. doi: 10.1016/S0167-2738(00)00277-0
37. Kanno R, Murayama M (2001) Lithium ionic conductor thio-LISICON: The Li[sub 2]S-GeS[sub 2]-P[sub 2]S[sub 5] system. *J Electrochem Soc* 148:A742. doi: 10.1149/1.1379028
38. Murayama M, Sonoyama N, Yamada A, Kanno R (2004) Material design of new lithium ionic conductor, thio-LISICON, in the $Li_2S-P_2S_5$ system. *Solid State Ionics* 170:173–180. doi: 10.1016/j.ssi.2004.02.025
39. Liu Z, Huang F, Yang J, et al. (2008) New lithium-ion conductor, thio-LISICON lithium zirconium sulfide system. *Solid State Ionics* 179:1714–1716. doi: 10.1016/j.ssi.2008.01.055
40. Murayama M, Kanno R, Kawamoto Y, Kamiyama T (2002) Structure of the thio-LISICON, Li_4GeS_4. *Solid State Ionics* 154–155:789–794. doi: 10.1016/S0167-2738(02)00492-7
41. Tatsumisago M, Nagao M, Hayashi A (2013) Recent development of sulfide solid electrolytes and interfacial modification for all-solid-state rechargeable lithium batteries. *J Asian Ceram Soc* 1:17–25. doi: 10.1016/j.jascer.2013.03.005
42. Murayama M, Kanno R, Irie M, et al. (2002) Synthesis of new lithium ionic conductor thio-LISICON - Lithium silicon sulfides system. *J Solid State Chem* 168:140–148. doi: 10.1006/jssc.2002.9701
43. Sun Y, Suzuki K, Hori S, et al. (2017) Superionic conductors: $Li10+\delta[SnySi1-y]1+\delta P2-\delta S12$ with a $Li10GeP2S12$-type structure in the $Li3PS4$-$Li4SnS4$-$Li4SiS4$ quasi-ternary system. *Chem Mater* 29:5858–5864. doi: 10.1021/acs.chemmater.7b00886
44. Xu M, Ding J, Ma E (2012) One-dimensional stringlike cooperative migration of lithium ions in an ultrafast ionic conductor. *Appl Phys Lett* 101:2012–2015. doi: 10.1063/1.4737397
45. Bron P, Johansson S, Zick K, et al. (2013) $Li_{10}SnP_2S_{12}$: An affordable lithium superionicconductor. *J. Am. Chem. Soc.* 135:15694-15697. doi.org/10.1021/ja407393y
46. Kwon O, Hirayama M, Suzuki K, et al. (2015) Synthesis, structure, and conduction mechanism of the lithium superionic conductor $Li10+\delta Ge1+\delta P2-\delta S12$. *J Mater Chem A* 3:438–446. doi: 10.1039/x0xx00000x
47. Mo Y, Ong SP, Ceder G (2012) First principles study of the $Li_{10}GeP_2S_{12}$ lithium superionic conductor material. *Chem Mater* 24:15–17. doi.org/10.1021/cm203303y
48. Adams S, Prasada Rao R (2012) Structural requirements for fast lithium ion migration in $Li_{10}GeP_2S_{12}$. *J Mater Chem* 22:7687–7691. doi: 10.1039/c2jm16688g

49. Liang X, Wang L, Jiang Y, et al. (2015) In-channel and in-plane Li ion diffusions in the superionic conductor $Li_{10}GeP_2S_{12}$ probed by solid-state NMR. *Chem Mater* 27:5503–5510. doi: 10.1021/acs.chemmater.5b01384

50. Wenzel S, Randau S, Leichtweiß T, et al. (2016) Direct observation of the interfacial instability of the fast ionic conductor Li10GeP2S12 at the lithium metal anode. *Chem Mater* 28:2400–2407. doi: 10.1021/acs.chemmater.6b00610

51. Kuhn A, Duppel V, Lotsch BV (2013) Tetragonal $Li_{10}GeP_2S_{12}$ and Li_7GePS_8-exploring the Li ion dynamics in LGPS Li electrolytes. *Energy Environ Sci* 6:3548–3552. doi: 10.1039/c3ee41728j

52. Sun Y, Suzuki K, Hori S, et al. (2017) Superionic conductors: $Li_{10+\delta}[Sn_ySi_{1-y}]_{1+\delta}P_{2-\delta}S_{12}$ with a $Li_{10}GeP_2S_{12}$-type structure in the Li_3PS_4-$Li_{10}SnS<sub>4<$. *Chem Mater* 29:5858–5864. doi: 10.1021/acs.chemmater.7b00886

53. Kuhn A, Gerbig O, Zhu C, et al. (2014) A new ultrafast superionic Li-conductor: Ion dynamics in $Li_{11}Si_2PS_{12}$ and comparison with other tetragonal LGPS-type electrolytes. *Phys Chem Chem Phys* 16:14669–14674.

54. Krauskopf T, Culver SP, Zeier WG (2018) Bottleneck of diffusion and inductive effects in $Li_{10}Ge_{1-x}Sn_xP_2S_{12}$. *Chem Mater* 30:1791–1798. doi: 10.1021/acs.chemmater.8b00266

55. Kato Y, Hori S, Saito T, et al. (2016) High-power all-solid-state batteries using sulfide superionic conductors. *Nat Energy* 1:1–7. doi: 10.1038/nenergy.2016.30

56. Hori S, Taminato S, Suzuki K, et al. (2015) Structure-property relationships in lithium superionic conductors having a $Li_{10}GeP_2S_{12}$-type structure. *Acta Crystallogr Sect B Struct Sci Cryst Eng Mater* 71:727–736. doi: 10.1107/S2052520615022283

57. Zhu Y, He X, Mo Y (2015) Origin of outstanding stability in the lithium solid electrolyte materials: Insights from thermodynamic analyses based on first-principles calculations. *ACS Appl Mater Interfaces* 7:23685–23693. doi: 10.1021/acsami.5b07517

58. Lotsch BV, Maier J (2017) Relevance of solid electrolytes for lithium-based batteries: A realistic view. *J Electroceramics* 38:128–141. doi: 10.1007/s10832-017-0091-0

59. Pecher O, Kong ST, Goebel T, et al. (2010) Atomistic characterisation of Li^+ mobility and conductivity in $Li_{7-x}PS_6$-xix argyrodites from molecular dynamics simulations, solid-state NMR, and impedance spectroscopy. *Chem - A Eur J* 16:8347–8354. doi: 10.1002/chem.201000501

60. Deiseroth H-J, Kong S-T, Eckert H, et al. (2008) Li6PS5X: A class of crystalline Li-rich solids with an unusually high Li+ mobility. *Angew Chemie* 120:767–770. doi: 10.1002/ange.200703900

61. Rao RP, Adams S (2011) Studies of lithium argyrodite solid electrolytes for all-solid-state batteries. *Phys Status Solidi Appl Mater Sci* 208:1804–1807. doi: 10.1002/pssa.201001117

62. Boulineau S, Courty M, Tarascon JM, Viallet V (2012) Mechanochemical synthesis of Li-argyrodite Li 6PS 5X (X = Cl, Br, I) as sulfur-based solid electrolytes for all solid state batteries application. *Solid State Ionics* 221:1–5. doi: 10.1016/j.ssi.2012.06.008

63. Kraft MA, Culver SP, Calderon M, et al. (2017) Influence of lattice polarizability on the ionic conductivity in the lithium superionic argyrodites Li6PS5X (X = Cl, Br, I). *J Am Chem Soc* 139:10909–10918. doi: 10.1021/jacs.7b06327

64. Zhang Z, Shao Y, Lotsch B, et al. (2018) New horizons for inorganic solid state ion conductors. *Energy Environ Sci* 11:1945–1976. doi: 10.1039/c8ee01053f

65. De Klerk NJJ, Rosłoń I, Wagemaker M (2016) Diffusion mechanism of Li argyrodite solid electrolytes for Li-ion batteries and prediction of optimized halogen doping: The effect of Li vacancies, halogens, and halogen disorder. *Chem Mater* 28:7955–7963. doi: 10.1021/acs.chemmater.6b03630

66. Guo Z, Li J, Xia Y, et al. (2018) A flexible polymer-based Li-air battery using a reduced graphene oxide/Li composite anode. *J Mater Chem A* 6:6022–6032. doi: 10.1039/c8ta01117f

67. Rao RP, Sharma N, Peterson VK, Adams S (2013) Formation and conductivity studies of lithium argyrodite solid electrolytes using in-situ neutron diffraction. *Solid State Ionics* 230:72–76. doi: 10.1016/j.ssi.2012.09.014
68. Malugani JP, Robert G (1980) Preparation and electrical properties of the $0,37Li_2S$-$0,18P_2S_5$-$0,45LiI$ glass. *Solid State Ionics* 1:519–523. doi: 10.1016/0167-2738(80)90048-X
69. Mercier R, Malugani JP, Fahys B, Robert G (1981) Superionic conduction in Li_2S-P_2S_5-LiI-glasses. *Solid State Ionics* 5:663–666. doi: 10.1016/0167-2738(81)90341-6
70. Ujiie S, Hayashi A, Tatsumisago M (2012) Structure, ionic conductivity and electrochemical stability of Li_2S-P_2S_5-LiI glass and glass-ceramic electrolytes. *Solid State Ionics* 211:42–45. doi: 10.1016/j.ssi.2012.01.017
71. Aihara Y, Ito S, Omoda R et al. (2016) The electrochemical characteristics and applicability of an amorphous sulfide-based solid ion conductor for the next-generation solid-state lithium secondary batteries. *Front Energy Res* :18. doi: 10.3389/fenrg.2016.00018
72. Rangasamy E, Liu Z, Gobet M, et al. (2015) An iodide-based $Li_7P_2S_8I$ superionic conductor. *J Am Chem Soc* 137:1384–1387. doi: 10.1021/ja508723m
73. Liang C, Rangasamy E (2016) *Electrochemically stable $Li_7P_2S_8I$ superionic conductor.* (UT-Battelle, LLC) US 2016/0028104 A1 1.
74. Gabano JP, Duchange JP (1983) (Fr. Demande) FR 2525396 A1. 19831021, 1983; *Eur. Pat. Appl.*, EP 68307 A1 19830105, 1983.
75. Sedlmaier SJ, Indris S, Dietrich C, et al. (2017) Li_4PS_4I: A Li^+ superionic conductor synthesized by a solvent-based soft chemistry approach. *Chem Mater* 29:1830–1835. doi: 10.1021/acs.chemmater.7b00013
76. Phuc NHH, Yamamoto T, Muto H, Matsuda A (2017) Fast synthesis of Li_2S-P_2S_5-LiI solid electrolyte precursors. *Inorg Chem Front* 4:1660–1664. doi: 10.1039/c7qi00353f
77. Homma K, Yonemura M, Kobayashi T, et al. (2011) Crystal structure and phase transitions of the lithium ionic conductor Li3PS4. *Solid State Ionics* 182:53–58.
78. Tachez M, Malugani JP, Mercier R, Robert G (1984) Ionic conductivity of and phase transition in lithium thiophosphate Li_3PS_4. *Solid State Ionics* 14:181–185. doi: 10.1016/0167-2738(84)90097-3
79. Liang CC (1973) Conduction characteristics of the lithium iodide-aluminum oxide solid electrolytes. *J Electrochem Soc* 120:1289. doi: 10.1149/1.2403248
80. Liu Z, Fu W, Payzant EA, et al. (2013) Anomalous high ionic conductivity of nanoporous β-Li_3PS_4. *J Am Chem Soc* 135:975–978. doi: 10.1021/ja3110895
81. Sicolo S, Kalcher C, Sedlmaier SJ, et al. (2018) Diffusion mechanism in the superionic conductor Li_4PS_4I studied by first-principles calculations. *Solid State Ionics* 319:83–91. doi: 10.1016/j.ssi.2018.01.046
82. Minafra N, Culver SP, Krauskopf T, et al. (2018) Effect of Si substitution on the structural and transport properties of superionic Li-argyrodites. *J Mater Chem A* 6:645–651. doi: 10.1039/c7ta08581h
83. Belkly A, Helderman M, Karen VL, Ulkch P (2002) New developments in the Inorganic Crystal Structure Database (ICSD): Accessibility in support of materials research and design. *Acta Crystallogr Sect B Struct Sci* 58:364–369. doi: 10.1107/S0108768102006948
84. Jorgens S, Johrendt D, Mewis AZ (2002) Motive dichtester Kugelpackungen: Die Verbindungen $Zn_3(PS_4)_2$ und $LiZnPS_4$. *Anorg Allg Chem* 628:1765–1769. doi.org/10.1002/1521-3749(200208)628:8<1765::AID-ZAAC1765>3.0.CO;2-E
85. Richards WD, Wang Y, Miara LJ, et al. (2016) Design of $Li_{1+2x}Zn_{1-x}PS_4$, a new lithium ion conductor. *Energy Environ Sci* 9:3272–3278. doi: 10.1039/c6ee02094a
86. Kaup K, Lalère F, Huq A, et al. (2018) Correlation of structure and fast ion conductivity in the solid solution Series Li1+2xZn1-xPS4. *Chem Mater* 30:592–596. doi: 10.1021/acs.chemmater.7b05108

Solid-State Electrolytes for Lithium-Ion Batteries

87. Wang Y, Richards WD, Ong SP, et al. (2015) Design principles for solid-state lithium superionic conductors. *Nat Mater* 14:1026–1031. doi: 10.1038/nmat4369
88. Kuhn A, Holzmann T, Nuss J, Lotsch BV (2014) A facile wet chemistry approach towards unilamellar tin sulfide nanosheets from Li4xSn1-xS2 solid solutions. *J Mater Chem A* 2:6100–6106. doi: 10.1039/c3ta14190j
89. Brant JA, Massi DM, Holzwarth NAW, et al. (2015) Fast lithium ion conduction in Li_2SnS_3: Synthesis, physicochemical characterization, and electronic structure. *Chem Mater* 27:189–196. doi: 10.1021/cm5037524
90. Holzmann T, Schoop LM, Ali MN, et al. (2016) $Li_{0.6}[Li_{0.2}Sn_{0.8}S_2]$-a layered lithium superionic conductor. *Energy Environ Sci* 9:2578–2585. doi: 10.1039/c6ee00633g
91. Kaib T, Bron P, Haddadpour S, et al. (2013) Li/Sn/Se compounds. *Chem Mater* 25:2961–2969. doi: 10.1021/cm400541n
92. Smirnova OA, Nalbandyan VB, Petrenko AA, Avdeev M (2005) Subsolidus phase relations in Na2O-CuO-Sb2O n system and crystal structure of new sodium copper antimonate Na3Cu2SbO6. *J Solid State Chem* 178:1165–1170. doi: 10.1016/j.jssc.2005.02.002
93. Politaev VV, Nalbandyan VB, Petrenko AA, et al. (2010) Mixed oxides of sodium, antimony (5+) and divalent metals (Ni, Co, Zn or Mg). *J Solid State Chem* 183:684–691. doi: 10.1016/j.jssc.2009.12.002
94. Berthelot R, Schmidt W, Muir S, et al. (2012) New layered compounds with honeycomb ordering: Li 3Ni 2BiO 6, Li 3NiM'BiO 6 (M' = Mg, Cu, Zn), and the delafossite Ag 3Ni 2BiO 6. *Inorg Chem* 51:5377–5385. doi: 10.1021/ic300351t
95. Zvereva EA, Evstigneeva MA, Nalbandyan VB, et al. (2012) Monoclinic honeycomb-layered compound Li 3Ni 2SbO 6: Preparation, crystal structure and magnetic properties. *Dalt Trans* 41:572–580. doi: 10.1039/c1dt11322d
96. Baumann V, Friedrich Röttgermann PJ, Haase F, et al. (2016) Highly stable and bio-compatible gold nanorod-DNA conjugates as NIR probes for ultrafast sequence-selective DNA melting. *RSC Adv* 6:103724–103739. doi: 10.1039/c6ra17156g
97. Greaves C, Katib SMA (1990) The structural chemistry of $Li_3Zn_2MO_6$ (M=Sb, Bi) and related phases. *Mater Res Bull* 25:1175–1182. doi: 10.1016/0025-5408(90)90148-U
98. Ratner MA, Johansson P, Shriver DF (2000) Polymer electrolytes: Ionic transport mechanisms and relaxation coupling. *MRS Bull* 25:31–37. doi: 10.1557/mrs2000.16
99. Shi QX, Xia Q, Xiang X, et al. (2017) Self-assembled polymeric ionic liquid-functionalized cellulose nano-crystals: Constructing 3D ion-conducting channels within ionic liquid-based composite polymer electrolytes. *Chem – A Eur J* 23:11881–11890. doi: 10.1002/chem.201702079
100. Subianto S, Mistry MK, Choudhury NR, et al. (2009) Composite polymer electrolyte containing ionic liquid and functionalized polyhedral oligomeric silsesquioxanes for anhydrous PEM applications. *ACS Appl Mater Interfaces* 1:1173–1182. doi: 10.1021/am900020w
101. Tikekar MD, Choudhury S, Tu Z, Archer LA (2016) Design principles for electrolytes and interfaces for stable lithium-metal batteries. *Nat Energy* 1:16114. doi: 10.1038/nenergy.2016.114
102. Stavila V, Talin AA, Allendorf MD (2014) MOF-based electronic and opto-electronic devices. *Chem Soc Rev* 43:5994–6010. doi: 10.1039/C4CS00096J
103. Thokchom JS, Gupta N, Kumar B (2008) Superionic conductivity in a lithium aluminum germanium phosphate glass–ceramic. *J Electrochem Soc* 155:A915. doi: 10.1149/1.2988731
104. Verma P, Maire P, Novak P (2010) A review of the features and analyses of the solid electrolyte interphase in Li-ion batteries. *Electrochim Acta* 55:6332–6341. doi: DOI:101016/jelectacta201005072

105. Scrosati B, Garche J (2010) Lithium batteries: Status, prospects and future. *J Power Sources* 195:2419–2430. doi: 10.1016/j.jpowsour.2009.11.048
106. Siqueira LJA, Ribeiro MCC (2006) Molecular dynamics simulation of the polymer electrolyte poly(ethylene oxide)/LiClO$_4$. II. Dynamical properties. *J Chem Phys* 125:214903. doi: 10.1063/1.2400221
107. Srivastava N, Tiwari T (2009) New trends in polymer electrolytes: A review. *e-Polymers* 9:146. doi: 10.1515/epoly.2009.9.1.1738
108. Thangadurai V, Kaack H, Weppner WJF (2003) Novel fast lithium ion conduction in garnet-type Li$_5$La$_3$M$_2$O$_{12}$ (M = Nb, Ta). *J Am Ceram Soc* 86:437–440. doi: 10.1111/j.1151-2916.2003.tb03318.x
109. Quartarone E, Mustarelli P (2011) Electrolytes for solid-state lithium rechargeable batteries: Recent advances and perspectives. *Chem Soc Rev* 40:2525–2540. doi: 10.1039/c0cs00081g
110. Sheng J, Tong S, He Z, Yang R (2017) Recent developments of cellulose materials for lithium-ion battery separators. *Cellulose* 24:4103–4122. doi: 10.1007/s10570-017-1421-8
111. Sun B, Mindemark J, Edström K, Brandell D (2014) Polycarbonate-based solid polymer electrolytes for Li-ion batteries. *Solid State Ionics* 262:738–742. doi: 10.1016/j.ssi.2013.08.014

3 Solid-State Electrolytes for Lithium-Ion Batteries

Novel Lithium-Ion Conducting Ceramic Materials: NASICON- and Garnet-Type Ionic Conductors

Prasanth Raghavan, Abhijith P. P., Jishnu N. S., Neethu T. M. Balakrishnan, Anjumole P. Thomas, Jabeen Fatima M. J., and Jou-Hyeon Ahn

CONTENTS

3.1 Introduction 51
3.2 Inorganic Li-ion Conductors..53
    3.2.1 NASICON Conductors 53
    3.2.2 Garnet-Type Conductors...56
3.3 Li-ion Diffusion Mechanism in Garnet-Type Conductors............................. 61
3.4 Conclusions...65
Acknowledgment 65
References...65

3.1 INTRODUCTION

With the expectation of the rapid depletion of conventional fossil fuels and, exponentially, the ever-increasing global demands on energy, recently there has been growing interest in developing alternative technologies for green (zero emissions) energy storage and conversion devices such as batteries, supercapacitors, fuel cells, and solar cells for transportation, stationary power, and distributed power generation applications. Compared to fuel cells, which require a constant supply of fuels and oxidants, batteries and supercapacitors can be completely self-contained, only requiring an occasional supply of chemical input or export across their entire lifetime. However, batteries have gained greater attention than supercapacitors due to their high energy density, constant output voltage, and very low self-discharge. Similar to other electrochemical devices, batteries also consist of three basic components viz., an electrolyte, which allows the transfer of ions from the negative (anode) to the positive (cathode) electrode during discharge, facilitating the continuous flow of electrons through an external circuit. During charging, the opposite reaction takes place with ions moving in the opposite direction, and the use of electrical energy pushes the electrons and ions back to the anode where they are stored in the galleries of the layered anode. Among the different battery technologies such as lead-acid, nickel-cadmium, and nickel-metal hydride batteries, so far, Li-ion batteries (LIBs) have exhibited the highest volumetric and gravimetric energy densities, with very low self-discharge and good power density [1–4]. Hence, during the past decades, lithium-ion batteries have gained much attention from the electronics industry and have become the primary power source for electronic gadgets [5–9]. However, to date, LIBs have suffered from serious safety issues, including the flammability of typical organic liquid electrolytes, which has caused serious incidents such as catching fire due to the thermal runway resulting from the failure of the electrolyte [10,11]. Compared to portable electronic devices, this is a particularly serious concern for hybrid/electrical vehicles and stationary power banks. Recent incidents in a unit of the Tesla Model S and the Boeing 787 Dreamliner airplane (fires in lithium-ion batteries) have impelled a mandatory safety policy on rechargeable lithium-ion batteries [12].

Elemental Li is a silvery-white alkali metal and is the lightest among the elements that are solids at room temperature (third lightest element with a density of 0.534 g cm^{-3}), is highly reactive, and is the most electropositive element, thus it could offer the highest nominal output cell voltage. The predominant electrode materials used in LIBs are graphite (anode) and $LiCoO_2$ (cathode). Unfortunately, these materials show low energy density, poor cycling performance, and poor rate capability due to their inferior theoretical capacity, and form a thick solid electrolyte interphase (SEI) layer at the electrolyte–electrode interfaces during the operation of the battery due to the unwanted reaction of the electrode with the electrolyte. The commercially used electrolyte in LIBs, either in a liquid electrolyte or a gel electrolyte, has a lithium salt such as $LiBF_4$, $LiPF_6$, lithium bis(trifluoromethanesulfonyl)imide (LiTFSI), or $LiCF_3SO_3$ that dissolves in aprotic solvents such as ethylene carbonate (EC), propylene carbonate (PC), or dimethyl carbonate (DMC), or their mixture. However, these carbonate solvents are flammable, have poor electrochemical stability, limited operating temperature, and exhibit leakage. Hence, solid-state electrolytes (SSEs) are considered one of the viable solutions for ensuring the safety of such applications in electric vehicles where high-power rechargeable lithium batteries are used as the power source [13]. Compared to conventional electrolytes, SSEs have several advantages such as non-volatility, low flammability, easy processability, and chemical and electrochemical stability [9,14]; therefore, replacing the flammable liquid electrolytes currently used in commercial Li-ion batteries with solid electrolytes can greatly enhance the safety of the devices [15–17]. In this context, solid polymer electrolytes (SPEs) are more popular and have aided in the tremendous development of new materials and hybrid/composite electrolytes [9]. However, the main challenge

Solid-State Electrolytes for Lithium-Ion Batteries

of such SPEs is their limited ionic conductivity at room temperature, and dendrite growth in the case of the Li-metal anode, which again suffers from safety issues and short-circuiting [12,18]. SPEs show practical ionic conductivity ($>10^{-4}$ S cm^{-1}) mostly at temperatures above 60°C, which restricts their practical use in room temperature applications [18–21]. Additionally, in certain high-end applications such as automotive and power storage, the use of SPEs is restricted at elevated operating temperatures due to their thermal degradation and tendency to decompose or melt at elevated temperatures [18]. Hence, the use of solid-state (ceramic) electrolytes has been proposed for the development of safe LIBs due to their desired physical, chemical, and thermal properties which provide higher power density compared to conventional polymer electrolyte–based LIBs. Generally, ceramic electrolytes have low room temperature ionic conductivity that is several orders of magnitude lower than that of liquid electrolytes and a poor lithium transference number limiting their practical use, hence the increasing interest in fast Li-ion conducting solid electrolytes for the next generation of Li-ion batteries. In addition to the safety benefits, solid electrolytes have the potential to enable the use of Li-metal anodes, resulting in increased energy densities and extended electrochemical windows [22–24]. A large number of inorganic oxides and non-oxides exhibiting amorphous and crystalline structures, including sodium superionic conductor (NASICON)-type phosphates [25], perovskite-type $La_{(2/3)x}Li_{3x}TiO_3$ (LLT) [26], anti-perovskite type [27], Li-b-alumina, Li_3N, and Li_4SiO_4, have been investigated. Figure 3.1 shows the idealized crystal structures of the most studied fast lithium-ion conductors for solid-state electrolyte LIBs. Among these different lithium-ion conductors, this chapter's main focus is on the ionic conductivity and lithium-ion conduction mechanism of NASICON- and garnet-type inorganic fast lithium-ion conductors.

3.2 INORGANIC Li-ion CONDUCTORS

3.2.1 NASICON Conductors

NASICON-type ceramics ($Na_{1+x}Zr_2P_{3-x}Si_xO_{12}$) are promising fast ion conductors (aka "sodium super ion conductor"). They were first discovered in 1968 with a composition of $NaM_2(PO_4)_3$ (M = Ge, Ti, Zr) [28] and the first lithium-ion conducting NASICON-type solid electrolyte $LiZr_2(PO_4)_3$ was reported by Surdrean et al. in 1989. Promising fast lithium-ion conductors with high conductivity are derived from $NaZr_2(PO_4)_3$ after the replacement of P with Si due to the poor ionic conductivity of P. The lithium-ion conducting NASICON has the general formula of $LiM_2(XO_4)_3$, in which $[M_2(XO_4)_3]$ constitutes the basic structure of NASICON. Studies on the ion conduction mechanism have shown that the enhanced conductivity of $Na_{1+x}Zr_2P_{3-x}Si_xO_{12}$ may be due to the following reasons [29]:

- the increased mobility of Na$^+$ ions in the structure,
- the higher density of the sintered pellets, and
- the more favorable environment for Na$^+$ ion migration through the 3D structure with enlarged tunnel sizes.

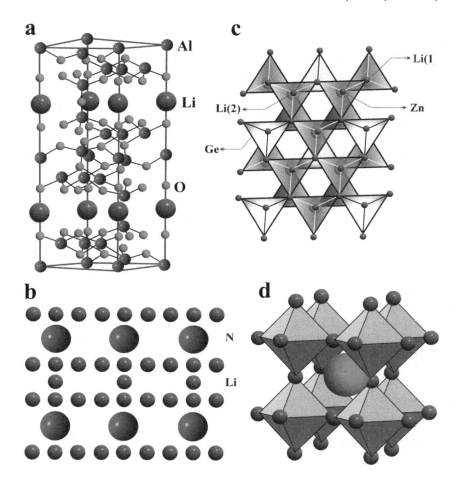

FIGURE 3.1 Idealized crystal structure for solid-state Li-ion conductors: (a) Li-b-alumina, (b) sodium super ion conducting (NASICON) phosphate $LiM_2(PO_4)_3$ (M = Ti, Zr), (c) lithium superior conducting (LISICON) $Li_3Zn_{0.5}GeO_4$, (d) Li_3N, and (e) A-site deficient perovskite-type $La_{(2/3)x}Li_{3x}TiO_3$. Isotropic Li-ion conduction is shown in (a) and (d) while all other members exhibit anisotropic Li-ion conduction.

Among the different NASICON-type conductors, the first lithium-ion conducting iso-structural $LiM_2(PO_4)_3$ (M = Zr, Ti, Hf, Ge, or Sn) was reported in 1977. The skeletons of these $LiM_2(PO_4)_3$ consist of MO_6 octahedra and PO_4 tetrahedra sharing oxygen atoms (Figure 3.2 NASICON structure) [30,31]. The MO_6 octahedron and the XO_4 tetrahedron are connected in a common angle to form a Li-ion transmission channel. This $LiM_2(PO_4)_3$ series can be further divided into $LiM_2(PO_4)_3$ (M = Ti, Ge) with rhombohedral symmetry and $LiM_2(PO_4)_3$ (M = Zr, Hf, or Sn) with a triclinic phase and lower symmetry. Here, alkaline ions in the rhombohedral phase are likely to occupy two crystallographic sites in which M1 sites are surrounded by six oxygens and M2 sites are positioned between two adjacent M1

Solid-State Electrolytes for Lithium-Ion Batteries

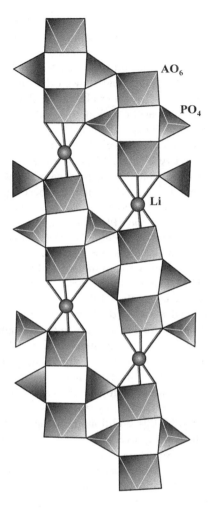

FIGURE 3.2 Idealized schematic visualization of the crystal structure of sodium super ion conducting (NASICON) phosphate.

positions with 10-fold oxygen coordination. As for the triclinic phase, Li cations are driven by structural distortions in four-fold coordination at the intermediate M12 sites. In 1990, Aono et al. [29] first reported doped trivalent ions in $LiTi_2(PO_4)_3$ with significantly improved ionic conductivity at room temperature. Following this study, many researchers prepared $Li_{1+x}Al_xTi_{2-x}(PO_4)_3$ (LATP) and demonstrated an ionic conductivity of $\geq 6.76 \times 10^{-4}$ S cm^{-1} at 60°C. Trivalent cations such as Al^{3+}, Sc^{3+}, Ga^{3+}, Fe^{3+}, In^{3+}, and Cr^{3+} replacing partial Ti^{4+} cations in $Li_{1+x}R_xTi_{2-x}(PO_4)_3$ also enhance ionic conductivity and show the ionic conductivity of 7×10^{-4} S cm^{-1} for $Li_{1.3}Al_{0.3}Ti_{1.7}(PO_4)_3$ (LATP). Also, it was demonstrated that the ionic conductivity of $LiTi_2(PO_4)_3$ outperforms other $LiM_2(PO_4)_3$ (M = Zr, Ge, or Hf) due to its optimal

56 Ceramic and Specialty Electrolytes

lattice size for conducting Li^+ ions. Hence, NASICON-type electrolytes gained the attention of battery researchers due to their unique properties such as their high ionic conductivity (over 10^{-3} S cm^{-1}) at ambient temperature and their stability in ambient atmosphere. Yang et al. [32] fabricated SPE based on poly(ethylene oxide) (PEO) incorporated with $Li_{1.3}Al_{0.3}Ti_{1.7}(PO_4)_3$ and showed that lithium-ion cells assembled with LiFePO$_4$/Li using this solid polymer electrolyte delivered a discharge capacity of 158.2 and 94.2 mAh g^{-1} at 0.1 and 2C-rate, respectively. Similar to LATP, lithium aluminum germanium phosphate (LAGP) is also a NASICON-type fast ion conducting glass ceramic having relatively high ionic conductivity (>10^{-4} S cm^{-1}). Using this NASICON-type LAGP, a PEO-based SPE ($Li_{1.5}Al_{0.5}Ge_{1.5}(PO_4)_3$ (LAGP) by Zhao et al. [33] and a stretchable SPE membrane with LiCLO$_4$ were prepared by Jung et al. [34]. An evaluation of the electrochemical performance of composite SPE displayed a wide electrochemical window of 0–5.3 V and an ionic conductivity of 6.76×10^{-4} S cm^{-1} at 60°C. Also, the SPE-based LiFePO$_4$/Li-metal battery showed a prominent cycling stability of 50 cycles with 90% capacity retention [33]. The PEO/LiCLO$_4$–LAGP stretchable composite electrolyte composed of 60–80 wt.% LAGP is still capable of providing enough mechanical modulus and a good electrochemical performance. The Li/LiFePO$_4$ cells assembled with these stretchable SPEs delivered an initial discharge capacity of 138.5 mAh g^{-1} and showed good capacity retention [34]. The improved ionic conductivity and electrochemical performance of these composite electrolytes are due not only to the formation of LATP or LAGP lithium-ion conduction pathways at the polymer–ceramic filler interphase, leading to improved ionic conductivity, but also to physically resisting lithium dendrite growth.

Detailed studies on the crystal structure and ionic conducting mechanism in NASICONs reported that the ionic radius of M^{4+} cations can influence the lattice constants of $LiM_2(PO_4)_3$ (M = Ge, Hf, or Zr) and significantly contribute to the tunnel size for Li^+ diffusion [35]. In addition, the ionic conductivity of NASICON-type conductors can be further improved by increasing the mobile ion content in the structure by augmenting densification (compacting or increasing the density) and reducing the activation energy by doping with trivalent ions [29]. Arbi et al. [35] systematically investigated the influence of cation miscibility on the optimization of the transport properties of the $Li_{1+x}Ti_{2-x}Sc_x(PO_4)_3$ ($0{\leq}x{\leq}0.5$) series. In the study, they observed NASICON phases with rhombohedral symmetry in Sc-poor samples, and the existence of secondary TiO_2, $LiScO_2$, and $LiScP_2O_7$ phases in Sc-rich structures, which were found to suppress the incorporation of Li in the NASICON phase. To further enhance ionic conductivity, Aono et al. [29] proposed another strategy by introducing secondary Li compounds such as Li_2O, Li_3PO_4, and Li_3BO_3 to serve as fluxes to promote crystallization and form conductive components at the grain boundary. Supported with experimental results, this proposed strategy showed that adding 20% Li_2O to $LiTi_2(PO_4)_3$ leads to an ionic conductivity of 5×10^{-4} S cm^{-1}.

3.2.2 GARNET-TYPE CONDUCTORS

Garnet-type lithium-ion conductors are a promising candidate for solid-state electrolytes on the way toward all-solid-state lithium-ion batteries. The first garnet-type

Solid-State Electrolytes for Lithium-Ion Batteries

lithium solid-state electrolyte was reported in 2007, even though the novel composition of $Li_5La_3M_2O_{12}$ (M = Nb, Ta) was proposed by Thangadurai et al. [36] in 2003. The ideal garnet crystals have the chemical formula $A_3B_2(XO_4)_3$ where A = Ca, Mg, Y, La, or rare-earth elements and B = Al, Fe, Ga, Ge, Mn, Ni, or V (X = Si, Ge, Al). In this general formula, A, B, and C are eight, six, and four oxygen-coordinated cation sites, which crystallize in a face-centered cubic structure with the space group Ia3d [37]. These ionically conducting Li-excess garnet-type materials attracted wide interest due to their unique crystal structures, high ionic conductivity, and wide electrochemical window [38]. Commonly studied ionically conducting garnets typically contain five to seven Li atoms per formula unit, and are referred to as Li-stuffed (Li-rich) garnets, meaning they have more Li than can be accommodated at the tetrahedral sites, leaving excess Li which occupies the octahedral sites in the garnet structure. In comparison with solid lithium-ion conductors such as lithium phosphorous oxy-nitride (LiPON, having the general formula $Li_xPO_yN_z$, where $x = 2y + 3z - 5$, Li_9AlSiO_8, and Li-β-alumina), the room temperature ionic conductivity of these garnet-type $Li_5La_3M_2O_{12}$ (M = Nb, Ta) could reach 10^{-3} S cm^{-1} and the bulk conductivity of both niobium and tantalum compounds could reach a similar order of magnitude (~10^{-6} S cm^{-1} at 25°C) with activation energies of 0.43 and 0.56 eV, respectively. In addition, the Ta members ($Li_5La_3Ta_2O_{12}$) exhibit outstanding chemical stability over a wide temperature range even in molten Li and moisture. However, when the all-solid-state battery is assembled using garnet-type ceramic ionic conductors, the electrode–electrolyte interface always shows poor conductivity (higher interfacial resistance), resulting in a deteriorated battery performance and rate capability [39]. $Li_3Ln_3Te_2O_{12}$ (Ln = Y, Pr, Nd, Sm–Lu) (Li_3-phases) $Li_{3+x}Nd_3Te_{2-x}Sb_xO_{12}$ (x = 0.05–1.5), $Li_5La_3M_2O_{12}$ (M = Nb, Ta, Sb) (Li_5-phases), $Li_6ALa_2M_2O_{12}$ (A = Mg, Ca, Sr, Ba; M = Nb, Ta) (Li_6-phases), and $Li_7La_3M_2O_{12}$ (M = Zr, Sn) (Li_7-phases) are the major garnet-type lithium-ion conductors.

In systematic studies of the relationship between Li-site occupation and Li-ion conductivity, O'Callaghan et al. [40] report that the lattice constant increases with increasing Ln-ionic radius in $Li_3Ln_3Te_2O_{12}$, and Li-ions are located exclusively in the tetrahedral (24d) sites in the space group Ia3d in the garnet crystal. These $Li_3Ln_3Te_2O_{12}$ garnets exhibited very low ionic conductivity at room temperature and even at 600°C the ionic conductivity was low at ~10^{-5} S cm^{-1} with a high activation energy of >1 eV [40]. This low ionic conductivity and high activation energy of $Li_3Ln_3Te_2O_{12}$ garnets suggests that Li in the tetrahedral sites is less mobile and, ultimately, seems not to be responsible for the high Li-ion conduction in the Li-stuffed Li_5-, Li_6-, or Li_7-phase garnets such as $Li_5La_3M_2O_{12}$, $Li_6ALa_2M_2O_{12}$, and $Li_7La_3Zr_2O_{12}$ (LLZO) [37,41–45]. Hence, to increase the ionic conductivity of Li_3-phase garnets, it would be feasible to optimize the amount of Li present in the octahedral sites in the garnet crystals. Based on this concept, O'Callaghan et al. [46] prepared a series of Li-excess $Li_{3+x}Nd_3Te_{2x}Sb_xO_{12}$ (x = 0.05–1.5) with lattice parameters ranging from 12.55576(12) Å (for x = 0.05) to 12.6253(2) Å (for x = 1.5) and, interestingly, found that the Li-ion conductivity increased with increasing Li content, reaching an ionic conductivity value of ~10^{-2} S cm^{-1} at 400°C for $Li_{3.5}Nd_3Te_{1.5}Sb_{0.5}O_{12}$ [46], which is much higher (1000 times) than that of $Li_3Ln_3Te_2O_{12}$ at 600°C [40]. Compared to the ideal garnet structure, all the excess Li in Li$_5$La$_3$M$_2$O$_{12}$ could not be incorporated into the ideal garnet tetrahedral sites; therefore, the excess Li in Li-rich garnet crystals must be incorporated into the octahedral sites, which results in Li$_5$La$_3$M$_2$O$_{12}$ and both tetrahedral and octahedral sites are partially filled [47].

Among the different garnet-type conductors, orthosilicate garnets possess the general empirical formula A$_3^{II}$B$_2^{III}$ (SiO$_4$)$_3$ in which A and B represent the eight- and six-coordinated cation sites. In this garnet structure, separate SiO$_4$ tetrahedra are bonded to each other through ionic bonds between interstitial B cations and by replacing silicon with other elements. It was reported that various complex oxides have been shown to crystallize in the garnet-like conductors with a general chemical formula of A$_3$B$_5$O$_{12}$ where A = Ca, Mg, Y or Ln = La, or rare-earth elements and B = Al, Fe, Ga, Ge, Mn, Ni, V, resulting in a 3D structure made up of BO$_4$ tetrahedra and BO$_6$ octahedra sharing corners with each other. For instance, in the Li$_5$La$_3$M$_2$O$_{12}$ (M = Nb, Ta) crystal structure (Figure 3.3), eight- and six-coordination sites are occupied by La and Ta ions with Li-ions on both the octahedral and tetrahedral sites, which was confirmed by Thangadurai et al. [48] using neutron diffraction investigations. They also demonstrated that the crystal Li(I)O$_6$ was much more distorted than Li(II)O$_6$ [48]. In addition, the researchers reported that six LiO$_6$ octahedra and two vacant sites of Li-ions surrounding MO$_6$ octahedra [49] or the partial substitution of K$^+$ or In^{3+} can result in high Li$^+$-ion conduction [43]. In addition, high sintering temperatures can enhance ionic conductivity [43,45] because

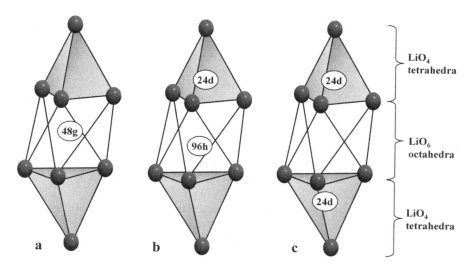

FIGURE 3.3 Li occupancy in the garnet-type structure Li$_{5+x}$La$_{3-x}$A$_x$M$_{2-y}$B$_y$O$_{12}$ where A = divalent, B = tri or tetravalent, and M = pentavalent ions. The following three arrangements are possible Li-ion distributions: (a) both tetrahedra are empty and Li$^+$ occupies a central position in the octahedron; (b) one Li$^+$ occupies a single tetrahedron shifting the octahedral Li$^+$ away from the shared face; and (c) both tetrahedra are occupied leaving the octahedral site empty. Adapted and reproduced with permission from Ref. [51]. Copyright © 2007 Royal Society of Chemistry.

Solid-State Electrolytes for Lithium-Ion Batteries

sintering at high temperatures can facilitate more Li-ions in octahedral sites. In their studies, Thangadurai et al. [45] reported that garnet-like $Li_5La_3Nb_2O_{12}$ enhances the ionic conductivity through the partial substitution of K^+ for La^{3+} and In^{3+} for Nb^{5+} or with increases in the ionic radius of alkaline earth ions [42,45]. In addition, the ionic conductivity of $Li_5La_3Nb_2O_{12}$ can also be enhanced by Y and Li co-doping to create a novel Li-rich $Li_{5+2x}La_3Nb_{2-x}Y_xO_{12}$ structure in which trivalent ions such as Y^{3+} surpass other dopants such as M^{2+} (alkaline earth ions), In^{3+}, and Zr^{4+} [50]. In their subsequent studies, Thangadurai et al. [42,45] synthesized original garnet-like conductors through the replacement of La with alkaline earth elements and reported a series of garnet-type crystals. Among the various garnet crystals prepared, Ba compound $Li_6BaLa_2Ta_2O_{12}$ showed optimal ionic conductivity of 4×10^{-5} S cm^{-1} at room temperature with an activation energy of 0.40 eV.

Highly conductive cubic $Li_7La_3Zr_2O_{12}$ is another important garnet-like structure first introduced by Murugan et al. in 2007 [44]. These materials possess high Li-ion conductivity ($\sim 10^{-4}$ S cm^{-1}), high chemical stability against metallic Li, and a high electrochemical window above 5 V. LLZO was found in the cubic and tetragonal phases [52]. Cubic LLZO exhibits a Li-ion conductivity close to the classic liquid Li-ion electrolytes, which is two orders of magnitude higher than that of tetragonal LLZO [52] because the structure greatly affects the distribution and subsequent migration pathway of the Li-ion [53]. The very first reported $Li_7La_3Zr_2O_{12}$ garnets by Murugan and co-workers showed an ionic conductivity of 3×10^{-4} S cm^{-1}. They synthesized $Li_7La_3Zr_2O_{12}$ by substituting Zr with M in $Li_5La_3M_2O_{12}$, confirming that the garnet structure can accommodate seven Li^+-ions per chemical formula [44]. These $Li_7La_3Zr_2O_{12}$ garnet crystals in which Li-ions are distributed over the octahedral 48g and the tetrahedral 24d Li(1) and 96h Li(2) sites [54] are much higher than any other previously reported Li garnet-like materials.

Awaka et al. [55,56] reported another tetragonal-type LLZO polymorph with low-temperature tetragonal symmetry [55,56]. These tetragonal-type LLZO exhibited an ionic conductivity of 10^{-6} S cm^{-1} that is much lower than the one reported by Murugan et al. [44], which resulted from the well-ordered arrangement of Li-ions at the octahedral 16f and 32g sites and the tetrahedral 8a sites in the garnet crystal [55,56]. Later, based on the studies of Hyooma et al. [49] and Thangadurai et al. [43], Rangasamy et al. [57] demonstrated that the addition of Al as a substitute for Li can generate more Li vacancies in the crystal, thereby enhancing the ionic conductivity and stability of LLZOs [49]. When Al^{3+} is doped in the LLZO, an additional charge compensation takes place through the emergence of Li^+-vacancies which reduce the free energy associated with the ordering of the Li-sublattice, eventually leading to a cubic symmetry change with disordered partially occupied Li-sites [52,53,58]. However, it is worth noting that only a minor concentration of Al in the LLZO (ca. 0.10–0.15 Al per formula unit of LLZO) [57,59] is required to stabilize the cubic LLZO phase. It is also reported that sintering at a temperature of $\geq 1000°C$ favors reaching the high Li^+-ion conducting cubic phase; however, it also results in micron-sized particles and potential Li loss, which is unfavorable for ionic conduction. The material's protonic exchange of Li^+ in humidified air also facilitates the phase transition to cubic LLZO [60]. Different studies demonstrate the significance of stabilizing the cubic phase in the LLZO. By stabilizing the cubic phase in the crystals, the ionic conductivity is improved by two orders of magnitude for $Li_{7-3x}(Al_x)La_3Zr_2O_{12}$ ($x = 0$ to 0.5), and the Li^+-ion conductivity is enhanced from 10^{-6} to 10^{-4} S cm^{-1} at ambient conditions. The enhancement of the ionic conductivity of the LLZO is dependent on the degree of structural Li-site occupancy, disorder, and relative density, and the microstructure of the pellets tuned by the stabilization of the cubic phase which is significantly influenced by the degree of doping with Al^{3+} [52,57,59,61,62]. It is a fact that the electrochemical performance of LIBs depends not only on the ionic conductivity of the electrolyte but also on the electrode–electrolyte interfacial resistance and compatibility of the electrolyte with the electrode [63–65]. Hu et al. [66] demonstrated that coating a garnet-type solid electrolyte (Nb and Ca co-doped LLZO) with an ultrathin layer of Al_2O_3 could lower the electrolyte–Li electrode interfacial resistance, in turn improving the specific capacity, which could lead to the fabrication of high-energy all-solid-state LIBs.

As Ga^{3+} have similar oxidation states and ionic radii to Al^{3+}, the stabilization of the cubic phase of LLZO has very recently been demonstrated by an alternative strategy through Ga^{3+} substitution of Li^+ [67–69] instead of Al^{3+} [52,57,59,61,62], but their ionic conductivity is in the order of 10^{-4} S cm^{-1} [67,68]. The enhancement in ionic conductivity is related to Ga^{3+} incorporation on tetrahedral lattice sites stabilizing cubic LLZO, which is spectroscopically confirmed through 71Ga Magic Angle Spinning (MAS) nuclear magnetic resonance (NMR) spectroscopy at high magnetic fields [69–71]. In recent studies, Rettenwander et al. [71] reported that Ga^{3+} can occupy both the 24d and 96h sites in $Li_{73(x+y)}Ga_xAl_yLa_3Zr_2O_{12}$ garnet crystals; however, this finding is different from previous studies showing a single site residence for Ga^{3+} [69]. The ionic conductivity of a Ga-substituted garnet is also influenced by the pellet density and sintering temperature. The higher sintering temperature ensures the stabilization of the cubic phase, a higher density, and a high Li-ion conducting cubic phase [25,43], but leads to the formation of micron-sized particles and potential Li loss [72]. There are few reports on the synthesis of the cubic-LLZO nanoparticle at temperatures as low as 750°C, but its theoretical density is about 60% and its ionic conductivity is in the range of 10^{-6} S cm^{-1} [73,74], which is not favorable for practical battery applications. Wu et al. [38] report clear guidance on how to increase pellet bulk densities up to 94% and ionic conductivities to approximately 10^{-3} S cm^{-1} for a series of Ga-substituted garnet pellets by sintering in an O_2 atmosphere.

It is widely accepted that all-solid-state LIBs do not necessarily require high density ceramic electrolytes, as long as the electrolyte exhibits a throughput Li-ionic conductivity in the range of 10^{-4} S cm^{-1}, lower interfacial resistance, and good compatibility with electrodes, and allows fast electrode–electrolyte interface transfer kinetics with good mechanical interface stability. Afyon et al. [72] demonstrated a novel low-temperature synthesis processing route for the preparation of cubic phase $Li_{6.4}Ga_{0.2}La_3Zr_2O_{12}$ at a temperature as low as 600°C, resulting in the formation of Ga^{3+}-substituted LLZO with small nanocrystalline sizes of 200–300 nm. This synthesis temperature is much lower compared to previous low-temperature preparations of cubic LLZO densities of about 60% and ionic conductivities in the range of 10^{-6} S cm^{-1} [73,74]. The sintered pellets of the $Li_{6.4}Ga_{0.2}La_3Zr_2O_{12}$ exhibited high

Solid-State Electrolytes for Lithium-Ion Batteries

bulk Li-ion conductivity in the range 4.0×10^{-4} S cm^{-1} at 20°C, and a wide thermal operation window through a lower characteristic activation energy of 0.32 eV by preventing Li-loss during the sintering process through low-temperature (600°C) processing [72]. The studies also give an insight into the conditions influencing the tetragonal to cubic phase transformation via homogeneous Ga-diffusion with incorporation occurring at a surprisingly low temperature of 100°C for a post-annealing step.

To further enhance the ionic conductivity and electrochemical properties of LLZO, in 2017, for the first time, a large radius R_b was doped at the La-site of the cubic $Li_{6.10}Ga_{0.30}La_3Zr_2O_{12}$. This strategic doping led to the highest ionic conductivity of 1.62×10^{-3} S cm^{-1} at room temperature and 4.56×10^{-3} S cm^{-1} at 60°C with an activation energy in the range of 0.25–0.28 eV, which was the highest conductivity reported until then. Also, direct current (DC) polarization studies demonstrated that the transference number of Li$^+$-ions in the $Li_{6.10+2y}Ga_{0.30}La_{3-y}Rb_yZr_2O_{12}$ electrolytes is approximately unity. An investigation of an all-solid-state Li-ion battery fabricated with a Li-metal anode and a LiFePO$_4$ cathode that underwent long charge/discharge cycling testing between the voltage profile of 2.8 and 4.0 V under the C-rate of 0.05 C at 60°C found that the battery delivers a specific capacity of 152 mAh g^{-1} in the first cycle, which is about 88% of the theoretical capacity of LiFePO$_4$ (170 mAh g^{-1}). Under continuous charge/discharge cycling, the battery maintained a specific capacity of 110 mAh g^{-1} even after 20 cycles, which is a retention of 72% of the initial capacity. Compared to other all-solid-state Li-ion batteries based on garnet-type electrolytes, LIBs with the $Li_{6.20}Ga_{0.30}La_{2.95}Rb_{0.05}Zr_2O_{12}$ electrolyte show high capacity and good cycling stability [38]. Table 3.1 shows the room temperature Li-ion conductivity of different garnet-type ion conductors reported in the literature.

3.3 Li-ion DIFFUSION MECHANISM IN GARNET-TYPE CONDUCTORS

The Li-ion diffusion mechanism in garnet-type conductors remains controversial. The Li mobility in these garnet crystals is noted to be a complex process due to the diversity in composition (and by extension Li content), accessibility of pathways, and vacancy configurations. Hence, a better understanding of the Li$^+$-transport mechanisms requires advanced characterization techniques to determine the exact location of the Li-ions. In garnet-like structures, two distinct sites are available for Li-ions, namely, the 24d tetrahedral (T^d cage) site and the six-fold-coordinated 48g position (O^g) and its distorted four-fold-coordinated split site 96h (O^h), collectively called the O^{g,h} cage. In the garnet, these 24d, 48g, and 96h sites form a 3D network of conduction pathways in which each 24d tetrahedron is connected to its neighbors by four face-sharing bridging octahedra. There are nine potential sites per host formula unit which lead to an average of seven Li occupied-two Li vacancy and five Li occupied-four Li vacancy for LLZO and LLTaO, respectively. In the Li-poor regime, such as for $Li_3Nd_3Te_2O_{12}$, full occupancy of the T^d site is suggested as the preferred configuration which leads to very low ionic mobility with an activation energy (E_a) of 1.22 eV, resulting in poor ionic conductivity even at higher temperatures with

TABLE 3.1

Chemical Composition, Synthesis Temperature, and Room Temperature Li-Ion Conductivity of Garnet-Type Ion Conductors Reported in the Literature

Garnet-type ionic conductors (LLZO) compound and composition	Synthesis temperature	Ionic conductivity (S cm^{-1}/°C)		Activation energy E_a (eV)	References
		Conductivity	Temperature		
$Li_7La_3Zr_2O_{12}$	750	2.85×10^{-6}		0.36	[74]
$Li_7La_3Zr_2O_{12}$	750	2.85×10^{-6}	25	0.36	[74]
$Li_7La_3Zr_2O_{12}$	800	3.12×10^{-7}	25	0.67	[75]
$Li_7La_3Zr_2O_{12}$	1200	3.10×10^{-4}	25	0.34	[76]
$Li_7La_3Zr_2O_{12}$	1050	2.30×10^{-5}	25	0.41	[67]
$Li_7La_3Zr_2O_{12}$	1230	5.11×10^{-4}	25	0.32	[44]
$Li_7La_3Zr_2O_{12}$ (1.2 wt.% Al)	1200	2.00×10^{-4}	25	0.33	[61]
$Li_7La_3Zr_2O_{12}$ (1.2 wt.% Al)	1200	2.00×10^{-4}		0.31	[61]
$Li_7La_3Zr_2O_{12}$ (1.2 wt.% Al)	1200	2.00×10^{-4}		0.32	[77]
$Li_{6.24}Al_{0.24}La_3Zr_2O_{11.98}$	1000	4.00×10^{-4}		0.26	[57]
$Li_{6.55}Al_{0.15}La_3Zr_2O_{12}$	1000	4.40×10^{-6}		0.49	[59]
$Li_{5.82}Al_{0.30}La_3Zr_{1.93}O_{11.72}$	1100	2.30×10^{-4}		0.37	[62]
$Li_{5.5}Ga_{0.5}La_3Zr_2O_{12}$	900	1.00×10^{-4}		0.34	[69]
$Li_{6.4}Ga_{0.2}La_3Zr_2O_{12}$	800	9.00×10^{-4}		0.30	[78]
$Li_{6.4}Ga_{0.2}La_3Zr_2O_{12}$	650	4.00×10^{-4}		0.32	[72]
$Li_{6.25}La_3Zr_2Ga_{0.25}O_{12}$	1000	3.50×10^{-4}	23		[67]
$Li_{6.25}Ga_{0.25}La_3Zr_2O_{12}$	1000	3.50×10^{-4}		0.32	[67]
$Li_{7.8}La_3Zr_2O_{12}$ (1.0 Ga per one mole)	1085	5.40×10^{-4}		0.32	[68]
$Li_7La_3Zr_2O_{12}$ (CO_2 doped)	1180	5.80×10^{-4}	25		[73]
$Li_7La_3Zr_2O_{12}$ (CO_2 doped)	800	3.30×10^{-6}	25		[73]

(Continued)

TABLE 3.1 (CONTINUED)
Chemical Composition, Synthesis Temperature, and Room Temperature Li-Ion Conductivity of Garnet-Type Ion Conductors Reported in the Literature

Garnet-type ionic conductors (LLZO) compound and composition	Synthesis temperature	Ionic conductivity (S cm^{-1}/°C)		Activation energy E_a (eV)	References
		Conductivity	Temperature		
$Li_7La_3Zr_2O_{12}$ (CO_2 doped)	450	1.30×10^{-6}	25	0.31	[73]
$Li_7La_3Zr_2O_{12}$ (1.7 wt.% Sr)	1200	5.00×10^{-4}	24	0.31	[79]
$Li_7La_3Zr_2O_{12}$ (0.4 mol.% Ce)	1050	1.44×10^{-5}	23	0.48	[57]
$Li_6La_3ZrTaO_{12}$	1120	2.50×10^{-4}	25	0.42	[80]
$Li_{6.4}La_3Zr_{1.4}Ta_{0.6}O_{12}$	1140	1.00×10^{-3}	25	0.35	[41]
$Li_{6.7}La_3Zr_{1.7}Ta_{0.3}O_{12}$	1130	0.96×10^{-3}	25	0.37	[81]
$Li_{6.15}La_3Zr_{1.75}Ta_{0.25}Al_{0.2}O_{12}$	1050	0.37×10^{-3}	25	0.30	[41]
$Li_{6.15}La_3Zr_{1.75}Ta_{0.25}Ga_{0.2}O_{12}$	1050	0.41×10^{-3}	25	0.27	[82]
$Li_{6.5}La_{2.5}Ba_{0.5}ZrTaO_{12}$	1100	2.00×10^{-4}	23	0.31	[83]
$Li_{6.5}La_{2.5}Ba_{0.5}ZrTaO_{12}$	1100	8.76×10^{-5}	24	0.34	[84]
$Li_{6.625}La_3Zr_{1.625}Ta_{0.375}O_{12}$ (29 mol.% Al) (cubic)	1000	5.00×10^{-4}	25	0.41	[85]
$Li_{6.55}La_3Hf_{1.55}Ta_{0.45}O_{13}$	1130	3.45×10^{-4}	22	0.44	[86]
$Li_7La_3Hf_2O_{13}$	1000	9.85×10^{-7}	23	0.53	[87]
$Li_7La_3Hf_2O_{13}$	1250	2.40×10^{-4}	23	0.29	[88]
$Li_6SrLa_2Bi_2O_{12}$	750	5.20×10^{-5}	22	0.42	[89]
$Li_{6.75}La_3Zr_{1.75}Nb_{0.25}O_{12}$	1200	0.80×10^{-3}	25	0.31	[90]
$Li_{7.06}La_3Zr_{1.94}Y_{0.06}O_{12}$	1200	9.56×10^{-4}	25	0.29	[44]
$Li_{7.06}La_3Zr_{1.94}Y_{0.06}O_{12}$	950	10^{-6}	23	0.47	[91]
$Li_{7.16}La_3Zr_{1.84}Y_{0.16}O_{12}$	950	10^{-6}	23	0.47	[91]

a maximum observed value of 1×10^{-5} S cm^{-1} at 600°C. Surprisingly, significant ionic conductivity is observed when the occupancy shifts to a distribution of Li in the T^d and O^{g,h} cages [92].

Compared to LLZO, there is relatively less direction-dependent E_a along the diffusion path in LLTaO, which can be explained by LLZO's lower electrostatic site potential difference (i.e., between T^d and O^{g,h}). This characteristic, coupled with the presence of vacancy dimers, leads to the unique cooperative hopping mechanism in LLTaO, characterized by long, multiple-site successive jump events with a very small timescale for fluctuations at intermediate positions. However, in LLZO, ion transport also follows a cooperative mechanism but is mainly limited to single-site successive hopping [93]. Two crucial factors that affect ionic conductivity appear to be associated with the restriction imposed by site-to-site interatomic separation between T^d and O^{g,h} cages and the Li content within the garnet structure. For LLZO, the combination leads to a cooperative-type migration instead of a single hopping-dominated process; this has been demonstrated by ab initio and classical molecular dynamics (MD) studies on LLZO [94,95]. Jalem et al. [54] were one of the first to investigate the ion dynamics and Li occupancy of LLZO using ab initio–based molecular dynamics study. Based on their studies, they concluded that the complex mechanism for the self-diffusion of Li-ions can be viewed as a concerted migration governed by two crucial features: (i) the restriction imposed on occupied site-to-site interatomic separation, and (ii) the unstable residence of Li-ions at the 24d site, which can serve as the trigger for ion mobility and the reconfiguration of surrounding Li neighbors to accommodate the initiated movement. As for the migration mechanism of LLZOs, this is typically determined by the imposed restrictions of occupied site-to-site interatomic isolation allowing only 48g/96h-24d-48g/96h and the temporal stay of Li$^+$ at the 24d site which can promote ion mobility and reconfigure surrounding Li neighbors [54]. Wüllen et al. [96] also reached a similar conclusion by employing advanced NMR strategies to study the mechanism of Li-ion transport in the garnet Li$_5$La$_3$Nb$_2$O$_{12}$. Using density functional theory, Xu et al. [97] concluded that the Li$^+$ ions jumped from one tetrahedral site to a neighboring octahedral site and then leaped forward to another tetrahedral site in the Li$_7$La$_3$Zr$_2$O$_{12}$ structure. Some preliminary studies have also been carried out to investigate Li migration and jumping via neutron powder diffraction (NPD) in Li$_7$La$_3$Zr$_2$O$_{12}$, yielding a similar conclusion [56,98]. However, Thompson et al. [99] drew the opposite conclusion with NPD results and claimed that the ionic conductivity of Li$_7$La$_3$Zr$_2$O$_{12}$ trended with the occupancy of octahedral sites; they deduced that the lithium jumps from one octahedral site to a neighboring octahedral site, bypassing tetrahedral sites entirely. Thangadurai et al.'s [45] studies on Li$_5$La$_3$M$_2$O$_{12}$ also support Thompson et al.'s [99] findings. In their studies, Thangadurai et al. [45] adopted the Bond Valence Sum method to explore the characteristic structure of Li$_5$La$_3$M$_2$O$_{12}$ and confirmed possible ion transport pathways through a minimization procedure of a bond valence mismatch in which the obtained results revealed that Li-ions exclusively occupied octahedral sites [100], further elaborating on the effects of binary aliovalent substitution on enhancing the ionic conductivity and bolstering the lithium transport mechanism in Li$_{7-2x-3y}$Al$_y$La$_3$Zr$_{2-x}$W$_x$O$_{12}$ ($0 \leq x \leq 1$) with a cubic garnet structure.

Using high-resolution NMR studies, ionic exchange between the 24d and 96h sites was clearly observed, demonstrating a lithium transport route of 24d-96h-48g-96h-24d. The results show evidence that the 24d, 96h, and 48g sites can be well-resolved. The lithium mobility at the 24d site is found to dominate the total ionic conductivity of the samples, with diffusion coefficients of 10^{-9} and 10^{-12} m^2 s^{-1} at the octahedral and tetrahedral sites, respectively [100]. In addition, simulation methods are useful tools to gain deeper understandings of Li-ion migration mechanisms in the crystals. Xu et al. [97] adopted the nudged elastic band (NEB) method to find the minimum energy path for Li diffusion in $Li_{3+x}La_3M_2O_{12}$ ($x = 0, 2, 4$) and to probe the mechanism for Li$^+$-ionic transport in LLZO. However, only limited insights can be drawn from this method since inherently it cannot take into account the dynamic aspect arising from the very large number of conceivable Li/Li vacancy arrangements in the LLZO framework.

3.4 CONCLUSIONS

The investigation of electrolytes with enhanced thermal stability has moved on to inorganic electrolytes. These solid-state electrolytes with enhanced ionic conductivity and thermal stability have led to the emergence of a new class of electrolytes. Among the inorganic solid-state electrolytes, NASICON- and garnet-type electrolytes are being widely explored owing to their inherent properties to more rapidly conduct lithium-ion. A detailed analysis was performed on the ionic conductivity, electrochemical performance, thermal stability, and structures of these inorganic systems. These inorganic compounds were found to be highly stable at elevated temperatures with enhanced ionic conductivity ($\sim 10^{-4}$ S cm^{-1}), upgrading them to an excellent candidate for high-temperature lithium-ion batteries. Lithium-excess inorganic solid-state electrolytes tend to show about 10^2 times enhancement in ionic conductivity at elevated temperatures. Hence, these inorganic solid-state compounds can be considered a promising electrolyte for next-generation devices.

ACKNOWLEDGMENT

Anjumole P. Thomas, Dr. Jabeen Fatima M. J., and Dr. Prasanth Raghavan would like to acknowledge the Department of Science and Technology (DST), India, and Kerala State Council for Science, Technology and Environment (KSCSTE), Kerala, for financial assistance.

REFERENCES

1. Raghavan P, Lim DH, Ahn JH, et al. (2012) Electrospun polymer nanofibers: The booming cutting edge technology. *React Funct Polym* 72:915–930. doi: 10.1016/j.reactfunctpolym.2012.08.018
2. Raghavan P, Choi JW, Ahn JH, et al. (2008) Novel electrospun poly(vinylidene fluoride-co-hexafluoropropylene)-in situ SiO2 composite membrane-based polymer electrolyte for lithium batteries. *J Power Sources* 184:437–443. doi: 10.1016/j.jpowsour.2008.03.027

3. Raghavan P, Manuel J, Zhao X, et al. (2011) Preparation and electrochemical characterization of gel polymer electrolyte based on electrospun polyacrylonitrile nonwoven membranes for lithium batteries. *J Power Sources* 196:6742–6749. doi: 10.1016/j.jpowsour.2010.10.089
4. Raghavan P, Zhao X, Kim J-K, et al. (2008) Ionic conductivity and electrochemical properties of nanocomposite polymer electrolytes based on electrospun poly(vinylidene fluoride-co-hexafluoropropylene) with nano-sized ceramic fillers. *Electrochim Acta* 54:228–234. doi: 10.1016/j.electacta.2008.08.007
5. Etacheri V, Marom R, Elazari R, et al. (2011) Challenges in the development of advanced Li-ion batteries: A review. *Energy Environ Sci* 4:3243–3262. doi: 10.1039/c1ee01598b
6. Wang Y, Liu B, Li Q, et al. (2015) Lithium and lithium ion batteries for applications in microelectronic devices: A review. *J Power Sources* 286:330–345. doi: 10.1016/j.jpowsour.2015.03.164
7. Thackeray MM, Wolverton C, Isaacs ED (2012) Electrical energy storage for transportation: Approaching the limits of, and going beyond, lithium-ion batteries. *Energy Environ Sci* 5:7854–7863. doi: 10.1039/c2ee21892e
8. Hayner CM, Zhao X, Kung HH (2012) Materials for rechargeable lithium-ion batteries. *Annu Rev Chem Biomol Eng* 3:445–471. doi: 10.1146/annurev-chembioeng-062011-081024
9. Scrosati B, Hassoun J, Sun YK (2011) Lithium-ion batteries. A look into the future. *Energy Environ Sci* 4:3287–3295. doi: 10.1039/c1ee01388b
10. Lu L, Han X, Li J, et al. (2013) A review on the key issues for lithium-ion battery management in electric vehicles. *J Power Sources* 226:272–288. doi: 10.1016/j.jpowsour.2012.10.060
11. Kim JG, Son B, Mukherjee S, et al. (2015) A review of lithium and non-lithium based solid state batteries. *J Power Sources* 282:299–322. doi: 10.1016/j.jpowsour.2015.02.054
12. Khurana R, Schaefer JL, Archer LA, Coates GW (2014) Suppression of lithium dendrite growth using cross-linked polyethylene/poly(ethylene oxide) electrolytes: A new approach for practical lithium-metal polymer batteries. *J Am Chem Soc* 136:7395–7402. doi: 10.1021/ja502133j
13. Tarascon JM, Armand M (2001) Issues and challenges facing rechargeable batteries. *Nature* 414:359–67. doi: 10.1038/35104644
14. Cha H, Kim J, Lee Y et al. (2017) Issues and Challenges Facing Flexible Lithium-Ion Batteries for Practical Application, Small 14: 1702989. doi.org/10.1002/smll.201702989
15. Janek J, Zeier WG (2016) A solid future for battery development. *Nat Energy* 1:1–4. doi: 10.1038/nenergy.2016.141
16. Bachman JC, Muy S, Grimaud A, et al. (2016) Inorganic solid-state electrolytes for lithium batteries: Mechanisms and properties governing ion conduction. *Chem Rev* 116:140–162. doi: 10.1021/acs.chemrev.5b00563
17. Manthiram A, Yu X, Wang S (2017) Lithium battery chemistries enabled by solid-state electrolytes. *Nat Rev Mater* 2:1–16. doi: 10.1038/natrevmats.2016.103
18. Kwon SJ, Kim DG, Shim J, et al. (2014) Preparation of organic/inorganic hybrid semi-interpenetrating network polymer electrolytes based on poly(ethylene oxide-co-ethylene carbonate) for all-solid-state lithium batteries at elevated temperatures. *Polymer (Guildf)* 55:2799–2808. doi: 10.1016/j.polymer.2014.04.051
19. Grünebaum M, Hiller MM, Jankowsky S, et al. (2014) Synthesis and electrochemistry of polymer based electrolytes for lithium batteries. *Prog Solid State Chem* 42:85–105. doi: 10.1016/j.progsolidstchem.2014.04.004
20. Manuel Stephan A, Nahm KS (2006) Review on composite polymer electrolytes for lithium batteries. *Polymer (Guildf)* 47:5952–5964. doi: 10.1016/j.polymer.2006.05.069

21. Meyer WH (1998) Polymer electrolytes for lithium-ion batteries. *Adv Mater* 10:439–448. doi: 10.1002/(SICI)1521-4095(199804)10:6<439::AID-ADMA439>3.0.CO;2-I
22. Lin D, Zhao J, Sun J, et al. (2017) Three-dimensional stable lithium metal anode with nanoscale lithium islands embedded in ionically conductive solid matrix. *Proc Natl Acad Sci USA* 114:4613–4618. doi: 10.1073/pnas.1619489114
23. Wang Y, Richards WD, Ong SP, et al. (2015) Design principles for solid-state lithium superionic conductors. *Nat Mater* 14:1026–1031. doi: 10.1038/nmat4369
24. Guo Y, Ouyang Y, Li D, et al. (2019) PMMA-assisted Li deposition towards 3D continuous dendrite-free lithium anode. *Energy Storage Mater* 16:203–211. doi: 10.1016/j.ensm.2018.05.012
25. Thangadurai V, Narayanan S, Pinzaru D (2014) Garnet-type solid-state fast Li ion conductors for Li batteries: Critical review. *Chem Soc Rev* 43:4714–4727. doi: 10.1039/c4cs00020j
26. Li J, Wen Z, Xu X, Zhang J (2007) Synthesis and characterization of Li ion conducting $La_{2/3-x}Li_{3x}TiO_3$ by a polymerizable complex method. *Ceram Int* 33:1591–1595. doi: 10.1016/j.ceramint.2006.06.008
27. Lu J, Li Y, Kong Y, Zhang N (2018) Study of structure and conductivity of $Li_{3/8}Sr_{7/16-3x/2}La_xZr_{1/4}Nb_{3/4}O_3$ solid electrolytes. *Ceram Int* 44:4744–4750. doi: 10.1016/j.ceramint.2017.12.058
28. Epp V, Ma Q, Hammer EM, et al. (2015) Very fast bulk Li ion diffusivity in crystalline $Li_{1.5}Al_{0.5}Ti_{1.5}(PO_4)_3$ as seen using NMR relaxometry. *Phys Chem Chem Phys* 17:32115–32121. doi: 10.1039/c5cp05337d
29. Aona H, Sugimota E, Sadaoka Y, et al. (1993) The electrical properties of ceramic electrolytes for $LiM_xTi_{-x}(PO) + yLi$ O, M = Ge, Sn, Hf, and Zr systems. *Soc J Electrochem* 140:1–7.
30. Giarola M, Sanson A, Tietz F, et al. (2017) Structure and vibrational dynamics of NASICON-type $LiTi_2(PO_4)_3$. *J Phys Chem C* 121:3697–3706. doi: 10.1021/acs.jpcc.6b11067
31. Tolchard J (2009) Electrolytes | Solid: Protons. *Encycl Electrochem Power Sources,* Jürgen G (Ed.), : Elsevier Science, ISBN: 9780444527455, pp. 188–195. doi: 10.1016/B978-044452745-5.00019-8
32. Yang L, Wang Z, Feng Y, et al. (2017) Flexible composite solid electrolyte facilitating highly stable "soft contacting" Li–electrolyte interface for solid state lithium-ion batteries. *Adv Energy Mater* 7:1–9. doi: 10.1002/aenm.201701437
33. Zhao Y, Huang Z, Chen S, et al. (2016) A promising PEO/LAGP hybrid electrolyte prepared by a simple method for all-solid-state lithium batteries. *Solid State Ionics* 295:65–71. doi: 10.1016/j.ssi.2016.07.013
34. Jung Y-C, Lee S-M, Choi J-H, et al. (2015) All solid-state lithium batteries assembled with hybrid solid electrolytes. *J Electrochem Soc* 162:A704–A710. doi: 10.1149/2.0731504jes
35. Kahlaoui R, Arbi K, Sobrados I, et al. (2017) Cation miscibility and lithium mobility in NASICON $Li_{1+x}Ti_{2-x}Sc_x(PO_4)_3$ ($0 \leq x \leq 0.5$) series: A combined NMR and impedance study. *Inorg Chem* 56:1216–1224. doi: 10.1021/acs.inorgchem.6b02274
36. Thangadurai V, Kaack H, Weppner WJ (2003) Novel fast lithium ion conduction in garnet-type Li5 La3M2O12 (M: Nb, Ta). *J Am Ceramic Soc* 86:437–440. doi: 10.1111/j.1151-2916.2003.tb03318.x
37. Wells AF (1971) Structural inorganic chemistry. *Nature* 229:453. doi: 10.1038/229453c0
38. Wu JF, Pang WK, Peterson VK, et al. (2017) Garnet-type fast Li-ion conductors with high ionic conductivities for all-solid-state batteries. *ACS Appl Mater Interfaces* 9:12461–12468. doi: 10.1021/acsami.7b00614

39. Chen L, Li Y, Li SP, et al. (2018) PEO/garnet composite electrolytes for solid-state lithium batteries: From "ceramic-in-polymer" to "polymer-in-ceramic." *Nano Energy* 46:176–184. doi: 10.1016/j.nanoen.2017.12.037

40. Cussen EJ, Yip TWS, O'Neill G, O'Callaghan MP (2011) A comparison of the transport properties of lithium-stuffed garnets and the conventional phases Li3Ln3Te2O12. *J Solid State Chem* 184:470–475. doi: 10.1016/j.jssc.2010.12.021

41. Li Y, Han JT, Wang CA, et al. (2012) Optimizing Li+ conductivity in a garnet framework. *J Mater Chem* 22:15357–15361. doi: 10.1039/c2jm31413d

42. Thangadurai V, Weppner W (2005) $Li_6ALa_2Ta_2O_{12}$ (A=Sr, Ba): Novel garnet-like oxides for fast lithium ion conduction. *Adv Funct Mater* 15:107–112. doi: 10.1002/adfm.200400044

43. Thangadurai V, Weppner W (2006) Effect of sintering on the ionic conductivity of garnet-related structure $Li_5La_3Nb_2O_{12}$ and In- and K-doped $Li_5La_3Nb_2O_{12}$. *J Solid State Chem* 179:974–984. doi: 10.1016/j.jssc.2005.12.025

44. Murugan R, Thangadurai V, Weppner W (2007) Fast lithium ion conduction in garnet-type $Li_7La_3Zr_2O_{12}$. *Angew Chemie - Int Ed* 46:7778–7781. doi: 10.1002/anie.200701144

45. Thangadurai V, Weppner W (2005) $Li_6ALa_2Nb_2O_{12}$ (A = Ca, Sr, Ba): A new class of fast lithium ion conductors with garnet-like structure. *J Am Ceram Soc* 88:411–418. doi: 10.1111/j.1551-2916.2005.00060.x

46. Cussen EJ, O'Callaghan MP, Powell AS, et al. (2008) Switching on fast lithium ion conductivity in garnets: The structure and transport properties of $Li_{3+x}Nd_3Te_{2-x}Sb_xO_{12}$. *Chem Mater* 20:2360–2369. doi: 10.1021/cm703677q

47. Cussen EJ (2006) The structure of lithium garnets: Cation disorder and clustering in a new family of fast Li+ conductors. *J Chem Commun* 4:412–413.

48. Thangadurai V, Kaack H, Weppner WJF (2003) Novel fast lithium ion conduction in garnet-type $Li_5La_3M_2O_{12}$ (M = Nb, Ta). *J Am Ceram Soc* 86:437–440. doi: 10.1111/j.1151-2916.2003.tb03318.x

49. Hyooma H, Hayashi K (1988) Crystal structures of $La_3Li_5M_2O_{12}$ (M=Nb, Ta). *Mater Res Bull* 23:1399–1407. doi: 10.1016/0025-5408(88)90264-4

50. Narayanan S, Ramezanipour F, Thangadurai V (2012) Enhancing Li ion conductivity of garnet-type $Li_5La_3Nb_2O_{12}$ by Y- and Li-codoping: Synthesis, structure, chemical stability, and transport properties. *J Phys Chem C* 116:20154–20162. doi: 10.1021/jp304737x

51. O'Callaghan MP, Cussen EJ (2007) Lithium dimer formation in the Li-conducting garnets $Li_{5+x}Ba_xLa_{3-x}Ta_2O_{12}$ (0 < x ≤ 1.6). *Chem Commun* 12:2048–2050. doi: 10.1039/b700369b

52. Geiger CA, Alekseev E, Lazic B, et al. (2011) Crystal chemistry and stability of "$Li_7La_3Zr_2O_{12}$" garnet: A fast lithium-ion conductor. *Inorg Chem* 50:1089–1097. doi: 10.1021/ic101914e

53. Bernstein N, Johannes MD, Hoang K (2012) Origin of the structural phase transition in Li 7La 3Zr 2O 12. *Phys Rev Lett* 109:2–6. doi: 10.1103/PhysRevLett.109.205702

54. Jalem R, Yamamoto Y, Shiiba H, et al. (2013) Concerted migration mechanism in the Li ion dynamics of garnet-type $Li_7La_3Zr_2O_{12}$. *Am Chem Soc* 296:1042–1045. doi: 10.1021/acsami.9b11439

55. Awaka J, Kijima N, Hayakawa H, Akimoto J (2009) Synthesis and structure analysis of tetragonal $Li_7La_3Zr_2O_{12}$ with the garnet-related type structure. *J Solid State Chem* 182:2046–2052. doi: 10.1016/j.jssc.2009.05.020

56. Awaka J, Takashima A, Kataoka K, et al. (2011) Crystal structure of fast lithium-ion-conducting cubic $Li_7La_3Zr_2O_{12}$. *Chem Lett* 40:60–62. doi: 10.1246/cl.2011.60

57. Rangasamy E, Wolfenstine J, Sakamoto J (2012) The role of Al and Li concentration on the formation of cubic garnet solid electrolyte of nominal composition $Li_7La_3Zr_2O_{12}$. *Solid State Ionics* 206:28–32. doi: 10.1016/j.ssi.2011.10.022

Solid-State Electrolytes for Lithium-Ion Batteries

58. Rettenwander D, Blaha P, Laskowski R, et al. (2014) DFT study of the role of Al^{3+} in the fast ion-conductor $Li_{7-3x}Al_{3+x}La_3Zr_2O_{12}$ garnet. *Chem Mater* 26:2617–2623. doi: 10.1021/cm5000999
59. Djenadic R, Botros M, Benel C, et al. (2014) Nebulized spray pyrolysis of Al-doped $Li_7La_3Zr_2O_{12}$ solid electrolyte for battery applications. *Solid State Ionics* 263:49–56. doi: 10.1016/j.ssi.2014.05.007
60. Larraz G, Orera A, Sanjuán ML (2013) Cubic phases of garnet-type $Li_7La_3Zr_2O_{12}$: The role of hydration. *J Mater Chem A* 1:11419–11428. doi: 10.1039/c3ta11996c
61. Jin Y, McGinn PJ (2011) Al-doped $Li_7La_3Zr_2O_{12}$ synthesized by a polymerized complex method. *J Power Sources* 196:8683–8687. doi: 10.1016/j.jpowsour.2011.05.065
62. Cheng L (2010) Effect of microstructure and surface impurity segregation on the electrical and electrochemical properties of dense Al-substituted $Li_7La_3Zr_2O_{12}$. *J. Mater. Chem. A* 2:172–181.
63. Phan VP, Pecquenard B, Le Cras F (2012) High-performance all-solid-state cells fabricated with silicon electrodes. *Adv Funct Mater* 22:2580–2584. doi: 10.1002/adfm.201200104
64. Zhu J, Lu L, Zeng K (2013) Nanoscale mapping of lithium-ion diffusion in a cathode within an all-solid-state lithium-ion battery by advanced scanning probe microscopy techniques. *ACS Nano* 7:1666–1675. doi: 10.1021/nn305648j
65. Haruta M, Shiraki S, Suzuki T, et al. (2015) Negligible "negative space-charge layer effects" at oxide-electrolyte/electrode interfaces of thin-film batteries. *Nano Lett* 15:1498–1502. Doi: 10.1021/nl5035896
66. Han X, Gong Y, Fu K, et al. (2017) Negating interfacial impedance in garnet-based solid-state Li metal batteries. *Nat Mater* 16:572–579. doi: 10.1038/nmat4821
67. Wolfenstine J, Ratchford J, Rangasamy E, et al. (2012) Synthesis and high Li-ion conductivity of Ga-stabilized cubic $Li_7La_3Zr_2O_{12}$. *Mater Chem Phys* 134:571–575. doi: 10.1016/j.matchemphys.2012.03.054
68. El Shinawi H, Janek J (2013) Stabilization of cubic lithium-stuffed garnets of the type "$Li_7La_3Zr_2O_{12}$" by addition of gallium. *J Power Sources* 225:13–19. doi: 10.1016/j.jpowsour.2012.09.111
69. Howard MA, Clemens O, Kendrick E, et al. (2012) Effect of Ga incorporation on the structure and Li ion conductivity of $La_3Zr_2Li_7O_{12}$. *Dalt Trans* 41:12048–12053. doi: 10.1039/c2dt31318a
70. Rettenwander D, Redhammer G, Preishuber-Pflügl F, et al. (2016) Structural and electrochemical consequences of Al and Ga cosubstitution in $Li_7La_3Zr_2O_{12}$ solid electrolytes. *Chem Mater* 28:2384–2392. doi: 10.1021/acs.chemmater.6b00579
71. Rettenwander D, Langer J, Schmidt W, et al. (2015) Site occupation of Ga and Al in stabilized cubic $Li_{7-3(x+y)}Ga_xAl_yLa_3Zr_2O_{12}$ garnets as deduced from 27Al and 71Ga MAS NMR at ultrahigh magnetic fields. *Chem Mater* 27:3135–3142. doi: 10.1021/acs.chemmater.5b00684
72. Afyon S, Krumeich F, Rupp JLM (2015) A shortcut to garnet-type fast Li-ion conductors for all-solid state batteries. *J Mater Chem A* 3:18636–18648. doi: 10.1039/c5ta03239c
73. Toda S, Ishiguro K, Shimonishi Y, et al. (2013) Low temperature cubic garnet-type $CO2$-doped $Li_7La_3Zr_2O_{12}$. *Solid State Ionics* 233:102–106. doi: 10.1016/j.ssi.2012.12.007
74. Xue W, Yang Y, Yang Q, et al. (2018) The effect of sintering process on lithium ionic conductivity of $Li_{6.4}Al_{0.2}La_3Zr_2O_{12}$ garnet produced by solid-state synthesis. *RSC Adv* 8:13083–13088. doi: 10.1039/c8ra01329b
75. Kokal I, Somer M, Notten PHL, Hintzen HT (2011) Sol-gel synthesis and lithium ion conductivity of Li7La 3Zr2O12 with garnet-related type structure. *Solid State Ionics* 185:42–46. doi: 10.1016/j.ssi.2011.01.002

76. Li Y, Han JT, Wang CA, et al. (2012) Ionic distribution and conductivity in lithium garnet Li 7La 3Zr 2O 12. *J Power Sources* 209:278–281. doi: 10.1016/j.jpowsour.2012.02.100

77. Dai Y, Xiao H, Liu J, et al. (2013) In vivo multimodality imaging and cancer therapy by near-infrared light-triggered trans -platinum pro-drug-conjugated upconversion nanoparticles. *J Am Chem Soc* 135:18920–18929. doi: 10.1021/ja410028q

78. Bernuy-Lopez C, Manalastas W, del Amo JML, et al. (2014) Atmosphere controlled processing of Ga-substituted garnets for high Li-ion conductivity ceramics. *Chem Mater* 26:3610–3617.

79. Dumon A, Huang M, Shen Y, Nan C (2013) High Li ion conductivity in strontium doped Li 7 La 3 Zr 2 O 12 garnet. *Solid State Ionics* 243:36–41. doi: 10.1016/j.ssi.2013.04.016

80. Li Y, Wang CA, Xie H, et al. (2011) High lithium ion conduction in garnet-type Li6La 3ZrTaO12. *Electrochem Commun* 13:1289–1292. doi: 10.1016/j.elecom.2011.07.008

81. Wang Y, Lai W (2012) High ionic conductivity lithium garnet oxides of Li 7-xLa 3Zr 2-xTa xO 12 compositions. *Electrochem Solid-State Lett* 15:4–8. doi: 10.1149/2.024205esl

82. Allen JL, Wolfenstine J, Rangasamy E, Sakamoto J (2012) Effect of substitution (Ta, Al, Ga) on the conductivity of Li7La3Zr2O12. *J Power Sources* 206:315–319. doi: 10.1090/dimacs/029/20

83. Ramzy A, Thangadurai V (2010) Tailor-made development of fast Li ion conducting garnet-like solid electrolytes. *ACS Appl Mater Interfaces* 2:385–390. doi: 10.1021/am900643t

84. Narayanan S, Epp V, Wilkening M, Thangadurai V (2012) Macroscopic and microscopic Li + transport parameters in cubic garnet-type "$Li_{6.5}La_{2.5}Ba_{0.5}ZrTaO_{12}$" as probed by impedance spectroscopy and NMR. *RSC Adv* 2:2553–2561. doi: 10.1039/c2ra01042a

85. Buschmann H, Berendts S, Mogwitz B, Janek J (2012) Lithium metal electrode kinetics and ionic conductivity of the solid lithium ion conductors "$Li_7La_3Zr_2O_{12}$" and $Li_{7-x}La_3Zr_{2x}Ta_xO_{12}$ with garnet-type structure. *J Power Sources* 206:236–244. doi: 10.1016/j.jpowsour.2012.01.094

86. Gupta A, Murugan R, Paranthaman MP, et al. (2012) Optimum lithium-ion conductivity in cubic $Li_{7-x}La_3Hf_{2-x}Ta_xO_{12}$. *J Power Sources* 209:184–188. doi: 10.1016/j.jpowsour.2012.02.099

87. Awaka J, Kijima N, Kataoka K, et al. (2010) Neutron powder diffraction study of tetragonal $Li_7La_3Hf_2O_{12}$ with the garnet-related type structure. *J Solid State Chem* 183:180–185. doi: 10.1016/j.jssc.2009.10.030

88. Zaiß T, Ortner M, Murugan R, Weppner W (2010) Fast ionic conduction in cubic hafnium garnet $Li_7La_3Hf_2O_{12}$. *Ionics (Kiel)* 16:855–858. doi: 10.1007/s11581-010-0486-2

89. Murugan R, Weppner W, Schmid-Beurmann P, Thangadurai V (2007) Structure and lithium ion conductivity of bismuth containing lithium garnets Li5La3Bi2O12 and $Li_6SrLa_2Bi_2O_{12}$. *Mater Sci Eng B Solid-State Mater Adv Technol* 143:14–20. doi: 10.1016/j.mseb.2007.07.009

90. Ohta S, Kobayashi T, Asaoka T (2011) High lithium ionic conductivity in the garnet-type oxide Li_{7-X} La$_3$(Zr$_{2-X}$, NbX)O$_{12}$ (X = 0–2). *J Power Sources* 196:3342–3345. doi: 10.1016/j.jpowsour.2010.11.089

91. Hitz GT, Wachsman ED, Thangadurai V (2013) Highly Li-stuffed garnet-type $Li_{7+x}La_3Zr_{2-x}Y_xO_{12}$. *J Electrochem Soc* 160:A1248–A1255. doi: 10.1149/2.088308jes

92. O'Callaghan MP, Lynham DR, Cussen EJ, Chen GZ (2006) Structure and ionic-transport properties of lithium-containing. *Am Chem Soc* 12:4681–4689.

93. Jalem R, Nakayama M, Manalastas W, et al. (2015) Insights into the lithium-ion conduction mechanism of garnet-type cubic $Li_5La_3Ta_2O_{12}$ by ab-initio calculations. *J Phys Chem C* 119:20783–20791. doi: 10.1021/acs.jpcc.5b05068

94. Adams S, Rao RP (2012) Ion transport and phase transition in $Li_{7-x}La_3(Zr_{2-x}M_x)O_{12}$ (M = Ta 5+, Nb 5+, x = 0, 0.25). *J Mater Chem* 22:1426–1434. doi: 10.1039/c1jm14588f
95. Meier K, Laino T, Curioni A (2014) Solid-state electrolytes: Revealing the mechanisms of Li-ion conduction in tetragonal and cubic LLZO by first-principles calculations. *J Phys Chem C* 118:6668–6679. doi: 10.1021/jp5002463
96. Van Wüllen L, Echelmeyer T, Meyer HW, Wilmer D (2007) The mechanism of Li-ion transport in the garnet $Li_5La_3Nb_2O_{12}$. *Phys Chem Chem Phys* 9:3298–3303. doi: 10.1039/b703179c
97. Xu M, Park MS, Lee JM, et al. (2012) Mechanisms of Li + transport in garnet-type cubic Li $_{3+}$x$La_3M_2O_{12}$ (M = Te, Nb, Zr). *Phys Rev B - Condens Matter Mater Phys* 85:1–5. doi: 10.1103/PhysRevB.85.052301
98. Han J, Zhu J, Li Y, et al. (2012) Experimental visualization of lithium conduction pathways in garnet-type $Li_7La_3Zr_2O_{12}$. *Chem Commun* 48:9840–9842. doi: 10.1039/c2cc35089k
99. Thompson T, Sharafi A, Johannes MD, et al. (2015) A tale of two sites: On defining the carrier concentration in garnet-based ionic conductors for advanced Li batteries. *Adv Energy Mater* 5:1500096–1500105. doi.org/10.1002/aenm.201500096
100. Wang D, Zhong G, Pang WK, et al. (2015) Toward understanding the lithium transport mechanism in garnet-type solid electrolytes: Li^+ ion exchanges and their mobility at octahedral/tetrahedral sites. *Chem Mater* 27:6650–6659. doi: 10.1021/acs.chemmater.5b02429

4 Polymer and Ceramic-Based Quasi-Solid Electrolytes for High Temperature Rechargeable Energy Storage Devices

Sajan Chinnan, Nikhil Medhavi,
Akhila Das, Neethu T. M. Balakrishnan,
Leya Rose Raphael, Jishnu N. S.,
Jabeen Fatima M. J., Prasanth Raghavan

CONTENTS

4.1 Introduction 73
4.2 Single-Phase to Dual-Phase Electrolyte 75
4.3 Inorganic Quasi-Solid Electrolytes.. 76
    4.3.1 Silica-Based Quasi-Solid-State Electrolytes 76
    4.3.2 Bentonite Clay-Based Quasi-Solid-State Electrolytes...................... 87
    4.3.3 Hexagonal Boron Nitride-Based Quasi-Solid-State Electrolytes 92
    4.3.4 Barium Titanate-Based Quasi-Solid-State Electrolytes 97
    4.3.5 Siloxane-Based Quasi-Solid-State Electrolytes.............................. 99
4.4 Conclusion and Future Outlook.. 103
Acknowledgment 103
References... 103

4.1 INTRODUCTION

Portable consumer electronics, spanning from wristwatches, mobile phones, laptops, and cameras, to electric vehicles and stationary power supply, are turning out to be an everyday necessity, demanding superior energy storage devices with improved safety [1, 2]. Among the different energy storage devices, batteries and supercapacitors (SCs) have been the most promising candidates in the arena [3]. The wide combination of electrodes and electrolytes has enabled the tailored use of these energy storage devices in extensive applications. However, heavy-duty applications such as electric vehicles or batteries used in abusive environments, such as petroleum mines, demand high tolerance of temperature and pressure [4, 5]. For the development of batteries or SCs with improved safety, the electrolyte plays a major role, unlike other device components, such as cathode, anode, or packaging materials. The conventional batteries had been using single-phase electrolytes (liquid electrolytes prepared by dissolving a suitable lithium salt in organic aprotic solvents, e.g., 1 M lithium hexafluorophosphate ($LiPF_6$) in ethylene carbonate (EC)/dimethyl carbonate (DMC), or all-solid-state electrolyte prepared by mixing solid-state matrix with a lithium salt, e.g.. poly(ethylene oxide) (PEO) mixed with lithium perchlorate ($LiClO_4$) along with a polymeric separator (Celgard®), which have higher ionic conductivity, but shows severe safety issues, even at room temperature applications, due to the low boiling point of the aprotic solvents, such as ethylene carbonate (EC), dimethyl carbonate (DMC), or propylene carbonate (PC). On that account, the development of electrolytes for high temperature applications remains a great challenge. For high temperature applications, conventional battery electrodes (carbon or metal oxide-based electrodes) are employable, but an electrolyte alternative was little known. Molten salt electrolytes came as a temporary solution, but it demanded higher operating temperatures to ensure the best conductivity properties. Solid-state electrolytes based on polymeric materials and lithium ion (Li-ion) conducting ceramic materials such as lithium superionic conductor (LISICON) and sodium superionic conductor (NASICON) were studied; however, they possessed poor ionic conductivity and processability, but they were safer. Ergo, there was a need to bring the safety offered by solid electrolytes and the superior conductivity offered by the liquid electrolytes into a single frame covering a wide range of operating temperatures [6–10].

The prior approach to prepare the conventional single-phase electrolyte was to add a minimum amount of liquid electrolyte to the solid electrolyte, which paved the way for the development of the other two electrolyte types, called gel electrolytes (GEs) and quasi-solid-state electrolyte (QSSEs). The conductivity and range of operating temperatures of these electrolytes can be tuned by the right selection of lithium salts, solvents, and matrix materials. Generally, in the gel electrolyte, a polymer material used as the matrix is gelled with an aprotic solvent containing a lithium salt, such as $LiPF_6$, lithium tetrafluoroborate ($LiBF_4$), lithium bis oxalate borate (LIBOB), etc., also called gel polymer electrolytes (GPE). Whereas, in the QSSEs, ceramic materials, such as nanoclay, hexagonal boron nitride (h-BN), or Li-ion, conducting glass ceramics, such as lithium aluminum titanium phosphate (LATP), lithium aluminum germanium phosphate (LAGP), etc., are employed as the matrix wetted with an aprotic solvent containing a lithium salt. In the resulting semisolid electrolyte, the coexistence of both phases (liquid and solid) puts the intrinsic safety of the solid-state electrolyte and ionic conductivity of the liquid electrolyte at risk. Compared to the all-solid-state batteries (ASSBs), the electrochemical performance of the device fabricated with GPE or QSSE is improved significantly. For instance, in a lithium sulfur battery, the replacement of solid-state electrolyte by QSSE improved the areal capacity from 1 mAh cm^{-2} to 2–4 mAh cm^{-2} [11], and lithium ion batteries (LIBs)

Rechargeable Energy Storage

made of QSSE improve the operating temperature to 150° C [12] and SC to 200° C [13]. Tackling the issues faced by the single-phase electrolyte, the QSSEs make their way into a state-of-the-art LIB structure. The second approach was by combining the advantages of a polymer with that of the inorganic and conventional organic electrolytes. Depending on the choice of polymer matrices and the inorganic and organic electrolytes employed, the electrolyte can be engineered for improved conductivity and efficient cell performance.

4.2 SINGLE-PHASE TO DUAL-PHASE ELECTROLYTE

The concept of quasi-solid-state batteries (QSSBs) emerged as a modification on conventional single-phase electrolytes. Their origin can be thought of as a progressive thinking strategy in which the flaws observed in single-phase solid electrolytes and single-phase liquid electrolytes were removed step by step with ad-hoc modifications. Though there are several problems, especially serious safety issues in LIBs using the conventional polymer separator, QSSEs are an advantageous system from the electrolyte perspective. So, to understand their origin, it is better to take a look at some significant limitations of batteries employing single-phase electrolytes (liquid electrolytes and solid-state electrolytes) that were overcome by using dual-phase GEs or QSSEs [14]. The most important properties of an electrolyte for a battery are the ionic conductivity and safety from electrolyte leakage or explosion. The conventional liquid electrolytes offer superior ionic conductivity and transference number (>5), but the safety of the battery, even at room temperature operation, is not promising [15]. The formation of the solid electrolyte interface (SEI) layer or dendrite formation due to the continuous charge–discharge cycling of the batteries was the primary issue causing the thermal runaway, which may lead to the explosion of batteries and the reported explosions of LIBs made of single-phase liquid electrolytes or GEs [16–20]. The SEI layer formation in the LIBs results from the unwanted electrochemical reaction between the electrolyte and battery electrode, especially with lithium metal. The chemicals used in the electrolytes laid the foundation for the formation for the SEI layer, hence, as an alternative for a single-phase liquid electrolyte system, all-solid-state electrolytes were introduced [15]. On the contrary, to single-phase liquid electrolyte or dual-phase QSSEs, the solid-state electrolytes exhibit reduced room temperature ionic conductivity, leading to inferior charge–discharge capacity, cycling stability, and rate capability performance of batteries/SCs. The interfacial resistance (R_f) offered by the electrode–electrolyte interface determines the ease of transfer of ions between the electrode and electrolyte. Apart from the poor ionic conductivity (higher bulk resistance, R_b), the single-phase solid-state electrolytes also show poor interfacial conductivity (higher interfacial resistance, R_f) at electrode and electrolyte interphase, which is due to the poor contact between the rigid natured electrode and solid-state electrolyte. Therefore, it causes the inadequate ion transference number and charge–discharge cycling performance of the battery or SC [21]. The aforementioned disadvantage of the single-phase electrolyte is addressed by the dual-phase QSSEs, opening up a new avenue in the development of high performance electrolytes with suitable ionic conductivity and

76 Ceramic and Specialty Electrolytes

electrochemical performance, coupled with safety at higher temperatures. Popularly, the quasi-solid electrolytes (QSEs) are inorganic in nature because the matrix used for the fabrication of QSSEs are ceramic materials (generally metal oxide or phosphates), such as silicon dioxide (SiO_2), h-BN, barium titanate ($BaTiO_3$), alumina (Al_2O_3), LAGP, LATP, nanoclay, etc; hence, they are broadly called inorganic QSSEs. In general, the inorganic QSEs are prepared by wetting the ceramic powder with a solution of lithium salt in room-temperature ionic liquid (RTIL) for the device to have high temperature safety; however, they can also be prepared by using aprotic solvents instead of RTILs.

4.3 INORGANIC QUASI-SOLID ELECTROLYTES

"Soggy sand" electrolyte is a term coined for inorganic-based QSEs, comprised of nanoparticles dispersed in nonaqueous electrolyte medium. Various oxides are known to be dispersed in the nonaqueous medium, providing enhanced surface area for the medium to be adsorbed and dried, forming an apparently solid QSE. The study was extended to ionic liquid-based electrolytes [22]. There are several reports on the solidification of ionic liquid (IL) with nanoparticles, such as SiO_2 [23–25], titanium dioxide (TiO_2) [26], and carbon nanotubes (CNTs) [26]. There are different methods adopted to solidify the ILs into mechanically self-supporting solid-state electrolytes: (i) impregnation into an organic polymer [27–30], (ii) copolymerization with an ionic-liquid monomer [31–38], (iii) solidification using low-molecular-weight gelating agents [39–41], (iv) confinement within inorganic gels [42–44], and (v) gelation with nanoparticles [23–26, 45]. This increase in the field of QSSEs was the consequence of the study of molecular layering of ILs on oxide surfaces opening a gateway to a generation of QSEs. A large number of QSSEs based on various RTILs and oxide substrates were studied in recent decades. The surface layer formation of ILs on the oxide substrate is formed in two ways. Strong interaction between ion pairs forces the formation of a checker-board-type structure in which an equal number of cations and anions are present in each layer. Contrary to the checker-board-type structure, systems with strong correlations between the ions and preference of either cations or anions form a distinct and alternative double layer of ionic species (cations and anions). The layers extend a few nanometers in thickness into the IL bulk and can be exploited to facilitate ionic conductivity through them [46]. The choice of oxide surface was explored to facilitate the drying of ILs, leading to QSEs with tailored thermomechanical properties. Because the thermal stability and nonflammability of ILs and ceramics materials are well established for crafting the electrolytes for high temperature LIBs, the conduction properties are the main concern. Several ceramic compounds have been attempted to prepare QSE systems, such as SiO_2 [47], nanoclay (aluminum silicates) [48], $BaTiO_3$ [49], and h-BN [12].

4.3.1 SILICA-BASED QUASI-SOLID-STATE ELECTROLYTES

SiO_2 is one of the most abundant ceramic materials known in the earth's crust. The low cost, inertness, and eco-friendliness of SiO_2 are advantageous properties,

Rechargeable Energy Storage

leading to a wide variety of applications, especially in electrolytes. SiO_2 is a colorless solid with a molecular mass of 60.08 g mol^{-1} and has extended thermal stability up to 1700° C. The ILs are also well known for their excellent thermal stability and flame-retardant properties with enhanced ionic conductivity. Combining the SiO_2 nanoparticles with IL generates a synergistic mechanism supporting the ionic conductivity and the dual-phase properties of the electrolyte. The presence of the second phase (inorganic solid phase) can increase the total ion conductivity of the soggy sand electrolytes because of the interfacial interactions. A drastic change in the ion-conducting properties of salt solutions in the solid insulating particles has been reported by A. J. Bhattacharyya et al. [50, 51]. Since Bhattacharya et al. [50] proposed layering IL on oxide surfaces, SiO_2 was immediately studied as an inorganic matrix to a vast combination of electrolytes. In a couple of studies, SiO_2 nanoparticles are prepared from a silicate precursor, primarily because of its availability and cost-effectiveness [52, 53]. Confinement of ILs into a neutral solid substrate has been a challenging task; however, Wang et al. [23–25] prepared the QSSEs by gelating the ILs with SiO_2 nanoparticles for electrolyte applications in dye-sensitized solar cells to enhance the thermal stability of the device. QSSEs based on SiO_2 particles (micro- or nanoparticles) with various RTILs dissolved with lithium salts were studied for the effect of SiO_2 size on the ionic conductivity and electrochemical performance in LIBs [15, 22, 47, 54–61]. The SiO_2 nanoparticles of 7 nm [56, 57] and different microsized to nanosized SiO_2 particles, ranging from 7 nm to 100 μm [22], have been widely used as the ceramic moiety.

The mechanical mixing of oxide nanoparticles and ILs to form the dry hybrid composite is a prevalent technique but, contrary to ordinary routes, Lu et al. [56] investigated the physical and electrochemical properties of a family of organic-inorganic hybrid electrolytes based on the IL 1-methyl-3-propylimidazolium bis(trifluoromethanesulfone)imide covalently tethered to SiO_2 nanoparticles (SiO_2-IL-TFSI). In the study, the investigators tried anchoring the IL 1-methyl-3-propyl-imidazolium bis(trifluoromethanesulfone)imide on SiO_2 nanoparticles, as shown in Figure 4.1. The first step was the functionalization of trimethoxysilane with RTIL to get 1-methyl-3-trimethoxysilane imidazolium chloride. The reaction product (1-methyl-3-trimethoxysilane imidazolium chloride), 3-chloropropyl trimethoxy silane precursor with 1-methyl imidazole, is then added into an aqueous solution of colloidal SiO_2 (30 wt% aqueous suspension) to form SiO_2-IL chloride (SiO_2-IL-Cl) nanoparticles [56]. The product was then subjected to anionic exchange with lithium bis(trifluoromethanesulfone)imide (LiTFSI) to form SiO_2-IL-TFSI. Because of the hydrophobic nature of the TFSI anion, the preparation is carried out in an aqueous medium, hence SiO_2-IL-TFSI immediately separates from the water phase and settles to the bottom of the vessel. The transmission electron microscope (TEM) image of SiO_2-IL-TFSI is shown in Figure 4.2a. Finally, the electrolyte was prepared by mixing SiO_2-IL-TFSI with LiTFI. The schematic illustration on the resulting SiO_2-IL-TFSI/LiTFSI mixture is displayed in Figure 4.2b.

The SiO_2-based SiO_2-IL-TFSI/LiTFSI electrolytes showed a potential stability window of 4.25 V, enhanced ionic conductivity, and thermal stability up to 400° C. It was observed that thermal stability increases with increasing content of SiO_2-IL-TFSI,

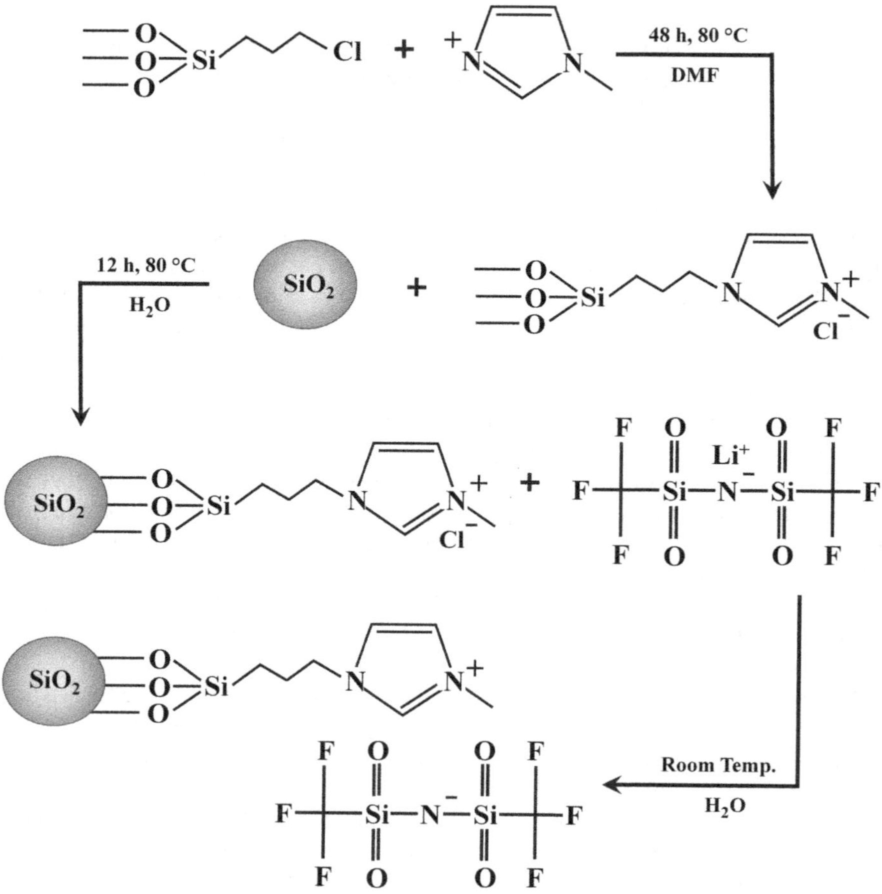

FIGURE 4.1 Schematic illustration on the synthesis method used for the preparation organic–inorganic hybrid electrolytes based on of RTIL covalently tethered to silica nanoparticles (SiO_2-RTIL-TFSI). Adapted and reproduced with permission from reference [56]. Copyright 2012 The Royal Society of Chemistry.

and the glass transition temperature (Tg) of the mixtures increased with increased doping of LiTFSI. The pristine SiO_2-IL-TFSI has a Tg of -78° C, while the Tg of SiO_2-IL-TFSI/LiTFSI mixture increased from -73° C to -55° C with a doping level of 50 wt%–95 wt% of LiTFSI. Ionic conductivities of SiO_2-IL-TFSI/LiTFSI mixtures exhibit a pronounced maximum, with SiO_2-IL-TFSI/LiTFSI mixtures containing 13.4 wt% SiO_2-IL-TFSI displaying the highest ionic conductivity. At room temperature, the ionic conductivity of the 13.4 wt% SiO_2-IL-TFSI/LITFI mixture is approximately 10^{-4} S cm^{-1}, which is more than three orders of magnitude higher than that of either of the pristine components or the previously reported hybrid electrolytes with 1-Butyl-3-methylimidazolium bis(trifluoromethanesulfonyl)imide ([BMIm][TFSI]),

Rechargeable Energy Storage

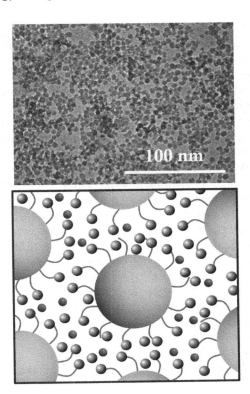

FIGURE 4.2 (a) Transmission electron micrograph of SiO$_2$-IL-TFSI deposited from solution on to a carbon grid and (b) schematic of ion distribution in SiO$_2$-IL-TFSI/LiTFSI electrolytes illustrating particle-induced ion dissociation, Gray circles represent impermeable particles and green and red dots represent the TFSI anions and lithium cations, respectively. The immobile particle surfaces or the cations tethered to the surface absorb TFSI and promote ion-pair dissociation in LiTFSI. Adapted and reproduced with permission from reference [56]. Copyright 2012 The Royal Society of Chemistry.

2-ethyl imidazolium bis(trifluoromethanesulfonyl)amide ([EtIm]$_4$[HTFSI]), or imidazolium bis(trifluoromethanesulfonyl)amide ([Im]$_4$[HTFSI]), which showed the ionic conductivity in the range of 10^{-5} S–10^{-6} S cm^{-1} [22]. The higher ionic conductivity of QSSEs prepared by solution mixing may be due to the presence of a liquid medium that facilitates effective dissociation of lithium salt, leading to the availability of a higher number of mobile Li-ions than those prepared by mechanical mixing [56]. In addition to the good ionic conductivity, the SiO$_2$-IL-TFSI/LiTFSI with 13.4 wt% SiO$_2$-IL-TFSI shows a Li-ion transfer number of (T_{Li+}) 0.54, while the electrolyte containing 7.5 wt% and 20 wt% SiO$_2$-IL-TFSI exhibit measurably lower T_{Li+} values of 0.33 and 0.21, respectively. These transference numbers are all notably larger than the reported T_{Li+} values for untethered IL electrolytes, directly attesting to the benefits of tethering the IL, which agrees with the physics existing in the zirconium dioxide (ZrO$_2$) hybrid IL electrolytes reported [62].

A similar maximum conductivity has been reported in soggy sand hybrid electrolytes with a higher content of ceramic particles [50]. Generally, the enhancement in ionic conductivity with ceramic-particle (SiO_2-IL-TFSI) loading is unexpected because the loading of ceramic particles considerably increases the electrolyte's viscosity and decreases the free-volume for ion transport. In their studies, Bhattacharyya and Maier [50] introduced the concept of adsorption-induced electrolyte polarization to explain the increasing ionic conductivity with the loading of ceramic fillers in the electrolyte. It was specifically explained that an increasing ionic conductivity with particle loading resulted from the interactions between ions in solution and charged species on the particle surface that weaken ion-pair interactions in the electrolytes, which enhances ion mobility. Because there are a finite number of dissociable ions in solution, the increase of ionic conductivity resulted from polarization beyond a critical particle loading. It should eventually give way to the more usual tendency of particles to decrease void fraction, which increases viscosity and reduces conductivity. Considering the two factors (rising ion mobility due to particle-induced polarization and falling ion mobility due to increasing suspension viscosity), it nicely explains the conductivity maximum in soggy sand hybrid electrolytes. A similar particle-induced polarization mechanism is responsible for the conductivity maximum observed for the SiO_2-IL-TFSI/TFSI system in which the bulky TFSI anion in the LiTFSI can associate with the particle-tethered cation, allowing the associated Li-ions to move more freely in response to an imposed field.

The uptake of ILs by SiO_2 particles considerably depends on the size of the ceramic SiO_2 particles. In many studies, it is reported that the ILs' uptake improves with increasing SiO_2 content and decreasing particle size of the SiO_2 due to the enhanced surface area (as particle size decreases, the surface area increases), which, in turn, increases the available surface area for the adsorption of ILs. In addition to that, the oxide nanoparticles' surface area affects the rate of drying of ILs. Shimano et al. [22] demonstrated the size effect of SiO_2 nanoparticles on the uptake of ILs and ionic conductivity of the QSSEs. In the study, they used different micronsize to nanosize SiO_2 particles, ranging from 7 nm to 100 µm. They prepared the QSSEs by gelation of an IL with nanoparticles. In planetary mixing, the predried SiO_2 and IL were mixed in argon-filled glove box followed by mechanical milling for homogenization. The study also investigated the effect of various RTILs, such as [BMIm][TFSI], $[Im]_4[HTFSI]$, and $[EtIm]_4[HTFSI]$, on ionic conductivity and electrochemical properties of the resulting QSSEs. The systematic study showed that for 7 nm-size SiO_2 particles with a surface area of 390 $m^2 g^{-1}$ showed quasi-solid properties on uptake above 70 wt% RTIL ([BMIm][TFSI]), whereas, for up to 70 wt%, the hybrid soggy sand type electrolyte maintained a solid-state morphology [22]. The surface morphology of QSSEs $[Im]_4[HTFSI]/SiO_2$ (70 wt% IL) and 40 wt%, (soggy sand) is displayed in Figure 4.3. As revealed in the scanning electron microscope (SEM) image, up to the loading of 40 wt% RTILs, no dense body of solid particle aggregates were observed; however, with 70 wt% IL loading, spherical liquid-like droplets with large diameters (50 nm–300 nm) were formed.

The synergistic effect of nanosize SiO_2 and bulk SiO_2 is demonstrated in the schematic illustration given in Figure 4.4. The electrolytes' physical state changed

Rechargeable Energy Storage

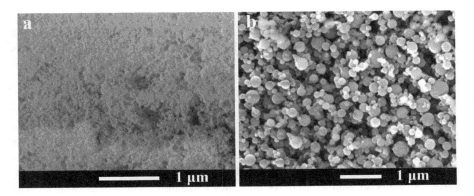

FIGURE 4.3 FE-SEM images on the surface morphology of RTIL [Im]$_4$[HTFSI]/SiO$_2$ (7 nm) hybrid materials with different ionic liquid compositions: (a) 40 wt% RTIL, soggy sand (powder state) and (b) 70 wt% RTIL QSSE (gel state). Adapted and reproduced with permission from reference [22]. Copyright 2007 American Chemical Society.

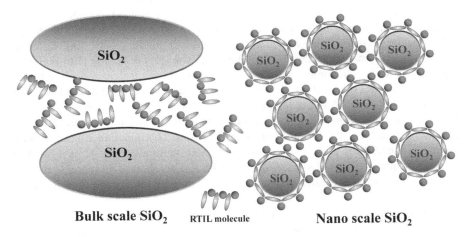

FIGURE 4.4 Comparison on synergistic mechanism of RTILs with bulk and nanosilica surfaces. Adapted and reproduced with permission from reference [22]. Copyright 2007 American Chemical Society.

from opaque solid to transparent gel as the mixing concentration of RTIL increases. The SiO$_2$/RTIL composite pellets prepared with [BMIm][TFSI], containing 70 wt%–90 wt% RTIL, were semitransparent gels, which increased with the volume fraction of RTIL. In contrast, materials containing less than 60 wt% IL were entirely solid-state bulky materials, and they exhibited excellent thermal stability (300° C to 350° C). When SiO$_2$ with a particle size less than 14 nm were used as solidifying agents, the hybrid electrolyte containing more than 90 wt% of IL were solid materials, for all the three ILs ([BMIm][TFSI], [Im]$_4$[HTFSI] and [EtIm]$_4$[HTFSI]) that were subjected to study [22].

The impedance spectroscopic studies showed that ionic conductivity is directly proportional to the amount of RTIL incorporated as the conducting phases in the electrolyte. The relationship between the RTIL concentration was given by Archie's law [63].

$$\sigma_{IL/SiO_2} = a\sigma_{IL}\varphi_{IL}{}^m$$

where σ_{IL/SiO_2} is the conductivity of RTIL-SiO$_2$ composite, σ_{IL} is the conductivity of IL alone, φ_{IL} is the volume fraction of RTIL, and a is the proportionality factor. As the size of SiO$_2$ particles decreases, the value of m (order to which the volume fraction affects the conductivity) increases. The hybrid electrolyte with nanosize SiO$_2$ particles (diameter smaller than 14 nm) shows a marked enhancement in m. The hybrid electrolyte containing 7 nm size SiO$_2$ showed the highest value of m, around 5–6, for different RTILs, indicating the effect of oxide/ceramic particle size on ionic conductivity and ion-conducting mechanism with nanoscale media.

SiO$_2$-based QSSE for battery applications became more attractive after Shimano et al. [22] reported ionic conductivity studies of hybrid electrolytes with ILs dried on SiO$_2$ nanoparticles of various sizes. The 7-nm fumed SiO$_2$ nanoparticles showed the best drying nature up to a loading capacity of 60 wt% IL without losing the solid powder texture. There was guaranteed thermal stability until 300° C for all three imidazolium-based ILs, [BMIm][TFSI], [EtIm]$_4$[HTFSI], and [Im]$_4$[HTFSI], used in the study. The ionic conductivity of the hybrid electrolyte was close to that of the pristine RTILs in the order of 10^{-3} S cm^{-1} at room temperature. This ionic conductivity is quite similar to the gel polymer electrolyte [63–79] and quite high for a solid-state electrolyte [80–87] and is larger than that of lithium conducting solid-polymer electrolytes [88–95] used in various devices. The impedance spectroscopic studies compared the ionic conductivity of hybrid materials at 25° C as a function of their volume ratios of ILs to SiO$_2$ (Figure 4.5a). This showed an increase in ionic conductivity with the volume fraction of the IL up to 80 vol% and then remained almost constant.

Temperature-dependent ionic conductivity studies on SiO$_2$/[BMIm][TFSI] composite QSSE over the temperature range 25° C–300° C showed a sharp increase in ionic conductivity up to 150° C for the QSSEs having 40 wt%–80 wt% RTILs as displayed in Figure 4.5(b). The SiO$_2$/[BMIm][TFSI] composite QSSE with 60 wt% RTIL showed a monotonic increase in ionic conductivity up to 300° C and reached the ionic conductivity value to the order of 10^{-2} S cm^{-1} in the temperature range of 200°–300 °C, which was claimed as the highest ionic conductivity reported for solid-state materials. The nanosize confinement of liquid molecules within the SiO$_2$ nanoparticles is presumed to be responsible for this liquid-like conductivity in the solid phase and the ILs' stability to fluidity and evaporation.

Several research groups have investigated the physical and electrochemical properties of a family of organic-inorganic hybrid electrolytes based on the IL 1-methyl-3-propylimidazolium bis(trifluoromethanesulfone)imide covalently tethered to SiO$_2$ nanoparticles (SiO$_2$-IL-TFSI). In 2012, Lu et al. [56, 57] demonstrated the effect of 7 nm SiO$_2$ particles on the thermal and electrochemical properties of SiO$_2$-IL-TFSI/PC

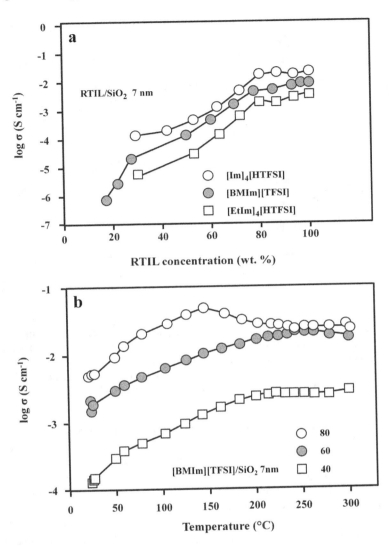

FIGURE 4.5 Comparison of ionic conductivity of RTIL/SiO$_2$-based QSSEs: (a) ionic conductivity of QSSEs based on different RTILs and silica (7 nm) as a function of RTIL loading (vol%) and (b) temperature dependent ionic conductivity of BMII TFSI/SiO$_2$ QSSEs with different RTIL loading (wt%) Adapted and reproduced with permission from reference [22]. Copyright 2007 American Chemical Society.

electrolyte systems with nanoparticle compositions ranging from 0 wt%–100 wt% in PC. Predetermined amounts of the as-synthesized SiO$_2$-IL-TFSI nanoparticles prepared as per Scheme 01 were blended directly with PC and LiTFSI to prepare SiO$_2$-IL-TFSI/PC blend containing 1 M LiTFSI electrolytes. The resulting QSSE with 1-methyl-3-propylimidazolium bis(tri-fluoromethanesulfone)imide RTIL covalently

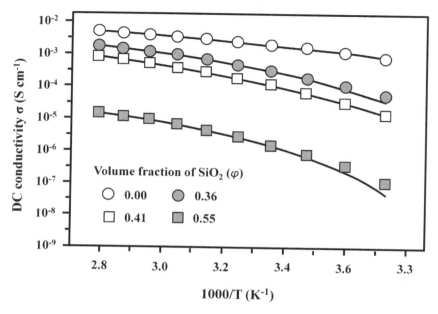

FIGURE 4.6 Temperature dependent ionic conductivity of SiO_2-RTIL-TFSI/PC hybrid electrolytes with various SiO_2 volume fractions (from pristine PC to pristine hybrid particle) as a function of temperature. The solid lines in the figure are VTF fits for the temperature-dependent ionic conductivity. Adapted and reproduced with permission from reference [57]. Copyright 2012 Wiley-VCH Verlag GmbH & Co. KGaA, Weinheim.

tethered to SiO_2 nanoparticles (SiO_2-IL-TFSI) is thermally stable up to temperatures as high as 400° C [56], and their temperature dependent conductivity follows the Vogel-Tamman-Fulcher (VTF) equation rather than Arrhenius equation. It should be noted that VTF-like temperature-dependent ionic conductivities are found in electrolytes where local segmental motion, chain relaxation, and crystallinity play essential roles. Furthermore, the motion of the ions themselves from one electrolyte site to another is of minor importance [96]. The impedance spectroscopic studies and nuclear magnetic resonance spectroscopy (NMR) analyses are two crucial tools for studying the ion dynamics in electrolyte systems. The linearity observed on temperature dependent ionic conductivity of SiO_2-IL-TFSI/PC QSSEs over the temperature range of -10° C–80° C and NMR studies implies that the motion of ions is controlled by molecular relaxation and by exaggerated swinging motions of SiO_2-IL-TFSI tethered to the nanoparticles [9, 56, 97]. Additionally, it was found that the thickness of the confined ionic species was close to 5 nm–10 nm, which also significantly influenced the Li-ion transport mechanism in the QSSEs.

The ionic conductivity of SiO_2-IL-TFSI/PC electrolytes as a function of temperature with various nanoparticle volume fractions, φ except for the pristine SiO_2-IL-TFSI electrolyte, is found to be 0.55, as displayed in the Figure 4.6 [57]. The results showed all the SiO_2-IL-TFSI/PC electrolytes having different volume fractions (φ)

Rechargeable Energy Storage

of nanoparticles exhibit attractive room-temperature ionic conductivities. Also the SiO_2-IL-TFSI/PC (φ = 0.11, 0.23, 0.36, 0.41, and 0.55) electrolytes show an electrochemical stability window up to around 4 V vs. Li/Li^+, which is much higher (3.2 times) than that of PC/1M LiTFSI, (φ = 0) (LSV, 1.25 V vs. Li/Li^+). These results indicate that the addition of SiO_2-IL-TFSI to PC may enhance the electrolyte's electrochemical stability, which could be due to the SiO_2-tethered IL's ability to form a mechanically strong, passivation film on metallic lithium.

For understanding the lithium plating mechanism and cycling stability or rate capability, a representative SiO_2-IL-TFSI/PC electrolyte system with particle content φ = 0.23 in a symmetric Li/Li^+ lithium metal coin cell was evaluated for bulk (R_b) and interfacial (R_i) resistances by impedance analysis as a function of time up to 1200 h [57]. At 25° C, a grain boundary resistance, R_b of around 630 Ω cm^{-2}, and interfacial resistance, R_i of around 1900 Ω cm^{-2}, were observed; however, at higher temperatures, R_b decreases gradually, while R_i drops rapidly, eventually becoming around 270 Ω cm^{-2} at 50° C, implying that, while the electrolytes are marginally suitable for room-temperature battery operation, they should function even better at moderately higher temperatures. The time-dependent impedance analysis shows that the bulk and interfacial resistances (R_b and R_i) reach steady-state values after around 100 hours and remain exceptionally stable after that, probably indicating that the electrolyte forms a stable passivation film during the first phase, which protects it subsequently.

The demonstration on the suitability of these SiO_2-IL-TFSI/PC hybrid electrolytes for room-temperature lithium metal batteries (a representative hybrid electrolyte with φ = 0.23) are investigated at 25° C under galvanostatic conditions with carbon-coated molybdenum disulfide (MoS_2) and anatase TiO_2, as electrodes, displays good charge–discharge capacity, cycling stability, and rate capability. The results are generally consistent with the characteristic profiles of MoS_2 obtained from galvanostatic cycling measurements in commercial 1 M Li^+-EC/DMC electrolytes [98]. At a current density of 100 mA g^{-1}, MoS_2 exhibits a capacity of 1310 mAh g^{-1} in the first discharge cycle and discharge plateaus at 1.1 V and 0.6 V. In the subsequent first charge and second discharge cycles, the capacities are 752 mAh g^{-1} and 800 mAh g^{-1} with voltage plateaus at 2.3 V and 1.9 V, respectively. The electrolyte shows excellent stability over the measured 15 charge–discharge cycles with a capacity of 750 mAh g^{-1} after the 15th cycle. Similar charge–discharge profiles and cycling stability were observed with a commercial EC/DMC-based electrolyte [98], signifying that SiO_2-IL-TFSI/PC electrolytes are tolerant to high energy density electrodes.

The charge–discharge profiles obtained for the SiO_2-IL-TFSI/PC, φ=0.23, hybrid electrolyte system with TiO_2 electrodes exhibit charge–discharge profiles with distinct potential plateaus at 1.77 V and 1.91 V for the discharging and charging processes with a capacity of around 325 and 245 mAh g^{-1} respectively. In the subsequent cycles, the discharging and charging capacities fall to 255 mAh g^{-1} and 235 mAh g^{-1}, respectively. These results are nearly identical to what was obtained using anatase TiO_2 electrodes with commercial electrolytes [99]. It is apparent from the Figure 4.7 that the electrolyte can sustain current rates as high as 10C with an average capacity of 20 mAh g^{-1}. Therefore, these results strongly suggest that the bulk and interfacial

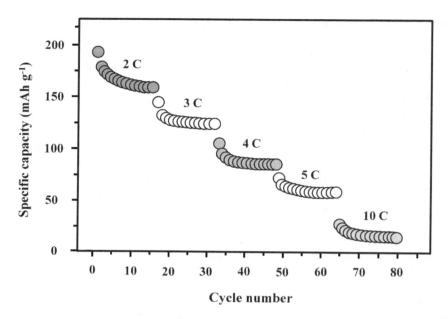

FIGURE 4.7 Variation of specific capacity with cycle number for Li/QSSE/TiO$_2$ coin cells at various current rates. The electrolyte used is a SiO$_2$-RTIL-TFSI/PC hybrid with $\phi = 0.23$. Adapted and reproduced with permission from reference [99]. Copyright 2010 The Royal Society of Chemistry.

mobility of Li-ions in SiO$_2$-IL-TFSI/PC electrolytes (Figure 4.6) is sufficient to sustain high power density electrodes even for room-temperature battery operation [99].

The increase in conductivity with RTIL loading cannot be viewed as a general trend for solid-liquid composites in which the properties just appear to be cumulative; instead, the effect is synergistic for which the interfacial interactions play a significant role. As discussed earlier, the mechanism for this interfacial adsorption induced polarization was also introduced by Bhattacharya et al. [50]. A specific ion tends to get adsorbed on the surface, and this facilitates the dissociation of the molecules and further enhances the ionic conductivity due to an increase in the number of generated ions. The high ionic conductivity, thermal stability, and excellent thermomechanical properties were demonstrated for fumed SiO$_2$ nanoparticle-based QSEs by a series of study by Honma group [15, 54, 55, 58–61], even though the complete cell studies did not show promising results for the higher number of charge–discharge cycles.

Li-ion conducting salts lithium bis(trifluoromethanesulfonyl)amide (Li-TFSA) or lithium bis(fluorosulfonyl)amide (Li-FSA) with 1-ethyl-3-methylimidazolium bis(trifluoromethanesulfonyl)amide (EMI-TFSA) or 1-ethyl-3-methylimidazolium bis(fluorosulfonyl)amide (EMI-FSA) RTIL–Li-salt mixtures, 1M Li-TFSA/EMI-TFSA and 1M Li-FSA/EMI-FSA, were quasi-solidified at fumed SiO$_2$ (390 m^2 g^{-1} and 7 nm in relative surface areas and grain diameter) particle surfaces by simple mixing followed by drying on a hot plate. The surface of the SiO_2 particles was etched by a piranha solution consisting of sulfuric acid (H_2SO_4) and hydrogen peroxide (H_2O_2) (7:3 v/v). The electrical conductivities and self-diffusion coefficients of the constituent species of the RTIL–Li-salt bulks and the composite materials with x vol% 1M Li-TFSA/EMI-TFSA or 1M Li-FSA/EMI-FSA (x=100, 75, and 50) were evaluated. We have successfully quasi-solidified RTIL–Li-salts at fumed SiO_2 surfaces, even though most of the composites consist of RTIL–Li-salts such as $x = 75$–80. The quasi-solid-state composites had liquid-like high conductivities, e.g. 3.2×10^{-4} to 4.4×10^{-3} S cm^{-1} for 75 vol%, 1M Li-TFSA/EMI-TFSA-fumed SiO_2 and 6.4×10^{-4} to 5.4×10^{-3} S cm^{-1} for 75 vol% 1M Li-FSA/EMI-FSA-fumed SiO_2, in the temperature range of 283–348 K [100]. Figure 4.8b depicts the electrochemical impedance measurements of 1M Li-TFSA/EMI-TFSA-SiO_2 with 75 vol% RTIL composite QSSE pellet sandwiched between stainless (SUS) electrodes or Li metal electrodes. Stainless steel acts as a blocking electrode, hence a 45° inclination was observed in the plot. A semicircular shape was seen when the SUS electrodes were replaced with Li electrodes, in which lithium acts as an active electrode, hence the single electrode-electrolyte interfacial impedance (R_i) was observed with an impedance value of ~1750 W from the Nyquist impedance plot. These results indicated that the Li-ion was one of the carrier species in the composite pellet.

The 1M Li-TFSA/EMI-TFSA-SiO_2 QSSE with 75 vol% RTIL was evaluated for the electrochemical performance in an all-solid-state lithium secondary battery cell by using three-dimensional (3D) structural cathode mixing the solid electrolyte and a cathode material lithium cobalt oxide ($LiCoO_2$, simply LCO) (the modified cathode), for which the electrolyte employed was water-like thick transparent films (pellets with diameters of 5.0 mm and 0.5 mm in height). The charge–discharge measurement of the ASSB cell using the 3D cathode showed a capacity value at the first, second, and fifth discharge as 126 mAh g^{-1}, 124 mAh g^{-1}, and 122 mAh g^{-1} for $LiCoO_2$, respectively, which corresponds to the 88%–90% of the theoretical capacity of the $LiCoO_2$ cathode (138 mAh g^{-1}) [47]. The charge–discharge plateau was observed between 3.8V and 4 V, indicating its compatibility with the lithium anode and $LiCoO_2$ cathode and thus stood up as a potential candidate for application in secondary batteries. Charge–discharge measurement of the all-solid secondary battery cell showed significant cycle decay (Figure 4.8a) above eighth cycle. Additionally, SiO_2 is not stable against Li in general; therefore, it influences the capacity decay.

The stability issues of SiO_2 against Li (possibly the Li may electrochemically react with SiO_2) is thought to be the reason for the fast decay in discharge capacity. The nanoparticulate, powdered nature of this hybrid electrolyte provides the upper hand in the facile preparation of a 3D cathode by mixing active cathode materials. Despite a few disadvantages, SiO_2-based QSEs showed thermal stability and excellent charge–discharge properties at a temperature close to 65° C.

4.3.2 Bentonite Clay-Based Quasi-Solid-State Electrolytes

Clay is a weathering product produced by disintegration of igneous rocks with a fine texture and particle size less than 2 mm. There are two types of clay; the first is

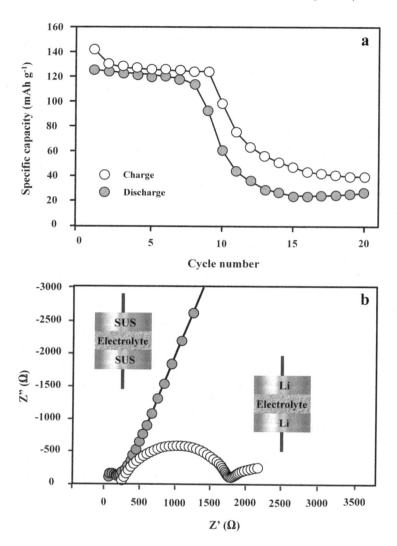

FIGURE 4.8 (a) Charge discharge cycle for the cell assembly with modified cathode and silica-based QSSE cycled at 65° C and 0.1 C-rate, and (b) Nyquist plot of 75 vol% Li-RTIL/ fumed silica composite electrolyte sandwiched by SUS electrodes and Li electrode. Adapted and reproduced with permission from reference [47]. Copyright 2012 Elsevier.

called 2:1 clay (montmorillonite/bentonite) and the second is called 1:1 clay (kaolinite). The 2:1 clay is used for many applications. A schematic representation on the special arrangement of layers in 2:1 clay (montmorillonite/bentonite) and 1:1 clay (kaolinte) is depicted in Figure 4.9. The planes of cations in clay minerals may be tetrahedrally or octahedrally coordinated with oxygen. In montmorillonite/bentonite clay, the planes are composed of two tetrahedral and one octahedral sheet,

Rechargeable Energy Storage

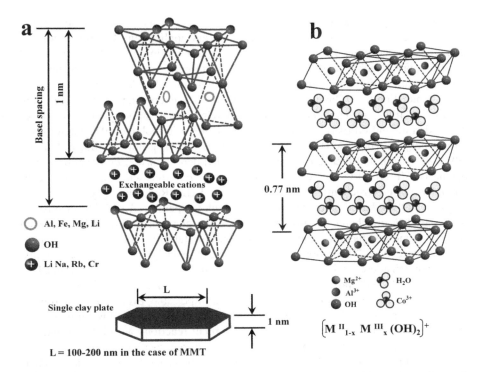

FIGURE 4.9 A schematic representation of structure of layered silicates/nanoclay and its constituent elements: (a) 2:1 clay (montmorillonite/bentonite) and (b) 1:1 clay (kaolinte). Adapted and reproduced with permission from reference [78]. Copyright 2013 Elsevier.

whereas, in kaolinite, the planes are composed of alternating tetrahedral and octahedral sheets. Bentonite clay is a natural clay derived from reworking and altering the glassy volcanic materials and is rich in smectites regardless of their origin. It has super adsorbing properties and is used widely in cosmetics and other medical applications. The unique layered structure of the clay facilitates the intercalation of various cations and promotes ionic conduction due to the superior cation exchange capacity (CEC) [101–103]. The bentonite clay consists of stalked aluminosilicate platelets, having other metal oxides, such as iron oxides, calcium oxides, potassium oxide, sodium ions, etc., between the clay platelets (clay galleries) depending on the area of mining [104]. One of the first occurrences of bentonite was found in the Cretaceous Benton Shale near Rock River, Wyoming. It is a type of montmorillonite clay, and the linkage of SiO_2 tetrahedra enables these aluminosilicates to adopt a variety of structural morphologies. These layered oxide structures offer unique wet chemistries within their interlayer gallery region. They can expand and contract their structure while maintaining their two-dimensional (2D) crystallographic integrity. A typical mineral of 2:1 group, montmorillonite has an ideal chemical formula of $R_{0.33}(Al_{1.67}Mg_{0.33})Si_4O_{10}(OH)_2$. Natural clays are hydrophilic owing to the presence of charges in the minerals. For electrolyte or energy storage applications, the solvent

90 Ceramic and Specialty Electrolytes

preferred is lyophilic rather than hydrophilic, so the clay is usually organically modified by ion-exchange reactions for the energy storage applications. Organic modification is achieved usually by using surfactant moieties containing both hydrophilic and lyophilic parts, such as cationic surfactants including primary, secondary, tertiary, and quaternary alkyl ammonium or alky phosphonium salts [78, 105].

Montmorillonite or bentonite clay is used as ion conduction promoter cum reinforcing filler and enhancing the electrolyte's thermal stability in the composite solid-state and GPEs of LIBs [63–79, 88]. Composite polymer electrolyte based on polyacrylonitrile (PAN) [63, 64, 72–75], PEO [76, 77], polyvinylidene fluoride (PVdF) [76–78], and their co-polymer poly(vinylidene fluoride)-*co*-hexafluoro propylene (PVdF-*co*-HFP) [65–69, 79, 106], etc. are reported with higher ionic conductivity and electrochemical properties for the LIBs. Recently, Ajayan et al. [48] reported a QSSE based on bentonite clay for high temperature LIBs. The electrolyte is prepared by mechanically mixing the predried clay with RTIL, which showed superior ionic conductivity and excellent thermal stability. The synergistic chemistry of the clay–RTIL combination is still under investigation. However, usually, clay is not considered to be a good candidate for the preparation electrolyte in LIBs, as, owing to its hydrophilic nature, they tend to absorb moisture, making complete removal of hydration or bound moisture almost impossible, even if it is dried overnight at a temperature above 600° C under vacuum. The presence of water molecules in the battery electrolyte causes vigorous chemical reactions with lithium and can cause the battery's explosion or poor charge–discharge, cycling stability, and electrochemical performance. However, due to the unique properties of the clay, such as layered structure, interesting interlayer chemistry in the clay platelets or clay galleries, and exceptional thermal as well as electrochemical stability, are the key parameters leading to research in clays as a promising nanomaterial for the preparation electrolyte in battery applications, especially when the safety at high temperature is a vital concern.

The bentonite clay shows remarkable adsorbing properties, causing enhanced uptake of RTIL and for the preparation of QSSE. The study used 1-methyl-1-propylpiperidinium bis(trifluoromethyl sulfonyl)imide (PPMI) as the RTIL because of its higher thermal and electrochemical stability and room temperature ionic conductivity as a result of localized electrons on the N-atom of its cation [48] and LiTFSI as lithium salt for the presence of the same sulfonylimide anion as that of PPMI (Figure 4.10) [48]. The clay-based QSSE was prepared by mechanical milling and then purified and dehydrated (by calcination in a vacuum oven at 650° C for 1 hour in a mortar with a homogenous solution of LiTFSI/PPMI [0.2M, 0.6M, and 1M molar solution]) and maintaining the ratio of clay to LiTFSI-RTIL as 1:1 wt/wt. During mechanical milling, the RTILs are easily intercalated into the clay galleries because of their exceptional affinity toward RTILs. Then the RTIL molecules start to pull out the clay platelets to exfoliate, which leads to the collapsing of the layered structure by ion intercalation method, which eventually leads to a sizeable interaction between the ions and the clay platelets in the composite QSSEs. A minimal mechanical agitation is required to exfoliate the clay at their edges to obtain the QSSE with stable composition with suitable consistency [107, 108].

Rechargeable Energy Storage 91

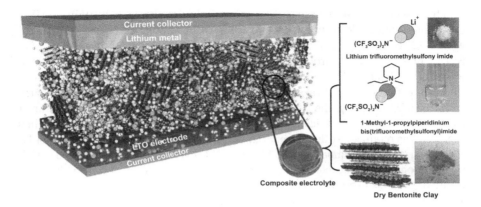

FIGURE 4.10 A schematic representation of the components employed for synthesis of clay-RTIL quasi-solid-state electrolyte, along with the envisioned structure of lithium-ion battery. Adapted and reproduced with permission from reference [48]. Copyright 2015 American Chemical Society.

In the study, LiTFSI is the doping salt that donates Li-ions for ionic conduction. The ionic conductivity increased with LiTFSI concentration and operating temperature. At elevated temperatures, the viscosity of the QSSEs decreased, which brings down the activation energy for ionic conduction, and the higher salt concentration contributed more mobile ions for ionic conduction, leading to the increase in ionic conductivity. The lowering of viscosity of the QSSEs with increasing operating temperature and decreasing salt concentration causes the decrease in the diffusion coefficient. The ionic conductivity dependency with temperature was not linear for the electrolyte, following the Arrhenius equation; instead, it favored VTF behavior. Ionic conductivity value of ~3.35 × 10^{-3} S cm^{-1} was obtained with 1 M LiTFSI/PPMI at a temperature of 120° C. The nature of clay tends to have more mobile cations; therefore, the overall conductivity is not an accurate measure of the mobility of Li^+ ion. Generally, transference number of Li^+ ions (T_{Li+}) is measured using the applied current/direct current (AC/DC) polarization method with Bruce-Vincent correction and was measured to be 0.06 at 25° C and close to 0.08 at 120° C for 1 M solution of LiTFSI in PPMI QSSE as compared to the 0.10 ± 0.03 at room temperature for a pristine 1 M solution of LiTFSI in PPMI. ILs tend to have a very low ion transference number in general, and this value seemed to be comparable with the reported values [109–111]. The exfoliation of layered clay causes a diminishing effect on the T_{Li+} values of the composite QSSE because it may release metal cations into the composite electrolyte and induces trapping of piperidinium ions in the cation exchange sites to counter the negative charge of the clay platelets. Up to 370° C, 1 M LiTFSI/PPMI was thermally stable, which is considerably higher (about 15° C) than clay/PPMI/LiTFSI QSSE. On further heating, the electrolyte showed a 50% weight loss of around 450° C due to the decomposition. Electrochemical studies with stainless steel (SS) working electrodes resulted in a linear potential sweep up to 3.1 V at 120° C. However the QSSE shows anodic stability up to 5 V at 25° C, which is comparable to the reported anodic stability of electrospun PVdF-*co*-HFP/clay composite gel electrolyte with 1 M $LiPF_6$ in EC/diethyl carbonate (DEC) (1:1, w/w) [112] or inferior to that of PVdF-*co*-HFP/ceramic filler (with 6 wt% SiO_2, $BaTiO_3$ or Al_2O_3) gel electrolyte with 0.5 M solution of LiTFSI in 1-butyl-3-methylimidazolium bis(trifluoromethylsulfonyl)imide (BMITFSI) [66]. Charge–discharge studies at different C-rates varying from C/16 to 1C at 120° C on the cells fabricated with $Li_4Ti_5O_{12}$ (LTO) as the working electrode and metallic lithium as the counter electrode displayed a significant decrease from 115 to 50 mAh g^{-1}, and the nominal capacity was retained, as the current rate was reverted to C/3 from 1C (Figure 4.11) [48]. At an operating temperature of 120° C, stable cycling stability with good capacity retention after 120 cycles at a current density of 50 mA g^{-1}, corresponding to a C rate of C/3 was displayed, and the cells delivered a stable capacity of 65 mAh g^{-1} after 120 cycles with excellent coulombic efficiency (about 100%) [48].

The same group also reported a high temperature SC that can safely operate at 200° C with bentonite clay/1-butyl-2,3-dimethylimidazolium bis(trifluoromethylsuphonyl)imide (BMMI-TFSI) electrolyte having a specific capacitance of 33 F g^{-1} [13]. These studies showed that, for the high temperature applications, the most suitable candidates for the choice of ILs are the imidazolium-based or piperidinium-based ILs. In imidazolium-based electrolytes, the positive charge is delocalized over the aromatic ring, whereas the positive charge is localized on the nitrogen atom of piperidinium-based electrolytes [113].

4.3.3 Hexagonal Boron Nitride-Based Quasi-Solid-State Electrolytes

Hexagonal boron nitride is a compound with an analogous structure to that of graphite with the chemical formula BN and is also known as white graphene. It is chemically and thermally stable and is thus exploited for various electrical insulation and heat-resistance applications. The h-BN has high thermal stability above 1000° C, possesses a direct bandgap of 5.9 eV, and shows excellent electrochemical stability [114]. The h-BN is formed by sp^2 hybridization of boron and nitrogen to form strong covalent bonds with a bond length of 1.45 Å. Adjacent layers of h-BN are combined with weak van der Waal's forces of attraction with an interatomic layer spacing of 0.333 nm [115]. The 2D boron nitride possesses similar properties of graphene with semimetallic conduction. The h-BN shows optical properties due to its anisotropic structure, and they have high exciton-binding energy. A single crystal's basal plane is not broken easily because of its strong in-plane bonds [116].

The layered structure of h-BN facilitates the exceptionally high intake of ILs in the synthesis of electrolytes, similar to the nanoclay (montmorillonite/bentonite clay). In 2016, Ajayan et al. [12] found h-BN as an exciting counterpart for bentonite clay used for the preparation of hybrid electrolytes for high-temperature LIBs [48] or SC [13], which was reported earlier from the same research group. Considering the superior ionic conductivity of piperidinium-based RTIL, the present study focused on 1-methyl-1-propyl piperidinium bis(trifluoromethylsulfonyl)imide (PP13) RTIL. Ceramic fillers used as a spacer for IL QSSEs tend to interact very weakly with the RTILs; however, at small concentrations, they have been widely reported to improve

Rechargeable Energy Storage

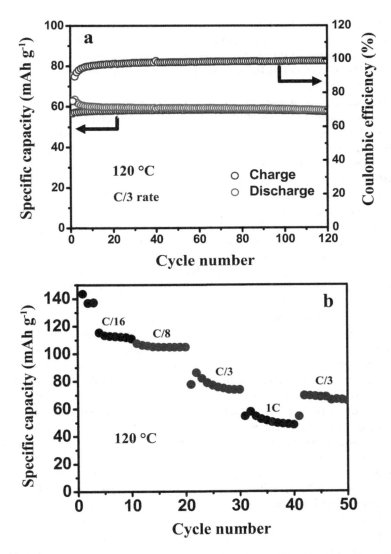

FIGURE 4.11 Electrochemical performance of Li/QSSE/LTO cells: (a) cyclic stability at 120° C at C/3-rate, and (b) rate capability at 120° C cycled at different C-rates using clay/PPMI- (1 M) LiTFSI composite electrolyte. Adapted and reproduced with permission from reference [48]. Copyright 2015 American Chemical Society.

transport properties in polymer electrolytes by facilitating salt dissociation and also by avoiding chain recrystallization. The electrolytes were prepared by blending the ceramics with a convenient weight of 1 mol L^{-1} solution of LiTFSI in the PP13 RTIL. A higher specific volume of h-BN enabled to improve the uptake of the RTIL. Though bentonite clay and h-BN powder had a similar flake size close to 1 micron, the intake of RTIL by h-BN was approximately twice that of the clay while maintaining the

94   Ceramic and Specialty Electrolytes

paste-like consistency during the mixing process. At $24°$ C, the h-BN composite electrolyte's conductivity was found to be 0.2×10^{-4} S cm^{-1}, which was higher than the benchmark value of 0.1×10^{-4} S cm^{-1} for battery electrolytes [117], while the clay/RTIL QSSE system lies below [48]. The temperature-dependent ionic conductivity of h-BN/RTIL QSSE was found to be curved in nature following the VTF equation instead of the Arrhenius equation, suggesting a free volume model of ionic transportation mechanism. The Li$^+$- ion conductivity deduced from the overall conductivity by measuring the Li$^+$-ion transference number (T_{Li+}), and T_{Li+} was found to be 0.093 ± 0.029 for 1 M LiTFSI in PP13 and 0.076 ± 0.009 for the h-BN/RTIL QSSE composite electrolyte at $23°$ C. The Li-ion transference number obtained for the h-BN composite electrolyte was comparable with the previously reported values [12, 118]. The h-BN electrolyte showed a slight increase in T_{Li+} above $80°$ C, thus the temperature-dependent diffusion coefficients of all species in the liquid phase were nearly the same. The electrochemical analysis of the h-BN/RTIL composite QSSE displayed anodic stability of ~5 V vs. Li/Li$^+$ at $120°$ C, which is significantly higher compared to clay/RTIL composite QSSE (~3.1 V).

The cell studies carried out with LTO-based half cells with a lithiation potential close to 1.5 V reported good charge–discharge capacity and cycling stability even at a higher temperature of $150°$ C. At room temperature, LTO half cells seemed to have a high resistance dwelling from the lower ionic conductivity of the electrolyte due to the lower wetting efficiency and higher viscosity, which leads to a sluggish charge transfer kinetics resulting from large cell polarization. The capacity values at room temperature were not consistent and ranged from 54 mAh g^{-1} to 101 mAh g^{-1} and were highly dependent on the thickness of the QSSE. However, the cells delivered a stable capacity of 158 mAh g^{-1} when cycled at C/8 rate at $120°$ C, as given in Figure 4.12 [48]. The lithiation kinetics were tremendously fast at a high temperature, which was evident when an exceptional coulombic efficiency and a stable discharge capacity of about 150 mAh g^{-1} were observed for a wide range of current densities between C/2 and 3C at $120°$ C. Moreover, the cell cycled at a current density of 600 mA g^{-1} (3 C rate) displayed a stable capacity for more than 600 cycles at $120°$ C, with a total capacity fade of less than 3% (Figure 4.13) [12]. Pushing to a higher operating temperature of $150°$ C, the cells still delivered a stable capacity of 150 mAh g^{-1} with high coulombic efficiency of 97% for 50 cycles at a current density of C/2 rate (Figure 4.14) and claimed that this is the highest temperature of operation ever reported for an LIB that can also perform at room temperature [12]. The authors suggest that cycling behavior at $150°$ C may be further improved by using an appropriate binder instead of PVdF for the electrode preparation and employing appropriate electrode processing techniques. PVdF is the commonly used binder for the preparation of the battery electrode. It was reported that cycling a cell with organic electrolytes at high temperatures causes diffusion of the PVdF binder within the cathode, forming a thin polymer-rich layer on the electrode surface, and the part of the binder was transferred through the separator to the anode [119]. This process was found to increase the total cell resistance and contributed to the fast capacity fade. Additionally, it is essential to note that the operating temperature of the cells, $120°$ C and $150°$ C, is

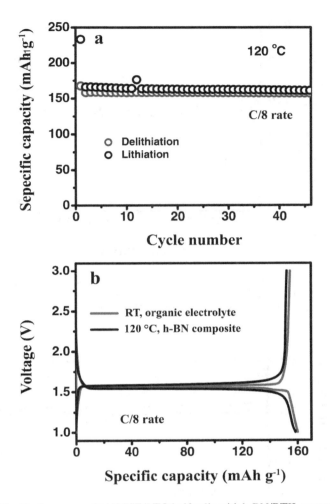

FIGURE 4.12 Performance of Li/QSSE/LTO half cells with h-BN/RTIL composite electrolyte: (a) cyclic stability for a cell operated for 32 days at a C/8 rate at 120° C, showing stable capacity of 158 mAh g^{-1} and (b) comparison between the charge–discharge profiles of a Li/QSSE/LTO half-cell containing the h-BN/RTIL composite electrolyte (cycled at 120° C) and a Li/QSSE/LTO half-cell containing 1 mol L^{-1} LiPF$_6$ in EC:DMC 1:1 (v/v) (cycled at 23° C), at C/8 rate. The performance is very similar with both systems showing low polarization. Adapted and reproduced with permission from reference [12]. Copyright 2016 Wiley-VCH Verlag GmbH & Co. KGaA, Weinheim.

close to the heat-deflection temperature (HDT) (145° C) and melting temperature (170° C) of PVdF [65, 78, 79, 120]. Therefore, the loosing of mechanical properties above the HDT can affect its binding properties, which leads to the contact issues, thereby contributing to reduced specific capacity, cycling stability, and coulombic efficiency.

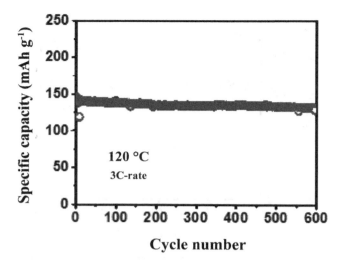

FIGURE 4.13 Cyclic stability at 120° C for Li/QSSE/LTO half-cells prepared using the h-BN/RTIL composite QSSE at a current density of 3C. Adapted and reproduced with permission from reference [12]. Copyright 2016 Wiley-VCH Verlag GmbH & Co. KGaA, Weinheim.

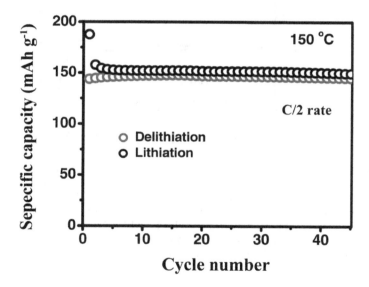

FIGURE 4.14 Charge discharge cycling stability of h-BN/RTIL composite electrolyte in Li/QSSE/LTO half-cell cycled at 150° C. Although there are changes in the electrode kinetics over time, the electrolyte is electrochemically stable, and the capacity fade is negligible. Adapted and reproduced with permission from reference [12]. Copyright 2016 Wiley-VCH Verlag GmbH & Co. KGaA, Weinheim.

Thermal stability is a very typical property exhibited by ILs; however, the long-term exposure to high temperatures during application may induce chemical transformations resulting in deteriorated cell performance, which was analyzed by the aging test of a sealed QSSE at 120° C for 20 days [12]. The performance was compared using electrochemical impedance spectroscopy, and the origin of a semicircle was observed in the impedance spectra at the higher frequency region due to the charge transfer resistance. The possibility of the formation of a passivation layer could be neglected due to its meager resistance. Charge–discharge cycles were analyzed with extra lithiated manganese oxide ($LiMn_2O_4$ [LMO]) as the cathode and LTO as the anode in the full cell configuration at 120° C, which displayed stable voltage profiles, resulting in reasonable cyclic stability up to 20 cycles (initial discharge capacity ~70 mAh g^{-1} and ~30 mAh g^{-1} after 20th cycle) (Figure 4.14) [12]. In the current scenario, there is a need for high-temperature LIBs, and the h-BN-based hybrid electrolyte system is considered an up-and-coming candidate for the near future because of its exceptional stability at elevated temperatures (>150° C) [12].

4.3.4 Barium Titanate-Based Quasi-Solid-State Electrolytes

$BaTiO_3$ is a ferroelectric ceramic (ferroelectric oxides) material having piezoelectric nature and a very high thermal stability above 1600° C. Its nanoparticles are exploited profoundly in material chemistry because of the ease of tuning the physical properties and morphology of the material. The high dielectric constant of $BaTiO_3$ and large surface area of nanoparticles favors the adsorption of high amounts of anions. Depending on the morphology, $BaTiO_3$ tends to have shown high dielectric values for nanoparticles (k~1200) and for thin films (k~2500) [121, 122]. The nanoparticles of $BaTiO_3$ provide an exceptionally high active surface area for the RTIL to anchor on the surface. Thus, the hybrid electrolyte adopts a coexisting liquid phase of IL and solid phase of $BaTiO_3$, however, with a dry texture. The candidates for ceramic fillers are analyzed based on pH of zero charge (pzc), ion exchange capacity, and Brunauer–Emmett–Teller (BET) surface area [123, 124]. The material is studied well as inorganic filler cum ion promoter with various polymer electrolytes made with [66, 125] or without RTILs [65, 125].

In 2017, Choi et al. [49] worked on an inorganic-based QSSEs with $BaTiO_3$ and RTIL N-methyl-N-butyl pyrrolidinium bis(trifluoromethane-sulfonyl)imide ($Pyr_{14}TFSI$). Pyridinium-based ILs always prove their quality with challenging values of conductivity and thermal stability. In addition to that, Pyr_{14}-TFSI was found to prevent undesired reactions at carbon anode by forming the SEI electrode layer. The QSSE was synthesized by milling the mixture of 0.2 M LiTFSI, 0.8 M $Pyr_{14}TFSI$, and $BaTiO_3$, where the weight ratio of ceramics vs. ILs was 60:40. The electrolytic mixture was pelletized at 10000 Kg force, so the RTIL could uniformly coat the $BaTiO_3$ spheres without the aggregation of nanoparticles. The conduction mechanism of Li$^+$ ions was assumed to be similar to that of SiO_2-based QSSEs. The linked network of the surface coated RTIL provided a conduction pathway for Li-ions. The impedance spectroscopic studies within a temperature range of -40° C–80° C displayed an ionic conductivity of ~2.0 × 10^{-4} S cm^{-1} at 0° C, which increased as temperatures increased to $\sim 1.3 \times 10^{-3}$ S cm^{-1} at 30° C following VTF behavior similar to that of clay/RTIL [48] or h-BN/RTIL [12] composite electrolyte. The Li$^+$ ion transference number for the QSSE was reported to be 0.35, which was substantially larger than pristine RTIL (0.08) or clay/RTIL [48] or h-BN/RTIL [12] composite QSSEs. The sample showed excellent thermal stability up to 400° C, and, on further heating, the decomposition of RTIL was initiated. Nevertheless, the BaTiO$_3$ is thermally stable above 600° C and has outstanding flame resistance.

The BaTiO$_3$/RTIL QSSE exhibited electrochemical stability up to 5.7 V against the lithium metal at room temperature, instead of about 5 V for clay/RTIL or h-BN/RTIL QSSE, which was attributed to the high loading capacity of ceramic fillers and the associated IL and their conductive network structure. The stability window suggested its potential to be compatible with high-voltage intercalation-compound cathodes such as LiCoO$_2$, lithium cobalt phosphate (LiCoPO$_4$, simply LCP), lithium iron phosphate (LiFePO$_4$, simply LFP) and lithium nickel manganese cobalt oxide (LiNi$_{1/3}$Mn$_{1/3}$Co$_{1/3}$O$_2$, simply NMC). Impedance spectra with LiCoO$_2$ electrodes suggested better contact with the electrodes and a significantly lesser interface resistance, which puts this in the league of solid-state electrolytes for ASSB applications. The charge–discharge cycles studies with Li/QSSE/LiFePO$_4$ and Li/QSSE/LiCoO$_2$ cell configurations at a current density of 0.1C at room temperature displayed a discharge capacity 145 mAhg^{-1} and 118 mAhg^{-1}, respectively. The difference in charge–discharge voltage (ΔV) was 0.19 and 0.07, respectively, for the LiFePO$_4$ and LiCoO$_2$ cells, indicating good charge transfer kinetics. At higher C-rate, the cell with LiFePO$_4$ displayed a discharge capacity of 108, 75 mAh g^{-1} at 0.5, and 1 C respectively at room temperature. At a higher temperature of 80° C, the Li/QSSE/LiCoO$_2$ cell displayed a higher discharge capacity of 128 mAh g^{-1} with 100% coulombic efficiency, which is about 8% (10 mAh g^{-1}) higher than that at room temperature. The cell also showed stable cycling stability for 70 cycles, which delivered a discharge capacity of 118 mAh g^{-1} after 70 cycles with a high capacity retention of 92% compared to the first discharge capacity, which are values that are sufficient for producing solid-state batteries with high energy densities. Therefore, BaTiO$_3$-RTIL hybrid QSSE demonstrated as a potential candidate for high temperature applications in ASSBs for high capacity applications, such as electric vehicles.

In 2008, Mezger et al. [46] reported high-resolution studies on temperature-dependent structure of three tris(pentafluoroethyl) trifluorophosphate anion- (FAP) based ILs at a charged solid Al$_2$O$_3$ (0001) interface, which revealed molecular level alternate-ion layering. A similar investigation was observed in BaTiO$_3$/IL composite electrolytes [49]. The interfacial van der Waals interaction utilizing the anions adsorbed on the nanoparticles promoted the dissociation and aggregation of ionic pairs. This interaction created a space charge layer around the nanoparticles, forming a negative-charge space on the nearest surface by the collected anions. The free cations on the negative-charge space formed a positive-charge space. These interfacial regions promoted the conductivity of the carrier ions in the electrolyte, enhancing the ionic conductivity of the QSSE. At higher filler concentrations, the ceramic particles were in contact, and a continuous network by the overlapping of space

Rechargeable Energy Storage 99

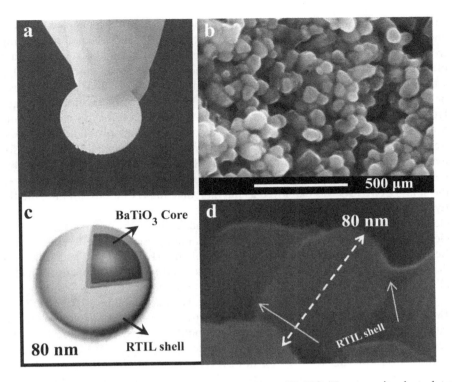

FIGURE 4.15 Schematic illustration and morphology of BaTiO$_3$/IL composite electrolyte: (a) optical image of the BaTiO$_3$/IL composite electrolytes, (b) FE-SEM monograph on surface morphology at lower magnification, (c) schematic illustration on the core shell structure with BaTiO$_3$ as the core and IL as the shell, and (d) FE-SEM monograph on surface morphology at a higher magnification. Adapted and reproduced with permission from reference [49]. Copyright 2017 Springer.

charge layers facilitated the lithium cation mobility. The IL with ceramic particles, such as BaTiO$_3$, with high thermal stability provides QSSE for high-temperature applications. An optical image of the BaTiO$_3$/IL composite electrolytes is depicted in Figure 4.15a, clearly demonstrating the opaque nature of the electrolyte. The field emission (FE) SEM surface morphology of BaTiO$_3$/IL composite electrolyte shows a spherical morphology, and, on higher magnification, the core shell structure of the spherical particle is shown in Figure 4.15b and c. The schematic illustration on the core shell structure with BaTiO$_3$ as core and IL as shell is demonstrated in Figure 4.15c.

4.3.5 Siloxane-Based Quasi-Solid-State Electrolytes

The term siloxane is denoting Si-O-Si bonds in organosilicon chemistry. These cyclic or linear organosilicon compounds possess high thermal and electrochemical stability and offer great opportunities for electrolytic applications in energy storage devices. Polysilsesquioxanes (PSQs) form a class of compounds with siloxane linkage. The word "poly" indicates the chain structure and "sesqui," originating from Latin, means one and a half, thus collectively, the term silsesquioxanes are often referred to a class of compounds denoted by the empirical formula $RSiO_{1.5}$, where R is hydrogen or any organo-functional derivative of alkyl, alkylene, aryl, or arylene groups [126]. Few studies explored PSQs for the fabrication of electrolytes for LIBs [127, 128]. Based on the fundamental idea of having an inorganic filler or crosslinker to bind RTILs to it, Lee et al. [129] demonstrated PSQs crosslinked with 1M LiTFSI/ N-butyl-N-methylpyrrolidinium bis(trifluoromethyl sulfonyl)imide (BMPTFSI) as high-temperature QSSE, in which the PSQs used were a novel ladder-structured poly-(methacryloxypropyl) silsesquioxane (LPMASQ). In the study, LPMASQ was employed as the inorganic matrix for crosslinking the IL. Even though LPMASQ is polymeric, the SiO_2-based framework differentiates these electrolytes from the other polymeric GEs and identifies as a particular class of electrolyte called hybrid ionogel electrolytes, an inorganic–organic hybrid QSSEs. Because the inorganic matrix employed is a polymer (LPMASQ), it had to be synthesized through a common synthesis procedure, unlike the SiO_2 [65, 66, 79], clay [48, 78, 112], or h-BN filler [12].

The QSSE was prepared by crosslinking various amounts of LPMASQ in 1M LiTFSI/BMPTFSI by thermal crosslinking at 70° C using azobisisobutyronitrile (AIBN) as thermal initiator. These could be processed as free-standing gels (QSSEs). BMPTFSI can be solidified completely using very low concentrations of LPMASQ (~ 2 wt%); however, two weight concentrations, 2 wt% and 5 wt% of LPMASQ were studied [129]. Thermograms of individual components and the hybrid ionogel assemblies showed excellent thermal stability up to 400° C and exceptionally low thermal shrinkage, pointing to the superior thermal and thermomechanical properties for application at elevated temperatures. The 3D network structure of the cured electrolyte obstructs ionic mobility, which is correlated with the diffusion of ions compared to neat 1 M LiTFSI/BMPTFSI. Because of the relatively low content of the crosslinker, the ionic conductivity was as expected to be close to the values of neat RTIL. With a trend of decreasing ionic conductivity with increased crosslinker concentration, their ionic conductivity values were in close proximity. The neat RTIL displayed an ionic conductivity of 0.96 mS cm^{-1}, whereas the hybrid electrolyte with 2 wt% LPMASQ showed the ionic conductivity 0.79 mS cm^{-1} at 30° C (Figure 4.16a) and anodic stability of >5.0 V against lithium metal at 90° C with a shift to a higher voltage with decreasing temperature, which indicates their application in high-voltage LIBs over a wide range of operating temperatures. The compatibility studies of LPMASQ 2 wt% QSSE with Li metal electrodes in symmetric cell assembly Li/QSSE/Li, for 25 days, the R_i increased gradually from 250 Ω to 450 Ω with time and attained a steady-state value after 10 days. In contrast, the bulk resistance, R_b, for hybrid electrolytes remained stable and constant with the storage time, which confirmed the excellent compatibility and stability of QSSE against lithium metal electrodes.

Rechargeable Energy Storage

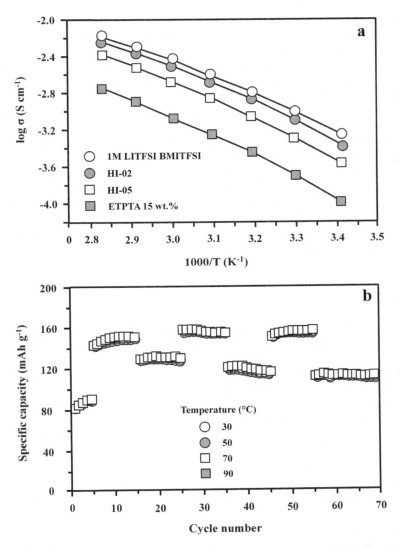

FIGURE 4.16 Ionic conductivity and electrochemical performance of QSSEs with ladder-structured poly-(methacryloxypropyl)silsesquioxane: (a) temperature dependent ionic conductivity of different hybrid electrolytes with poly-(methacryloxypropyl)silsesquioxane at different compositions (2 wt% and 5 wt%, commercially available organic-based crosslinker, ETPTA) and pristine ionic liquid with doping salt, and (b) discharge capacity at various temperatures and C-rates for LiFePO$_4$/QSSE/Li cells with QSSE have 2 wt% poly-(methacryloxypropyl)silsesquioxane. Adapted and reproduced from with permission from reference [131]. Copyright 2015 The Royal Society of Chemistry.

Although there is much work being done on hybrid QSEs to make it congenial for high temperatures, most of them do not include the cell studies at high temperatures. With hybrid LPMASQ- (2 wt%) based QSSE, the high-temperature charge–discharge cycles at varying temperatures from 30–90° C (Figure 4.16b) with the Li/LiFePO$_4$ cell in a voltage range of 2.5 V–4.2 V was studied. Upon cycling, a gradual decrease in discharge capacity and voltage with an increase in current density was observed because of an increase in cell polarization caused by the poor charge transfer kinetics at the electrode–electrolyte interface [130]. It was seen that the discharge capacity and voltage increases with increasing temperature due to the better ionic conductivity and charge transfer kinetics at higher temperatures. The initial cycles at 50° C displayed a discharge capacity of 88.3 mAh g^{-1} with a current density of 0.5 C; meanwhile, at 90° C, the cells exhibited a capacity of 156.2 mAh g^{-1}, which is comparable to the theoretical capacity of LiFePO$_4$ (170 mAh g^{-1}). From the analysis of discharge profiles obtained at various temperatures at a 0.1 C charge-0.1 C discharge, a flat voltage plateau was seen repeatedly close to 3.4 V (vs. Li/Li$^+$), corresponding to the LiFePO$_4$/FePO$_4$ conversion. A well-defined voltage plateau was not observed for 30° C unlike for 50° C, which indicated that sufficient mobility of Li$^+$ ions is essential for the maintenance of electrochemical performance. At a low temperature, the low diffusion of Li$^+$ ions in electrodes and electrolytes might limit the conversion process.

A comparison of electrochemical performance of the Li/LiFePO$_4$ cells prepared with QSSEs based on organic–inorganic hybrid crosslinker LPMASQ (2 wt%) against well-known organic crosslinker, trimethylolpropane ethoxylate triacrylate (ETPTA) [131], showed that the QSSE containing LPMASQ ionogels exhibited relatively stable cycling performance even at a high current density of 0.5C and an operating temperature of 90° C. Additionally, the discharge capacities for LPMASQ ionogels were comparable to cells containing the pristine 1 M LiTFSI BMPTFSI liquid. The discharge capacity of the cell with LPMASQ (2 wt%) QSSE maintained a value of 147 mAh g^{-1} after 50 cycles, i.e., 94% of its largest discharge capacity (15.2 mAh g^{-1}) with 98% coulombic efficiency.

On the contrary, the cells containing an organic crosslinker ETPTA-based ionogel displayed a rapid capacity loss over a repeatable cycling process, and the discharge capacity decreased to 118.7 mA g^{-1} after 50 times, which corresponds to a capacity retention of 82.7% on the maximum capacity obtained for the same in the initial cycles. The study also demonstrated that the inorganic–organic hybrid LPMASQ fully solidifies the IL at a mere 2 wt%. In contrast, the organic ionogel fabricated using ETPTA required a high concentration (15 wt%) of the crosslinker, leading to significantly lower ionic conductivity than inorganic–organic hybrid LPMASQ (Figure 4.16a). This study implies that the improved electrochemical performances of the cell with ionogel-based QSSEs may be due to the soft network structure formed by LPMASQ, which could improve the Li-ion diffusion and transference number through the QSSE. Thus inorganic–organic hybrid ionogels using the ladder-like PSQ (LPMASQ) were demonstrated as a thermally stable and efficient electrolyte for high-temperature battery applications [132–134].

4.4 CONCLUSION AND FUTURE OUTLOOK

The QSSEs discussed above are the most significant work in the field of high-temperature application. The scheme of construction of a QSSE lays a variety of choices for the candidature for ILs, and extensive research can undoubtedly bring out the best combination of inorganic matrix and IL that can create safe batteries. So far, the studies have been generating cell assemblies stable up to 150° C, and limits are still to be pushed beyond. To overcome the limitations of organic and nonaqueous electrolytes that limit batteries' application temperature to < 70° C, QSSEs have been successful in recent years to demonstrate prototypes. The electrode compatibility and the separator issues stand out as major challenges in completing the full cell studies of such electrolytes. Hopefully, the discovery of better nanomaterials and oxide surfaces can help solve these challenges. There is no question that studies have successfully brought the superior conductivity of liquid electrolytes and safety offered by solid electrolyte into a single frame. The conductivity of all the discussed QSSEs was close to the order of 10^{-4} Scm^{-1}, which is close to the IL component, and thermal stabilities confirmed a stable nature till 300° C. The problems with the conventional binder and separator are being dealt with and modified to prepare cells for high-temperature applications. The future in which we will be employing these electrolytes for real-life, day-to-day applications is not far.

ACKNOWLEDGMENT

Authors Dr. Jabeen Fatima M. J. and Dr. Prasanth Raghavan would like to acknowledge Kerala State Council for Science, Technology and Environment (KSCSTE), Kerala, India, for financial assistance.

REFERENCES

1. Brodd RJ, Bullock KR, Leising RA, et al. (2004) Batteries, 1977 to 2002. *J Electrochem Soc* 151:K1. doi: 10.1149/1.1641042
2. Liang Y, Zhao C, Yuan H, et al. (2019) A review of rechargeable batteries for portable electronic devices. *InfoMat* 1:6–32. doi: 10.1002/inf2.12000
3. Simon P, Gogotsi Y, Dunn B (2014) Where do batteries end and supercapacitors begin? *Science* 343:1210–1211. doi: 10.1126/science.1249625
4. Kaun TD, Nelson PA, Redey L, et al. (1993) High temperature lithium/sulfide batteries. *Electrochim Acta* 38:1269–1287. doi: 10.1016/0013-4686(93)80057-7
5. Vissers DR, Tomczuk Z, Steunenberg RK (1974), Brief communications: a preliminary investigation of high temperature lithium/iron sulfide secondary cells. *J Electrochem Soc* 121:665–667. doi: 10.1149/1.2401882
6. Kalhoff J, Eshetu GG, Bresser D, Passerini S (2015) Safer electrolytes for lithium-ion batteries: State of the art and perspectives. *ChemSusChem* 8:2154–2175. doi: 10.1002/cssc.201500284
7. Quartarone E, Mustarelli P (2011) Electrolytes for solid-state lithium rechargeable batteries: Recent advances and perspectives. *Chem Soc Rev* 40:2525–2540. doi: 10.1039/c0cs00081g

8. Zhang J, Zhao N, Zhang M, et al. (2016) Flexible and ion-conducting membrane electrolytes for solid-state lithium batteries: Dispersion of garnet nanoparticles in insulating polyethylene oxide. *Nano Energy* 28:447–454. doi: 10.1016/j.nanoen.2016.09.002
9. Nugent JL, Moganty SS, Archer LA (2010) Nanoscale organic hybrid electrolytes. *Adv Mater* 22:3677–3680. doi: 10.1002/adma.201000898
10. Martinet S (2016) Nanomaterials for rechargeable lithium batteries. In: Li Q. (eds) Nanomaterials for Sustainable Energy,.*Nanosci Technol*, Springer, Cham. ISBN: 978-3-319-32021-2, pp. 471–512. doi: 10.1007/978-3-319-32023-6_13
11. Judez X, Martinez-Ibañez M, Santiago A, et al. (2019) Quasi-solid-state electrolytes for lithium sulfur batteries: Advances and perspectives. *J Power Sources* 438:226985. doi: 10.1016/j.jpowsour.2019.226985
12. Rodrigues MTF, Kalaga K, Gullapalli H, et al. (2016) Hexagonal boron nitride-based electrolyte composite for Li-ion battery operation from room temperature to 150°C. *Adv Energy Mater* 6:1–7. doi: 10.1002/aenm.201600218
13. Borges RS, Reddy ALM, Rodrigues MTF, et al. (2013) Supercapacitor operating at 200 degrees celsius. *Sci Rep* 3:1–6. doi: 10.1038/srep02572
14. Cho SJ, Jung GY, Kim SH, et al. (2019) Monolithic heterojunction quasi-solid-state battery electrolytes based on thermodynamically immiscible dual phases. *Energy Environ Sci* 12:559–565. doi: 10.1039/c8ee01503a
15. Ramakumar S, Deviannapoorani C, Dhivya L, et al. (2017) Lithium garnets: Synthesis, structure, Li+ conductivity, Li+ dynamics and applications. *Prog Mater Sci* 88:325–411. doi: 10.1016/j.pmatsci.2017.04.007
16. Fire APUB (2014) Japan Airlines Boeing 787--8, JA829J, Boston, Massachusetts. https://en.wikipedia.org/wiki/Boeing_787_Dreamliner_battery_problems
17. Lenovo recalls 200,000 Thinkpad batteries. *The Register.* https://www.theregister.com/2007/03/01/lenovo_sanyo_battery_recall/
18. Samsung says two separate battery issues were to blame for all of its Galaxy Note 7 problems. *Vox.* https://www.vox.com/2017/1/22/14330404/samsung-note-7-problems-battery-investigation-explanation
19. Tesla's third models fire brings call for U.S. inquiry. *Bloomberg.* https://www.bloomberg.com/news/articles/2013-11-07/tesla-s-third-model-s-fire-brings-call-for-u-s-inquiry
20. Tesla says car fire started in battery. *The New York Times.* https://www.nytimes.com/2013/10/04/business/car-fire-a-test-for-high-flying-tesla.html
21. Quartarone E, Mustarelli P (2020) Review—Emerging trends in the design of electrolytes for lithium and post-lithium batteries. *J Electrochem Soc* 167:050508. doi: 10.1149/1945-7111/ab63c4
22. Shimano S, Zhou H, Honma I (2007) Preparation of nanohybrid solid-state electrolytes with liquidlike mobilities by solidifying ionic liquids with silica particles. *Chem Mater* 19:5216–5221. doi: 10.1021/cm0707814
23. Wang P, Zakeeruddin SM, Comte P, et al. (2003) Gelation of ionic liquid-based electrolytes with silica nanoparticles for quasi-solid-state dye-sensitized solar cells. *J Am Chem Soc* 125:1166–1167. doi: 10.1021/ja029294+
24. Wang P, Zakeeruddin SM, Exnar I, Grätzel M (2002) High efficiency dye-sensitized nanocrystalline solar cells based on ionic liquid polymer gel electrolyte. *Chem Commun* 5:2972–2973. doi: 10.1039/b209322g
25. Wang P, Zakeeruddin SM, Grätzel M (2004) Solidifying liquid electrolytes with fluorine polymer and silica nanoparticles for quasi-solid dye-sensitized solar cells. *J Fluor Chem* 125:1241–1245. doi: 10.1016/j.jfluchem.2004.05.010

26. Usui H, Matsui H, Tanabe N, Yanagida S (2004) Improved dye-sensitized solar cells using ionic nanocomposite gel electrolytes. *J Photochem Photobiol A Chem* 164:97–101. doi: 10.1016/j.jphotochem.2003.12.020
27. Fuller J (1997) Ionic liquid-polymer gel electrolytes. *J Electrochem Soc* 144:L67. doi: 10.1149/1.1837555
28. Fuller J, Breda AC, Carlin RT (1998) Ionic liquid-polymer gel electrolytes from hydrophilic and hydrophobic ionic liquids. *J Electroanal Chem* 459:29–34. doi: 10.1016/S0022-0728(98)00285-X
29. Noda A, Watanabe M (2000) Highly conductive polymer electrolytes prepared by in situ polymerization of vinyl monomers in room temperature molten salts. *Electrochim Acta* 45:1265–1270. doi: 10.1016/S0013-4686(99)00330-8
30. Susan MABH, Kaneko T, Noda A, Watanabe M (2005) Ion gels prepared by in situ radical polymerization of vinyl monomers in an ionic liquid and their characterization as polymer electrolytes. *J Am Chem Soc* 127:4976–4983. doi: 10.1021/ja045155b
31. Yoshimoto N, Shirai T, Morita M (2005) A novel polymeric gel electrolyte systems containing magnesium salt with ionic liquid. *Electrochim Acta* 50:3866–3871. doi: 10.1016/j.electacta.2005.02.036
32. Yoshizawa M, Ogihara W, Ohno H (2002) Novel polymer electrolytes prepared by copolymerization of ionic liquid monomers. *Polym Adv Technol* 13:589–594. doi: 10.1002/pat.261
33. Yoshizawa M, Ohno H (2001) Synthesis of molten salt-type polymer brush and effect of brush structure on the ionic conductivity. *Electrochim Acta* 46:1723–1728. doi: 10.1016/S0013-4686(00)00777-5
34. Ohno H (2001) Molten salt type polymer electrolytes. *Electrochim Acta* 46:1407–1411. doi: 10.1016/S0013-4686(00)00733-7
35. Ohno H, Yoshizawa M, Ogihara W (2004) Development of new class of ion conductive polymers based on ionic liquids. *Electrochim Acta* 50:255–261. doi: 10.1016/j.electacta.2004.01.091
36. Hirao M, Ito K, Ohno H (2000) Preparation and polymerization of new organic molten salts; N-alkylimidazolium salt derivatives. *Electrochim Acta* 45:1291–1294. doi: 10.1016/S0013-4686(99)00334-5
37. Hirao M, Ito-Akita K, Ohno H (2000) Polymerization of molten salt monomers having a phenylimidazolium group. *Polym Adv Technol* 11:534–538. doi: 10.1002/1099-1581(200008/12)11:8/12<534::AID-PAT2>3.0.CO;2-R
38. Washiro S, Yoshizawa M, Nakajima H, Ohno H (2004) Highly ion conductive flexible films composed of network polymers based on polymerizable ionic liquids. *Polymer (Guildf)* 45:1577–1582. doi: 10.1016/j.polymer.2004.01.003
39. Kubo W, Murakoshi K, Kitamura T, et al. (1998) Fabrication of quasi-solid-state dye-sensitized TiO$_2$ solar cells using low molecular weight gelators. *Chem Lett* 27:1241–1242. doi.org/10.1246/cl.1998.1241
40. Kubo W, Kambe S, Nakade S, et al. (2003) Photocurrent-determining processes in quasi-solid-state dye-sensitized solar cells using ionic gel electrolytes. *J Phys Chem B* 107:4374–4381. doi: 10.1021/jp034248x
41. Ikeda A, Sonoda K, Ayabe M, et al. (2001) Gelation of ionic liquids with a low molecular-weight gelator showing Tgel above 100 °C. *Chem Lett* 30:1154–1155. doi: 10.1246/cl.2001.1154
42. Néouze MA, Le Bideau J, Leroux F, Vioux A (2005) A route to heat resistant solid membranes with performances of liquid electrolytes. *Chem Commun* 8:1082–1084. doi: 10.1039/b416267f

43. Shi F, Zhang Q, Li D, Deng Y (2005) Silica-gel-confined ionic liquids: A new attempt for the development of supported nanoliquid catalysis. *Chem - A Eur J* 11:5279–5288. doi: 10.1002/chem.200500107

44. Shi F, Deng Y (2005) Abnormal FT-IR and FTRaman spectra of ionic liquids confined in nano-porous silica gel. *Spectrochim Acta - Part A Mol Biomol Spectrosc* 62:239–244. doi: 10.1016/j.saa.2004.12.031

45. Stathatos E, Lianos P, Zakeeruddin SM, et al. (2003) A quasi-solid-state dye-sensitized solar cell based on a sol-gel nanocomposite electrolyte containing ionic liquid. *Chem Mater* 15:1825–1829. doi: 10.1021/cm0213568

46. Mezger M, Schröder H, Reichert H, et al. (2008) Molecular layering of fluorinated ionic liquids at a charged sapphire (0001) surface. *Science* 322:424–428.

47. Ito S, Unemoto A, Ogawa H, et al. (2012) Application of quasi-solid-state silica nanoparticles-ionic liquid composite electrolytes to all-solid-state lithium secondary battery. *J Power Sources* 208:271–275. doi: 10.1016/j.jpowsour.2012.02.049

48. Kalaga K, Rodrigues MTF, Gullapalli H, et al (2015) Quasi-solid electrolytes for high temperature lithium ion batteries. *ACS Appl Mater Interfaces* 7:25777–25783. doi: 10.1021/acsami.5b07636

49. Choi H, Kim HW, Ki JK, et al. (2017) Nanocomposite quasi-solid-state electrolyte for high-safety lithium batteries. *Nano Res* 10:3092–3102. doi: 10.1007/s12274-017-1526-2

50. Bhattacharyya AJ, Maier J (2004) Second phase effects on the conductivity of non-aqueous salt solutions: "Soggy sand electrolytes." *Adv Mater* 16:811–814. doi: 10.1002/adma.200306210

51. Maier J (2005) Nanoionics: Ion transport and electrochemical storage in confined systems. *Nat Mater* 4:805–815. doi: 10.1038/nmat1513

52. Rao KS, El-Hami K, Kodaki T, et al. (2005) A novel method for synthesis of silica nanoparticles. *J Colloid Interface Sci* 289:125–131. doi: 10.1016/j.jcis.2005.02.019

53. Le VH, Thuc CNH, Thuc HH (2013) Synthesis of silica nanoparticles from Vietnamese rice husk by sol–gel method. *Nanoscale Res Lett* 8:58. doi: 10.1186/1556-276x-8-58

54. Unemoto A, Iwai Y, Mitani S, et al. (2011) Electrical conductivity and dynamics of quasi-solidified lithium-ion conducting ionic liquid at oxide particle surfaces. *Solid State Ionics* 201:11–20. doi: 10.1016/j.ssi.2011.08.008

55. Unemoto A, Ogawa H, Ito S, Honma I (2013) Electrical conductivity, self-diffusivity and electrolyte performance of a quasi-solid-state pseudo-ternary system, bis(trifluoromethanesulfonyl) amide-based room temperature ionic liquid-lithium bis (trifluoromethanesulfonyl) amide-fumed silica nanoparticles. *J Electrochem Soc* 160:A138 doi: 10.1149/2.024302jes

56. Lu Y, Moganty SS, Schaefer JL, Archer LA (2012) Ionic liquid-nanoparticle hybrid electrolytes. *J Mater Chem* 22:4066–4072. doi: 10.1039/c2jm15345a

57. Lu Y, Das SK, Moganty SS, Archer LA (2012) Ionic liquid-nanoparticle hybrid electrolytes and their application in secondary lithium-metal batteries. *Adv Mater* 24:4430–4435. doi: 10.1002/adma.201201953

58. Ueno K, Kasuya M, Watanabe M, et al. (2010) Resonance shear measurement of nano-confined ionic liquids. *Phys Chem Chem Phys* 12:4066–4071. doi: 10.1039/b923571j

59. Katakabe T, Kawano R, Watanabe M (2007) Acceleration of redox diffusion and charge-transfer rates in an ionic liquid with nanoparticle addition. *Electrochem Solid-State Lett* 10:23–25. doi: 10.1149/1.2720636

60. Ueno K, Hata K, Katakabe T, et al. (2008) Nanocomposite ion gels based on silica nanoparticles and an ionic liquid: Ionic transport, viscoelastic properties, and micro-structure. *J Phys Chem B* 112:9013–9019. doi: 10.1021/jp8029117

Rechargeable Energy Storage

61. Ueno K, Sano Y, Inaba A, et al. (2010) Soft glassy colloidal arrays in an ionic liquid: Colloidal glass transition, ionic transport, and structural color in relation to microstructure. *J Phys Chem B* 114:13095–13103. doi: 10.1021/jp106872w

62. Dlubek G, Yu Y, Krause-Rehberg R, et al. (2010) Free volume in imidazolium triflimide ([C3MIM] [NTf 2]) ionic liquid from positron lifetime: Amorphous, crystalline, and liquid states. *J Chem Phys* 133:124502 . doi: 10.1063/1.3487522

63. Raghavan P, Manuel J, Zhao X, et al. (2011) Preparation and electrochemical characterization of gel polymer electrolyte based on electrospun polyacrylonitrile nonwoven membranes for lithium batteries. *J Power Sources* 196:6742–6749. doi: 10.1016/j.jpowsour.2010.10.089

64. Raghavan P, Zhao X, Shin C, et al. (2010) Preparation and electrochemical characterization of polymer electrolytes based on electrospun poly(vinylidene fluoride-co-hex afluoropropylene)/polyacrylonitrile blend/composite membranes for lithium batteries. *J Power Sources* 195:6088–6094. doi: 10.1016/j.jpowsour.2009.11.098

65. Raghavan P, Zhao X, Kim JK, et al. (2008) Ionic conductivity and electrochemical properties of nanocomposite polymer electrolytes based on electrospun poly(vinylidene fluoride-co-hexafluoropropylene) with nano-sized ceramic fillers. *Electrochim Acta* 54:228–234. doi: 10.1016/j.electacta.2008.08.007

66. Raghavan P, Zhao X, Manuel J, et al. (2010) Electrochemical performance of electrospun poly(vinylidene fluoride-co-hexafluoropropylene)-based nanocomposite polymer electrolytes incorporating ceramic fillers and room temperature ionic liquid. *Electrochim Acta* 55:1347–1354. doi: 10.1016/j.electacta.2009.05.025

67. Raghavan P, Zhao X, Manuel J, et al. (2010) Electrochemical studies on polymer electrolytes based on poly(vinylidene fluoride-co-hexafluoropropylene) membranes prepared by electrospinning and phase inversion-A comparative study. *Mater Res Bull* 45:362–366. doi: 10.1016/j.materresbull.2009.12.001

68. Zhao X, Kim DS, Raghavan P, et al. (2010) Effect of processing parameters on the electrochemical properties of a polymer electrolyte prepared by the phase inversion process. *Phys Scr* 014036 doi: 10.1088/0031-8949/2010/T139/014036

69. Aravindan V, Shubha N, Chui Ling W, Madhavi S (2013) Constructing high energy density non-aqueous Li-ion capacitors using monoclinic TiO_2-B nanorods as insertion host. *J Mater Chem A* 1:6145–6151. doi: 10.1039/c3ta11103b

70. Raghavan P, Zhao X, Choi H, et al. (2014) Electrochemical characterization of poly(vinylidene fluoride-co-hexafluoro propylene) based electrospun gel polymer electrolytes incorporating room temperature ionic liquids as green electrolytes for lithium batteries. *Solid State Ionics* 262:77–82. doi: 10.1016/j.ssi.2013.10.044

71. Cheruvally G, Kim JK, Choi JW, et al. (2007) Electrospun polymer membrane activated with room temperature ionic liquid: Novel polymer electrolytes for lithium batteries. *J Power Sources* 172:863–869. doi: 10.1016/j.jpowsour.2007.07.057

72. Prasanth R, Aravindan V, Srinivasan M (2012) Novel polymer electrolyte based on cob-web electrospun multi component polymer blend of polyacrylonitrile/poly(methyl methacrylate)/polystyrene for lithium ion batteries – Preparation and electrochemical characterization. *J Power Sources* 202:299–307. doi: 10.1016/j.jpowsour.2011.11.057

73. Joyner J, Javvaji B, Owuor PS, et al. (2020) Shear exfoliation synthesis of large-scale graphene-reinforced nanofibers. *Carbon N Y* 166:405–413. doi: 10.1016/j.carbon.2020.05.009

74. Gopalan AI, Santhosh P, Manesh KM, et al. (2008) Development of electrospun PVdF-PAN membrane-based polymer electrolytes for lithium batteries. *J Memb Sci* 325:683–690. doi: 10.1016/j.memsci.2008.08.047

75. Yanilmaz M, Zhang X (2015) Polymethylmethacrylate/polyacrylonitrile membranes via centrifugal spinning as separator in Li-ion batteries. *Polymers (Basel)* 7:629–643. doi: 10.3390/polym7040629

76. Prasanth R, Shubha N, Hng HH, Srinivasan M (2014) Effect of poly(ethylene oxide) on ionic conductivity and electrochemical properties of poly(vinylidenefluoride) based polymer gel electrolytes prepared by electrospinning for lithium ion batteries. *J Power Sources* 245:283–291. doi: 10.1016/j.jpowsour.2013.05.178

77. Shubha N, Prasanth R, Hng HH, Srinivasan M (2014) Study on effect of poly (ethylene oxide) addition and in-situ porosity generation on poly (vinylidene fluoride)-glass ceramic composite membranes for lithium polymer batteries. *J Power Sources* 267:48–57. doi: 10.1016/j.jpowsour.2014.05.074

78. Prasanth R, Shubha N, Hng HH, Srinivasan M (2013) Effect of nano-clay on ionic conductivity and electrochemical properties of poly(vinylidene fluoride) based nano-composite porous polymer membranes and their application as polymer electrolyte in lithium ion batteries. *Eur Polym J* 49:307–318. doi: 10.1016/j.eurpolymj.2012.10.033

79. Raghavan P, Choi JW, Ahn JH, et al. (2008) Novel electrospun poly(vinylidene fluoride-co-hexafluoropropylene)-in situ SiO_2 composite membrane-based polymer electrolyte for lithium batteries. *J Power Sources* 184:437–443. doi: 10.1016/j.jpowsour.2008.03.027

80. Thangadurai V, Weppner W (2006) Recent progress in solid oxide and lithium ion conducting electrolytes research. *Ionics (Kiel)* 12:81–92. doi: 10.1007/s11581-006-0013-7

81. Knauth P (2009) Inorganic solid Li ion conductors: An overview. *Solid State Ionics* 180:911–916. doi: 10.1016/j.ssi.2009.03.022

82. Stramare S, Thangadurai V, Weppner W (2003) Lithium lanthanum titanates: A review. *Chem Mater* 15:3974–3990. doi: 10.1002/chin.200352244

83. Bohnke O, Bohnke C, Fourquet JL (1996) Mechanism of ionic conduction and electrochemical intercalation of lithium into the perovskite lanthanum lithium titanate. *Solid State Ionics* 91:21–31. doi: 10.1016/s0167-2738(96)00434-1

84. Yashima M, Itoh M, Inaguma Y, Morii Y (2005) Crystal structure and diffusion path in the fast lithium-ion. *J Am Chem Soc* 127:3491.

85. Zhu P, Yan C, Dirican M, et al. (2018) $Li_{0.33}La_{0.557}TiO_3$ ceramic nanofiber-enhanced polyethylene oxide-based composite polymer electrolytes for all-solid-state lithium batteries. *J Mater Chem A* 6:4279–4285. doi: 10.1039/c7ta10517g

86. Liu W, Liu N, Sun J, et al. (2015) Ionic conductivity enhancement of polymer electrolytes with ceramic nanowire fillers. *Nano Lett* 15:2740–2745. doi: 10.1021/acs.nanolett.5b00600

87. Fu K, Gong Y, Dai J, et al. (2016) Flexible, solid-state, ion-conducting membrane with 3D garnet nanofiber networks for lithium batteries. Edited by Yi Cui, Stanford University, Stanford, CA. In: *Proceedings of the National Academy of Sciences of the United States of America (PNAS)*, USA, pp. 113:7094–7099. doi.org/10.1073/pnas.1600422113

88. Choi JW, Cheruvally G, Kim YH, et a.l (2007) Poly(ethylene oxide)-based polymer electrolyte incorporating room-temperature ionic liquid for lithium batteries. *Solid State Ionics* 178:1235–1241. doi: 10.1016/j.ssi.2007.06.006

89. Zhang ZC, Jin JJ, Bautista F, et al. (2004) Ion conductive characteristics of cross-linked network polysiloxane-based solid polymer electrolytes. *Solid State Ionics* 170:233–238. doi: 10.1016/j.ssi.2004.04.007

90. Song D, Cho W, Lee JH, Kang YS (2014) Toward higher energy conversion efficiency for solid polymer electrolyte dye-sensitized solar cells: Ionic conductivity and TiO_2 pore-filling. *J Phys Chem Lett* 5:1249–1258. doi: 10.1021/jz5002727

91. Kwon SJ, Kim DG, Shim J, et al. (2014) Preparation of organic/inorganic hybrid semi-interpenetrating network polymer electrolytes based on poly(ethylene oxide-co-ethylene carbonate) for all-solid-state lithium batteries at elevated temperatures. *Polymer (Guildf)* 55:2799–2808. doi: 10.1016/j.polymer.2014.04.051

92. Rodríguez J, Navarrete E, Dalchiele EA, et al. (2013) Polyvinylpyrrolidone-LiClO4 solid polymer electrolyte and its application in transparent thin film supercapacitors. *J Power Sources* 237:270–276. doi: 10.1016/j.jpowsour.2013.03.043

93. Wu H, Wu I, Chang FC (2001) The interaction behavior of polymer electrolytes composed of poly(vinyl pyrrolidone) and lithium perchlorate (LiClO4). *Polymer (Guildf)* 42:555–562. doi: 10.1016/S0032-3861(00)00213-5

94. Chiu CY, Yen YJ, Kuo SW, et al. (2007) Complicated phase behavior and ionic conductivities of PVP-co-PMMA-based polymer electrolytes. *Polymer (Guildf)* 48:1329–1342. doi: 10.1016/j.polymer.2006.12.059

95. Zhou S, Fang S (2007) High ionic conductivity of all-solid polymer electrolytes based on polyorganophosphazenes. *Eur Polym J* 43:3695–3700. doi: 10.1016/j.eurpolymj.2007.06.001

96. Kerr JB, Sloop SE, Liu G, et al. (2002) From molecular models to system analysis for lithium battery electrolytes. *J Power Sources* 110:389–400. doi: 10.1016/S0378-7753(02)00202-1

97. Bower DI, Solis FJ (2003) An introduction to polymer physics. *Am J Phys* 71:285–286. doi: 10.1119/1.1533063

98. Das SK, Mallavajula R, Jayaprakash N, Archer LA (2012) Self-assembled MoS 2-carbon nanostructures: Influence of nanostructuring and carbon on lithium battery performance. *J Mater Chem* 22:12988–12992. doi: 10.1039/c2jm32468g

99. Das SK, Darmakolla S, Bhattacharyya AJ (2010) High lithium storage in micrometre sized mesoporous spherical self-assembly of anatase titania nanospheres and carbon. *J Mater Chem* 20:1600–1606. doi: 10.1039/b919139a

100. Unemoto A, Iwai Y, Mitani S, et al (2012) Mass transport properties in quasi-solidified lithium-ion conducting ionic liquids at oxide particle surfaces. *Solid State Ionics* 225:416–419. doi: 10.1016/j.ssi.2012.01.020

101. Grim RE, Bradley WF (1948) Rehydration and dehydration of the clay minerals. *Am Mineral* 33:50.

102. Stankovic N, Logar M, Lukovic J, et al (2011) Characterization of bentonite clay from "Greda" deposit. *Process Appl Ceram* 5:97–101. doi: 10.2298/pacl102097s

103. King RD, Nocera DG, Pinnavaia TJ (1987) On the nature of electroactive sites in clay-modified electrodes. *J Electroanal Chem* 236:43–53. doi: 10.1016/0022-0728(87)88017-8

104. Abdullahi SL, Audu AA (2017) Comparative analysis on chemical composition of bentonite clays obtained from Ashaka and tango deposits in Gombe State, Nigeria. *ChemSearch J* 8:35–40.

105. Joshi M, Banerjee K, Prasanth R, Thakare V (2006) Polymer/clay nanocomposite based coatings for enhanced gas barrier property. *Indian J Fiber Text Res* 31:202–214.

106. Shubha N, Prasanth R, Hoon HH, Srinivasan M (2014) Plastic crystalline-semi crystalline polymer composite electrolyte based on non-woven poly(vinylidenefluoride-c o-hexafluoropropylene) porous membranes for lithium ion batteries. *Electrochim Acta* 125:362–370. doi: 10.1016/j.electacta.2014.01.024

107. Wang X, Fulvio PF, Baker GA, et al. (2010) Direct exfoliation of natural graphite into micrometre size few layers graphene sheets using ionic liquids. *Chem Commun* 46:4487–4489. doi: 10.1039/c0cc00799d

108. Nicolosi V, Chhowalla M, Kanatzidis MG, et al. (2013) Liquid exfoliation of layered materials. *Science* 340:72–75. doi: 10.1126/science.1226419

109. Frömling T, Kunze M, Schönhoff M, et al. (2008) Enhanced lithium transference numbers in ionic liquid electrolytes. *J Phys Chem B* 112:12985–12990. doi: 10.1021/jp804097j

110. Zygadło-Monikowska E, Florjańczyk Z, Kubisa P, et al. (2014) Lithium electrolytes based on modified imidazolium ionic liquids. *Int J Hydrogen Energy* 39:2943–2952. doi: 10.1016/j.ijhydene.2013.06.003

111. Ferrari S, Quartarone E, Mustarelli P, et al. (2009) A binary ionic liquid system composed of N-methoxyethyl-N-methylpyrrolidinium bis(trifluoromethanesulfonyl)-imide and lithium bis(trifluoromethanesulfonyl)imide: A new promising electrolyte for lithium batteries. *J Power Sources* 194:45–50. doi: 10.1016/j.jpowsour.2008.12.013

112. Shubha N, Prasanth R, Hoon HH, Srinivasan M (2013) Dual phase polymer gel electrolyte based on non-woven poly(vinylidenefluoride-co-hexafluoropropylene)-layered clay nanocomposite fibrous membranes for lithium ion batteries. *Mater Res Bull* 48:526–537. doi: 10.1016/j.materresbull.2012.11.002

113. Shukla M, Sah S (2013) A comparative study of piperidinium and imidazolium based ionic liquids: Thermal, spectroscopic and theoretical studies. Jun-ichi Kadokawa *(eds)* : Ionic Liquids - New Aspects for the Future, IntechOpen, ISBN: 978-953-51-0937-2, pp: 9–12. doi: 10.5772/51797

114. Tarrio C, Schnatterly SE (1989) Interband transitions, plasmons, and dispersion in hexagonal boron nitride. *Phys Rev B* 40:7852–7859. doi: 10.1103/PhysRevB.40.7852

115. Wang J, Ma F, Sun M (2017) Graphene, hexagonal boron nitride, and their heterostructures: Properties and applications. *RSC Adv* 7:16801–16822. doi: 10.1039/c7ra00260b

116. Kubota Y, Watanabe K, Tsuda O, Taniguchi T (2007) Deep ultraviolet light-emitting hexagonal boron nitride synthesized at atmospheric pressure. *Science* 317:932–934. doi: 10.1126/science.1144216

117. Goodenough JB, Kim Y (2010) Challenges for rechargeable Li batteries. *Chem Mater* 22:587–603. doi: 10.1021/cm901452z

118. Gao G, Mathkar A, Martins EP, et al. (2014) Designing nanoscaled hybrids from atomic layered boron nitride with silver nanoparticle deposition. *J Mater Chem A* 2:3148–3154. doi: 10.1039/c3ta12892j

119. Bodenes L, Naturel R, Martinez H, et al. (2013) Lithium secondary batteries working at very high temperature: Capacity fade and understanding of aging mechanisms. *J Power Sources* 236:265–275. doi: 10.1016/j.jpowsour.2013.02.067

120. Pramoda KP, Mohamed A, Phang IY, Liu T (2005) Crystal transformation and thermomechanical properties of poly(vinylidene fluoride)/clay nanocomposites. *Polym Int* 54:226–232. doi: 10.1002/pi.1692

121. Brien SO, Brus L, Murray CB (2001) Synthesis of Monodisperse Nanoparticles of Barium Titanate: Toward a Generalized Strategy of Oxide Nanoparticle Synthesis. *J. Am. Chem. Soc.* 123:12085–12086. doi: 10.1021/ja011414a

122. Ihlefeld JON, Laughlin B, Hunt-lowery A, et al. (2005) Copper compatible barium titanate thin films for embedded passives. *Journal of Electroceramics* 14:95–102. doi. org/10.1007/s10832-005-0866-6

123. Bhattacharyya AJ (2012) Ion transport in liquid salt solutions with oxide dispersions: "Soggy Sand" electrolytes. *J Phys Chem Lett* 3:744–750. doi: 10.1021/jz201617w

124. Pfaffenhuber C, Göbel M, Popovic J, et al. (2013) Soggy-sand electrolytes: Status and perspectives. 15:18318–18335. doi: 10.1039/c3cp53124d

125. Raghavan P, Lim DH, Ahn JH, et al. (2012) Electrospun polymer nanofibers: The booming cutting edge technology. *React Funct Polym* 72:915–930. doi: 10.1016/j.reactfunctpolym.2012.08.018

126. Baney RH, Itoh M, Sakakibara A, et al. (1995) Silsesquioxanes. *Chem. Rev.* 95:1409–1430. doi: 10.1021/cr00037a012

Rechargeable Energy Storage

127. Popall M, Andrei M, Kappel J, et al. (1998) ORMOCERs as inorganic-organic electrolytes for new solid state lithium batteries and supercapacitors. *Electrochim Acta* 43:1155–1161. doi: 10.1016/S0013-4686(97)10014-7
128. Puthirath AB, Patra S, Pal S, et al. (2017) Transparent flexible lithium ion conducting solid polymer electrolyte. *J Mater Chem A* 5:11152–11162. doi: 10.1039/c7ta02182h
129. Lee JH, Lee AS, Lee JC, et al. (2015) Hybrid ionogel electrolytes for high temperature lithium batteries. *J Mater Chem A* 3:2226–2233. doi: 10.1039/c4ta06062h
130. Wetjen M, Navarra MA, Panero S, et al. (2013) Composite poly(ethylene oxide) electrolytes plasticized by N-alkyl-N-butylpyrrolidinium bis(trifluoromethanesulfonyl)imide for lithium batteries. *ChemSusChem* 6:1037–1043. doi: 10.1002/cssc.201300105
131. Lee JH, Lee AS, Lee JC, et al. (2015) Hybrid ionogel electrolytes for high temperature lithium batteries. *J Mater Chem A* 3:2226–2233. doi: 10.1039/c4ta06062h
132. Wen Z, Li Y, Zhao Z, et al. (2020) A leaf-like Al_2O_3 -based quasi-solid electrolyte with a fast Li + conductive interface for stable lithium metal anodes. *J Mater Chem A*. 8: 7280–7287, doi: 10.1039/d0ta02098b
133. Sacco A, Lamberti A, Gerosa M, et al. (2015) Toward quasi-solid state dye-sensitized solar cells: Effect of γ-Al_2O_3 nanoparticle dispersion into liquid electrolyte. *Sol Energy* 111:125–134. doi: 10.1016/j.solener.2014.10.034
134. Bertasi F, Pagot G, Vezzù K, et al. (2019) Lithiated nanoparticles doped with ionic liquids as quasi-solid electrolytes for lithium batteries. *Electrochim Acta* 307:51–63. doi: 10.1016/j.electacta.2019.03.167

5 Quasi-Solid-State Electrolytes for Lithium-Ion Batteries

Hiren K. Machhi, Keval K. Sonigara,
Saurabh S. Soni

CONTENTS

5.1 Introduction 114
5.2 Essential Criteria for QSSEs.. 115
    5.2.1 Ionic Conductivity 115
    5.2.2 Electrochemical Window 117
    5.2.3 Cationic Transport Number (t_+) 117
    5.2.4 Chemical and Thermal Stability 118
    5.2.5 Porosity and Electrolyte Uptake 118
    5.2.6 Mechanical Robustness 118
    5.2.7 Interface with Electrode Materials 118
5.3 Various Polymeric Host Used for the Quasi-Solid State Electrolytes 120
    5.3.1 PEO-Based Quasi-Solid State Electrolytes 120
        5.3.1.1 Mechanism of Ionic Conductivity and Ion Transport........ 121
        5.3.1.2 Solubility of Salts in Polymer Matrix 121
        5.3.1.3 Plasticizer Containing PEO Electrolytes 121
        5.3.1.4 Enhancement of Ionic Conductivity and Transport
                  Number in PEO-Based Electrolytes 123
        5.3.1.5 Composite Electrolyte.. 124
    5.3.2 PVdF-Based QSSEs... 125
    5.3.3 PAN- and PMMA-Based QSSEs... 125
    5.3.4 Single Li-ion Conducting Polymer-Based QSSEs 127
    5.3.5 Ionic Liquid-Based QSSEs 129
    5.3.6 Special Class of QSSEs for LIBs... 129
5.4 Conclusion and Future Outlook.. 130
Acknowledgement 131
References.. 131

5.1 INTRODUCTION

The rapid increase in global population has created an urgent need to find alternative sustainable energy sources and energy storage provisions with minimal environmental hazards. In the past two decades, efficient energy storage devices, such as lithium-ion batteries (LIBs), have been receiving attention and have been widely commercialized in vehicles and portable wearable electronic gadgets. Being a prime component among the anode, cathode, electrolyte, and separator, liquid electrolytes have emerged as long-term stable lithium (Li)-based energy storage systems with high ionic conductivity, high ionic transport number, and stable interface with electrodes. However, the scientific community is still wrestling with some key issues, such as leakage, use of toxic organic solvents, flammability, low mechanical strength, and dendrite formation brought by liquid electrolytes during their operational period. In this regard, solid polymer electrolytes [1] are found to be a promising alternative that does not incorporate any liquid solvent, but they suffer from lower ionic conductivities (order of 10^{-6} to 10^{-5} S cm^{-1}), poor interface with electrodes, and lower mechanical robustness, all of which restrict them from ensuring high performance in LIBs. The answer to these issues was found in quasi-solid-state electrolytes (QSSEs), which provide combined advantages of liquid and solid electrolyte systems, including high ionic conductivity, high Li$^+$-transport number, low flammability, and stable electrode–electrolyte interface. In addition to this, the tunable mechanical properties provide potential applicability toward the flexible energy storage devices. With the enormous significance of QSSEs, the recent trend makes it as a desirable alternative over various liquid electrolytes for the efficient energy storage devices, such as LIBs, Li-air/sulfur batteries, sodium-ion batteries (SIBs), zinc-ion batteries (ZIBs), supercapacitors (SCs), and fuel cells [2].

Typically, a QSSE comprises a host matrix, Li salt with or without additives, and solvent, all of which are selected to provide a perfect combination for the proficient electrolytic species, resulting in efficient LIBs. The Li salts selected must consist of large anions, resulting in fast migration of lithium ions, hence various Li salts have been studied, as shown in Figure 5.1. However, the polymer host matrix must follow the given criterias: (i) high thermal stability, (ii) inertness for wide electrochemical window, (iii) low glass transition temperature, (iv) functional groups that increase and stabilize the dissolution of salt, (v) suitable molecular weight, (vi) electrolyte uptake capacity, etc. In lieu of finding the appropriate host, various polymers listed as poly(ethylene oxide) (PEO), polymethyl methacrylate (PMMA), polyacrylonitrile (PAN), polyvinylidene fluoride (PVdF), and other biopolymer-derived QSSEs are studied in detail [3].

Looking toward the recent advancement and upcoming significant challenges related to QSSE preparation, mechanisms, and applications in LIBs, this contribution is focused on investigating the state-of-the-art QSSEs from the varieties of host matrix and their physicochemical parameters and performances. In addition to this, the role of QSSEs in advancement in the flexible and wearable LIB devices along with various strategies for the betterment of mechanical and chemical properties have been covered. Simultaneously, various Li salts along with polymer hosts, such

Ceramic and Specialty QSSEs for LIBs

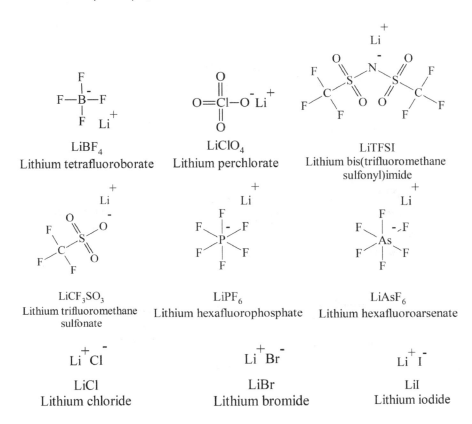

FIGURE 5.1 Various Li salts studied in LIB systems.

as PEO, PMMA, PVdF, PAN, etc., including ionic liquids and single lithium-ion- (Li-ion) conducting electrolytes have been explained.

5.2 ESSENTIAL CRITERIA FOR QSSES

In order to construct LIBs' high capacity and long-term stable system, electrolytes attain special emphasis, as they are placed between anode and cathode, and hence, efforts are ongoing to discover an efficient electrolyte system. For this purpose, several key parameters affecting the efficiency are represented in Figure 5.2 and discussed.

5.2.1 Ionic Conductivity

A chief role of QSSEs is the conduction of Li$^+$ ion transport within the gel matrix, simultaneously obstructing the self-discharge of the electrode material. Hence, it is essential to possess high ionic conductivity along with electronic insulation.

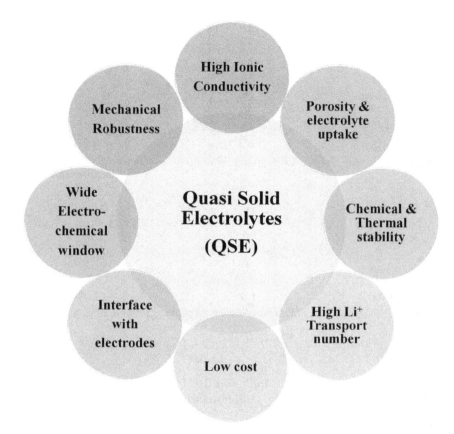

FIGURE 5.2 Critical desired properties for efficient QSSEs for high power LIBs.

Generally, the QSSEs' ionic conductivity values range between 10^{-3} and 10^{-2} S cm^{-1}, which is relatively higher than solid-state electrolytes. Ionic conductivity depends on chief factors including crystalline packing, porosity, thickness, and solvent uptake ability of the host matrix. In order to increase ionic conductivity, the system is chosen in such a manner that it provides high charge carrier mobility along with high electrolyte uptake concentration.

The ionic conductivity, σ, is given in Equation 5.1, which states that it is directly proportional to concentration and mobility of the charge carrier ions [4]

$$\sigma = \sum n_i q_i u_i \qquad 5.1$$

where, n_i, u_i, and q_i are the concentration, mobility, and ionic charge, respectively, on the charge carrier species. As the equation depicts, an increase in the charge carrier concentration or the mobility of the ionic species, ultimately, is responsible for the increase in the total ionic conductivity, σ, of QSSE. In practice, ionic conductivity

Ceramic and Specialty QSSEs for LIBs

is measured by the applied current (AC) impedance method, where QSSE is sandwiched between two identical stainless steel/platinum electrodes and measured in a blocking-type cell. The ionic conductivity is calculated using Equation 5.2

$$\sigma = \frac{l}{R_b A} \qquad 5.2$$

where, σ represents the ionic conductivity in S cm^{-1}, l is the thickness of the QSSE in cm, R_b is the bulk resistance in Ω, and A in cm^2 is the total effective area of contact between two electrodes [5].

5.2.2 ELECTROCHEMICAL WINDOW

Apart from ionic conductivity, the electrochemical window of QSSE would be a critical parameter, as it decides the total operational potential window of LIBs. Generally, it can be defined as the difference between the oxidation and reduction reaction potentially present in the system. For an efficient QSSE, the fundamental necessity is to be inert to the anode and the cathode, which means that the oxidation potential must be higher than the embedding potential of Li$^+$ in the cathode, and the reduction potential must be lower than the Li metal at the anode. The operational potential window is measured by linear or cyclic voltammetry sweeps. In general, QSSE-based devices find the electrochemical operational window of 3 V–4 V vs. Li/Li$^+$, but, in some cases, it also exceeds even 4.5 V [6].

5.2.3 CATIONIC TRANSPORT NUMBER (T$_+$)

For an efficient QSSE, the Li$^+$ transference number has to be close to unity. Generally, it is cation mobility measurement relative to the anion species in the salt of QSSE, and suppressing the mobility of anions can yield a prominent increase in the Li$^+$ transport number. In order to achieve the same, the concept of anchoring of anion, using a polymeric backbone, has been developed and is the most common method for single-ion conducting QSSEs [6]. Another approach is the introduction of anion receptors that undergo selective complex formation with anionic species in the electrolyte system. Therefore, a Li$^+$ transport number close to unity will lead to an effective reduction in the concentration polarization of QSSE during the charge–discharge cycles, yielding high power densities. In general, for a simple binary electrolyte system dissociated into Li$^+$ and X$^-$ ions, Li$^+$-transport number can be given as shown in Equation 5.3,

$$t_+ = I_{Li}^+ / I_{Li}^+ + I_x^- \qquad 5.3$$

Where, t_+ is the cationic transfer number, and I_{Li}^+ and I_x^- represent current observed by Li$^+$ and X$^-$ ions, respectively, when electrolytes are embedded between blocking electrodes.

5.2.4 CHEMICAL AND THERMAL STABILITY

An important aspect of the QSSE is that it must be chemically inert toward the other components of LIBs, such as anode, cathode, separator, current collectors, and various additive materials and do not undergo any side reactions during its operational period. Apart from chemical stability, excellent thermal stability is also a desirable parameter, as LIBs must withstand the heat generated due to short circuit, overcharge, improper operation, or external thermal abuse. Therefore, thermally stable matrices will prevent the decomposition, evaporation, melting, and side reactions of the species present within the QSSE. These parameters can be evaluated using various thermal analyses, such as thermogravimetric analysis (TGA) and differential scanning calorimetry (DSC) analysis, with the temperature range of -50° C–70° C, prior the application, where parameters, such as decomposition temperature (T_d), glass transition temperature (T_g), melting point (T_m), and phase transition of QSSE, are determined for thermal stability of LIBs.

5.2.5 POROSITY AND ELECTROLYTE UPTAKE

The porosity is defined as the ratio of the volume occupied by voids to the total geometric volume [7], as it is directly proportional to the electrolyte uptake. An increase in porosity simultaneously increases electrolyte uptake, which yields to high ionic conductivity, but simultaneously changes mechanical properties, too. Therefore, it is crucial to balance the porosity and electrolyte uptake, which can possess good mechanical strength, too. The uptake can be expressed as shown in Equation 5.4

$$\text{Uptake \%} = \left(\frac{W_1 - W_0}{W_0} \right) \times 100\% \qquad 5.4$$

where, W_1 is the weight after electrolyte uptake, and W_0 is the weight before uptake [8].

5.2.6 MECHANICAL ROBUSTNESS

The high mechanical strength of QSSEs is again a critical parameter, as they must withstand various mechanical stress/strain during large-scale manufacturing, cell assembly, storage, and real-scale applications, especially for flexible LIBs on the market. Therefore, various mechanical properties of QSSEs are investigated prior to their application. Generally, cross-linkable components are preferred over linear polymer chains because of good mechanical strength with high ionic conductivity [9].

5.2.7 INTERFACE WITH ELECTRODE MATERIALS

It is essential to understand the compatibility and the reactions between the electrode–electrolyte interface for an efficient device to have long cycling life and safety.

Ceramic and Specialty QSSEs for LIBs

For efficient LIBs, efforts are ongoing to form stable an electrode–electrolyte interface and dendrite suppression, which is conductive to Li$^+$, yielding high voltage efficiency, long cycle life, and safety. In practice, various advanced techniques are used to investigate the interface mechanism.

As discussed in the previous section, the QSSE provides more significant potential as it combines the fundamental properties of liquid and solid electrolytes, which results in high performing LIBs. Specifically, a fixed quantity of polymer–host matrix is chosen with Li salt with an appropriate solvent that yields better QSSEs. In general, Li$^+$-transport number and conductivity are typically governed by liquid electrolytes, while mechanical and morphological properties are governed by polymeric matrix. Although, disputes are observed in some special cases in which researchers find that polymer matrix contributes to Li$^+$ transport number [10]. The concept of trapping alkali metal salt into polymer matrices, such as polyvinylformal (PVF) and PAN, resulting in quasi state was reported in 1975. After consecutive efforts, utilization of QSSEs into LIBs specially entailing poly(vinylidene fluoride)-co-hexafluoro propylene (PVdF-co-HFP) with lithium iron phosphate (LiPF$_6$, simply LFP) electrolyte were reported [11]. In recent years, many reports using various polymer matrices (as given in Figure 5.3) have come up using PEO, PVdF, PMMA, PAN, polyvinyl alcohol (PVA), polyvinyl chloride (PVC), polyethylene glycol diacrylate (PEGDA), PVdF-co-HFP, and naturally available matrix, such as cellulose and other inorganic fillers [4, 6].

However, the addition of these plasticizers bring shortcomings, such as low ionic conductivity and Li$^+$-transport number, when compared to liquid electrolytes, but

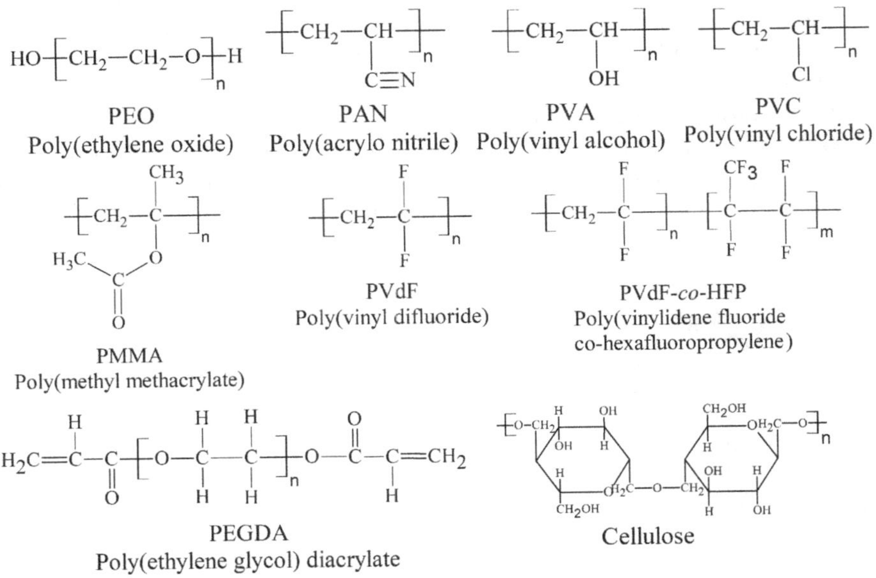

FIGURE 5.3 Various polymer matrices used to prepare QSSEs for LIBs.

they show improvements in other parameters, such as mechanical strength, thermal stability, and chemical stability. Additionally, because they are leakage-free and have better electrode–electrolyte interface contact with comparable conductivity and transport number, they are suitable for the application of QSSE into LIBs. Efforts are being made to overcome the existing limitations of QSSEs by adding inorganic fillers, cross-linking polymers, and introducing anisotropy, single-ion conduction polymers as well as adding chemically bonded anion of Li-salt to improve the structural design of polymers for LIBs. In the following sections, some well-known QSSEs with different polymer matrix are discussed with their properties and mechanism.

5.3 VARIOUS POLYMERIC HOST USED FOR THE QUASI-SOLID STATE ELECTROLYTES

5.3.1 PEO-Based Quasi-Solid State Electrolytes

PEO is a polymer with low toxicity, and thus it has many applications in a variety of fields, such as chemical, biological, medical, and industrial. Li⁺ions can easily form a complex with PEO by electrostatic interactions to form QSSE. The available lone pair of electrons present on the ethylene oxide (EO) facilitates the binding of Li⁺, and because of the high flexibility of the PEO chain, migration of Li⁺ is easy, which leads to good conductivity. However, the semicrystalline nature of PEO hinders the conductivity below glass transition temperature (T_g) [12], but the presence of the crystalline segment, as shown in Figure 5.4a, and their effects on transportation, is a matter of debate because some reports indicate that crystalline PEO has higher conductivity than amorphous nature, but the former leads to dendrite formation at electrodes [13]. Therefore, in the majority of cases, suppression of crystallinity in PEO is one of the most important criteria for designing of PEO-based quasi-electrolyte.

Hence, various strategies, such as the addition of plasticizers [14], preparation of polymer blends [15] and cross-linked PEO based polymer [16], and creation of a block copolymer with PEO as the active block [17], have been adopted to control the crystallinity for improvement in conductivity of polymer electrolytes.

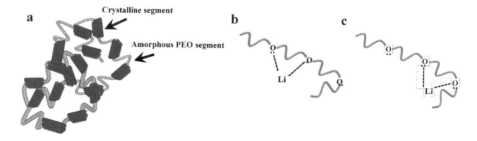

FIGURE 5.4 (a) Structural morphology of PEO and (b, c) possible mechanism of Li⁺-ion transport in PEO.

5.3.1.1 Mechanism of Ionic Conductivity and Ion Transport

Ionic conductivity and transport number are the key and basic requirement for electrolytes of an efficient and stable LIB. As Li salts have excellent solubility in PEO-based electrolyte, a high number of Li^+-ion are available for coordination with an available electron donor element of EO units. Additionally, high chain flexibility also promotes rapid ion transport in PEO matrix. As shown in Figure 5.4(b, c), through the bond breaking and forming of Li-O bonds, hopping of Li^+-ions between inter- or intrachain occurs in PEO-based electrolytes [18]. This process of Li^+-ion transport through PEO matrix is continuous and leads to segmental rearrangement, which leads to long-range transport of Li-ion and also promotes ionic conductivity through amorphous PEO regions in QSSE. Since the first report of QSSE, the ion transport in crystalline and amorphous segments of the PEO chain is still a complex phenomenon and is, therefore, a popular topic of debate among various research groups [13].

Apart from ionic conductivity and better Li^+-ion transport in PEO-based QSSEs, it exhibits mechanical properties that are in competencewith solid electrolytes because solvated Li-ion behaves as a liquid-like microscopic environment in entangled polymer chains in the PEO host [12].

5.3.1.2 Solubility of Salts in Polymer Matrix

A typical PEO-based QSSE is generally composed of PEO polymer matrix and Li salts. Solubility of Li salts in polymer matrix is a prime requirement, but not all Li salts are dissociated and act as free ions in a PEO matrix. Therefore, the choice of Li salt is important for PEO-based QSSEs, as it affects the ionic conductivity of Li salts with smaller anions, such as Cl^-, F^-, I^- etc., and do not provide high conductivity and transport because of uncontrolled mobility of anions. Therefore, Li salts with bulkier anions are first choice as they provide high conductivity as larger anion induced free Li cations. Traditionally, $LiPF_6$, $LiClO_4$, $LiPF_6$, $LiAsF_6$, $LiBF_4$ etc. have been used for PEO-based electrolytes [12]. Among all LI^+ salts, $LiClO_4$ and $LiPF_6$ exhibit good conductivity, electrochemical stability, and strong oxidation ability, however, their decomposition nature in presence of moisture limits their use in LIBs. At room temperature, the PEO-LiX complex possesses ionic conductivities below 1×10^{-4} S cm^{-1}. As ionic mobility in the amorphous phase has local relaxation and better segmental motion of the PEO host that govern the efficient Li-ion transport in electrolytes, salts with large anions, such as TFSI bis(trifluoromethanesulfonyl)imide (TFSI), fluorosulphonylamide (FSI), trifluromethanesulphonimide (BETI), and trifluoromethanesulfonate (TFS), are widely used. The structures of various anions containing Li salts along with organic anions are given in Figure 5.1. Numerous strategies have been adopted for increasing conductivity by improving parameters that govern the conductivity in PEO-based electrolytes.

5.3.1.3 Plasticizer Containing PEO Electrolytes

Adding plasticizer is one way to reduce crystallinity by increasing the amorphous phase in PEO electrolytes that increases room-temperature ionic conductivity. Table 5.1 shows various examples of PEO-based electrolytes with various plasticizers and their conductivity. Generally, liquid plasticizers, such as polyethylene

TABLE 5.1

Ionic Conductivity and Transport Properties of PEO-Based QSSEs with Different Li Salts Employed in LIBs

Sr. No.	Polymer-Plasticizer Combination	Lithium Salt	Conductivity S cm⁻¹	Li⁺ Transport Number	Reference
	PEO-based polymer electrolytes with different plasticizers				
1	PEO/EC	$LiCF_3SO_3$	1.6×10^{-4}	-	[19]
2	PEO/PC	$LiCF_3SO_3$	5.2×10^{-5}	-	[14]
3	PEO/EC/PC	$LiCF_3SO_3$	1.2×10^{-4}	-	[20]
4	PEO/PEG	$LiCF_3SO_3$	$\sim 10^{-4}$	> 0.5	[21]
5	PEO/TEG	$LiCF_3SO_3$	6.5×10^{-5}	-	[22]
6	PEO/DOP	$LiClO_4$	9.76×10^{-5}	-	[23]
7	PEO/DBP	$LiClO_4$	$\sim 10^{-5}$	-	[23]
8	PEO/DMP	$LiClO_4$	$\sim 10^{-5}$	-	[23]
9	PEO/CP	$Li(SO_2)_2(CF_3)_2$	$\sim 10^{-5}$	-	[24]
10	PEO/SN	$Li(SO_2)_2(CF_3)_2$	1.0×10^{-3}		[25]
	PEO-based polymer electrolytes with different ionic liquids as plasticizers				
11	PEO/EMITf	$LiCF_3SO_3$	3.0×10^{-4}	> 0.99	[26]
12	PEO/BMITFSI	$Li(SO_2)_2(CF_3)_2$	3.2×10^{-4}	-	[14]
13	PEO/EMITFSI	$Li(SO_2)_2(CF_3)_2$	2.67×10^{-4}	0.108	[27]
14	PEO/PP$_{13}$TFSI	$Li(SO_2)_2(CF_3)_2$	8.93×10^{-5}	0.0934	[27]
15	PEO/Pyr$_{24}$TFSI	$Li(SO_2)_2(CF_3)_2$	$\sim 10^{-5}$	0.30	[28]
16	PEO/MMPIPF$_6$	$LiPF_6$	1.13×10^{-3}	-	[29]
17	PEO/ MMPIBF$_4$	$LiBF_4$	2.06×10^{-3}	-	[29]
	PEO-based electrolytes prepared with different polymers				
18	PEO/PMMA	$LiClO_4$	1.30×10^{-5}	-	[30]
19	PEO/PVdF	$LiClO_4$	2.62×10^{-5}	-	[31]
20	PEO/PVdF	$Li(SO_2)_2(CF_3)_2$	4.9×10^{-3}	-	[32]
21	PEO/MEEP	$LIBF_4$	4.0×10^{-6}	-	[33]
22	PEO/PES	$LiClO_4$	3.0×10^{-5}	0.37	[34]
23	PEO/PET	$LiClO_4$	2.0×10^{-5}	-	[35]
24	PEO/PEI	$LiClO_4$	$\sim 10^{-4}$	-	[36]
25	PEO/PDMS	$LiPF_6$	5.6×10^{-5}	-	[37]
26	PEO/NC	$LiClO_4$	$\sim 10^{-5}$	-	[38]
	PEO-based nanopolymer composite electrolyte				
27	PEO/Al$_2$O$_3$	$LiClO_4$	$\sim 10^{-5}$	-	[39]
28	PEO/Al$_2$O$_3$	$LiCF_3SO_3$	$\sim 10^{-4}$	0.48	[40]
29	PEO/TiO$_2$	$LiCF_3SO_3$	1.6×10^{-4}	-	[19]
30	PEO/SiO$_2$	$LiCF_3SO_3$	-	-	[41]
31	PEO/ZnO	$Li(SO_2)_2(CF_3)_2$	$\sim 10^{-5}$	0.40-0.55	[18]
32	PEO/ZrO$_2$	$LiCF_3SO_3$	$\sim 10^{-4}$	0.42	[42]

(Continued)

TABLE 5.1 (CONTINUED)
Ionic Conductivity and Transport Properties of PEO-Based QSSEs with Different Li Salts Employed in LIBs

Sr. No.	Polymer-Plasticizer Combination	Lithium Salt	Conductivity S cm⁻¹	Li⁺ Transport Number	Reference
33	PEO/CuO	$LiCF_3SO_3$	2.64×10^{-4}	-	[43]
34	PEO/CdO	LiI	3.0×10^{-4}	-	[44]
35	PEO/Li$_2$O	$Li(SO_2)_2(CF_3)_2$	~ 10^{-5}	0.49	[45]
36	PEO/LiAlO$_2$	$LiClO_4$	2.24×10^{-5}	-	[46]
37	PEO/BaTiO$_3$	$Li(SO_2)_2(CF_3)_2$	3.4×10^{-4}	-	[47]
38	PEO/MgAl$_2$O$_4$	$LiPF_6$	10^{-7} to 10^{-5}	0.49 to 0.53	[48]
39	PEO/Urea	$LiCF_3SO_3$	5.1×10^{-6}	0.55	[49]
40	PEO/Boron	$LiCF_3SO_3$	4.3×10^{-5}	0.89	[50]

glycol (PEG) and aprotic organic solvents (ethylene carbonate, propylene carbonate, etc.), are the first choice to enhancing room-temperature ionic conductivity, as they have the ability to decrease the crystallinity and increase the mobility of cation in the PEO-based electrolyte.

A two- to threefold enhancement in ionic conductivity has been observed in the presence of a plasticizer. Apart from the conventional plasticizers, plastic crystal and room-temperature ionic liquids (RTILs) have also received much attention as a new class of plasticizers [25, 51]. Succinonitrile (SN) is used as an organic nonionic plastic material that can dissolve Li salts to make a solution at room temperature. These electrolytes exhibit high conductivity and appropriate mechanical properties. Unique physical properties such as nonflammability, nonvolatility, wide electrochemical window, high conductivity, and thermal stability make RTILs a popular choice to be used as electrolytes or plasticizers in LIBs. Pure RTILs as an electrolyte has already explored in LIBs, and it will be discussed in detail later in this chapter. Imidazolium and pyrrolidinium cation containing RTILs were introduced in PEO–LiTFSI PGEs [14, 52]. In both the cases, ionic conductivity of ~3×10^{-4} S cm⁻¹ at room temperature were achieved with good compatibility with an Li electrode. Other than conventional RTILs, special RTILs, such as 1-n-propyl-2,3-dimethylimidazolium-tetrafluoroborate (MMPIBF$_4$), 1-n-propyl-2,3-dimethylimidazolium hexafluorophosphate (MMPIPF$_6$), and n-butyl-n-ethyl pyrrolidinium bis(trifluromethylsulfonyl)imide (Pyr$_{24}$TFSI), exhibit good ionic conductivities along with cell performance over a temperature range of 49°C–90° C and also showed a wide electrochemical potential window of ~4.9 V [14, 53].

5.3.1.4 Enhancement of Ionic Conductivity and Transport Number in PEO-Based Electrolytes

As mentioned above, both ionic conductivity and transport number are prime particulars for PEO-based electrolytes for application in LIBs. Researchers have adopted various strategies to achieve this task by developing new material that retains amorphous segments that are responsible for good ionic conductivity.

5.3.1.5 Composite Electrolyte

Composite is a mixture of filler and matrix, and each component of the composite retains its properties, or the properties of the composite depend on each component of the composite. In addition, intramolecular interaction between filler and matrix also governs the properties of composite [54, 55]. It is well established that the presence of filler in PEO-based electrolytes can improve the ionic conductivity and the interfacial properties between electrolytes and electrodes. Moreover, it enhances the amorphous phase of PEO along with controlling recrystallization of PEO [11]. However, studies confirm the properties of composite polymer electrolytes are affected by the size and characteristics of the filler.

5.3.1.5.1 Nanopolymer Composite Electrolyte

Since 1982, a good number of studies have reported on the use of nanoparticles of metal oxides in PEO-based electrolytes to improve the properties of QSSEs. The nanoparticles of alumina (Al_2O_3), titanium dioxide (TiO_2), silicon dioxide (SiO_2), zinc oxide (ZnO), zirconium dioxide (ZrO_2), magnesium oxide (MgO), copper oxide (CuO), cadmium oxide (CdO), lithium oxide (Li_2O), etc., have been added as filler in PEO-based electrolytes. Addition of these inorganic nanoparticles can improve the mechanical properties that are otherwise lower because of the presence of lower crystallinity. Additionally, the presence of these particles can pave the way in the interphase for the ion transformation, which results in improved ionic conductivity [56]. It has been observed that fillers such as Al_2O_3 and TiO_2 in PEO-based electrolytes lead to increased conductivity by the factor of 1 or 2. However, no systematic trends were obtained as a function of size and surface area [57, 58]. Other than metal oxides, many mixed metal oxides (e.g. $LiAlO_2$, $BaTiO_3$, SiC, $MgAl_2O_4$, etc.), urea, boron compounds, and silica gel were also used as filler to improve the properties of PEO-based polymer electrolytes [41, 46–48, 59, 60]. Among these inorganic materials, using mesoporous $LiAlO_2$ as a filler enhanced not only an ionic conductivity but also exhibited good electrochemical stability up to 5.0 V.

5.3.1.5.2 Polymer Blend Composite Electrolytes

The percentage of amorphous phase in PEO matrix can also be increased by blending PEO with other polymers. The main advantage of the polymer blend electrolyte is to overcome serious complications in preparing electrolytes for suitable practical application. Additionally, the blending method can simplify preparation and control of physical properties by changing the composition of each component present in the electrolytes. Beginning in 1983, numerous studies were conducted using polymer blend electrolytes with PMMA, poly(methyl vinyl ether-maleic acid (PMVE-Mac), poly(bisphenyl A-co-epichlorohydrin (PBE), etc. [21, 22, 30, 61]. The miscibility of all these polymers in PEO electrolyte is governed by intermolecular hydrogen bonds between polymers. Table 5.1 gives examples of PEO-based polymer electrolytes prepared via blending method.

Ceramic and Specialty QSSEs for LIBs

5.3.2 PVdF-Based QSSEs

After PEO, PVdF is a frequently studied polymer to prepare QSSEs because its strong electron-withdrawing-group decorated chains in the back bone of PVdF which facilitate much more dissolution of Li salts, providing high concentration of charge carriers inside the polymer matrix. In comparison with PEO, PVdF provides much better thermal, mechanical, and electrochemical stability and is a promising alternative to PEO-based QSSEs. Because of its adaptable electrochemical properties, the first hybrid PVdF+LiClO$_4$ film was prepared in 1981, and ionic conductivities were investigated [62]. However, the crystalline arrangement in PVdF-based QSSEs still limits the electrochemical properties due to a lessening in the Li$^+$ mobility, and as with PEO, the addition of other additives, such as amorphous polymers, fillers were introduced to reduce the crystallinity and fine tuning of the properties. Many reports have investigated healthier combinations of PVdF with hexafluoropropylene (HFP), in which copolymerization strategies are adopted to yield PVdF-*co*-HFP. Because of this, effective improvement in ionic conductivity was observed due to a reduction in overall crystalline nature of the mixture, and the result was far superior to commercialized polypropylene (PP) separator in flexible LIBs [63].

However, to improve the parameters, strategic mixing of PVdF-*co*-HFP with other natural polymer were also implemented such as cellulose/PVdF-*co*-HFP mixture with pore forming characteristics to achieve high Li$^+$ transport number of 0.89 with stable 5.35 V (Vs Li$^+$) of wide electrochemical window [64]. The combination of PVdF and graphene also was studied, in which 0.002 wt% graphene was introduced that effectively increased the ionic conductivity nearly twofold along with rate capability and the cycling performances of the device. However, combining it with other organic polymers, such as polyvinyl chloride-*co*-vinyl acetate P(VC-*co*-VAc), and their electrochemical properties were investigated [65]. Another approach was carried out by preparing polymeric Li salts, such as lithium polyvinyl alcohol oxalate borate (LiPVAOB) and lithium polyacrylic acid oxalate borate (LiPAAOB), mixed with PVdF. These studies found it to be comparable with the commercialized sample [66]. Polyurethane Li salt (PLS) was prepared by condensing PEG, diphenylmethane6 diisocyanate, and PVdF/PLS, with an 80:20 weight ratio, and several composites with PVdF, such as polyethene (PE), PEO, polydimethylsiloxane (PDMS), polystyrene, cellulose, etc., were prepared to enhance the overall electrochemical properties. Table 5.2 summarizes the various PVdF-based electrolytes that were prepared and studied.

5.3.3 PAN- and PMMA-Based QSSEs

Unlike PEO- and PVdF-based QSSEs, PAN- and PMMA-based QSSEs also possess promising electrolyte properties for energy storage systems. PAN delivers excellent electrochemical, thermal, mechanical, and ion solvation properties along with good compatibility with Li anodes. However, a decrease in the Li$^+$ conductivity due to the presence of adjacent –CN groups leads to crystallinity; therefore various aspects have been investigated to increase the conductivity and transference number for

TABLE 5.2
Ionic Conductivity and Transport Properties of PVdF- and PVdF-*co*-HFP-Based QSSEs Used in LIBs

Sr. No.	Polymer-Host Combination	Lithium Salt	Conductivity S cm^{-1}	Li$^+$ Transport Number	Reference
1	PVdF	LiClO$_4$	10^{-5} to 10^{-4}	-	[62]
2	PVdF-*co*-HFP	LiPF$_6$	2.3×10^{-3}	-	[63]
3	Cellulose/PVdF-HFP	LiPF$_6$	1.89×10^{-3}	0.89	[64]
4	PVdF-PVP/graphene	LiPF$_6$	3.61×10^{-3}	0.59	[63]
5	PVdF/P(VC-VAc)	LiPF$_6$	3.57×10^{-3}	-	[65]
6	PVdF-LiPVAOB	LiPF$_6$	0.26×10^{-3}	0.58	[66]
7	PVdF-LiPAAOB	LiPF$_6$	0.35×10^{-3}	0.58	[67]
8	PVdF-PLS	LiPF$_6$	4.49×10^{-3}	0.489	[68]
9	PVdF/PDMS	LiPF$_6$	1.17×10^{-3}	-	[69]
10	PVdF/PS	LiClO$_4$	3.05×10^{-3}	-	[70]
11	PVdF-CAB	LiPF$_6$	2.48×10^{-3}	-	[71]
12	PVdF-PEO	LiPF$_6$	4.9×10^{-3}	-	[32]
13	PVdF/HEC/PVdF	LiPF$_6$	0.88×10^{-3}	0.57	[72]
14	PPC/PVdF	LiPF$_6$	4.05×10^{-3}	-	[73]
15	PVdF-*co*-HFP/Al$_2$O$_3$	LiPF$_6$	4.1×10^{-3}	-	[74]
16	PVdF-Mg(OH)$_2$	LiPF$_6$	0.542×10^{-3}	-	[75]
17	PVdF-*co*-HFP/TiO$_2$	LiClO$_4$ + LiPF$_6$	0.99×10^{-2} to	-	[76]
18	PVdF-*co*-HFP/SiO$_2$	LiClO$_4$ + LiPF$_6$	1.56×10^{-3}	-	[76]
19	PVdF-*co*-HFP/ Li$_7$La$_3$Zr$_2$O$_{12}$	LiPF$_6$	3.71×10^{-4}	0.58	[77]

superior performance of LIBs. PMMA is the most common polymer among the polyacrylates family for the QSSEs. As expected, having polar carbonyl functional group in the backbone will further facilitate the solvation of Li$^+$ inside the polymeric matrix and benefit the migration of Li$^+$-ions.

Therefore, because it has been established that PMMA has the ability to work as a gelating agent [43], PMMA was used to prepare QSSE with propylene carbonate (PC)–ethylene carbonate (EC) plasticizers [78]. However, PMMA finds good affinity toward the liquid electrolyte because of carbonyl groups in its backbone but, simultaneously, has poor mechanical strength, which can be improved by blending, copolymerization, and introducing fillers. Therefore, the additivity/copolymerizing approach is also adopted by many researchers to improve the electrochemical and physicomechanical properties further.

To create mobile Li$^+$ ion, it is important to limit the Li$^+$ affinity toward –CN group in PAN, hence it is blended with other polymer matrix, such as PMMA and PVA, is used, in which poly(acrylonitrile-co-vinyl acetate) (P(AN-co-VAc)) copolymer is blended with PMMA host by PAN-based electrolytes have observed supreme electrochemical potential range of >6.5 V. Table 5.3 lists QSSEs based on PAN and PMMA along with different plasticizer or additives.

TABLE 5.3
Ionic Conductivity and Transport Properties of PAN- and PMMA-Based QSSEs Employed in LIBs

Sr. No.	Polymer-Host Combination	Lithium Salt	Conductivity S cm^{-1}	Li$^+$ Transport Number	Reference
		PAN-based QSSEs			
1	PAN/PMMA/PAV	LiPF$_6$	3.50×10^{-3}	0.60	[80]
2	PAN-POSS	LiPF$_6$	6.06×10^{-3}	0.59	[81]
3	PAN/PMMA	LiPF$_6$	5.10×10^{-3}	0.46	[82]
4	PAN/TEGDA-BA	LiPF$_6$	5.90×10^{-3}	0.48	[83]
5	PAN/OMMT	LiPF$_6$	-	-	[84]
6	PAN/SiO$_2$	LiPF$_6$	1.80×10^{-3}	-	[85]
7	PAN/TiO$_2$/SiO$_2$	LiPF$_6$	9.8×10^{-4}	-	[86]
8	PAN/Na-MMT	LiPF$_6$	-	-	[87]
9	PAN-MAH	LiPF$_6$	3.03×10^{-3}	0.57	[88]
10	PBMA-AN-St/SiO$_2$	LiPF$_6$	1.90×10^{-3}	-	[89]
11	PAN-TiO$_2$-LiClO$_4$	LiClO$_4$	1.80×10^{-4}	-	[90]
		PMMA-based QSSEs			
1	PMMA	LiClO$_4$, LiAsF$_6$ or LiN(CF$_3$SO$_2$)$_2$]	-	-	[78]
2	PMMA-MAH	LiClO$_4$	1.22×10^{-3}	-	[91]
3	PMA/PEG	LiClO$_4$	0.57×10^{-3}	-	[92]
4	PBMA-St/SiO$_2$	LiPF$_6$	2.15×10^{-3}	-	[93]
5	OEGMA/BnMA	LiPF$_6$	1.80×10^{-3}	-	[94]
6	P(MMA-co-BA)	LiPF$_6$	1.20×10^{-3}	-	[95]
7	PMMA-PS	LiClO$_4$	-	-	[96]
8	PMMA/POSS	LiPF$_6$	1.27×10^{-3}	-	[89]
9	PMMA/PPC	LiPF$_6$	1.71×10^{-3}	-	[97]
10	PMMA-PC	LiClO$_4$	2.30×10^{-3}	-	[98]
11	PMMA	LiClO$_4$	5×10^{-3}-5×10^{-5}	-	[99]
12	PMMA/PC	LiClO$_4$	-	-	[100]
13	PMMA	LiBF$_4$	-	-	[101]

5.3.4 SINGLE Li-ion CONDUCTING POLYMER-BASED QSSEs

In order to enhance the transference number of Li$^+$-ions, an introductory report in 1984 suggested preparing single Li-ion conducting polymer- (SLIC) based electrolytes via two approaches [79]. The first approach consists of restricting the mobility of anions by choosing bulkier anionic species, and incorporating anions as polymeric side chain is the second approach. The conductivities observed using the first approach were very low; therefore, various chemical structures have been designed and synthesized with specific modifications in polymeric species with specific functionalized groups. In order to formulate SLICs, effective strategies have been investigated: (i) covalent linkage of anions to main polymeric chains that involves direct polymerization of Li salt monomers and synthetic modification of standing polymers, (ii) linking anions to an inorganic backbone, and (iii) the addition of anion-trapping agents. The study of altering the polymeric backbone chains reported direct polymerization by co-polymerization of Li (4-styrenesulfonyl) (trifluoromethanesulfonyl)imide (LiSTFSI) and methoxy-polyethylene glycol acrylate (MPEGA) named (Li[PSTFSI-co-MPEGA]) with coupled TFSI salt to the original backbone chain, which effectively suppressed the migration of anions and provided a path only for mobile Li^+-ions. The study revealed that the transport number exhibited a fivefold increase compared to the LiPSTFSI/PEO structure.

Alternative approaches use chemical modification of existing polymers, in which a polystyrene chain is the main back bone to which trifluoromethanesulfonamide ($CF_3SO_2NH_2$) is introduced, and then using the cation exchange method, the Li poly[(4-styrenesulfonyl) (trifluoromethanesulfonyl)imide] (LiPSTFSI) was prepared. Alternatively, various strategies have been adopted to alter different polymeric backbones with various anionic functional groups, mainly carboxylate ($-COO^-$), sulfonate ($-SO_3^-$), and sulfonylimide. Moreover, organic–inorganic combinations also have been explored to determine how much it enhances electrochemical properties of SLICs. PEO and poly(ethylene glycol) dimethyl ether (PEGDME) was selected as the primary backbone with anions that are grafted/cografted onto SiO_2, Al_2O_3 nanoparticles with Li salt in which anions are grafted/cografted onto ceramic nanoparticles, for which a maximum conductivity value of 0.19 mS cm^{-1} was found and a high electrochemical stability window up to 5 V. Instead of silica, polyhedral oligomeric silsesquioxanes (POSS) nanofillers were cross-linked with PEO chains grafted with anionic groups via sol gel process, which resulted in a transparent, flexible, hybrid organic–inorganic SLIC that possess low ionic conductivity but relatively good mechanical strength. In hybrid Li electrolyte of polyelectrolyte-grafted nanoparticles and polyethylene glycol dimethyl ether (PEGDME), reduction of anion mobility was obtained through polyanions immobilized by the silica nanoparticles. Though it had poor conductivity (~10^{-7} S cm^{-1}), further enhancement (up to ~10^{-6} S cm^{-1}) was observed by copolymerization of the polyethylene oxide methacrylate with Li 4-styrene sulfonate monomers that provide more support for Li^+ migration. However, alteration of anions from sulfonate to triflate, which is more delocalized, results in further enhancement of conductivity up to ~10^{-5} S cm^{-1}.

Finding the new horizons of SLICs supramolecular anion receptors, such as calixarene, which forms a stable complex with iodide ions and Li triflate salt to suppress the growth of electrode–electrolyte interface, were also investigated. However, the transfer number was increased up to only 0.5 because of lower Li-ion affinity. Other studies reported using slight modifications, using calix[6]-pyrrole and calix[2]-p-benzo[4] pyrrole with $LiBF_4$ and LiTf with transport numbers of nearly 0.8 in both cases. However, low ionic conductivity is the key drawback of these SLICs for large scale applications; therefore, much more research is needed.

5.3.5 Ionic Liquid-Based QSSEs

Ionic liquids (ILs) are also being studied to overcome problems observed during the use of organic solvents in LIBs. ILs are highly viscous, possess negligible vapor pressure, have low flammability, and are superior hydrophobic liquids at room temperature with a stable electrochemical window. However fine tuning in viscosity, melting point, and solubility can provide better alternatives to current liquid electrolytes. Recently, highly concentrated electrolytes, called quasi-ionic liquids (QILs), were also studied because of their quasi state for battery applications. In general, they are prepared by increasing the salt concentration in ILs, which increases viscosity and leads to QILs. This concept was initially proposed in 1993 [102], and such systems are termed as "highly concentrated electrolytes" or "solvent-in-salt electrolytes," which is reverse to conventional "salt-in-solvent electrolytes." In order to further enhance the viscosity, gelating agents have been utilized to prepare QSSEs based on ILs, for which various nanofillers, such as polymer matrix or inorganic materials, have been utilized. Adding active ceramic filler $Li_{1.5}Al_{0.5}Ge_{1.5}(PO_4)_3$ (LAGP) and PVdF-*co*-HFP to 1-ethyl-3-methylimidazolium triluoromethanesufonate (EMITFSI) resulted in EMITFSI/PVdF-HFP/LAGP hybrid system, which increased both ionic conductivity and transport number. QILs composed of LiTFSI, PYR14TFSI, and PMMA with a various Li^+/PYR^+ molar ratio have a single-electron transfer mechanism, which overcomes problems such as high charge overpotential, short cycle life, and poor kinetics in $Li-O_2$ batteries. EMITFSI, another example of amino-functionalized silica nanofiber fillers to ILs, provides a quasi state at 3.5 wt% of silica, a conductivity range of mS cm^{-1}, and an improved transfer number. Moreover, self-assembled ionic transport channels of TiO_2-based QILs, using sol-gel with varying ratios, was used with 1-butyl-3-methyl-imidazolium bis(trifluoromethylsulfonyl)imide [Bmim][TFSI] and titanium precursor ($TiCl_4$), which showed remarkable ionic conductivity ranging about 10^{-2} S cm^{-1} at elevated temperature. Another sol-gel route was used to prepare TiO_2-based QILs in which N-methoxyethyl-N-methylpyrrolidinium bis(trifluoromethanesulfonyl)imide (PYR1(201)TFSI), mixed with LiTFSI salt, was confined within the TiO_2 matrix prepared using tetrabutyl titanate (TBT) precursor. The addition of the TiO_2 matrix can immobilize the IL, suppressing leakage of the electrolyte. In addition to this, many studies used other metal oxides, such as α-Al_2O_3, γ-Al_2O_3, CeO_2, ZrO_2, and nanoporous mixed ILs resulted in QILs. Metal organic frameworks (MOFs), representing high porosity and surface area, may be candidates for incorporation into the ILs to allow for diffusion of Li^+-ion through channels or host-filler interaction and studied as hosts for ILs to create QILs. One study investigated 1-ethyl-3-methylimidazolium bis(trifluoromethylsulfonyl)amide (EMI-TFSA) IL with LiTFSI salt incorporated into ZIF-8. The resulting decrease in mobility of the TFSI anion suggests that the Li^+ cations diffuse through the micropores of the MOF structure.

5.3.6 Special Class of QSSEs for LIBs

While there has been improvement in energy density and life cycle of LIBs, the safety issue has yet to be addressed. As normal LIBs operate within the limited temperature range and electrochemical window, a short circuit, overcharging, or other abuse lead to several exothermic reactions that will shut down the battery and can also lead to fire or explosion; therefore, it is necessary to resolve these problems by using smart QSSEs that are temperature sensitive and have a self-healing ability. So, other than the traditional QSSEs mentioned above, different classes of functional QSSEs also have been developed in recent years that possess sol-gel transition or phase separation at elevated temperatures to meet the safe operation of LIBs. Generally, thermally responsive electrolytes have a blend of thermally responsive polymer and conductive ions that undergo reversible phase transition, leading to separation of polymer phase and ions when they are exposed to elevated temperatures and reversibly mix together to form a uniform electrolyte upon cooling [73]. When temperature is elevated, QSSEs undergo phase transition, which leads to decreased ion concentration and conductivities [103]. To understand the concept further, $Li_4Ti_5O_{12}/LiFePO_4$ -based LIBs are created by mixing the thermoresponsive polymer polybenzyl methacrylate (PBMA) with 1-ethyl-3-methylimidazolium bis(trifluoromethanesulfonyl)imide (EMIM-TFSI) ionic liquid, resulting in a hybrid QSSE that loses conductivity at elevated temperatures because of phase transition, as PBMA becomes insulator at elevated temperature, and suppresses device performance when subjected to 150° C, preventing the LIB system to go beyond the unsafe temperature [104]. Furthermore, thermally responsive sol-gel QSSEs are reported to have tunable transition temperatures using a thermally responsive poly(N-isopropy lacrylamide-co-acrylamide) (PNIPAM/AM). Due to elevation in temperature, the electrolyte undergoes sol to gel transition, which inhibits the migration of ions and cuts off the performance of the device.

The rapid development observed in flexible and wearable LIBs has the potential against deformations during their operational life, but self-healing materials can repair the damages. Aqueous LIB system use cross-linked Li sulfate/sodium carboxymethylcellulose (Li_2SO_4/CMC) with ionic conductivity of 0.12 S cm^{-1}. The Li_2SO_4/CMC QSSE shows good contact with electrodes and self-healing with electrochemical properties, which proved to be a dynamic QSSE for efficient flexible LIBs.

5.4 CONCLUSION AND FUTURE OUTLOOK

To resolve several drawbacks driven by liquid electrolyte systems, it is necessary to develop a family of QSSEs with superior electrochemical parameters, such as higher conductivity, transport number, and electrochemical operational window with better interfacial contact, as well as better mechanical properties. Therefore, QSSEs derived from a variety of polymeric species, including PEO, PVdF, PMMA, PAN, PVA, PVC, PEGDA, PVdF-*co*-HFP, and natural matrices with inorganic fillers are summarized and explained with mechanism in detail. Furthermore, single Li-ion conducting polymers, ionic-liquid-based QSSEs, and some stimuli responsive, self-healing QSSEs for advanced LIBs were also discussed. However, lower conductivity, poor interfacial contact, and flexibility in some specific QSSE composites are areas in which scientists are still developing new matrices and concepts for efficient LIBs for large scale commercialization.

Ceramic and Specialty QSSEs for LIBs

It is also equally important to incorporate smart functionalities, such as self-curing/healing properties with larger operational electrochemical windows, to expand the applications of QSSEs for LIBs storage. In the rapid global commercialization of flexible energy storage devices for wearable and portable electronic gadgets, QSSEs with superior flexible and stretchable properties and good mechanical strength must replace the existing liquid-based electrolytes. As advancements in biocompatible and implantable devices are growing rapidly, it is highly desirable to focus safer, aqueous, and pH resistant QSSEs to create safer energy storage devices for the human body. However, tuning the properties of existing QSSEs with effective manipulation of various organic, inorganic, or hybrid additives along with introducing various functionalities are again the key areas in which a huge amount of work must be done to yield the best QSSEs for resourceful battery systems. The development of QSSEs represents the prime direction in making high power LIBs for sustainable energy storage devices.

ACKNOWLEDGEMENT

The authors are thankful to University Grants Commission- Department of Atomic Energy-Consortium for Scientific Research (UGC-DAE-CSR) (sanctioned letter no. UDCSR/MUM/AO/CRS-M-290/2017/587) and University Grants Commission-Centers with Potential for Excellence in a Particular Areas (UGC-CPEPA) (Phase–II) program. The authors are also thankful to special assistant programs funded by UGC, New Delhi, India.

REFERENCES

1. Famprikis T, Canepa P, Dawson JA, et al. (2019) Fundamentals of inorganic solid-state electrolytes for batteries. *Nat. Mater.* 18:1278–1291. doi: 10.1038/s41563-019-0431-3
2. Cheng X, Pan J, Zhao Y, et al. (2017) Gel polymer electrolytes for electrochemical energy storage. *Adv. Energy Mater.* 8:1702184. doi: 10.1002/aenm.201702184
3. Zhu M, Wu J, Wang Y, et al. (2019) Recent advances in gel polymer electrolyte for high-performance lithium batteries. *J. Energy Chem.* 37:126–142. doi: 10.1016/j.jechem.2018.12.013
4. Baskoro F, Wong HQ, Yen HJ (2019) Strategic structural design of a gel polymer electrolyte toward a high efficiency lithium ion battery. *ACS Appl. Energy Mater.* 2:3937–3971. doi: 10.1021/acsaem.9b00295
5. Sonigara KK, Machhi HK, Vaghasiya JV, et al. (2018) A smart flexible solid state photovoltaic device with interfacial cooling recovery feature through thermoreversible polymer gel electrolyte. *Small* 14:1800842. doi: 10.1002/smll.201800842
6. Long L, Wang S, Xiao M, et al. (2016) Polymer electrolytes for lithium polymer batteries. *J. Mater. Chem. A* 4:10038–10069. doi: 10.1039/C6TA02621D
7. Liang S, Yan W, Wu X, et al. (2018) Gel polymer electrolytes for lithium ion batteries: Fabrication, characterization and performance. *Solid State Ionics* 318:2–18. doi: 10.1016/j.ssi.2017.12.023
8. Arya A, Sharma AL (2019) Electrolyte for energy storage/conversion (Li^+, Na^+, Mg^{2+}) devices based on PVC and their associated polymer: A comprehensive review. *J. Solid State Electrochem.* 23:997–1059. doi: 10.1007/s10008-019-04203-x

9. Song JY, Wang YY, Wan CC, et al. (1999) Review of gel-type polymer electrolytes for lithium ion batteries. *J. Power Sources* 77:183–197. doi: 10.1016/S0378-7753(98)00193-1

10. Xu K (2014) Electrolytes and interphases in Li-ion batteries and beyond. *Chem. Rev.* 114:11503–11618. doi: 10.1021/cr500003w

11. Dias FB, Plomp L, Veldhuis JBJ (2000) Trends in polymer electrolytes for secondary lithium batteries. *J. Power Sources* 88:169–191. doi: 10.1016/S0378-7753(99)00529-7

12. Xue Z, He D, Xie X (2015) Poly(ethylene oxide)-based electrolytes for lithium ion batteries. *J. Mater. Chem. A* 3:19218–19253. doi: 10.1039/C5TA03471J

13. Gadjourova Z, Andreev YG, Tunstall DP, et al. (2001) Ionic conductivity in crystalline polymer electrolytes. *Nature* 412:520–523. doi: 10.1038/35087538

14. Bandara LRAK, Dissanayake MAKL, Mellander BE (1998) Ionic conductivity of plasticized(PEO)-LiCF$_3$SO$_3$ electrolytes. *Electrochim. Acta* 43:1447–1451. doi: 10.1016/S0013-4686(97)10082-2

15. Park CH, Sun Y-K, Kim D-W (2004) Blended polymer electrolytes based on poly(lithium 4-styrene sulfonate) for the rechargeable lithium polymer batteries. *Electrochim. Acta* 50:375–378. doi: 10.1016/j.electacta.2004.01.110

16. Magistris A, Singh K (1992) PEO-based polymer electrolytes. *Polym. Int.* 28:277–280. doi: 10.1002/pi.4990280406

17. Panday A, Mullin S, Gomez ED, et al. (2009) Effect of molecular weight and salt concentration on conductivity of block copolymer electrolytes. *Macromolecules* 42:4632–4637. doi: 10.1021/ma900451e

18. Xiong H-M, Wang Z-D, Xie D-P, et al. (2006) Stable polymer electrolytes based on polyether-grafted ZnO nanoparticles for all-solid-state lithium batteries. *J. Mater. Chem.* 16:1345–1349. doi: 10.1039/B514346B

19. Vignarooban K, Dissanayake MAKL, Albinsson I, et al. (2014) Effect of TiO$_2$ nanofiller and EC plasticizer on electrical and thermal properties of poly(ethylene oxide) (PEO) based solid polymer electrolytes. *Solid State Ionics* 266:25–28. doi: 10.1016/j.ssi.2014.08.002

20. Pitawala HMJC, Dissanayake MAKL, Seneviratne VA, et al. (2008) Effect of plasticizers (EC or PC) on the ionic conductivity and thermal properties of the (PEO)$_9$LiTf: Al$_2$O$_3$ nanocomposite polymer electrolyte system. *Solid State Electr.* 12:783–789. doi: 10.1007/s10008-008-0505-7

21. Niedzicki L, Kasprzyk M., Kuziak K, et al. (2009) Modern generation of polymer electrolytes based on lithium conductive imidazole salts. *J. Power Sources* 192:612–617. doi: 10.1016/j.jpowsour.2009.03.050

22. Chintapalli S, Frech R (1996) Effect of plasticizers on ionic association and conductivity in the (PEO)$_9$LiCF$_3$SO$_3$ system. *Macromolecules* 29:3499–3506. doi: 10.1021/ma9515644

23. Michael MS, Jacob MME, Prabaharan SRS, et al. (1997) Enhanced lithium ion transport in PEO-based solid polymer electrolytes employing a novel class of plasticizers. *Solid State Ionics* 98:167–174. doi: 10.1016/S0167-2738(97)00117-3

24. Li Y, Zhan H, Wu L, et al. (2006) Flame-retarding ability and electrochemical performance of PEO-based polymer electrolyte with middle MW cyclic phosphate. *Solid State Ionics* 177:1179–1183. doi: 10.1016/j.ssi.2006.05.015

25. Fan L-Z, Maier J (2006) Composite effects in poly(ethylene oxide)–succinonitrile based all-solid electrolytes. *Electrochem. Commun.* 8:1753–1756. doi: 10.1016/j.elecom.2006.08.017

26. Kumar Y, Hashmi SA, Pandey GP (2011) Lithium ion transport and ion–polymer interaction in PEO based polymer electrolyte plasticized with ionic liquid. *Solid State Ionics* 201:73–80. doi: 10.1016/j.ssi.2011.08.010

27. Zhu C, Cheng H, Yang Y (2008) Electrochemical characterization of two types of PEO-based polymer electrolytes with room-temperature ionic liquids. *J. Electrochem. Soc.* 155:A569–A575. doi: 10.1149/1.2931523

28. Wetjen M, Navarra MA, Panero S, et al. (2013) Composite poly(ethylene oxide) electrolytes plasticized by N-alkyl-N-butylpyrrolidinium bis(trifluoromethanesulfonyl)imide for lithium batteries. *ChemSusChem.* 6:1037–1043. doi: 10.1002/cssc.201300105

29. Sutto TE (2007) Hydrophobic and hydrophilic interactions of ionic liquids and polymers in solid polymer gel electrolytes. *J. Electrochem. Soc.* 154:P101–P107. doi: 10.1149/1.2767414

30. Tsuchida E, Ohno H, Tsunemi K, et al. (1983) Lithium ionic conduction in poly (methacrylic acid)-poly (ethylene oxide) complex containing lithium perchlorate. *Solid State Ionics* 11:227–233. doi: 10.1016/0167-2738(83)90028-0

31. Jacob MME, Prabaharan SRS, Radhakrishna S (1997) Effect of PEO addition on the electrolytic and thermal properties of PVDF-$LiClO_4$ polymer electrolytes. *Solid State Ionics* 104:267–276. doi: 10.1016/S0167-2738(97)00422-0

32. Prasanth R, Shubha N, Hng HH, et al. (2014) Effect of poly(ethylene oxide) on ionic conductivity and electrochemical properties of poly(vinylidenefluoride) based polymer gel electrolytes prepared by electrospinning for lithium ion batteries. *J. Power Sources* 245: 283–291. doi: 10.1016/j.jpowsour.2013.05.178

33. Abraham KM, Alamgir M, Reynolds RK (1989) Polyphosphazene-poly(olefin oxide) mixed polymer electrolytes: I. Conductivity and thermal studies of MEEP/PEO-$(LiX)_n$. *J. Electrochem. Soc.* 136:3576–3582. doi: 10.1149/1.2096512

34. Kim D-W, Park J-K, Rhee H-W (1996) Conductivity and thermal studies of solid polymer electrolytes prepared by blending poly(ethylene oxide), poly(oligo[oxyethylene] oxysebacoyl) and lithium perchlorate. *Solid State Ionics* 83:49–56. doi: 10.1016/0167-2738(95)00238-3

35. Oh J-S, Kim S-H, Kang Y, et al. (2006) Electrochemical characterization of polymer blend electrolytes based on poly(oligo[oxyethylene]oxyterephthaloyl) for rechargeable lithium metal polymer batteries. *J. Power Sources* 163:229–233. doi: 10.1016/j.jpowsour.2006.02.012

36. Tanaka R, Sakurai M, Sekiguchi H, et al. (2001) Lithium ion conductivity in polyoxyethylene/polyethylenimine blends. *Electrochim. Acta* 46:1709–1715. doi: 10.1016/S0013-4686(00)00775-1

37. Das A, Thakur A, Kumar K (2013) Exploring low temperature Li^+ ion conducting plastic battery electrolyte. *Ionics* 19:1811–1823. doi: 10.1007/s11581-013-0898-x

38. Samad YA, Asghar A, Lalia BS, et al. (2013) Networked cellulose entrapped and reinforced PEO-based solid polymer electrolyte for moderate temperature applications. *J. Appl. Polym. Sci.* 129:2998–3006. doi: 10.1002/app.39033

39. Zewde BW, Admassie S, Zimmermann J, et al. (2013) Enhanced lithium battery with polyethylene oxide-based electrolyte containing silane–Al_2O_3 ceramic filler. *ChemSusChem* 6:1400–1405. doi: 10.1002/cssc.201300296

40. Masoud EM, El-Bellihi AA, Bayoumy WA, et al. (2013) Organic–inorganic composite polymer electrolyte based on PEO–$LiClO_4$ and nano-Al_2O_3 filler for lithium polymer batteries: Dielectric and transport properties. *J. Alloy Compd.* 575:223–228. doi: 10.1016/j.jallcom.2013.04.054

41. Johansson P, Ratner MA, Shriver DF (2001) The influence of inert oxide fillers on poly(ethylene oxide) and amorphous poly(ethylene oxide) based polymer electrolytes. *J. Phys. Chem. B* 105:9016–9021. doi: 10.1021/jp010868r

42. Mural PKS, Rana MS, Madras G, et al. (2014) PE/PEO blends compatibilized by PE brush immobilized on MWNTs: Improved interfacial and structural properties. *RSC Adv.* 4:16250–16259. doi: 10.1039/C4RA01961J

43. Patil A, Patil V, Choi JW, et al. (2017) Solid electrolytes for rechargeable thin film lithium batteries: A review. *J. Nanosci. & Nanotechnol.* 17:29–71. doi: 10.1166/jnn.2017.12699

44. Karmakar A, Ghosh A (2011) Poly ethylene oxide (PEO)–LiI polymer electrolytes embedded with CdO nanoparticles. *J. Nanoparticle Res.* 13:2989–2996. doi: 10.1007/s11051-010-0194-x

45. Kumar J, Rodrigues SJ, Kumar B (2010) Interface-mediated electrochemical effects in lithium/polymer-ceramic cells. *J. Power Sources* 195:327–334. doi: 10.1016/j.jpowsour.2009.06.098

46. Hu L, Tang Z, Zhang Z (2007) New composite polymer electrolyte comprising mesoporous lithium aluminate nanosheets and PEO/LiClO$_4$. *J. Power Sources* 166:226–232. doi: 10.1016/j.jpowsour.2007.01.028

47. Ito Y, Kawakubo M, Ueno M, et al. (2012) Carbon anodes for solid polymer electrolyte lithium ion batteries. *J. Power Sources* 214:84–90. doi: 10.1016/j.jpowsour.2012.04.068

48. Angulakshmi N, Nahm KS, Nair JR, et al. (2013) Cycling profile of MgAl$_2$O$_4$-incorporated composite electrolytes composed of PEO and LiPF$_6$ for lithium polymer batteries. *Electrochim. Acta* 90:179–185. doi: 10.1016/j.electacta.2012.12.003

49. Zhang D, Yan H, Zhang H, et al. (2011) Electrochemical properties of the solid polymer electrolyte PEO20–LiSO3CF3–Urea1.5 *Solid State Ionics* 199–200:32–36. doi: 10.1016/j.ssi.2011.03.003

50. Mathews KL, Budgin AM, Beeram S, et al. (2013) Solid polymer electrolytes which contain tricoordinate boron for enhanced conductivity and transference numbers. *J. Mater. Chem. A* 1:1108–1116. doi: 10.1039/C2TA00628F

51. Ye Y-S, Rick J, Hwang B-J (2013) Ionic liquid polymer electrolytes. *J. Mater. Chem. A* 1:2719–2743. doi: 10.1039/C2TA00126H

52. Shin J-H, Henderson WA, Passerini S (2003) Ionic liquids to the rescue? Overcoming the ionic conductivity limitations of polymer electrolytes. *Electrochem. Commun.* 5:1016–1020. doi: 10.1016/j.elecom.2003.09.017

53. Kim Y-T, Smotkin ES (2002) The effect of plasticizers on transport and electrochemical properties of PEO-based electrolytes for lithium rechargeable batteries. *Solid State Ionics* 149:29–37. doi: 10.1016/S0167-2738(02)00130-3

54. Croce F, Appetecchi GB, Persi L, et al. (1998) Nanocomposite polymer electrolytes for lithium batteries. *Nature* 394:456–458. doi: 10.1038/28818

55. Krawiec W, Scanlon Jr LG, Fellner JP, et al. (1995) Polymer nanocomposites: A new strategy for synthesizing solid electrolytes for rechargeable lithium batteries. *J. Power Sources* 54:310–315. doi: 10.1016/0378-7753(94)02090-P

56. Feuillade G, Perche P (1975) Ion-conductive macromolecular gels and membranes for solid lithium cells. *J. Appl. Electrochem.* 5:63–69. doi: 10.1007/BF00625960

57. Best AS, Adebahr J, Jacobsson P, MacFarlane DR, et al. (2001) Microscopic interactions in nanocomposite electrolytes. *Macromolecules* 34:4549–4555. doi: 10.1021/ma001837h

58. Yang C-M, Kim H-S, Na B-K, et al. (2006) Gel-type polymer electrolytes with different types of ceramic fillers and lithium salts for lithium ion polymer batteries. *J. Power Sources* 156:574–580. doi: 10.1016/j.jpowsour.2005.06.018

59. Croce F. Persi L, Ronci F, et al. (2000) Nanocomposite polymer electrolytes and their impact on the lithium battery technology. *Solid State Ionics* 135:47–52. doi: 10.1016/S0167-2738(00)00329-5

60. Choi BK, Shin KH (1997) Effects of SiC and Si$_3$N$_4$ fillers on the electrical properties of (PEO)$_{16}$LiClO$_4$ electrolytes. *J. Appl. Electrochem.* 27:365–367. doi: 10.1023/A:1018497117353

Ceramic and Specialty QSSEs for LIBs

61. Rocco AM, da Fonseca CP, Pereira RP (2002) A polymeric solid electrolyte based on a binary blend of poly(ethylene oxide), poly(methyl vinyl ether-maleic acid) and $LiClO_4$. *Polymer* 43:3601–3609. doi: 10.1016/S0032-3861(02)00173-8
62. Watanabe M, Kanba M, Matsuda H, et al. (1981) High lithium ionic conductivity of polymeric solid electrolytes. *Makromol Chem Rapid Commun* 2:741–744. doi: 10.1002/marc.1981.030021208
63. Kim I, Kim BS, Nam S, et al. (2018) Cross-linked poly(vinylidene fluoride-co-hexafluoropropene) (PVDF-co-HFP) gel polymer electrolyte for flexible Li-ion battery integrated with organic light emitting diode (OLED). *Materials* 11:543. doi: 10.3390/ma11040543
64. Asghar MR, Zhang Y, Wu A, et al. (2018) Preparation of microporous cellulose/poly(vinylidene fluoride-hexafluoropropylene) membrane for lithium ion batteries by phase inversion method. *J. Power Sources* 379:197–205. doi: 10.1016/j.jpowsour.2018.01.052
65. Zhao M, Zuo X, Ma X, et al. (2017) Self-supported PVdF/P(VC-VAc) blended polymer electrolytes for LiNi0.5Mn1.5O4/Li batteries. *J. Memb. Sci.* 532:30–37. doi: 10.1016/j.memsci.2017.03.009
66. Zhu Y, Xiao S, Shi Y, et al. (2013) A composite gel polymer electrolyte with high performance based on poly(vinylidene fluoride) and polyborate for lithium ion batteries. *Adv. Energy Mater.* 4:1300647. doi: 10.1002/aenm.201300647
67. Zhu Y, Xiao S, Shi Y, et al. (2013) A trilayer poly(vinylidene fluoride)/polyborate/poly(vinylidene fluoride) gel polymer electrolyte with good performance for lithium ion batteries. *J. Mater. Chem. A* 1:7790–7797. doi: 10.1039/C3TA00167A
68. Xing Y, Wu Y, Wang H, et al. (2014) Preparation of hybrid polymer based on polyurethane lithium salt and polyvinylidene fluoride as electrolyte for lithium ion batteries. *Electrochim. Acta* 136:513–520. doi: 10.1016/j.electacta.2014.05.122
69. Li H, Chen YM, Ma XT, et al. (2011) Gel polymer electrolytes based on active PVDF separator for lithium ion battery. I: Preparation and property of PVDF/poly(dimethylsiloxane) blending membrane. *J. Memb. Sci.* 379:397–402. doi: 10.1016/j.memsci.2011.06.008
70. Guo M, Zhou B, Hu J, et al. (2018) Porous polymer electrolyte based on poly(vinylidene fluoride)/comb-liked polystyrene via ionic band functionalization. *J. Memb. Sci.* 564:663–671. doi: 10.1016/j.memsci.2018.07.078
71. Liu J, Li W, Zuo X, et al. (2013) Polyethylene-supported polyvinylidene fluoride–cellulose acetate butyrate blended polymer electrolyte for lithium ion battery. *J. Power Sources* 226:101–106. doi: 10.1016/j.jpowsour.2012.10.078
72. Zhang MY, Li MX, Chang Z, et al. (2017) A sandwich PVDF/HEC/PVDF gel polymer electrolyte for lithium ion battery. *Electrochim. Acta* 245:752–759. doi: 10.1016/j.electacta.2017.05.154
73. Huang X, Zeng S, Liu J, et al. (2015) High-performance electrospun poly(vinylidene fluoride)/poly(propylene carbonate) gel polymer electrolyte for lithium ion batteries. *J. Phys. Chem. C.* 119:27882–27891. doi: 10.1021/acs.jpcc.5b09130
74. Kim KW, Kim HW, Kim Y, et al. (2017) Composite gel polymer electrolyte with ceramic particles for $LiNi_{1/3}Mn_{1/3}Co_{1/3}O_2$-$Li_4Ti_5O_{12}$ lithium ion batteries. *Electrochim. Acta* 236:394–398. doi: 10.1016/j.electacta.2017.03.176
75. Kim S, Han T, Jeong J, et al. (2017) A flame-retardant composite polymer electrolyte for lithium ion polymer batteries. *Electrochim. Acta* 241:553–559. doi: 10.1016/j.electacta.2017.04.129
76. Naderi R, Gurung A, Zhou Z, et al. (2017) Activation of passive nanofillers in composite polymer electrolyte for higher performance lithium-ion batteries. *Adv. Sustainable Syst.* 1:1700043. doi: 10.1002/adsu.201700043

77. Liang YF, Deng SJ, Xia Y, et al. (2018) A superior composite gel polymer electrolyte of Li7La3Zr2O12- poly(vinylidene fluoride-hexafluoropropylene) (PVDF-HFP) for rechargeable solid-state lithium ion batteries. *Mater. Res. Bull.* 102:412–417. doi: 10.1016/j.materresbull.2018.02.051
78. Appetecchi GB, Croce F, Scrosati B (1995) Kinetics and stability of the lithium electrode in poly(methylmethacrylate)-based gel electrolytes. *Electrochim. Acta* 40:991–997. doi: 10.1016/0013-4686(94)00345-2
79. Bannister DJ, Davies GR, Ward IM, et al. (1984) Ionic conductivities for poly(ethylene oxide) complexes with lithium salts of monobasic and dibasic acids and blends of poly(ethylene oxide) with lithium salts of anionic polymers. *Polymer* 25:1291–1296. doi: 10.1016/0032-3861(84)90378-1
80. Wang SH, Kuo PL, Hsieh CT, et al. (2014) Poly(ethylene oxide)-co-poly(propylene oxide)-based gel electrolyte with high ionic conductivity and mechanical integrity for lithium ion batteries. *ACS Appl. Mater. Interfaces* 6:19360–19370. doi: 10.1021/am505448a
81. Liu B, Huang Y, Cao H, et al. (2018) A novel porous gel polymer electrolyte based on poly(acrylonitrile-polyhedral oligomeric silsesquioxane) with high performances for lithium ion batteries. *J. Memb. Sci.* 545:140–149. doi: 10.1016/j.memsci.2017.09.077
82. Bi H, Sui G, Yang X (2014) Studies on polymer nanofibre membranes with optimized core–shell structure as outstanding performance skeleton materials in gel polymer electrolytes. *J. Power Sources* 267:309–315. doi: 10.1016/j.jpowsour.2014.05.030
83. Wang Q, Song WL, Fan LZ, et al. (2015) Effect of polyacrylonitrile on triethylene glycol diacetate-2-propenoic acid butyl ester gel polymer electrolytes with interpenetrating crosslinked network for flexible lithium ion batteries. *J. Power Sources* 295:139–148. doi: 10.1016/j.jpowsour.2015.06.152
84. He C, Liu J, Cui J, et al. (2018) A gel polymer electrolyte based on polyacrylonitrile/organic montmorillonite membrane exhibiting dense structure for lithium ion battery. *Solid State Ionics* 315:102–110. doi: 10.1016/j.ssi.2017.12.014
85. Shin WK, Cho J, Kannan AG, et al. (2016) Cross-linked composite gel polymer electrolyte using mesoporous methacrylate-functionalized SiO_2 nanoparticles for lithium ion polymer batteries. *Sci. Reports* 6:26332. doi: 10.1038/srep26332
86. Kurc B (2014) Gel electrolytes based on poly(acrylonitrile)/sulpholane with hybrid TiO_2/SiO_2 filler for advanced lithium polymer batteries. *Electrochim. Acta* 125:415–420. doi: 10.1016/j.electacta.2014.01.117
87. Almuhamed S, Bonne M, Khenoussi N, et al. (2016) Electrospinning composite nanofibers of polyacrylonitrile/synthetic Na-montmorillonite. *J. Ind. & Engg. Chem.* 35:146–152. doi: 10.1016/j.jiec.2015.12.024
88. Huang Y, Huang Y, Liu B, et al. (2018) Gel polymer electrolyte based on p(acrylonitrile-maleic anhydride) for lithium ion battery. *Electrochim. Acta* 286:242–251. doi: 10.1016/j.electacta.2018.08.024
89. Huang Y, Liu B, Cao H, et al. (2017) Novel gel polymer electrolyte based on matrix of PMMA modified with polyhedral oligomeric silsesquioxane. *J. Solid State Electrochem.* 21:2291–2299. doi: 10.1007/s10008-017-3568-5
90. Rahman MYA, Ahmad A, Ismail LHC, et al. (2010) Fabrication and characterization of a solid polymeric electrolyte of $PAN-TiO_2–LiClO_4$. *J. Appl. Poly. Sci.* 115:2144–2148. doi: 10.1002/app.31299
91. Wang Y, Ma X, Zhang Q, et al. (2010) Synthesis and properties of gel polymer electrolyte membranes based on novel comb-like methyl methacrylate copolymers. *J. Memb. Sci.* 349:279–286. doi: 10.1016/j.memsci.2009.11.060

92. Huang W, Zhu Z, Wang L, et al. (2013) Quasi-solid-state rechargeable lithium-ion batteries with a Calix[4]quinone cathode and gel polymer electrolyte. *Angew. Chem. Int. Ed.* 52:9162–9166. doi: 10.1002/anie.201302586

93. Liao YH, Rao MM, Li WS, et al. (2010) Fumed silica-doped poly(butyl methacrylate-styrene)-based gel polymer electrolyte for lithium ion battery. *J. Memb. Sci.* 352:95–99. doi: 10.1016/j.memsci.2010.01.064

94. Isken P, Winter M, Passerini S, et al. (2013) Methacrylate based gel polymer electrolyte for lithium ion batteries. *J. Power Sources* 225:157–162. doi: 10.1016/j.jpowsour.2012.09.098

95. Luo X, Liao Y, Xie H, et al. (2016) Polyethylene-supported poly(methyl methacrylate-co-butyl acrylate)-based novel gel polymer electrolyte for lithium ion battery. *Ionics* 22:1035–1042. doi: 10.1007/s11581-015-1621-x

96. Guan X, Chen F, Li Z, et al. (2016) Influence of a rigid polystyrene block on the free volume and ionic conductivity of a gel polymer electrolyte based on poly(methyl methacrylate)-block-polystyrene. *J. Appl. Polym. Sci.* 133:43901. doi: 10.1002/app.43901

97. Huang X, Xu D, Chen W, et al. (2017) Preparation, characterization and properties of poly(propylene carbonate)/poly(methyl methacrylate)-coated polyethylene gel polymer electrolyte for lithium ion batteries. *J. Electroanal. Chem.* 804:133–139. doi: 10.1016/j.jelechem.2017.09.050

98. Bohnke O, Rousselot C, Gillet PA, et al. (1992) Gel electrolyte for solid-state electrochromic cell. *J. Electrochem. Soc.* 139:1862–1865. doi: 10.1149/1.2069512

99. Bohnke O, Frand G, Rezrazi M, et al. (1993) Fast ion transport in new lithium electrolytes gelled with PMMA. 1. Influence of polymer concentration. *Solid State Ionics* 66:97–104. doi: 10.1016/0167-2738(93)90032-X

100. Vondrak J, Sedlarikova M, Velicka J, et al. (2001) Gel polymer electrolytes based on PMMA. *Electrochim. Acta* 46:2047–2048. doi: 10.1016/S0013-4686(01)00413-3

101. Vondrak J, Sedlarikova M, Reiter J, et al. (1999) Polymer gel electrolytes for electrochromic devices. *Electrochim. Acta* 44:3067–3073. doi: 10.1016/S0013-4686(99)00022-5

102. Angell CA, Liu C, Sanchez E (1993) Rubbery solid electrolytes with dominant cationic transport and high ambient conductivity. *Nature* 362:137–139. doi: 10.1038/362137a0

103. Kelly JC, Pepin M, Huber DL, et al. (2012) Reversible control of electrochemical properties using thermally-responsive polymer electrolytes. *Adv. Mater.* 24:886–889. doi: 10.1002/adma.201103340

104. Kelly JC, Degrood NL, Roberts ME (2015) Li-ion battery shut-off at high temperature caused by polymer phase separation in responsive electrolytes. *Chem. Commun.* 51:5448–5451. doi: 10.1039/C4CC10282G

6 Electrolytes for High Temperature Lithium-Ion Batteries
Electric Vehicles and Heavy-Duty Applications

Leya Rose Raphael, Neethu T.M. Balakrishnan, Akhila Das, Nikhil Medhavi, Jabeen Fatima M. J., Jou-Hyeon Ahn, Prasanth Raghavan

CONTENTS

6.1 Introduction: Background and Driving Forces 139
6.2 The Role of Electrolytes 140
    6.2.1 Electrolyte Composition of LIBs 140
        6.2.1.1 Organic Solvents 141
        6.2.1.2 Lithium Salts 141
        6.2.1.3 Polymer Electrolytes 145
        6.2.1.4 RTILs 145
6.3 Electrolyte Reactions of the LIBs 147
    6.3.1 Thermal Decomposition of Electrolytes 147
    6.3.2 Thermal Reactions of Electrolytes with Electrode Surface 149
6.4 Thermally Stable Electrolytes 149
6.5 Conclusion: Electrolytes or LIBs on Fire 154
References 154

6.1 INTRODUCTION: BACKGROUND AND DRIVING FORCES

"Our house is on fire." These were the words remarked by a 16-year-old environmental activist, Greta Thunberg, that pinpoints the climate crisis our world is currently facing [1]. This irreversible climate change has been the result of various factors among which fueled vehicle emissions has contributed greatly. Setting aside the folly and ignorance on this matter, a great deal of effort has been put forward in both research and application to recuperate. The sustainable energy foundation will be strong and efficacious if the storage technologies of chemical, electrical, mechanical,

140   Ceramic and Specialty Electrolytes

electrochemical origin are robust. Out of these systems, the electrochemical storage of energy using secondary batteries are at the forefront. For nearly three decades, lithium-ion batteries (LIBs) have found a prominent place among the electrification of vehicles and powering of utility grids and consumer electronics, replacing other battery systems, such as nickel-cadmium and nickel metal hydride (NiMH), because of their non-toxic nature , higher energy, and low-cost [2]. In order to replace fossil-fuel-based vehicles with highly efficient and reliable electric vehicles (EV) and/ or hybrid electric vehicles (HEV), safety of the energy storage system is considered a basic requirement. The major drawback of LIBs in EVs is the thermal decomposition of the battery components due to overcharging and/or overheating. Even though many measures are adopted to avoid these, the improvisation of the battery system itself can yield better results, which can be made possible by using components that can withstand high temperature (HT) [3]. Being the only liquid component in conventional LIBs, it was easily established that the electrolyte is very unsafe when subjected to extreme conditions [4]. This is evident from various unfortunate incidents of recalls of mobile phones and laptops and explosions during transportation and in EVs [5–8]. The thermal runaway triggered by electrolytes at higher temperatures can easily lead to the downfall of LIB technology, which offers high power density, energy density, and high capacity when handled with skill (Figure 6.1) [9,10] et al. et al.. This chapter discusses electrolytes' existing deteriorating chemistry and their improvisational materialistic aspects in the LIB research.

6.2 THE ROLE OF ELECTROLYTES

The choice of electrolytes is of paramount importance because it is the only component physically in contact with the other components of an electrochemical system. A good electrolyte is considered to be electrically insulating and ionically conducting. The ionic transport should be high at higher temperatures and should be negligible during storage conditions in order to avoid self-discharge. To steer clear of electrolyte degradation, the electrolyte should be stable within its electrodes' potential, that is, it should have a wide electrochemical stability window. The electrolyte should maintain inert reactivity toward the other cell components, too. In terms of producing thermally safe LIB technology, the electrolytes primarily should be compatible with the evolving electrodes, which can be altered by understanding its composition [11–13].

6.2.1 ELECTROLYTE COMPOSITION OF LIBs

Typically, the LIB electrolytes are composed of nonaqueous organic solvents, including ethylene carbonate (EC), propylene carbonate (PC), dimethyl carbonate (DMC), diethyl carbonate (DEC), ethyl methyl carbonate (EMC), or their mixtures with a lithium salt, such as lithium hexaflourophosphahte ($LiPF_6$), lithium tetraflouroborate ($LiBF_4$), lithium bis(oxolato)borate (LiBOB), or lithium perchlorate ($LiClO_4$). However, various new electrolyte formulations are being considered that use polymers and room-temperature ionic liquids (RTILs) for advanced performance and improvements [14–16].

High Temperature LIBs

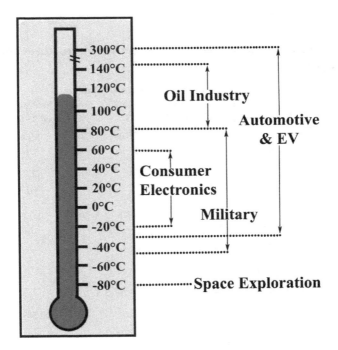

FIGURE 6.1 Temperature dependence of LIB applications. Adapted and reproduced with permission from reference [10]. Copyright 2016 Royal Society of Chemistry.

6.2.1.1 Organic Solvents

The utilization of organic solvents, specifically, their optimized combinations with lithium salts and/or the addition of additives to improve their dissolution in lithium salts are quite compelling [17, 18]. The reasons behind this being their reduced viscosity, good dielectric constant, and good ionic conductivity. But they are limited in operating successfully without any thermal runaway at higher temperatures due to their low volatility and low boiling point (Table 6.1) [19–21].

Efforts are being made to either improve the performance of the existing organic electrolyte systems or supplant them with better ones. Due to high dielectric constant, better flash point, and boiling points, linear sulfites, such as dimethyl sulfite (DMS) and diethyl sulfite (DES), are found to form better solid electrolyte interphase (SEI) compared to alkyl carbonates. The use of the organic solvent, sulfolane with DMS–DES solvents exhibited excellent electrochemical performance with lithium bis(oxolato)borate (LiBOB) salt at 60° C [25].

6.2.1.2 Lithium Salts

In a mixture of organic based solvents, $LiPF_6$ is the dominant lithium salt still used in the majority of the LIBs manufactured today; however, the formation of the corrosive product at elevated temperatures are the main reason for their electrochemical degradation [13, 26]. Figure 6.2 represents the common lithium-salt structures, and

TABLE 6.1
Commonly Used Organic Solvents in LIBs and Their Structures and Properties [22–24]

Organic Solvents	Structure	Molecular Mass g mol^{-1}	Melting point °C	Boiling point °C	Viscosity cP 25 °C	Density g cm^{-3} 25 °C
EC		88.06	36.4	248	1.93	1.32
PC		102.08	-48.8	242	2.53	1.2
DMC		90.08	4.6	90	0.589	1.0632
DEC		118.13	-73.3	126	0.75	0.9690
EMC		104.10	-53	110	0.648	1.0063
Acetonitrile		41.05	-48.8	81.6	0.341	0.7768
Υ-BL		86.09	-43.1	204.8	1.73	1.99

Table 6.2 shows their respective flaws. With the aim of upgrading these prevailing hitches, efforts are being made to develop new lithium salts that can operate on a long-term basis at higher temperatures. LiBOB is an unconventional salt with qualities such as low toxicity, good solubility in organic solvents, and good electrochemical and thermal stability, which makes them an attractive alternate lithium salt for

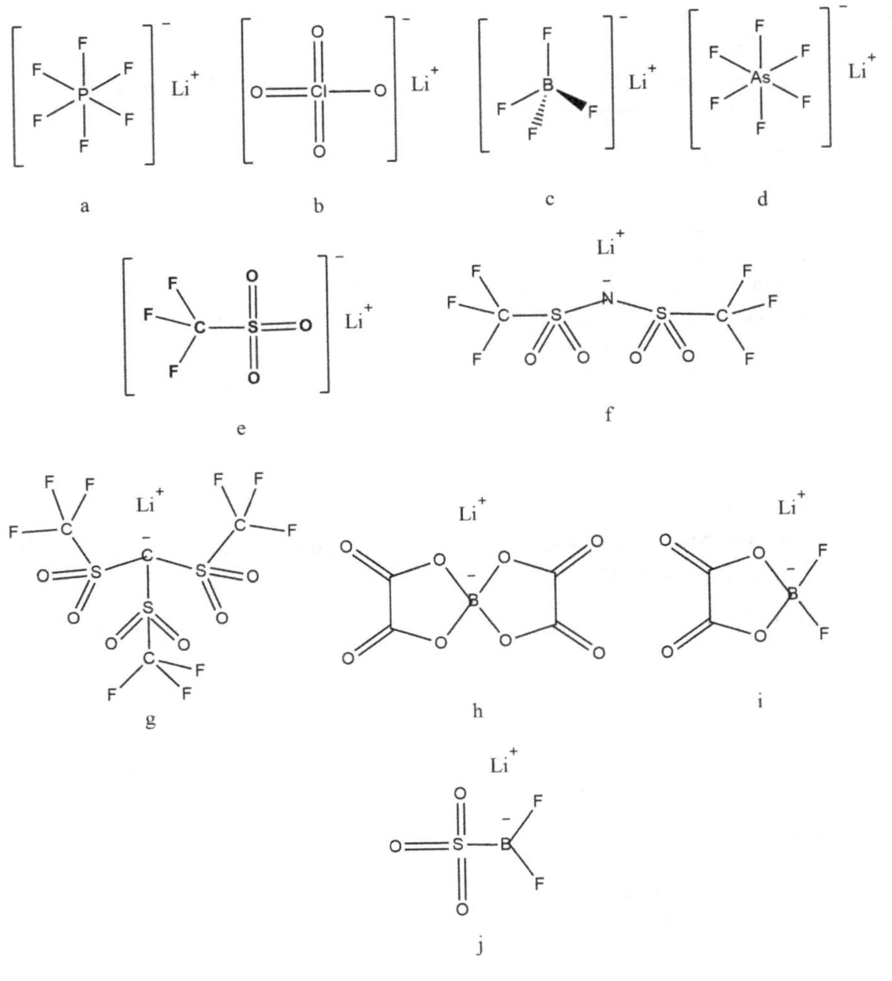

High Temperature LIBs

FIGURE 6.2 Chemical structures of commonly used lithium salts. (a) Lithium hexa-fluorophosphate (LiPF$_6$), (b) lithium perchlorate (LiClO$_4$), (c) lithium tetrafluoroborate (LiBF$_4$), (d) lithium hexafluoroarsenate (LiAsF$_6$), (e) lithium trifluoro methane sulpho-nate (Lithium triflate-LiCF$_3$SO$_3$), (f) lithium bis(trifluorosulphonylimide) (C$_2$F$_6$LiNO$_4$S$_2$), (g) lithium tris(trifluoromethanesulphonyl) methide (C$_4$F$_9$LiO), (h) lithium bis(oxalate) borate (LiB[C$_2$O$_4$]$_2$), (i) lithium difluoro (oxalato) borate (C$_2$BF$_2$LiO$_4$), and (j) lithium difluoro(sulphato) borate (LiBF$_2$SO$_4$).

the LIB electrolyte system. These unique properties that contribute to form a stable and less resistive SEI can thereby prevent anodic corrosion at HTs. In comparison with LiPF$_6$, LiBF$_4$, and lithium bis(triflouromethane)sulphonimide (LiN(CF$_3$SO$_2$)$_2$/ LiTFSI), this feature is ascribed to its bulky BOB anion in its structure. It is also evident from Table 6.3 that the higher decomposition temperature and its harm-less decomposition products make LiBOB a thermally feasible lithium salt [27–29].

TABLE 6.2
Limitations of Common Lithium Salts Employed in Electrolytes for LIBs [35–38]

Lithium Salt	Disadvantage
Lithium perchlorate ($LiClO_4$)	Explosive nature
Lithium tetraflouroborate ($LiBF_4$)	Inferior SEI forming ability
Lithium hexaflouroarsenate ($LiAsF_6$)	Highly toxic
Lithium triflouromethanesulphonate ($LiCF_3SO_3$)	Low ionic conductivity
Lithium bis(triflouromethane)sulphonimide ($LiN(CF_3SO_2)_2$/LiTFSI)	Corrosive toward current collectors
Perflouroalkyl sulphonyl lithium methide ($LiC(CF_3SO_2)_3$)	Corrosive toward current collectors

TABLE 6.3
Thermal Stability of Commonly Used Lithium Salts in Electrolytes for LIBs [37]

Lithium Salt	Structure	Melting Point (°C)
$LiPF_6$		200
LiTFSI		234
$LiBF_4$		310
LiBOB		>400

High Temperature LIBs 145

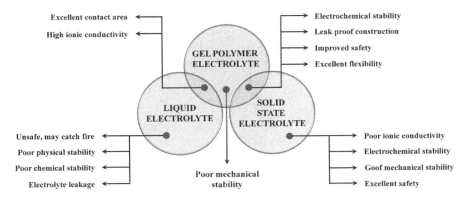

FIGURE 6.3 The nature and characteristics of different types of electrolytes employed in commercial LIBs.

Lithium diflouro(oxolato)borate (LiDFOB), an alternate to LiBOB, has stable fluorine atoms in its structure and has lower impedance values, stable SEI forming ability, and good performance at higher temperatures [30–33]. Recently, a novel salt named lithium diflouro(sulphato)borate (LiBF$_2$SO$_4$) has also found its place in the lithium salt genre as an excellent HT candidate [34].

6.2.1.3 Polymer Electrolytes

Since the discovery of ion-conductive, solvent-free polymer electrolytes (PE) and their application in electrochemical systems [39, 40], various efforts have been made to replace the flammable, volatile liquid systems as electrolytes in LIBs. PEs are basically comprised of a polymer matrix with a uniform dissolution of salts in them. In order to serve as an electrolyte in electrochemical storage systems, they should meet certain requirements, such as (i) good ionic conductivity in the range $\geq 10^{-4}$ S cm^{-1}, (ii) good mechanical strength, (iii) wide electrochemical stability window (4–5 V vs. Li/Li$^+$), (iv) good interfacial contact with the electrodes, and (v) good chemical and thermal stability. The classification of electrolytes based on their nature and characteristics are represented in the Figure 6.3. Without compromising the advantageous qualities of these systems, creating thermally feasible PEs is an exigency for high-end applications [41–48].

6.2.1.4 RTILs

Ionic liquids (ILs) are fused salts with melting points below 100° C, and its structure is made up of large cations with a delocalized anion. Because these low-temperature molten salts consisting of cations and anions exist in a liquid/molten state at room temperature (RT), they are also known as RTILs. These RTILs, which were accepted as an alternate option for organic solvents, found their practical platform of application in 1992 [49], even though they were reported earlier by Hurley et al. [50] and later by Wilkes et al. [51]. The factors that make these ILs a good component in LIB electrolyte systems are their nonflammability, meagre volatile nature, and good terms of stability chemically, electrochemically, and thermally. Figure 6.4 represents

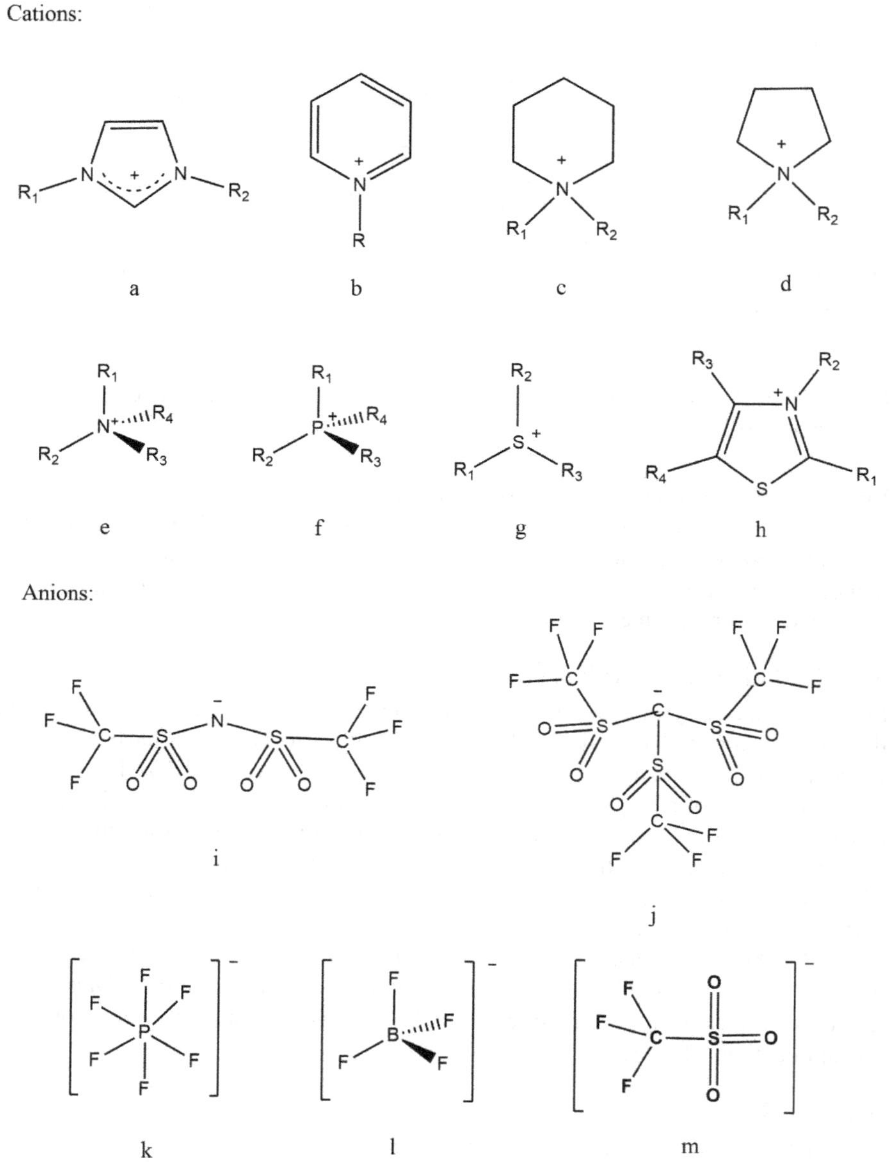

Cations:

Anions:

FIGURE 6.4 The structures of cations and anions of ILs (a) imidazolium, (b) pyridinium, (c) piperidinium, (d) pyrrolidinium, (e) quaternary ammonium, (f) phosphonium, (g) sulphonium, (h) thiazolium cations, (i) bis(trifluorosulphonylimide), (j) tris(trifluoromethanesulphonyl) methide, (k) hexafluorophosphate, (l) tetraborofluoride, and (m) trifluoro methane sulphonate anions.

High Temperature LIBs

the commonly used cations and anions of the ILs. With the aim to increase solubility of ILs with the lithium salts in the electrolyte systems, ILs are chosen with the same anion as that of the lithium salt. Thus, RTILs play a prominent role in the development of safe electrolytes when added with suitable components [52–55].

6.3 ELECTROLYTE REACTIONS OF THE LIBS

With the advent of the EV and HEV, LIBs must be operable at challenging conditions, especially if they are prone to damage even at normal conditions. The LIB systems are sensitive at temperatures near 100° C at which point several heat-generating, irreversible exothermic reactions take place. These complex processes of heat generation inside the cell can trigger more inimical reactions that can even disseminate to the nearby cells. The rapid increase of the internal battery temperature should be suppressed, which is potentially dangerous. Various studies have been carried out to understand the thermal runaway dynamics from which they have found the electrolytes guilty. This is governed by the fact that the interactions and the conditions of the LIB components with the electrolyte, other than the characteristics of the materials incorporated, do reflect in its performance [9, 56–60].

6.3.1 THERMAL DECOMPOSITION OF ELECTROLYTES

$LiPF_6$ has been the widely used salt, and this is unlikely to change until and unless an optimized lithium salt is formulated. This lithium salt undergoes dissociation, and their products are found to react with the organic electrolytes that are omnipresent in the conventional electrolyte systems. (Equation 6.1)

$$LiPF_6(sol) \rightleftarrows LiF(s) + PF_5(s) \tag{6.1}$$

The dissociation product, PF_5, is a strong Lewis acid and readily reacts with the conventional organic solvents even in the small amount of moisture content. (Equation 6.2–6.3) [27, 61]

$$LiPF_6(sol) + H_2O \rightarrow OPF_3(sol) + LiF(s) + 2HF(sol) \tag{6.2}$$

$$PF_5(sol) + H_2O \rightarrow OPF_3(sol) + 2HF(sol) \tag{6.3}$$

The proposed mechanism of the decomposition of the $LiPF_6$ salt with organic electrolytes such as EC and DEC is shown in Figure 6.5. Their decomposition pathway at elevated temperatures is shown in Figure 6.6. The compounds, such as hydrogen fluoride, lithium fluoride, carbon dioxide, ethylene, alkyl flourides, dialkyl ethers, fluorophosphates, flourophosphoric acids, and oligoethylene oxides are found to be the thermal decomposition products of the electrolytes [26, 62, 63].

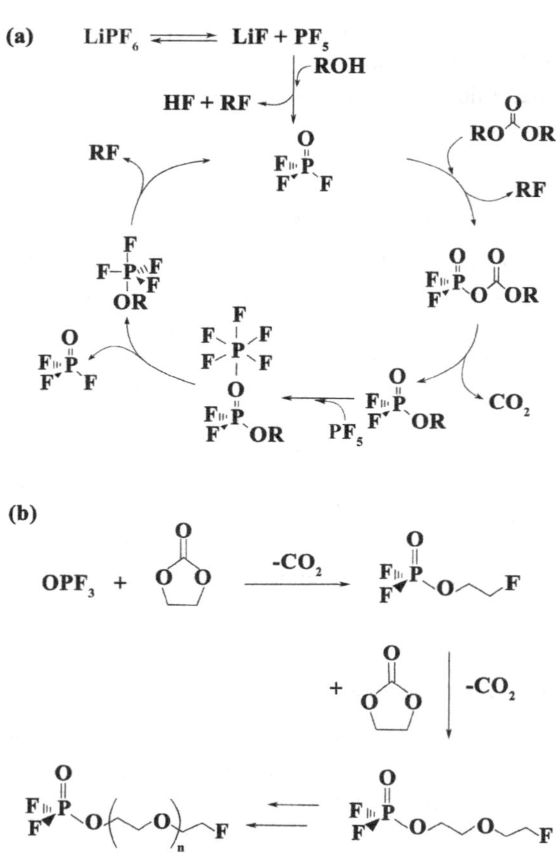

148 Ceramic and Specialty Electrolytes

FIGURE 6.5 The thermal decomposition of $LiPF_6$ in carbonyl solvents. (a) Diethyl carbonate (DEC) and (b) ethylene carbonate (EC). Adapted and reproduced with permission from reference [26]. Copyright 2005 IOP Science.

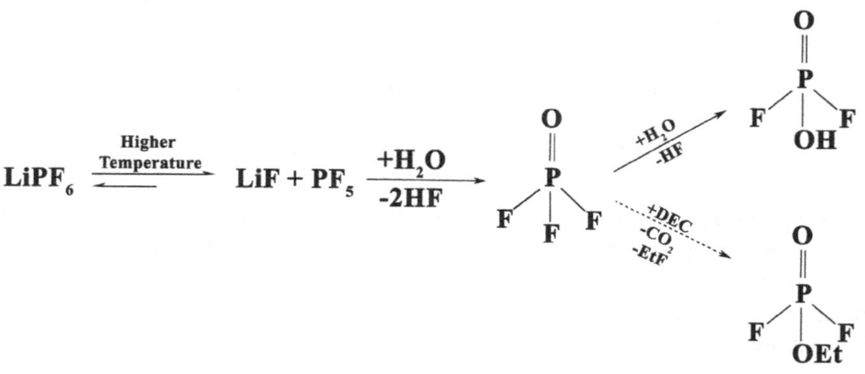

FIGURE 6.6 The decomposition pathway of $LiPF_6$ at HTs. Adapted and reproduced with permission from reference [63]. Copyright 2014 Elsevier.

High Temperature LIBs 149

6.3.2 Thermal Reactions of Electrolytes with Electrode Surface

The electrolytes' thermal reactions with the electrode materials at its interface are considered to be a lethal cause for the prevailing thermal instability of LIBs. As a result of the decomposition due to the initial reaction of the anode with the electrolyte consisting of the salt, organic solvent(s), and additives, if present, form a stable SEI. It is composed of lithium alkyl carbonate (LiOCOOR), lithium alkoxide (ROLi), polycarbonates, and ethers formed as a result of the decomposition of the electrolyte system. Even though the role of the SEI is to prevent the further reduction of the anode with the electrolyte, which it does not fail to do, it is, however, unstable at higher temperatures. The thermal stability of the SEI is affected by the attack of PF_5 that is formed as a result of the decomposition of the $LiPF_6$ salt. Upon aging, the SEI thickens, and a change in composition is observed. The passivation layer, which contains higher concentrations of several fluorine and phosphorus species, such as lithium fluoride (LiF), lithium fluorophosphates (Li_xPF_y and $Li_xPF_yO_z$), when thermally abused, increases the cell impedance. This formation of nonuniform impedance values are also portrayed by the cathode–electrolyte interface, which contributes to the power fade in the LIB system [26, 62, 64].

6.4 THERMALLY STABLE ELECTROLYTES

The electrolyte components mentioned above that are incorporated in the LIB electrolyte system have their own role to play in the HT paradigm. Recently, Wang et al. [65] developed a satisfactory flame-retardant solvent as a nonflammable electrolyte to replace conventional organic solvents. This highly concentrated electrolyte, composed of voguish flame retardant, trimethyl phosphate (TMP) and lithium bis(flourosulphonyl)imide (LiFSI) salt, formed an unusual passivation layer (Figure 6.7), which showed negligible degradation; therefore, it is a leap toward safe battery electrolytes.

The action of additives on the electrolyte system have demonstrated a significant difference over the additive-free electrolyte at a temperature of 55° C. This HT cyclability was shown by a maleimide-based branched oligomer with the conventional electrodes and electrolytes, such as $LiCoO_2$ (LCO), mesocarbon microbead (MCMB) and $LiPF_6$ in EC:DEC [66]. With respect to the ability to stabilize $LiPF_6$, a similar study involving a benzimidazole anion in the lithium salt as the additive portrayed a good battery performance at 60° C. This anion took part in a Lewis acid-base reaction with PF_5 that suppressed the unwanted side reactions and helped in the formation of a stable SEI. This additive salt showed no difference in its performance with the change in the cathode component [67, 68]. The borate-based salt, LiDFOB were reported capable of improving cycling performances at elevated temperatures of 60° C along with the suppression of thermal deterioration due to its synergistic phenomenon with $LiPF_6$ with different types of electrodes [30, 33]. Lithium tetraflouro oxalato phosphate (LTFOP) is a similar salt that is used as an electrolyte additive that shows beneficiary results at 55° C along with good capacity retention [69]. Several lithium salts with good cycling performance, rate performance and SEI forming ability at elevated temperatures of 60° C [70] and 80° C, such as lithium

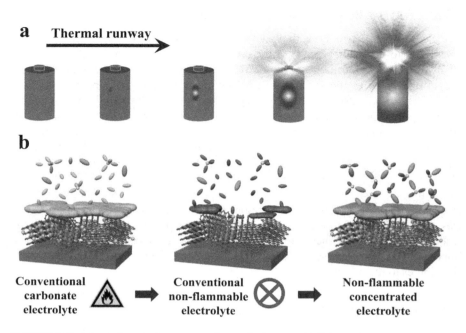

FIGURE 6.7 Electrolyte design concept for a safer battery. (a) Schematic diagram of battery explosion caused by the ejection of flammable electrolyte vapor heated following thermal runway, (b) intercalation behavior of cations into a carbonaceous anode in various electrolytes. A conventional EC-based electrolyte passivates the anode via preferential reduction of the EC solvent over anions, but its high flammability poses a severe safety risk. An electrolyte with nonflammable solvents (conventional nonflammable electrolyte) generally cannot passivate the anode to cause continuous solvent decomposition or solvent cointercalation. A concentrated electrolyte with nonflammable solvents can effectively passivate the anode via the formation of salt-derived SEI while functioning as a fire-extinguishing material. Adapted and reproduced with permission from reference [65]. Copyright 2018 Springer Nature.

dodecaflourododecaborate ($Li_{12}B_{12}F_{12}$/Li_2DFB) and $LiBF_2SO_4$, were investigated to replace $LiPF_6$ [34].

The ionic conductivity, which is a major criterion for the electrolytes in LIBs, has been found to be satisfactory for polymer-based and single-ion materials. This novel polymer electrolyte, lithium polyvinyl alcohol oxalate borate (LiPVAOB), had an increase in ionic conductivity with respect to temperature in its Arrhenius plot [32]. There has been special interest in a new class of lithium-ion conductors based on rare earth elements that show good conductivity at elevated temperatures of above 600° C. Lithium samarium holmium silicate is one such material with good ionic conductivity at 850° C with the possibility to replace conventional electrolytes for HT applications [71]. To address the thermal runaway problems in LIBs, which use liquid electrolytes susceptible to leakage, researchers are investigating solid-state lithium systems using unconventional electrolytes, especially over a wide temperature range. Lithium phosphorous oxynitride (LiPON) is one such aberrant material

High Temperature LIBs

over the traditional ones that has shown increased conductivity at higher temperatures when studied in the range 20° C–200° C [72].

Novel developments in the use of polymer materials as solid electrolytes, with optimum ionic conductivity, has had success, making them also suitable as HT materials in LIBs. One such material is a graft copolymer electrolyte made of poly(oxyethylene) methacrylate-g-poly(dimethyl siloxane) (POEM-g-PDMS) with lithium triflate salt, which showed good charge–discharge cycling at 120° C [73]. The study on polymer blends, such as polyethylene oxide/polyvinylidene diflouride (PEO/PVdF), in lithium salt has also resulted in finding good substitutes for liquid systems with amiable performance in ionic conductivity above room temperature [74]. The compatibility of polymer-based nonflammable material, such as perflourinated analogue of PEO with the (LiTFSI), was studied and proved to be an excellent candidate for intrinsically safe electrolyte system in LIB [75]. Along with good ionic conductivity, a stable electrochemical stability window was displayed by a polycarbonate-based material at 60° C [76].

The gel polymer electrolytes (GPE) are considered as an effective electrolyte alternative due to its various advantages (Figure 6.3). A PVdF-based GPE exhibited a good thermal stability individually at 150° C and, when coupled with nonconventional electrodes, it was extended up to 200° C [77]. A modification on this system using a nonflammable material, phosphonate-based copolymer, have also been reported recently, which are intrinsically safer than PVdF-based GPE [78]. Shin et al. [79] prepared a polyethylene glycol (PEG) cross-linked with poly(vinyl pyridine)-PEG-poly(vinyl pyridine) (PVP-PEG-PVP) copolymers with a good ionic conductivity at 80° C. This conductivity increase was found to be 33 times the value of poly(vinylidene fluoride-co-hexafluoropropylene)(PVdF-co-HFP)-based electrolytes, which makes these PEG-based GPEs superior in terms of thermomechanical properties. Recently, another triblock polymer of polystyrene-poly(ethylene oxide)-polystyrene (PS-PEO-PS) on PVdF exhibited good thermal dimensional stability with little shrinkage at temperature up to 260° C [80]. Considering that GPE lacks mechanical stability, Lv et al. [81] fabricated succinonitrile (SN) containing GPE with a polyurethane acrylate (PUA) skeleton with LiTFSI salt. This electrolyte showed mechanical robustness along with good ionic conductivity at the temperature of 50° C compared to the normal electrolytes.

The addition of fillers has also contributed to the thermal stability of polymer-based electrolytes [82]. Composite polymer electrolytes (CPE) with efficient fillers, such as titanium dioxide, alumina, and lithium aluminate, have shown good transport properties at temperatures in the range of 80° C–90° C with PEO matrix [83]. The use of the heat resister polytetraflouroethylene (PTFE) as filler in CPEs in the form LiBOB-SN-PEO-PTFE and $LiCF_3SO_3$-PEO-PTFE tend to increase the thermal feasibility at 160° C with good ionic conductivity [84]. A CPE consisting of cyanoethyl-β-polyvinyl alcohol (PVA-β-CN) with optimum amount of PC operated well at 120° C in LFP/Li half cells [85]. Apart from the ion-transporting ability, the electrolytes can also function as separators if constructed in a manner consistent with the abusive condition that the battery undergoes. A GPE with inorganic nanoparticles, such as SiO_2 and Al_2O_3, were found to overcome the problem of thermal shrinkage in the existing separators [86]. The silica nanoparticle has proven to be a good electrolyte additive with greater than 80% capacity retention in half-cell study at 60° C [87].

The IL-based electrolytes have found a role in replacing the conventional electrolytes with similar electrochemical performance because of their nonvolatile nature and good ionic conductivity. Several imide-based ILs, such as N-butyl-N-methylpyrrolidinium bis(triflourosulphonyl)imide ($PYR_{14}TFSI$) [88], N-propyl-N-methylpyrrolidinium bis(triflourosulphonyl)imide ($PYR_{13}TFSI$) [89], and 1-butyl-1-methylpiperidinium bis(triflourosulphonyk)imide ($Pip_{14}TFSI$) [90] in LiTFSI salt, have portrayed good cycling ability over the temperature range of 60° C–80° C. This has been accomplished not only with lithium iron phosphate (LFP) electrodes but also with the unconventional tin oxide (SnO_2) electrode. Combining ILs with poor capacity have shown no short-circuiting at 50° C, making them a safe system [91]. A practically adequate binary system composed of ILs and organic solvents has proven its workability from RT to 60° C [92]. The temperature effect of binary IL has reported an increase in charge–discharge specific capacity with temperature [93].

The compatibility between IL and polymer matrix has been explored since a long time, in which systems without thermal degradation at elevated temperatures up to 205 °C have been studied with conductivities upto 4.1×10^{-3} S cm^{-1} [94]. The ionic conductivity of an imide IL based GPEs increased with rise in temperature from 25 °C to 95 °C from 0.64×10^{-3} S cm^{-1} to 4.8×10^{-3} S cm^{-1} [95]. The electrolyte systems with imidazolium IL with different polymers have showed thermal stabilities near 300 °C which proves themselves to function as non-flammable safe electrolytes [96, 97]. An ionogel made up of IL, its lithium salt, and silane coupling agent, is not only reported to be stable at 195 °C but also exhibits high capacities till temperatures upto 90 °C [98].

The conventional cathode for LIB system has been lithium cobaltate (LCO), ever since its discovery by Yoshino et al. [99] and into its commercialization in 1991 [100]. However, LFP have attracted attention due to its high power capability, non-toxic nature, and thermal stability [101]. The study of IL-based GPE with LFP cathode and lithium metal as an anode has reflected appreciable ionic conductivities from RT to 50° C along with no significant discharge capacity loss [102]. A similar electrolyte with a different IL showed thermal stability with good ionic conductivity up to 80° C in addition to the good cycling performance at 60° C [103]. Although the GPEs tend to restrict the fluidic nature of ILs, their mechanical instability is addressed by the use of ceramic fillers. The incorporation of dry bentonite clay [104] and hexagonal boron nitride (h-BN) [105] particles in piperidinium-based IL exhibited good wetting properties along with an increase in the electrochemical stability window. These were studied with LTO half-cells with a wide thermal stability from RT to 120° C and 150° C with extended cycling stability (Figure 6.8), ensuring their practical usage under extreme requirements. The development of HT electrolytes in LIBs has expanded to various dimensions in which 3D printing of the electrolytes are even explored [106].

High Temperature LIBs 153

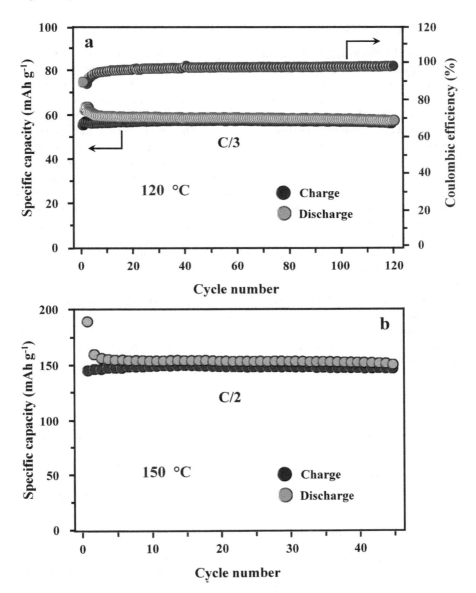

FIGURE 6.8 The cycling stability of Li/LTO half cells assembled with (a) bentonite clay (cell tested at 120° C at current density of C/3) and (b) h-BN- (cell tested at 150° C at current density of C/2) based Quasi Solid State Electrolyte (QSSEs). Although there are changes in the electrode kinetics over time, the electrolyte is electrochemically stable, and the capacity fade is negligible. Adapted and reproduced with permission from reference [104, 105]. Copyright 2015 American Chemical Society and 2016 Elsevier.

6.5 CONCLUSION: ELECTROLYTES OR LIBS ON FIRE

The use of HT electrolytes for the functioning of LIBs at extreme temperatures for various applications is a requirement. As this chapter indicates, there are a multitude of materials for this purpose; however, their practicality has not yet been fully accomplished even with the many impressive studies carried out to create safe electrolytes for LIBs. The research on these devices, which are applied in almost all facets of human development, have been exploratory. The deviation from the flammable organic solvents have explored many other candidates, such as polymers and their different combinations. The blends and cosystems have provided polymer-based electrolytes with ambient properties along with good compatibility with the electrodes. Various studies have even proven that the addition of nanoceramic particles to the polymer have contributed to good physiochemical properties. The polymer-salt systems consisting of thermally stable RTILs have opened a new wide range of practical electrolytes for the safe and smooth functioning of LIBs.

The possibility of polymeric printable ink-like electrolytes on elevated temperatures have been explored exclusively, which is found to be more methodical in preparation and embodiment in LIBs. Research to evolve LIBs has shown that the electrolytes have had their own thermal limits. Thus, the evolution of electrolytes has been going on with safety and operation at elevated temperatures as the prime focus. This chapter has presented valuable information on the existing transition occurring now on this Nobel Prize winning technology. We can optimistically look forward to witnessing LIBs that can even work in fire in the not-so-distant future.

REFERENCES

1. Workman J (2019) "Our house is on fire." 16 year-old Greta Thunberg wants action. In: World Econ. Forum Annu. Meet. 2019, https://www.weforum.org/agenda/2019/01/our-house-is-on-fire-16-year-old-greta-thunberg-speaks-truth-to-power/.
2. Whittingham MS (2012) History, evolution, and future status of energy storage. *Proc IEEE* 100:1518–1534. doi: 10.1109/JPROC.2012.2190170
3. Liu W (2013) Basic components of hybrid vehicle. In: *Introduction to Hybrid Vehicle System Modeling and Control.* John Wiley & Sons, Germany, ISBN:9781118308400, 11-24. doi:10.1002/9781118407400
4. Blomgren GE (2017) The development and future of lithium ion batteries. *J Electrochem Soc* 164:A5019–A5025. doi: 10.1149/2.0251701jes
5. Swapnil Mathur (2016) Samsung Galaxy Note 7 fiasco: Here is everything you need to know about lithium batteries. In: *Technol. News.* The Indian Express. https://indianexpress.com/article/technology/tech-news-technology/samsung-galaxy-note-7-li-ion-battery-explosion-everything-you-need-to-know-3030456/. Accessed 4 Dec 2020
6. Christen Costa Lenovo Recalls 200k Exploding Batteries | Gadget Review. In: Gadget Rev. https://www.gadgetreview.com/lenovo-recalls-200k-exploding-batteries. Accessed 4 Dec 2020
7. Adam Aitken (2017) *Dangerous Goods - Lithium Battery Fire - Redback Aviation.* In: Redback Aviat. http://www.redbackaviation.com/dangerous-goods-lithium-battery-fire/. Accessed 4 Dec 2020
8. BBC News (2019) *Crawley Tesla Fire: Half of Site Damaged in Fire.* https://www.bbc.com/news/uk-england-sussex-47427311. Accessed 4 Dec 2020

9. Ma S, Jiang M, Tao P, et al. (2018) Temperature effect and thermal impact in lithium-ion batteries: A review. *Prog Nat Sci Mater Int* 28:653–666. doi: 10.1016/j.pnsc.2018.11.002

10. Lin X, Salari M, Arava LMR, et al. (2016) High temperature electrical energy storage: Advances, challenges, and frontiers. *Chem Soc Rev* 45:5848–5887. doi: 10.1039/c6cs00012f

11. Robertson AD, West AR, Ritchie AG (1997) Review of crystalline lithium-ion conductors suitable for high temperature battery applications. *Solid State Ionics* 104:1–11.

12. Xu K (2004) Nonaqueous liquid electrolytes for lithium-based rechargeable batteries. *Chem Rev* 104:4303–4417. doi: 10.1021/cr030203g

13. Xu K (2014) Electrolytes and interphases in Li-ion batteries and beyond. *Chem Rev* 114:11503–11618. doi: 10.1021/cr500003w

14. Megahed S and BS (1994) Lithium-ion rechargeable batteries. *J Power Sources* 51:79–104.

15. Hayner CM, Zhao X, Kung HH (2012) Materials for rechargeable lithium-ion batteries. *Annu Rev Chem Biomol Eng* 3:445–471. doi: 10.1146/annurev-chembioeng-062011-081024

16. Li Q, Chen J, Fan L, et al. (2016) Progress in electrolytes for rechargeable Li-based batteries and beyond. *Green Energy Environ* 1:18–42. doi: 10.1016/j.gee.2016.04.006

17. Yaakov D, Gofer Y, Aurbach D, Halalay IC (2010) On the study of electrolyte solutions for Li-ion batteries that can work over a wide temperature range. *J Electrochem Soc* 157:A1383–A1391. doi: 10.1149/1.3507259

18. Xie B, Lee HS, Li H, et al. (2008) New electrolytes using Li 2 O or Li 2 O 2 oxides and tris (pentafluorophenyl) borane as boron based anion receptor for lithium batteries. *Electrochem Commun* 10:1195–1197. doi: 10.1016/j.elecom.2008.05.043

19. Zhu G, Wen K, Lv W, et al. (2015) Materials insights into low-temperature performances of lithium-ion batteries. *J Power Sources* 300:29–40. doi: 10.1016/j.jpowsour.2015.09.056

20. Raghavan P, Manuel J, Zhao X, et al. (2011) Preparation and electrochemical characterization of gel polymer electrolyte based on electrospun polyacrylonitrile nonwoven membranes for lithium batteries. *J Power Sources* 196:6742–6749. doi: 10.1016/j.jpowsour.2010.10.089

21. Rodrigue Y, Tessier C, El L, et al. (2013) Low pressure carbon dioxide solubility in lithium-ion batteries based electrolytes as a function of temperature. Measurement and prediction. *J Chem Thermodyn* 61:32–44. doi: 10.1016/j.jct.2012.12.025

22. Nishi Y (2001) Lithium ion secondary batteries: Past ten years and future. *J Power Sources* 100:101–106.

23. Thackeray MM, David WIF, Bruce PG, Goodenough JB (1983) Lithium insertion into magnesium spinels. *Mater Res Bull* 18:461–472. doi: 10.1016/0025-5408(83)90138-1

24. Wang Y, Cao G (2008) Developments in nanostructured cathode materials for high-performance lithium-ion batteries. *Adv Mater* 20:2251–2269. doi: 10.1002/adma.200702242

25. Mao L, Li B, Cui X, et al. (2012) Electrochemical performance of electrolytes based upon lithium bis(oxalate)borate and sulfolane/alkyl sulfite mixtures for high temperature lithium-ion batteries. *Electrochim Acta* 79:197–201. doi: 10.1016/j.electacta.2012.06.102

26. Campion CL, Li W, Lucht BL (2005) Thermal decomposition of LiPF 6-based electrolytes for lithium-ion batteries. *J Electrochem Soc* 152:2327–2334. doi: 10.1149/1.2083267

27. Xu K, Zhang S, Jow TR, et al. (2002) LiBOB as salt for lithium-ion batteries : A possible solution for high temperature operation service LiBOB as salt for lithium-ion batteries: A possible solution for high temperature operation. *Electrochem Solid State Lett* 5:2–6. doi: 10.1149/1.1426042

28. Zhang SS, Xu K, Jow TR (2006) LiBOB-based gel electrolyte Li-ion battery for high temperature operation. *J Power Sources* 154:276–280. doi: 10.1016/j.jpowsour.2005.03.196

29. Li Y, Wu X, Kim J, et al. (2013) A novel polymer electrolyte with improved high-temperature- tolerance up to 170 C for high-temperature lithium-ion batteries. *J Power Sources* 244:234–239. doi: 10.1016/j.jpowsour.2013.01.148
30. Xu M, Zhou L, Hao L, et al. (2011) Investigation and application of lithium difluoro (oxalate) borate (LiDFOB) as additive to improve the thermal stability of electrolyte for lithium-ion batteries. *J Power Sources* 196:6794–6801. doi: 10.1016/j.jpowsour.2010.10.050
31. Hu M, Wei J, Xing L (2012) Effect of lithium difluoro (oxalate) borate (LiDFOB) additive on the performance of high-voltage lithium-ion batteries. *J Appl Electrochem* 42:291–296. doi: 10.1007/s10800-012-0398-0
32. Zhu YS, Wang XJ, Hou YY, et al. (2013) A new single-ion polymer electrolyte based on polyvinyl alcohol for lithium ion batteries. *Electrochim Acta* 87:113–118. doi: 10.1016/j.electacta.2012.08.114
33. Jun S, Han J, Lee Y, et al. (2014) A bi-functional lithium difluoro (oxalato) borate additive for lithium cobalt oxide / lithium nickel manganese cobalt oxide cathodes and silicon / graphite anodes in lithium-ion batteries at elevated temperatures. *Electrochim Acta* 137:1–8. doi: 10.1016/j.electacta.2014.05.136
34. Li S, Zhao W, Cui X, et al. (2014) Lithium difluoro(sulfato)borate as a novel electrolyte salt for high-temperature lithium-ion batteries. *Electrochim Acta* 129:327–333. doi: 10.1016/j.electacta.2014.02.090
35. Aravindan V, Vickraman P (2007) A study on LiBOB-based nanocomposite gel polymer electrolytes (NCGPE) for lithium-ion batteries. *Ionics (Kiel)* 13:277–280. doi: 10.1007/s11581-007-0106-y
36. Aravindan V, Vickraman P (2009) Synthesis and characterization of LiBOB-based PVdF/PVC-TiO$_2$ composite polymer electrolytes. *Polym Eng Sci* 49:2109–2115. doi: 10.1002/pen
37. Ping P, Wang Q, Sun J, et al. (2010) Thermal stabilities of some lithium salts and their electrolyte solutions with and without contact to a LiFePO$_4$ electrode. *J Electrochem Soc* 157:1170–1176. doi: 10.1149/1.3473789
38. Zhang L, Chai L, Zhang L, et al. (2014) Synergistic effect between lithium bis(fluorosulfonyl)imide (LiFSI) and lithium bis-oxalato borate (LiBOB) salts in LiPF$_6$-based electrolyte for high-performance Li-ion batteries. *Electrochim Acta* 127:39–44. doi: 10.1016/j.electacta.2014.02.008
39. Fenton DE, Parker JM, Wright PV (1973) Complexes of alkali metal ions with poly(ethylene oxide). *Polymer (Guildf)* 14:589. doi: 10.1016/0032-3861(73)90146-8
40. Armand M (1986) Polymer electrolytes. *Annu Rev Mater Sci* 16:245–261.
41. Meyer WH (1998) Polymer electrolytes for lithium-ion batteries. *Adv Mater* 10:439–448. doi: 10.1002/(SICI)1521-4095(199804)10:6<439::AID-ADMA439>3.0.CO;2-I
42. Murata K (1995) An overview of the research and development of solid polymer electrolyte batteries. *Electrochim Acta* 40:2177–2184.
43. Murata K, Izuchi S, Yoshihisa Y (2000) An overview of the research and development of solid polymer electrolyte batteries. *Electrochim Acta* 45:1501–1508. doi: 10.1016/S0013-4686(99)00365-5
44. Dias FB, Plomp L, Veldhuis JBJ (2000) Trends in polymer electrolytes for secondary lithium batteries. *J Power Sources* 88:169–191. doi: 10.1016/S0378-7753(99)00529-7
45. Gerbaldi C (2010) All-solid-state lithium-based polymer cells for high-temperature applications. *Ionics (Kiel)* 16:777–786. doi: 10.1007/s11581-010-0484-4
46. Ngai KS, Ramesh S, Ramesh K, Juan JC (2016) A review of polymer electrolytes: Fundamental, approaches and applications. *Ionics (Kiel)* 22:1259–1279. doi: 10.1007/s11581-016-1756-4
47. Zhang H, Li C, Piszcz M, et al. (2017) Single lithium-ion conducting solid polymer electrolytes: Advances and perspectives. *Chem Soc Rev* 46:797–815. doi: 10.1039/c6cs00491a

48. Chua S, Fang R, Sun Z, Wu M, Zi Gu YW (2018) Hybrid solid polymer electrolytes with two-dimensional inorganic nanofillers. *Chem Eur J* 24:18180–18203.

49. Wilkes JS and Zaworotka MJ (1992) Air and water stable I-Ethyl-3-methylimidazolium based ionic liquids. *J Chem Soc Chem Commun* 13: 965–967. doi.org/10.1039/C39920000965

50. Hurley FH, Wier TP (1951) Electrodeposition of metals from fused quaternary ammonium salts. *J Electrochem Soc* 98:203–206. doi: 10.1149/1.2778132

51. Wilkes JS, Levisky JA, Wilson RA, Hussey CL (1982) Dialkylimidazolium chloroaluminate melts: A new class of room-temperature ionic liquids for electrochemistry, spectroscopy, and synthesis. *Inorg Chem* 21:1263–1264.

52. Lavalle S, Michot C, Armand M (2004) Room temperature molten salts as lithium battery electrolyte. *Electrochim Acta* 49:4583–4588. doi: 10.1016/j.electacta.2004.04.041

53. Nakagawa H, Fujino Y, Kozono S (2007) Application of nonflammable electrolyte with room temperature ionic liquids (RTILs) for lithium-ion cells. *J Power Sources* 174:1021–1026. doi: 10.1016/j.jpowsour.2007.06.133

54. Lewandowski A, Swiderska-mocek A (2009) Ionic liquids as electrolytes for Li-ion batteries — An overview of electrochemical studies. *J Power Sources* 194:601–609. doi: 10.1016/j.jpowsour.2009.06.089

55. Armand M, Endres F, Macfarlane DR, et al. (2009) Ionic-liquid materials for the electrochemical challenges of the future. *Nat Publ Gr* 8:621–629. doi: 10.1038/nmat2448

56. Bandhauer TM, Garimella S, Fuller TF (2011) A critical review of thermal issues in lithium-ion batteries. *J Electrochem Soc* 158:R1–R25. doi: 10.1149/1.3515880

57. Abraham DP, Dees DW, Knuth J, et al. (2005) Diagnostic examination of generation 2 lithium-ion cells and assessment of performance degradation mechanism (No. ANL-05/21). Chemical Engineering Division, Argonne National Laboratory (ANL), Argonne, IL (United States).

58. Burns JC, Kassam A, Sinha NN, et al. (2013) Predicting and extending the lifetime of Li-ion batteries. *J Electrochem Soc* 160:A1451–A1456. doi: 10.1149/2.060309jes

59. Finegan DP, Scheel M, Robinson JB, et al. (2015) In-operando high-speed tomography of lithium-ion batteries during thermal runaway. *Nat Commun* 6:1–10. doi: 10.1038/ncomms7924

60. Rodrigues M-TF, Babu G, Gullapalli H, et al. (2017) A materials perspective on Li-ion batteries at extreme temperatures. *Nat Energy* 2:17108. doi: 10.1038/nenergy.2017.108

61. Aravindan V, Vickraman P (2009) Synthesis and characterization of LiBOB-based PVdF/PVC-TiO 2 composite polymer electrolytes. *Polym Eng Sci* 49:2109–2115. doi: 10.1002/pen

62. Lucht BL Markmaitree T, Yang L (2010) Thermal Stability of Lithium-Ion Battery Electrolytes. Energy Production and Storage: Inorganic Chemical Strategies for a Warming World. Crabtree RH (Editor), John Wiley & Sons, Inc., Germany, p. 333. ISBN: 978-0-470-74986-9, 333. doi.org/10.1002/anie.201103012

63. Handel P, Fauler G, Kapper K, et al. (2014) Thermal aging of electrolytes used in lithium-ion batteries: An investigation of the impact of protic impurities and different housing materials. *J Power Sources* 267:255–259. doi: 10.1016/j.jpowsour.2014.05.080

64. Lee HH, Wan CC, Wang YY (2004) Thermal stability of the solid electrolyte interface on carbon electrodes of lithium batteries. *J Electrochem Soc* 151:542–547. doi: 10.1149/1.1647568

65. Wang J, Yamada Y, Sodeyama K, et al. (2018) Fire-extinguishing organic electrolytes for safe batteries. *Nat Energy* 3:22–29. doi: 10.1038/s41560-017-0033-8

66. Li YH, Lee ML, Wang FM, et al. (2012) Electrochemical characterization of a branched oligomer as a high-temperature and long-cycle-life additive for lithium-ion batteries. *Electrochim Acta* 85:72–77. doi: 10.1016/j.electacta.2012.08.062

67. Pradanawati SA, Wang FM, Rick J (2014) In situ formation of pentafluorophosphate benzimidazole anion stabilizes high-temperature performance of lithium-ion batteries. *Electrochim Acta* 135:388–395. doi: 10.1016/j.electacta.2014.05.038

68. Wang FM, Pradanawati SA, Yeh NH, et al. (2017) Robust benzimidazole-based electrolyte overcomes high-voltage and high-temperature applications in 5 v class lithium ion batteries. *Chem Mater* 29:5537–5549. doi: 10.1021/acs.chemmater.7b00824

69. Qin Y, Chen Z, Liu J, Amine K (2010) Lithium tetrafluoro oxalato phosphate as electrolyte additive for lithium-ion cells. *Electrochem Solid-State Lett* 13:11–14. doi: 10.1149/1.3261738

70. Arai J, Matsuo A, Fujisaki T, Ozawa K (2009) A novel high temperature stable lithium salt (Li2B12F12) for lithium ion batteries. *J Power Sources* 193:851–854. doi: 10.1016/j.jpowsour.2009.04.001

71. Ganesan M (2007) A new promising high temperature lithium battery solid electrolyte. *Electrochem commun* 9:1980–1984. doi: 10.1016/j.elecom.2007.05.012

72. Li D, Ma Z, Xu J, et al. (2014) High temperature property of all-solid-state thin film lithium battery using LiPON electrolyte. *Mater Lett* 134:237–239. doi: 10.1016/j.matlet.2014.07.092

73. Hu Q, Osswald S, Daniel R, et al. (2011) Graft copolymer-based lithium-ion battery for high-temperature operation. *J Power Sources* 196:5604–5610. doi: 10.1016/j.jpowsour.2011.03.001

74. Yoon MY, Hong SK, Hwang HJ et al. (2013) Fabrication of Li-polymer/silica aerogel nanocomposite electrolyte for an all-solid-state lithium battery. *Ceram Int* 39:9659–9663. doi: 10.1016/j.ceramint.2013.05.088

75. Wong DHC, Thelen JL, Fu Y, et al. (2014) Nonflammable perfluoropolyether-based electrolytes for lithium batteries. *Proc Natl Acad Sci* 111:3327–3331. doi: 10.1073/pnas.1314615111

76. Sun B, Mindemark J, Edström K, Brandell D (2014) Polycarbonate-based solid polymer electrolytes for Li-ion batteries. *Solid State Ionics* 262:738–742. doi: 10.1016/j.ssi.2013.08.014

77. Hassoun J, Reale P, Panero S, et al. (2010) Determination of the safety level of an advanced lithium ion battery having a nanostructured Sn-C anode, a high voltage $LiNi_{0.5}Mn_{1.5}O_4$ cathode, and a polyvinylidene fluoride-based gel electrolyte. *Electrochim Acta* 55:4194–4200. doi: 10.1016/j.electacta.2010.02.063

78. Jia H, Onishi H, Wagner R, et al. (2018) An intrinsically safe gel polymer electrolyte comprising flame retarding polymer matrix for lithium ion battery application. *ACS Appl Mater Interfaces* 10:42348–42355. doi: 10.1021/acsami.8b15505

79. Shin I, Nam J, Lee K, et al. (2018) Poly(ethylene glycol) (PEG)-crosslinked poly(vinyl pyridine)-PEG-poly(vinyl pyridine)-based triblock copolymers prepared by RAFT polymerization as novel gel polymer electrolytes. *Polym Chem* 9:5190–5199. doi: 10.1039/c8py01097h

80. Xiao Q, Deng C, Wang Q, et al. (2019) In situ cross-linked gel polymer electrolyte membranes with excellent thermal stability for lithium ion batteries. *ACS Omega* 4:95–103. doi: 10.1021/acsomega.8b02255

81. Lv P, Li Y, Wu Y, et al. (2018) Robust succinonitrile-based gel polymer electrolyte for lithium-ion batteries withstanding mechanical folding and high temperature. *ACS Appl Mater Interfaces* 10:25384–25392. doi: 10.1021/acsami.8b06800

82. Masoud EM (2019) Montmorillonite incorporated polymethylmethacrylate matrix containing lithium trifluoromethanesulphonate (LTF) salt: Thermally stable polymer nanocomposite electrolyte for lithium-ion batteries application. *Ionics (Kiel)* 25:2645–2656. doi: 10.1007/s11581-018-2802-1

High Temperature LIBs

83. Croce F, Persi L, Ronci F, Scrosati B (2000) Nanocomposite polymer electrolytes and their impact on the lithium battery technology. *Solid State Ionics* 135:47–52.
84. Wu X, Li Y, Wu N, et al. (2013) Enhanced working temperature of PEO-based polymer electrolyte via porous PTFE film as an efficient heat resister. *Solid State Ionics* 246:1–7. doi: 10.1016/j.ssi.2013.05.012
85. Wang Q, Zhang B, Zhang J, et al. (2015) Heat-resistant and rigid-flexible coupling glass-fiber nonwoven supported polymer electrolyte for high-performance lithium ion batteries. *Electrochim Acta* 157:191–198. doi: 10.1016/j.electacta.2015.01.083
86. Liao Y, Sun C, Hu S, Li W (2013) Anti-thermal shrinkage nanoparticles/polymer and ionic liquid based gel polymer electrolyte for lithium ion battery. *Electrochim Acta* 89:461–468. doi: 10.1016/j.electacta.2012.11.095
87. Caimi S, Klaue A, Wu H, Morbidelli M (2018) Effect of SiO_2 nanoparticles on the performance of PVdF-HFP/ionic liquid separator for lithium-ion batteries. *Nanomaterials* 8: 926. doi: 10.3390/nano8110926
88. Kühnel RS, Böckenfeld N, Passerini S, et al. (2011) Mixtures of ionic liquid and organic carbonate as electrolyte with improved safety and performance for rechargeable lithium batteries. *Electrochim Acta* 56:4092–4099. doi: 10.1016/j.electacta.2011.01.116
89. Yang B, Li C, Zhou J, et al. (2014) Pyrrolidinium-based ionic liquid electrolyte with organic additive and LiTFSI for high-safety lithium-ion batteries. *Electrochim Acta* 148:39–45. doi: 10.1016/j.electacta.2014.10.001
90. Kerner M, Scheers J, Johansson P, Edstr K (2017) Elevated temperature lithium-ion batteries containing SnO2 electrodes and LiTFSI-Pip 14 TFSI ionic liquid electrolyte. *J Electrochem Soc* 164:701–708. doi: 10.1149/2.0861704jes
91. Lane GH, Best AS, Macfarlane DR, et al. (2010) An Azo-Spiro mixed ionic liquid electrolyte for lithium metal – LiFePO 4 batteries. *J Electrochem Soc* 157:876–884. doi: 10.1149/1.3429138
92. Sato T, Maruo T, Marukane S, Takagi K (2004) Ionic liquids containing carbonate solvent as electrolytes for lithium ion cells. *J Power Sources* 138:253–261. doi: 10.1016/j.jpowsour.2004.06.027
93. Fu Y, Chen C, Qiu C, Ma X (2009) Vinyl ethylene carbonate as an additive to ionic liquid electrolyte for lithium ion batteries. *J Appl Electrochem* 39:2597–2603. doi: 10.1007/s10800-009-9949-4
94. Fuller J, Breda AC, Carlin RT (1997) Ionic liquid-gel polymer electrolytes. *J Electrochem Soc* 144:L67–L70.
95. Stepniak I, Andrzejewska E, Dembna A, Galinski M (2014) Characterization and application of N-methyl-N-propylpiperidinium bis (trifluoromethanesulfonyl) imide ionic liquid – based gel polymer electrolyte prepared in situ by photopolymerization method in lithium ion batteries. *Electrochim Acta* 121:27–33. doi: 10.1016/j.electacta.2013.12.121
96. Nakagawa H, Izuchi S, Kuwana K, et al. (2003) Liquid and gel polymer electrolytes for lithium batteries composed of room-temperature molten salt doped by lithium salt. *J Electrochem Soc* 150:A695–A700. doi: 10.1149/1.1568939
97. Li ZH, Xia QL, Liu LL, et al. (2010) Effect of zwitterionic salt on the electrochemical properties of a solid polymer electrolyte with high temperature stability for lithium ion batteries. *Electrochim Acta* 56:804–809. doi: 10.1016/j.electacta.2010.09.068
98. Wu F, Chen N, Chen R, et al. (2017) Organically modified silica-supported ionogels electrolyte for high temperature lithium-ion batteries. *Nano Energy* 31:9–18. doi: 10.1016/j.nanoen.2016.10.060
99. Yoshino A, Sanechika K and Nakajima T (1987) "Secondary battery." United States Patent No. 4,668,595. 26 May 1987.

100. Goodenough JB, Park K-S (2013) The Li-ion rechargeable battery: A perspective. *J Am Chem Soc* 135:1167–1176. doi.org/10.1021/ja3091438
101. Padhi AK, Nanjundaswamy KS (1997) Phospho-olivines as positive-electrode materials for rechargeable lithium batteries. *J Electrochem Soc* 144:1188–1194.
102. Li M, Yang L, Fang S, et al. (2011) Li/LiFePO$_4$ batteries with gel polymer electrolytes incorporating a guanidinium-based ionic liquid cycled at room temperature and 50 °C. *J Power Sources* 196:6502–6506. doi: 10.1016/j.jpowsour.2011.03.071
103. Liu L, Yang P, Li L, et al. (2012) Application of bis(trifluoromethanesulfonyl)imide lithium-N-methyl-N- butylpiperidinium-bis(trifluoromethanesulfonyl)imide-poly(vi nylidene difluoride-co-hexafluoropropylene) ionic liquid gel polymer electrolytes in Li/LiFePO$_4$ batteries at different temperatures. *Electrochim Acta* 85:49–56. doi: 10.1016/j.electacta.2012.08.066
104. Kalaga K, Rodrigues MTF, Gullapalli H, et al. (2015) Quasi-solid electrolytes for high temperature lithium ion batteries. *ACS Appl Mater Interfaces* 7:25777–25783. doi: 10.1021/acsami.5b07636
105. Rodrigues MTF, Kalaga K, Gullapalli H, et al. (2016) Hexagonal boron nitride-based electrolyte composite for Li-ion battery operation from room temperature to 150°C. *Adv Energy Mater* 6:1–7. doi: 10.1002/aenm.201600218
106. Cheng M, Jiang Y, Yao W, et al. (2018) Elevated-temperature 3D printing of hybrid solid-state electrolyte for Li-ion batteries. *Adv Mater* 30:1–10. doi: 10.1002/adma.201800615

7 Electrolytes for Low-Temperature Lithium-Ion Batteries Operating in Freezing Weather

Neethu T. M. Balakrishnan, Leya Rose Raphael, Akhila Das, Jishnu N. S., Jou-Hyeon Ahn, Jabeen Fatima M. J., Prasanth Raghavan

CONTENTS

7.1 Introduction 161
7.2 Electrolytes for LIBs.. 162
    7.2.1 GPEs for Low-Temperature LIBs 163
        7.2.1.1 Additives and Lithium Salts for Low-Temperature LIBs.......165
        7.2.1.2 Organic Solvents for Low-Temperature LIBs.................. 166
        7.2.1.3 Room-Temperature Ionic Liquids for
                Low-Temperature LIBs 169
7.3 Separators for Low-Temperature LIBs 170
7.4 Conclusion 172
Acknowledgment 173
References.. 173

7.1 INTRODUCTION

Today, energy storage devices are entering into a broader area owing to their ability to control greenhouse gas emissions by avoiding the combustion of fossil fuels. Apart from this, they play a key role in avoiding the extinction of nonrenewable sources of energy through proper usage of renewable, green energy sources such as wind, sun, water, etc. Different energy storage devices were explored for the proper storage of energy harvested from these different renewable sources. Batteries and supercapacitors are predominant among them and constitute common materials for the fabrication of electrodes and electrolyte. Batteries exhibit high energy density (150 Wh g^{-1}) and high coulombic efficiency, while supercapacitors possess high power density

(25–100 kW kg^{-1}) [1, 2]. Rechargeable batteries are mostly used because of their ability to store more energy for a given weight and volume and its possibility to reuse by recharging [3]. Among the different types of rechargeable batteries, lithium-ion batteries (LIBs) are used in most portable electronic devices [4, 5]; however, there are challenges in the working environment of the LIBs. The battery operation involves extreme conditions, such as high temperature, low temperature, high discharge rate, low discharge rate, etc. [6, 7], so the temperature at which they are going to be used is important. For LIBs, the acceptable temperature limit is generally in between -20° C and 60° C, which makes them practical for use in cold weather also. Compared to the lead acid, the low-temperature performance of these batteries is far better [8]. At 0° C, lead acid batteries suffer about 50% capacity reduction, but, for LIBs, it is only about 10%, although it is difficult for LIBs to completely accomplish best performance at low temperatures. At low temperatures, the internal rise in temperature will get compensated by the cold working temperature, while the internal resistance developed will cause a prolonged charging time.

At freezing temperature (0° C), it is hazardous for the battery to charge without reducing the charge current because of the mechanisms taking place inside the LIBs at this temperature. Below 0° C, the anode is inefficient at capturing the lithium ions (Li$^+$-ions), instead they get caught over the surface of the electrode that leads to the lithium plating, which decreases battery capacity. This leads to mechanical instability that may cause battery failure. Different methods were proposed to resolve this issue. Heating the battery before charging was one of the solutions, and that can be done either by warming the battery in a hot environment or by placing them in a thermal blanket or by a heater. Zhang et al. [9] developed the method of preheating the battery by using a sinusoidal alternative current. They found that by using this method the battery can heat up from -20° C to 50° C in only 15 minutes. Song et al. [10] proposed air heating by a stimulation system. They found that by heating up the surrounding air, the battery capacity can be retained to a great extent. While these modifications to the battery's surroundings can lead to satisfactory results, it would be more convenient if it is possible to modify the battery components to provide better capacity at cold temperatures. Being the most crucial component inside the battery, electrolytes are considered to be the component that can be modified to obtain the expected performance. This chapter gives the detailed examination of the performance of the electrolytes at low temperature as well as the different advancements that have been made to create high-performing LIBs at low temperatures.

7.2 ELECTROLYTES FOR LIBs

Being a crucial component inside the battery, electrolytes are gaining attention as improvements to low temperature performance are sought. During the early stages of LIBs, organic liquids with high ionic mobility, which is essential for the best electrochemical performance, were used as electrolytes. Moreover, the solid-electrolyte interface (SEI) formation inside the battery is greatly influenced by the presence of liquid electrolytes. The SEI formation helps to prevent electrolyte reduction, protect the electrodes, and permit the conduction of Li$^+$-ions, which, in turn, affect the

Low-Temperature LIBs

low-temperature performance of the LIBs; however, these volatile and flammable electrolytes made LIBs a nightmare by causing fire and explosions during continuous usage. The heat that builds up inside the battery heat the flammable liquid counterparts, which caused the battery to swell and, worst case, explode. At low temperatures, the ionic conductivity of these liquids are reduced because of an increase in viscosity [11, 12]. The increased viscosity results in the formation of lithium plating that deteriorates the performance of battery [13]. The exploration of polymer electrolytes by replacing the liquid counterparts enhanced the safety aspects in LIBs. Commonly used gel polymer electrolytes (GPEs) are made of polymers activated with a liquid electrolyte containing lithium salt. In evaluating the low-temperature properties of polymer electrolytes, it was discovered that, with decreasing temperature, the amorphous nature of the polymer is reduced and the chain flexibility is arrested, which leads to limited ionic movement and low ionic conductivity. In order to improve the amorphous nature of the polymer at low temperatures, different additives and salts were introduced [14, 15]. The different methods to modify the low-temperature performance of polymer electrolytes in LIBs will be discussed in later sections of this chapter.

7.2.1 GPEs FOR LOW-TEMPERATURE LIBs

The catastrophic failure caused by extreme condition applications is an important barrier for the wide temperature use of LIBs. Thermal or electrochemical abuse of the battery can cause exothermic reactions that combust the liquid electrolytes inside the battery. These can lead to thermal runway that may cause the storage system to explode. The highly reactive nature of these electrolytes necessitates the use of polymer electrolytes that produce more stable and reliable battery systems [16–19]. Solid polymer electrolytes improve the safety aspects of LIBs, but could not deliver an advantageous electrochemical performance, as they show very low ionic conductivity as compared to that of organic solvents. GPEs that can provide higher ionic conductivity than solid polymer electrolytes and that are more inflammable than liquid electrolytes are considered promising components to produce safer batteries [20]. GPEs consist of a polymer matrix with a liquid electrolyte and a lithium salt [21]. Different polymers are employed as the matrix for the electrolyte in LIBs, including polyethylene oxides (PEO) [22], polymethyl methacrylate (PMMA) [23], polyvinylidene difluoride-co-hexaflouropropylene (PVdF-co-HFP) [24], polyacrylonitrile (PAN), polyvinylidene fluoride (PVdF) [25], polyvinyl chloride (PVC) [26] and polystyrene (PS) [27]. GPEs were anticipated to be less effective at improving the low-temperature conductivity compared to liquid electrolytes [28], so different studies were conducted using variant polymer matrices in which the components, such as cosolvents, and salts can impart specific properties that make them capable of delivering better low-temperature performance. GPEs fabricated using the ionic liquid electrolyte (ILE) N-butyl-N-methyl-pyrrolidiniumbis(trifluoromethane sulfonyl)imide to form the liquid polymer electrolytes (ILPEs) that could exhibit a good low temperature ionic conductivity (between -50° C and -70° C), which is found to be four orders of magnitude higher than that of ILEs (Figure 7.1a)and the

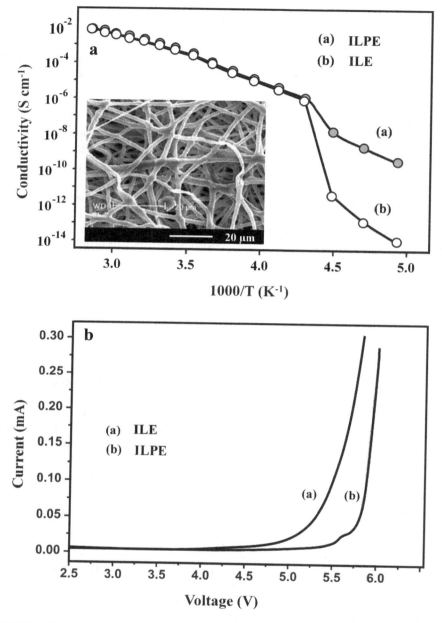

FIGURE 7.1 (a) Ionic conductivity as a function of temperature for the Py14TFSI room-temperature ILE and the Py14TFSI-based polymer electrolyte (ILPE). Inset figure is scanning electron microscope image of electrospun PVdF-*co*-HFP membrane (b) linear sweep voltammetry (LSV) plots of an cell with the Py14TFSI-based polymer electrolyte (ILPE). Adapted and reproduced with permission from reference [29]. Copyright 2013 Elsevier.

Low-Temperature LIBs

electrochemical window for the ionic liquid polymer electrolytes (ILPEs) (5.5 V) is higher than that of ILEs (4.75 V) versus Li/Li$^+$ (Figure 7.1b) [29]. Here, it is evident that, even if the ILs play a major role in enhancing low-temperature performance, the presence of polymer matrix also helps. However, the selection of different constituents in PEs, such as additives, ionic liquids (ILs), and cosolvents, are also important and will be discussed in later sections.

7.2.1.1 Additives and Lithium Salts for Low-Temperature LIBs

Salts are the key factor that determine the property of electrolyte in batteries. Using suitable salt, the viscosity and the freezing point of the electrolyte can be reduced at low temperatures. During the chemical reaction, the salt is reduced and is one of the important components of SEI that directly determines the conductivity [30]. Lithium hexafluoro phosphate (LiPF$_6$) is one of the widely used salts in electrolytes used in LIBs, but the spontaneous decomposition of this salt into LiF and PF$_5$ causes capacity fading [31, 32]. So, replacing this salt with others can improve the low-temperature performance. Lithium tetra flouroborate (LiBF$_4$) is the best substitute, as it offers excellent ionic conductivity and low charge-transfer resistance at cold temperatures [33, 34]. At -30° C, comparing the capacity of LiPF$_{66}$ with LiBF$_4$ in PC:EC:EMC (1:1:3) shows that the cell with LiBF$_4$ salt retained its 86% of room-temperature capacity, while it is only 72% for LiPF$_{66}$ [35]. Moreover, substituting LiPF$_6$ with LiBF$_4$ can reduce the R_{ct} up to a voltage of 4.4 V [36]. Lithium bis oxalate borate (LiBOB), such as LiBF$_4$, is a thermally stable salt that can be used for extreme temperatureLIBs [37, 38]. Exploring LiBOB along with the combination of organic electrolytes PC/EC/EMC (1:1:3) outcomes 75 and 64% room temperature capacity retention even at a temperature of -20 °C and -30 °C, respectively [35]. The combined advantage of both LiPF$_6$ and LiBF$_4$ are given by lithium diflouro oxalate borate (LiDFOB). It forms a stable SEI [39], however, as a low-temperature electrolyte salt, the application of LiDFOB is limited because its tendency to form a thicker SEI and increase the interface impedance may lead to poor electrochemical properties. But the 1:1 blend of LiDFOB and LiBF$_4$, along with the solvents ethylene carbonate (EC), dimethyl carbonate (DMC), and dimethyl sulfite (DMS) (1:2:1 volume respectively), exhibits excellent performance even with a fall in temperature. The combination of salt (0.6 M LiDFOB + 0.4 M LiBF$_4$) exhibits an ionic conductivity of 0.75 mS cm^{-1} even at -40°C which is slightly greater than that exhibited by 0.8 M LiBF$_4$ system (0.5 mS cm^{-1}) at the same temperature(Figure 7.2)[40].

Mandal et al. [41] reported that 0.9 M LiTFSI in a mixture of EC:DMC:EMC:PC in the ratio 15:37:38:10 is an efficient electrolyte over temperatures ranging from -30° C to 70° C. It has been reported that this electrolyte system can provide an ionic conductivity of 2 mS cm^{-1} even at a temperature of -40°C [41]. Certain lithium modified salts, such as lithium modified silica nanosalt (Li$_2$O$_2$), exhibit excellent cyclic performance, ionic conductivity, and superior electrochemical property over 5 V at -20° C The salt's ability to improve the ionic conductivity and form a moderate SEI layer makes it promising for electrolytes in LIBs [42]. Other polydimethylsilixane (PDMS) based additives, such as poly[dimethylsiloxane-co-(siloxane-g-acrylate)] (PDMS-A), poly(dimethylsiloxane-co-phenylsiloxane) (PDMS-P), and poly[dimet

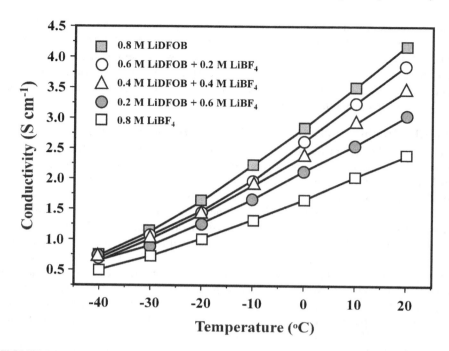

FIGURE 7.2 Dependence of ionic conductivity on temperature for different electrolyte systems that have LiDFOB and LiBF$_4$. Adapted and reproduced with permission from reference [40]. Copyright 2017 IOP Science.

hylsiloxane-co-(siloxane-g-ethylene oxide)] (PDMS-EO), enhance battery performance and exhibit an ionic conductivity of around 5×10^{-4} S cm^{-1} at -20° C (Figure 7.3), which indicate their ability to resist the freezing property of liquid electrolytes [43]. PDMS-A and Li$_2$O$_2$ are combined to exhibit electrochemical stability at about 5.5 V and ionic conductivity is 4×10^{-4} S cm^{-1}, respectively at -20° C [44].

7.2.1.2 Organic Solvents for Low-Temperature LIBs

The electrochemical performance of polymer electrolytes at low temperatures are limited by the restricted ionic mobility. This can be enhanced by adding suitable cosolvents with low viscosity and freezing point at low temperatures. For graphite-containing systems, EC is considered the best electrolyte cosolvent because of its ability to form a stable SEI layer. For systems using graphite electrodes in solution containing methyl formate (MF) and EC, increasing the EC content improves the cyclic stability of the graphite because the reduction product of EC favors the formation of a compact passivation layer. The high polar nature of EC and the low melting point of MF are favorable for low-temperature performance in LIBs. Systems containing LiAlF$_6$ exhibit an ionic conductivity of 25.3 and 8.4 mS cm^{-1} at temperatures of 22° C and -40° C respectively [45]. Plichta et al. [46] studied the low-temperature performance using a combination of EC, diethyl carbonate (DEC), DMC, and ethyl

Low-Temperature LIBs 167

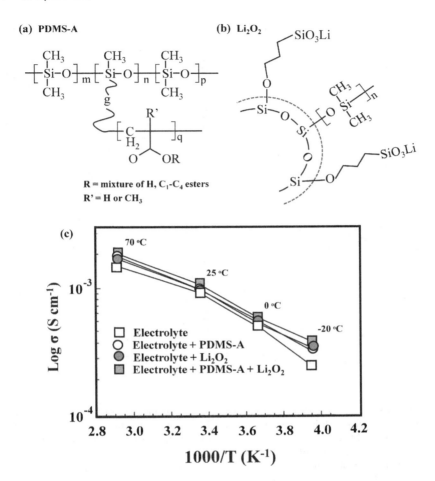

FIGURE 7.3 (a) Chemical structures of the additives PDMS-A and Li$_2$O$_2$, and (b) temperature dependence of ionic conductivity for the "electrolyte" solutions with and without the additives. Adapted and reproduced with permission from reference [43]. Copyright 2014 Elsevier.

methyl carbonate (EMC). They found that by increasing the EC content, the Li$^+$-ion kinetics are reduced at -40° C due to poor lithium transport characteristics and modest charge-transfer kinetics [46]; however, the EC ternary system is still considered effective for low-temperature performance of LIBs. Interfacial properties in the ternary mixtures are more favorable for the Li$^+$-ions intercalation and deintercalation [47]. Propylene carbonate (PC) is one of the organic solvents that can be used effectively with EC. A comparative study on the EC:EMC and EC:EMC:PC system was made. The study shows that the EC:EMC:PC ternary system exhibits superior low-temperature properties compared to the other because of the improved ionic conductivity along a stable SEI [48]. EC:PC:EMC (1:1:8) ternary system, consisting

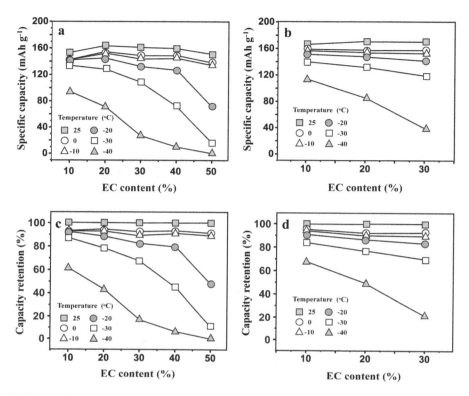

FIGURE 7.4 Variations of discharge capacity (a, b) and capacity retention (c, d) of graphite||NCA cells with EC content in EC:PC:EMC solvent mixtures at different temperatures. (a, c) 20% PC content (E1, E2, E3, E4, and E5) and (b) 10% PC content (E6, E7, and E8) in the solvent mixtures. Electrolyte used (E_W) is the mixture of 1 M $LiPF_6$ in EC:PC:EMC by weight and 0.05 M $CsPF_6$, where E1 = (5:2:3), E2 = (4:2:4), E3 = (3:2:5), E4 = (2:2:6), E5 = (1:2:7), E6 =(3:1:6), E 7=(2:1:7), and E8 = (1:1:8). Adapted and reproduced with permission from reference [50]. Copyright 2017 American Chemical Society.

of $LiPF_6$ salt and $CsPF_6$ additive, results in extended service temperature from -40° C to 60° C [49]. At -40° C, the system retained 68% of the room-temperature capacity and, even after 400 cycles, 82% capacity retention was observed. Figure 7.4 shows the variation of discharge capacity of the system with EC and PC content at low temperature. At -20 °C, the ionic conductivity decreases with EC content regardless of the presence of PC and it has been observed that less PC and more EMC is beneficial for high conductivity of electrolyte [49]. For instance, the discharge capacities and capacity retention exhibited by the system with 10%, 20%, and 30% EC content at -20° C are 150/91, 146.4/86.5, and 140.3 mAh g^{-1}/83.4%, respectively; at -30° C they are 138.7/84.2, 130.4/77.1, and 117.3 mAh g^{-1}/69.7 %, respectively; and at -40° C they are 112.3/68.1, 83.6/49.4, and 36.3 mAh g^{-1}/21.6 %, respectively in graphite/$LiNi_{0.8}OCo_{0.15}Al_{0.05}O_2$.

Low-Temperature LIBs

7.2.1.3 Room-Temperature Ionic Liquids for Low-Temperature LIBs

Room-temperature ionic liquids (RTILs) are salts that exist as liquids at room temperature. They are the novel electrolyte material that are thermally and chemically stable as well as nonflammable, and they exhibit very low vapor pressure and a wide electrochemical window [50]. Generally, RTILs are safer than conventional ILs, but some combinations perform poorly in terms of safety than conventional ones. One combination that did not perform well in terms of safety was 1-ethyl 3-methyl Imidazodium bis(fluorosulfonyl)imide (EMI-FSI) [51]. Li et al. [52] fabricated IL containing decorated PMMA nanoparticles with 1 M lithium triflouro sulfonyl imide (LiTFSI) by dissolving in a mixture of PC and methyl acetate. The unique grafting structure of IL on PMMA has a vital role in the enhancement of the low-temperature performance (Figure 7.5).

The scanning electron microscope (SEM) image of PMMA-IL-TFSI shows nanoparticles with an average particle size of 260 nm (Figure 7.6a). During

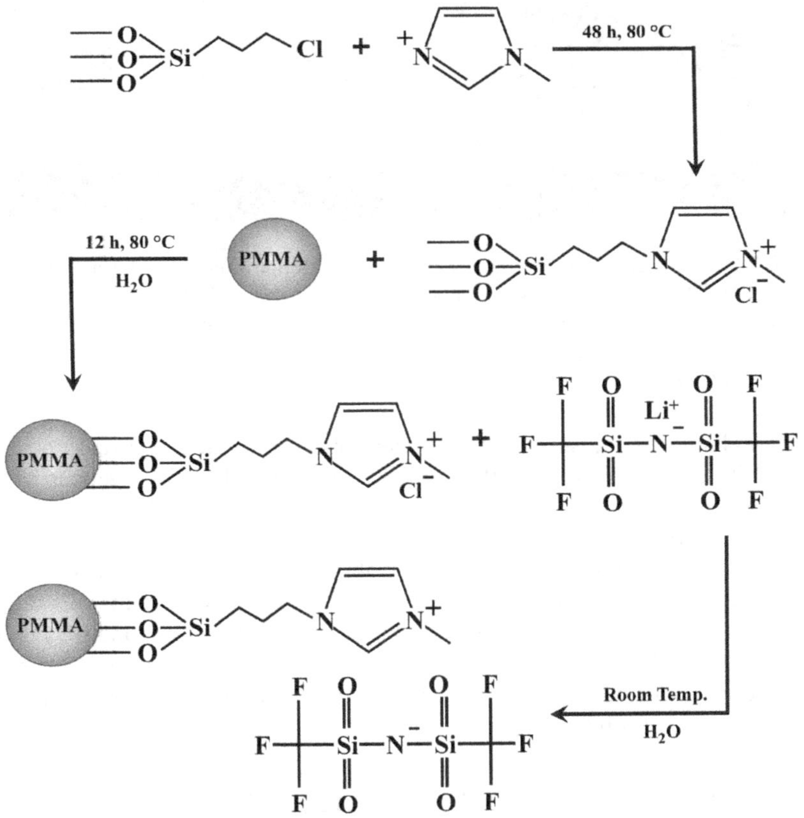

FIGURE 7.5 Schematic illustration on the synthesis strategy for the preparation of PMMA-IL-TFSI nanoparticles. Adapted and reproduced with permission from reference [52]. Copyright 2018 American Chemical Society.

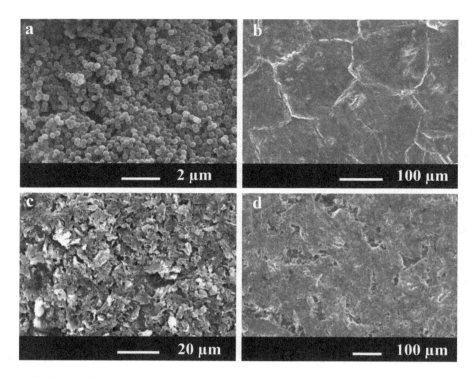

FIGURE 7.6 Field emission scanning electron microscope image on the morphology of (a) PMMA-IL-TFSI nanoparticles, Li anode after cycling at −20° C using electrolyte: (b) with PMMA-IL-TFSI, (c) without PMMA-IL-TFSI, and (d) after cycling at −40° C without PMMA-IL-TFSI. Adapted and reproduced with permission from reference [52]. Copyright 2018 American Chemical Society.

cycling, a change in the surface morphology of the lithium electrode is observed (Figure 7.6b–d), which indicates the influence of PMMA-IL-TFSI nanoparticles on the morphology of the electrode. This electrolyte forms a stable SEI film with high ionic conductivity. Ionic conductivity of about 9.15×10^{-4} S cm^{-1} was observed even at -20° C. Comparing the discharge capacity of polymer electrolyte with and without the IL at −20° C, high discharge capacity is observed for the system with ILs (80, 58, and 41 mAh g^{-1} at 0.5 C, 1 C, and 2 C) than without it (38, 18, and 0.1 mAh g^{-1} at 0.5 C, 1 C, and 2 C, respectively, LTO/Li cells). Table 7.1 shows the different electrolyte components and their mechanism in maintaining the low-temperature performance in electrolytes.

7.3 SEPARATORS FOR LOW-TEMPERATURE LIBs

Being a physical barrier between the electrodes, a separator system ensures the safety of LIBs. The main challenge of developing a separator is to implant both

TABLE 7.1

Electrolyte Components for the Low-Temperature Performance of Lithium-Ion Batteries

Compounds	Mechanism	References
Additives		
PDMS based additives	Resistant to the freezing of liquid	[43]
Lithium modified silica nano salt	electrolyte at low temperature	[44]
	Able to sustain a moderate SEI layer	
Lithium Salts		
Lithiumtetraflouroborate (LiBF$_4$)	Lower charge transfer resistance	[40]
Lithium bis(oxalate)borate	High stability at low temperature	[37, 38]
Solvents and Cosolvents		
Ethyl carbonate	Reducing the melting point of	[46]
Dimethyl carbonate	electrolyte, high conductivity of the	[45]
Propylene carbonate	SEI layer between the interface	

mechanical robustness and porosity or transport properties [53]. A safe separator should be stable, chemically inert to other materials, and it should facilitate ion transport inside the cell [54, 55]. Commonly used separators for LIBs include polyolefin, polypropylene, and polyethylene. Size and thickness of the separator is important in order to develop lightweight energy storage systems [56]. Another important property of a separator is its wettability, which necessitates ion transport by wetting with electrolytes [57]. The separators follow the shutdown mechanism that helps to limit the flow of temperature and to prevent venting in short circuited cells. Such a shutdown mechanism can easily be employed in a multilayer or multi-component separator in which low melting components are melted during heat development and which closes the micro pores in the separator, thereby ensuring thermal safety of the battery [56]. Separator properties depend mostly on the temperature and the strain rate. A separator should be thermally stable so that it will not shrink while varying temperature [58]. PMMA-TiO$_2$-coated PE composite membrane used as a separator shows low shrinkage on thermal variation. The surface coating provides homogeneous distribution of the nanospheres that results in a porous structure (Figure 7.7a, b). With the introduction of thermally stable titanate particles, the thermal shrinking resistance of the separator is enhanced, moreover the wettability of this separator was observed to be better than PE membranes (Figure 7.7 c, d). The properties of separators can be further enhanced by using wetting agents that can form grafting of hydrophilic functional groups on the surface and in pores. Surfactants can also improve the wettability but are unable to enhance the retention of the electrolyte [59–63].

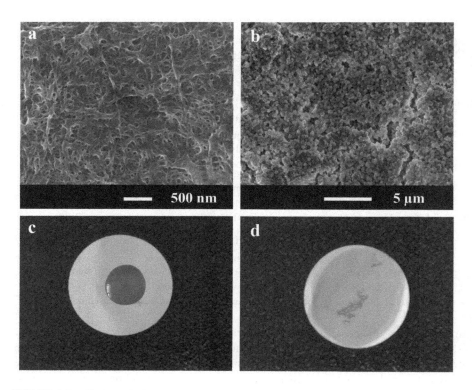

FIGURE 7.7 Field emission scanning electron microscope (FE-SEM) images on the surface morphology of separators: (a) PE membrane, and (b) TiO$_2$-PMMA/PE composite membrane, optical images of (c) PE membrane, and (d) TiO$_2$-PMMA/PE composite membrane separator in contact with electrolyte solution. Adapted and reproduced with permission from reference [62]. Copyright 2017 ESG.

7.4 CONCLUSION

The low-temperature performance of LIBs is determined by the components used in it. Electrolytes are the crucial component in a battery and exhibit a decisive role in determining the performance in cold environments. The limits in ionic conductivity that arise by the viscous nature of the electrolytes and internal resistance of the battery inversely affect the storage system and decay the energy storing capacity. In order to enhance the low-temperature performance, different modifications are proposed for the electrolyte components, including organic solvents, lithium salts, and polymer matrices. The modified system can promote the ionic conduction inside the polymer electrolyte system, even at low temperatures, that will make a sustainable energy storage device that can be used efficiently, even in low temperatures. Different lithium salts and a combination of salts and different organic solvents are used to improve performance at lower temperatures. Additionally, RTILs are essential to performance in both high and low temperatures. Combinations of ILs with

Low-Temperature LIBs

certain organic electrolytes has been shown to be the best medium to ensure enough ionic mobility even with the reduction in working temperature. Therefore, properly selecting and modifying battery components, it is conceivable to accomplish the high performance even at low temperatures.

ACKNOWLEDGMENT

Authors Dr. Jabeen Fatima M. J. and Dr. Prasanth Raghavan, would like to acknowledge Kerala State Council for Science, Technology and Environment (KSCSTE), Kerala, India, for financial assistance.

REFERENCES

1. Zhang F, Zhang T, Yang X, et al. (2013) A high-performance supercapacitor-battery hybrid energy storage device based on graphene-enhanced electrode materials with ultrahigh energy density. *Energy Environ Sci* 6:1623. doi: 10.1039/c3ee40509e
2. Li J, Du Z, Ruther RE, et al. (2017) Toward low-cost, high-energy density, and high-power density lithium-ion batteries. *Jom* 69:1484–1496. doi: 10.1007/s11837-017-2404-9
3. Horiba T, Maeshima T, Matsumura T, et al. (2005) Applications of high power density lithium ion batteries. *J Power Sources* 146:107–110. doi: 10.1016/j.jpowsour.2005.03.205
4. Mauger A, Julien C (2014) Surface modifications of electrode materials for lithium-ion batteries: Status and trends. *Ionics (Kiel)* 20:751–787. doi: 10.1007/s11581-014-1131-2
5. Cano ZP, Banham D, Ye S, et al. (2018) Batteries and fuel cells for emerging electric vehicle markets. *Nat Energy* 3:279–289. doi: 10.1038/s41560-018-0108-1
6. Belov D, Yang MH (2008) Failure mechanism of Li-ion battery at overcharge conditions. *J Solid State Electrochem* 12:885–894. doi: 10.1007/s10008-007-0449-3
7. Maleki H, Howard JN (2006) Effects of overdischarge on performance and thermal stability of a Li-ion cell. *J Power Sources* 160:1395–1402. doi: 10.1016/j.jpowsour. 2006.03.043
8. Wang K (2017) Study on low temperature performance of Li ion battery. *OALib* 04:1–12. doi: 10.4236/oalib.1104036
9. Zhang J, Ge H, Li Z, Ding Z (2015) Internal heating of lithium-ion batteries using alternating current based on the heat generation model in frequency domain. *J Power Sources* 273:1030–1037. doi: 10.1016/j.jpowsour.2014.09.181
10. Song HS, Jeong JB, Lee BH, et al. (2012) Experimental study on the effects of preheating a battery in a low-temperature environment. (2012) *IEEE Vehicle Power and Propulsion Conference (VPPC)* , 9-12 October, Seoul, Republic of Korea, pp. 1198–1201. doi: 10.1109/VPPC.2012.6422509
11. Zhang SS, Xu K, Jow TR (2002) A new approach toward improved low temperature performance of Li-ion battery. *Electrochem Commun* 4:928–932. doi: 10.1016/ S1388-2481(02)00490-3
12. Zhang SS, Xu K, Jow TR (2007) Low temperature performance of graphite electrode in Li-ion cells. *J Comb Chem* 9:20–28. doi: 10.1021/cc0601175
13. Petzl M, Kasper M, Danzer MA (2015) Lithium plating in a commercial lithium-ion battery - A low-temperature aging study. *J Power Sources* 275:799–807. doi: 10.1016/j. jpowsour.2014.11.065
14. Ketabi S, Lian K (2012) Effect of nano-fillers on the conductivity and structural properties of $EMIHSO_4$-based polymer electrolytes. The Electrochemical Society 23rd ECS Meething. Toronto, Canada, May 12-16, 2013, Abstarct # 1427:.

15. Yap YL, You AH, Teo LL, Hanapei H (2013) Inorganic filler sizes effect on ionic conductivity in polyethylene oxide (PEO) composite polymer electrolyte. *Int J Electrochem Sci* 8:2154–2163.
16. Sudiarti T, Wahyuningrum D, Bundjali B, Made Arcana I (2017) Mechanical strength and ionic conductivity of polymer electrolyte membranes prepared from cellulose acetate-lithium perchlorate. *IOP Conf Ser Mater Sci Eng* 223:0–8. doi: 10.1088/1757-899X/223/1/012052
17. Konnik OV, Shul'gin VF, Bekirova ZZ, et al. (2014) Coordination compounds of dysprosium(III) with 3-methyl-1-phenyl-4-formylpyrazol-5-one diacyldihydrazones. *Russ J Inorg Chem* 59:1237–1243. doi: 10.1134/S0036023614110126
18. Porcarelli L, Gerbaldi C, Bella F, Nair JR (2016) Super soft all-ethylene oxide polymer electrolyte for safe all-solid lithium batteries. *Sci Rep* 6:1–14. doi: 10.1038/srep19892
19. Wang SH, Lin YY, Teng CY, et al. (2016) Immobilization of anions on polymer matrices for gel electrolytes with high conductivity and stability in lithium ion batteries. *ACS Appl Mater Interfaces* 8:14776–14787. doi: 10.1021/acsami.6b01753
20. Zhang R, Chen Y, Montazami R (2015) Ionic liquid-doped gel polymer electrolyte for flexible lithium-ion polymer batteries. *Materials (Basel)* 8:2735–2748. doi: 10.3390/ma8052735
21. Kumar M (2018) A conceptual review on gel polymer electrolytes and its conduction mechanism. *Pharma Innov J* 7:194–198.
22. Kim YT, Smotkin ES (2002) The effect of plasticizers on transport and electrochemical properties of PEO-based electrolytes for lithium rechargeable batteries. *Solid State Ionics* 149:29–37. doi: 10.1016/S0167-2738(02)00130-3
23. Krejza O, Velická J, Sedlaříková M, Vondrák J (2008) The presence of nanostructured Al_2O_3 in PMMA-based gel electrolytes. *J Power Sources* 178:774–778. doi: 10.1016/j.jpowsour.2007.11.018
24. Stephan AM, Nahm KS, Anbu Kulandainathan M, et al. (2006) Poly(vinylidene fluoride-hexafluoropropylene) (PVdF-HFP) based composite electrolytes for lithium batteries. *Eur Polym J* 42:1728–1734. doi: 10.1016/j.eurpolymj.2006.02.006
25. Huang H, Wunder SL (2001) Preparation of microporous PVDF based polymer electrolytes. *J Power Sources* 97–98:649–653. doi: 10.1016/S0378-7753(01)00579-1
26. Ramesh S, Yahaya AH, Arof AK (2002) Dielectric behaviour of PVC-based polymer electrolytes. *Solid State Ionics* 152–153:291–294. doi: 10.1016/S0167-2738(02)00311-9
27. Rohan R, Sun Y, Cai W, et al. (2014) Functionalized polystyrene based single ion conducting gel polymer electrolyte for lithium batteries. *Solid State Ionics* 268:294–299. doi: 10.1016/j.ssi.2014.10.013
28. Smart MC, Ratnakumar BV, Behar A, et al. (2007) Gel polymer electrolyte lithium-ion cells with improved low temperature performance. *J Power Sources* 165:535–543. doi: 10.1016/j.jpowsour.2006.10.038
29. Kim JK, Niedzicki L, Scheers J, et al. (2013) Characterization of N-butyl-N-methyl-pyrrolidinium bis(trifluoromethanesulfonyl)imide-based polymer electrolytes for high safety lithium batteries. *J Power Sources* 224:93–98. doi: 10.1016/j.jpowsour.2012.09.029
30. Nie M, Lucht BL (2014) Role of lithium salt on solid electrolyte interface (SEI) formation and structure in lithium ion batteries. *J Electrochem Soc* 161:A1001–A1006. doi: 10.1149/2.054406jes
31. Yang H, Zhuang GV, Ross Jr PN (2006) Thermal stability of LiPF 6 salt and Li-ion battery electrolytes containing LiPF 6 Hui Yang. *J Power Sources* 161:573–579. doi.org/10.1016/j.jpowsour.2006.03.058
32. Zinigrad E, Larush-Asraf L, Gnanaraj JS, et al. (2005), On the thermal stability of $LiPF_6$. *Thermochimica Acta*, 438: 184–191. https://doi.org/10.1016/j.tca.2005.09.006

33. Zhang SS, Xu K, Jow TR (2003) Low-temperature performance of Li-ion cells with a LiBF$_4$based electrolyte. *J Solid State Electrochem* 7:147–151. doi: 10.1007/s10008-002-0300-9
34. Zhang SS, Xu K, Jow TR (2002) Study of LiBF[sub 4] as an electrolyte salt for a Li-ion battery. *J Electrochem Soc* 149:A586. doi: 10.1149/1.1466857
35. Jow TR, Ding MS, Xu K, et al. (2003) Nonaqueous electrolytes for wide-temperature-range operation of Li-ion cells. *J Power Sources* 119–121:343–348. doi: 10.1016/S0378-7753(03)00153-8
36. Ellis LD, Xia J, Louli AJ, Dahn JR (2016) Effect of substituting LiBF$_4$ for LiPF$_6$ in high voltage lithium-ion cells containing electrolyte additives. *J Electrochem Soc* 163:A1686–A1692. doi: 10.1149/2.0851608jes
37. Xu K, Zhang S, Jow TR, et al. (2002) LiBOB as salt for lithium-ion batteries. A possible solution for high temperature operation. *Electrochem Solid-State Lett* 5:A26. doi: 10.1149/1.1426042
38. Zhang SS, Xu K, Jow TR (2003) Low-temperature performance of Li-ion cells with a LiBF4-based electrolyte. *J Solid State Electrochem* 7:147–151. doi: 10.1007/s10008-002-0300-9
39. Hu M, Wei J, Xing L, Zhou Z (2012) Effect of lithium difluoro(oxalate)borate (LiDFOB) additive on the performance of high-voltage lithium-ion batteries. *J Appl Electrochem* 42:291–296. doi: 10.1007/s10800-012-0398-0
40. Zhao Q, Zhang Y, Tang F, et al. (2017) Mixed salts of lithium difluoro (oxalate) borate and lithium tetrafluorobotate electrolyte on low-temperature performance for lithium-ion batteries. *J Electrochem Soc* 164:A1873–A1880. doi: 10.1149/2.0851709jes
41. Mandal BK, Padhi AK, Shi Z, et al. (2006) New low temperature electrolytes with thermal runaway inhibition for lithium-ion rechargeable batteries. *J Power Sources* 162:690–695. doi: 10.1016/j.jpowsour.2006.06.053
42. Hamenu L, Lee HS, Latifatu M, et al. (2016) Lithium-silica nanosalt as a low-temperature electrolyte additive for lithium-ion batteries. *Curr Appl Phys* 16:611–617. doi: 10.1016/j.cap.2016.03.012
43. Kim KM, Ly NV, Won JH, et al. (2014) Improvement of lithium-ion battery performance at low temperature by adopting polydimethylsiloxane-based electrolyte additives. *Electrochim Acta* 136:182–188. doi: 10.1016/j.electacta.2014.05.054
44. Won JH, Lee HS, Hamenu L, et al. (2016) Improvement of low-temperature performance by adopting polydimethylsiloxane-g-polyacrylate and lithium-modified silica nanosalt as electrolyte additives in lithium-ion batteries. *J Ind Eng Chem* 37:325–329. doi: 10.1016/j.jiec.2016.03.045
45. Ein-Eli Y (1997) Li-ion battery electrolyte formulated for low-temperature applications. *J Electrochem Soc* 144:823. doi: 10.1149/1.1837495
46. Plichta EJ, Hendrickson M, Thompson R, et al. (2001) Development of low temperature Li-ion electrolytes for NASA and DoD applications. *J Power Sources* 94:160–162. doi: 10.1016/S0378-7753(00)00578-4
47. Smart MC (1999) Electrolytes for low-temperature lithium batteries based on ternary mixtures of aliphatic carbonates. *J Electrochem Soc* 146:486. doi: 10.1149/1.1391633
48. Zhang SS, Xu K, Allen JL, Jow TR (2002) Effect of propylene carbonate on the low temperature performance of Li-ion cells. *J Power Sources* 110:216–221. doi: 10.1016/S0378-7753(02)00272-0
49. Li Q, Jiao S, Luo L, et al. (2017) Wide-temperature electrolytes for lithium-ion batteries. *ACS Appl Mater Interfaces* 9:18826–18835. doi: 10.1021/acsami.7b04099
50. Yang J, Wang J, Wang D, et al. (2012) 3D porous LiFePO$_4$ graphene hybrid cathodes with enhanced performance for Li-ion batteries. *J Power Sources* 208:340–344. doi: 10.1016/j.jpowsour.2012.02.032

51. Wang Y, Zaghib K, Guerfi A, et al. (2007) Accelerating rate calorimetry studies of the reactions between ionic liquids and charged lithium ion battery electrode materials. *Electrochim Acta* 52:6346–6352. doi: 10.1016/j.electacta.2007.04.067
52. Li Y, Wong KW, Dou Q, et al. (2018) Improvement of lithium-ion battery performance at low temperature by adopting ionic liquid-decorated PMMA nanoparticles as electrolyte component. *ACS Appl Energy Mater* 1:2664–2670. doi: 10.1021/acsaem.8b00355
53. Gor GY, Cannarella J, Leng CZ, et al. (2015) Swelling and softening of lithium-ion battery separators in electrolyte solvents. *J Power Sources* 294:167–172. doi: 10.1016/j.jpowsour.2015.06.028
54. Song M, Kim Y-T, Kim YT, et al. (2003) Thermally stable gel polymer electrolytes. *J Electrochem Soc* 150:A439. doi: 10.1149/1.1556592
55. Zhang H, Wang X, Liang Y (2015) Preparation and characterization of a lithium-ion battery separator from cellulose nanofibers. *Heliyon* 1:1–16. doi: 10.1016/j.heliyon.2015.e00032
56. Rajagopalan Kannan DR, Terala PK, Moss PL, Weatherspoon MH (2018) Analysis of the separator thickness and porosity on the performance of lithium-ion batteries. *Int J Electrochem* 2018:1–7. doi: 10.1155/2018/1925708
57. Zhang, Z., Yuan, W., & Li, L. (2018). Enhanced wettability and thermal stability of nano-SiO$_2$/poly (vinyl alcohol)-coated polypropylene composite separators for lithium-ion batteries. *Particuology*, 37: 91–98. doi.org/10.1016/j.partic.2017.10.001
58. Avdeev I, Martinsen M, Francis A (2014) Rate- and temperature-dependent material behavior of a multilayer polymer battery separator. *J Mater Eng Perform* 23:315–325. doi: 10.1007/s11665-013-0743-4
59. Taskier HT (1982) Hydrophilic polymer coated microporous membranes capable of use as a battery separator, U.S. Patent No. 4,359,510. Washington, DC: U.S. Patent and Trademark Office..
60. Gineste JL (1995) Polypropylene separator grafted with hydrophilic monomers for lithium batteries. *J Memb Sci* 107:155–164. doi: 10.1016/0376-7388(95)00112-P
61. Ko JM, Min EG, Kim DW, et al. (2004) Thin-film type Li-ion battery, using a polyethylene separator grafted with glycidyl methacrylate. *Electrochim. Acta*, 50: 367–370. doi.org/10.1016/j.electacta.2004.01.127
62. Xi Y, Zhang P, Zhang H, et al. (2017) Membrane separators coated by TiO2-PMMA with low thermal shrinkage rate for lithium-ion batteries. *Int J Electrochem Sci* 12:5421–5430. doi: 10.20964/2017.06.69
63. Arora P, Zhang Z (2004) Battery separators. *Chem Rev* 104:4419–4462. doi: 10.1021/cr020738u

8 Electrolytes for Magnesium-Ion Batteries
Next Generation Energy Storage Solutions for Powering Electric Vehicles

Akhila Das, Anjumole P. Thomas, Neethu T.M. Balakrishnan, Jishnu N.S., Jabeen Fatima M. J., Jou-Hyeon Ahn, Prasanth Raghavan

CONTENTS

8.1 Introduction 177
    8.1.1 Mg-ion Battery Chemistry 178
8.2 Electrolytes for Mg-ion Batteries 179
    8.2.1 Liquid Electrolytes with Inorganic Salts for Mg-ion Batteries 179
    8.2.2 Organic/Inorganic Halo-Salt-Based Electrolytes for Mg-ion Batteries 180
    8.2.3 Polymer Electrolytes for Mg-ion Batteries 182
        8.2.3.1 Solid Polymer Electrolytes for Mg-ion Batteries 183
        8.2.3.2 Gel Polymer Electrolytes for Mg-ion Batteries 183
        8.2.3.3 Polymer Composite Electrolytes for Mg-ion Batteries 185
    8.2.4 Room-Temperature Ionic Liquid-Based Electrolytes for Mg-ion Batteries 186
8.3 Conclusion 187
Acknowledgment 188
References 188

8.1 INTRODUCTION

Rechargeable batteries are still in their infancy meeting the requirements of energy storage applications such as electric vehicles, portable energy storage devices, etc. [1, 2]. A need for sustainable and economically viable energy storage devices is crucial. Currently, lithium-ion batteries rule the electrochemical world, but they are handicapped by their risk of hazards and cost [3]. Magnesium-ion batteries are an alternative system for lithium-ion batteries and are superior in terms of safety. Redox

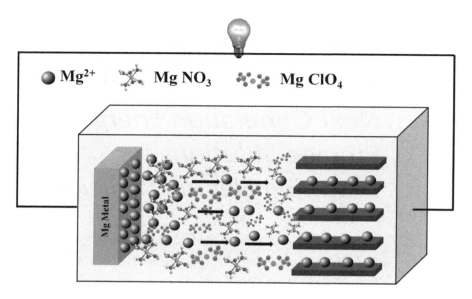

FIGURE 8.1 Schematic illustration of the structure and working principles of an Mg-ion battery (charging cycle).

potential of magnesium (Mg) is -2.38 V [4], which is greater than lithium (-3.04 V), paving the way for an easy charge–discharge process. The charging process of batteries leads to the intercalation of ions (Li$^+$/Mg^{2+}) in the cathodes; the volume of occupancy for two lithium (Li$^+$) ions is higher than that of a single Mg^{2+} ion [4, 5]. Therefore, because of the bivalency of Mg ions, more charge can be stored in a minimum volume, which is an added advantage for miniaturization of energy storage devices. During lithiation process, volume expansion occurs, and, as a result, structural deformation takes place in the process of delithation at the cathode, decreasing the electric contact and cyclability [6–8]. Alkali metals in anodes are not safe because they are reactive and have the potential for dendrite formation. Mg metals are compatible with anodes and are safe; a schematic diagram of Mg-ion battery is shown in Figure 8.1. Research on Mg-ion batteries has impelled its importance in many industries and academic institutions. Advanced Project Research Agency, Pellion Technologies, and Toyota Research Institute in North America initiated the development of Mg-ion batteries. Pellion Technologies focused mainly on the core issue related to Mg-ion deposition/dissolution and found an alternative method to tackle problems [8, 9]. At the same time, Toyota Research Institute's research focused mainly on developing high-energy, high-density Mg-sulfur (Mg-S) batteries.

8.1.1 Mg-ion Battery Chemistry

The basic chemistry behind the Mg-ion battery mechanism is similar to that of the lithium-ion battery. Mg-ion batteries consist of (i) anodes made of Mg metal/metal alloy; (b) electrolytes, which can be organic liquid electrolytes, non-nucleophilic

Magnesium-Ion Batteries

electrolytes, polymer electrolytes, etc.; (d) cathode materials capable of reacting with Mg ions; and (d) separators, such as microglass fiber, glass fiber, polypropylene non-woven membranes, etc. [10, 11]. Cathodes are layered materials capable of intercalating Mg ions, whereas anodes are materials that release Mg cations. During the charging process, electrons are ejected from the cathode through the external circuit, whereas Mg ions will pass to anodes through the electrolytes. During the discharging process, the reverse process takes place in which electrons move from anodes to cathodes through the external circuit. The deintercalation of Mg ions occurs during this time. The basic mechanism behind charging and discharging is given in Equations 8.1 and 8.2:

$$\text{Anode:} \text{Mg} \rightarrow \text{Mg}^{2+} + 2e^- \tag{8.1}$$

$$\text{Cathode:} \text{Mg}^{2+} + 2e^- \rightarrow \text{Mg} \tag{8.2}$$

Further research on Mg-ion batteries is favored because Mg metals are safer than lithium metals and it does not cause dendrite formation. However, when Mg metals come in contact with conventional organic solvents, a thin passivation layer develops on the surface of the Mg metal that is impermeable to the Mg-ion movement that imparts the electrochemical performance of the battery. Thus, the type of electrolytes chosen has a major role in the development of a sustainable battery. Therefore, researchers are focusing mainly on the development of suitable electrolytes that could avoid the problems experienced with conventional electrolytes.

8.2 ELECTROLYTES FOR Mg-ion BATTERIES

Electrolytes are the core part leading the development of Mg-ion battery. The type of electrolyte chosen has a major role in determining the electrochemical stability and Mg metal compatibility of the battery. Salt–solvent interactions, chemical reactions at electrode–electrolyte interfaces, migration mechanisms of Mg^{2+}, etc. are the major concerns when choosing electrolytes [5, 12, 13]. The major classification of electrolytes in Mg-ion batteries are given in the following sections.

8.2.1 LIQUID ELECTROLYTES WITH INORGANIC SALTS FOR Mg-ion BATTERIES

Gregory et al. [14] first synthesized organic electrolytes and anodes that are capable of Mg electrodeposition. The compounds, such as $Mg(BBu_2Ph_2)_2$, $Mg(ClO_4)_2$, $Mg(BF_4)_2$, and C_2H_5MgCl, were chosen and they inferred that the bulky groups connected with Mg ions have a tendency to behave in an ionic nature and share in a covalent nature. Among these compounds, reversible intercalation of Mg^{2+} ions with high specific capacity and energy densities are low. Solute–solvent interaction in electrode materials is also very low. Similarly, the type of solvent also has a major role. Aurbach et al. [15] chose tetrahydrofuran (THF), butyl triphenyl borates, and tetraphenyl borate to investigate the behavior of solvent in the electrochemical performance of the battery. Triphenyl borate and butyl triphenyl borates have low solubility. Similarly, the effect of organohalo-aluminate-based electrolytes were chosen by same group [16]. Organohalo aluminates such as $Mg(AlCl_3R)_2$, $Mg(AlCl_2R'R)_2$, are some of the electrolytes that exhibit high anodic stability. The use of organohalo aluminates along with THF solvent the electrolyte shows better ionic conductivity and electrochemical properties however the presence halide group in organohalo aluminates, for example Cl group in $Mg(AlCl_3R)_2$, $Mg(AlCl_2R'R)_2$ leads to corrosion of the electrodes and battery case. The first prototype cell was assembled with $Mg/0.25$ M $Mg(AlCl_2BuEt)_2$ /Chevrel phase and exhibited specific capacity of 122mAh g^{-1} (at current of 0.3 mAcm^{-2}). Replacing alkyl groups with phenyl groups increases anodic stability up to 3.3 V vs. Mg. Alkyl parts and halogen parts play an important role in the complex adsorption phenomena. Similarly, a group of compounds, including organomagnesium and amidomagnesium, dissolved in THF, for which good oxidative stability was observed by $Mg(BBu_2Ph_2)_2$ compounds [17]. Peter et al. [18] reported different metal oxides and sulfides dissolved in $MgClO_4$, whereas V_2O_5 have similar morphological characteristics of TiO_2. This matrix provides high coulombic efficiency because the water molecules in the electrolytes allow intercalation of Mg ions. Though many studies using $MgClO_4$ with different compounds were investigated, incorporation of ionic liquid is characterized with CoO_3 as working electrodes, as reported by Sutto et al. [19]. Cations of 1, 2-dimethyl-3-R-imidazolium with R = butyl (MMBI) or octyl (MMOI) ionic liquid was utilized with anion as bis(trifluoromethanesulfonyl)imide (TFSI). Though $MgClO_4$ is a powerful oxidizer, it has better solubility in ionic liquids compared to that of other electrolytes. Of these combinations, MMOITFSI provides the widest electrochemical stability window, although it has lower ionic conductivity. Figure 8.2 shows a schematic diagram of the three- and two-electrode systems. Copper foil/double-sided tape electrode intercalating Mg^{2+}/CoO_3 was shown below inferring CoO_3 is not suitable for the choice of anode materials (Figure 8.2).

Later, $MgClO_4$ was found to be incompatible with anode materials and borohydride-based materials appeared as common, which was first discovered by Mohtadi et al. [21] in which halide-free materials were used to avoid corrosion. Different solvents, such as THF and dimethyl ether (DME), were used, in which DME provides better solubility, low potential and high current density. Shao et al. [22] explained the detailed coordination chemistry in $MgBH_4$ with different ethereal solvents. Since electrochemical performance of Mg closely related to coulombic efficiency, denticity and donating strength of ethereal solvent is vital and these factors influences the thermodynamic as well as kinetic behavior on Mg. A solvated Mg complex was formed by oxygen donor denticity. New electrolytes are able to perform 100% coulombic efficiency with stable cycling performance.

8.2.2 Organic/Inorganic Halo-Salt-Based Electrolytes for Mg-ion Batteries

Organohalo aluminate systems were first introduced by Aurbach et al. [23], introducing different solvents, such as glymes, THF, polyethers, I,3-dioxine etc. Different $Mg(AX_{4-n}R_n)_2$ complexes were chosen [A = Al, B, Sb, P, As, Fe;

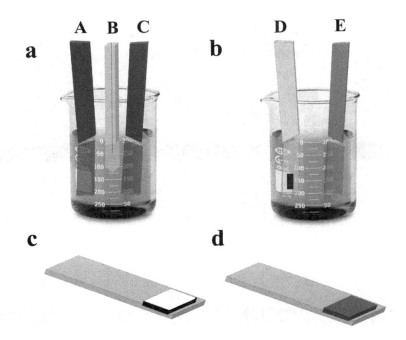

FIGURE 8.2 (a) Schematic illustration on the three electrode system used for the ionic conductivity measurements and electrochemical characterization ionic liquid characterization, (i) working electrode (glassy carbon), (ii) reference electrode (Vyccor tipped Ag/Ag+), and (iii) counter electrode (graphite rod), (b) two-electrode cell collecting charge–discharge cell, (iv) gold foil with CoO₃, and (v) anode (Mg foil), (c) copper foil electrode with graphitic tape, and (d) removing protecting backing and cathodic material being pressed. Adapted and reproduced with permission from reference [20]. Copyright 2012 Elsevier.

R = butyl, ethyl, phenyl, and benzyl; X = Cl, Br, and F]. The presence of chlorine increases ionic conductivity, and high anodic stability among different combinations of AlCl₂Et and Bu₂R mixtures delivers better efficiency. Because a matter of corrosion persisted in AlCl₃, AlOPh₃ was introduced by Nelson et al. [24] with a 1:4 ratio of AlOPh₃:PhMgCl. Later on, Barlie et al. [11] investigated the chemistry behind the Mg-ion stripping, deposition, dissolution, and operating mechanisms of organohalo aluminates with Grignard reagent of EtMgBr. Figure 8.3 shows gold nanoparticles deposited in the Mg metal after the first and 50th cycle. The morphology difference was noted only with EtMgBr, which appears to have cracked in the 50th cycle.

Inorganic halide-based electrolytes were synthesized with a non-nucleophilic source of MgCl₂ and Lewis acid, such as AlCl₃, AlPh₃, and AlEtCl₂ [25]. Both MgCl₂-AlEtCl₂ and MgCl₂-AlCl₃ are compatible with sulfur atoms and, therefore, can be used in Mg-S batteries. Robert et al. [9] chose the same system using different solvents having anodic stability greater than 3.1 V, including THF and DME. The Mg aluminum chloride complex was formed by an acid-based reaction similar

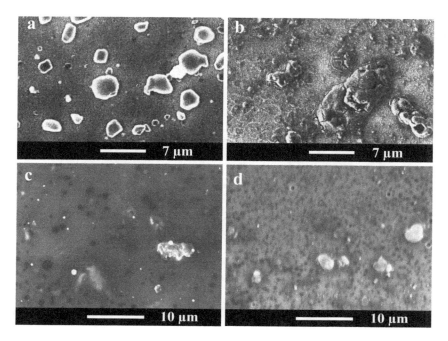

FIGURE 8.3 FE-SEM images on surface morphology of Au electrodes after charge–discharge cycling: with ethylene Mg bromide electrolyte (EtMgBr), (a) first cycle, and (b) 50th cycle, with organo haloaluminate electrolyte (Mg(AlCl$_2$EtBu)$_2$), (c) first cycle, and (d) 50th cycle. Adapted and reproduced with permission from reference [11]. Copyright 2014 Elsevier.

to that of transmetalation of a Grignard-based complex. Equation 8.3 represents the reaction:

$$mMgCl_2 + nAlCl_3 \rightarrow Mg_mAl_nCl_{[(2*m)+(3*n)]} \qquad (8.3)$$

Inorganic salts are capable of forming highly reversible Mg deposition. Homoleptic dialkoxide improves performance of halide ions containing Mg ions. Bulkier phenyl groups reduce deposition overpotential, low cycling performance, and cell impedance. Homoleptic compounds are a class of compounds containing Mg (HMDS)$_2$, Mg dialkoxide, and Mg bisamide compounds, but the reversible plating of halide-free Mg compounds is poor. Mg (OCPh$_3$)$_2$:AlCl$_3$ is reactive and imparts low deposition overpotentials. It is inferred that adding a small amount of alkoxide increases anodic stability and improves deposition morphologies [26].

8.2.3 Polymer Electrolytes for Mg-ion Batteries

Safety is an important criterion for the fabrication of all types of batteries. Most of the conventional liquid electrolytes are incapable of solving this issue. In this scenario, researchers developed polymer electrolytes that are an excellent substitute for

Magnesium-Ion Batteries

the organic electrolytes in batteries. The major highlights of polymer electrolytes are lightweight, flexible, noncombustible reaction products that avoid internal short circuiting and leakage [27, 28]. Polymer electrolytes, such as polyethylene oxide (PEO) [29], polyacrylonitrile (PAN) [30], polyvinylidene difluoride (PVdF) [31], polyvinyl acetate (PVAc) [32], etc., have been used in experiments in lithium-ion batteries. Solution casting [33], hot-press method [34], phase-inversion technique [35], and electrospinning [36] are some of the techniques used to prepare polymer electrolytes. The well-established polymer electrolytes in lithium-ion batteries led to the extension of the studies in Mg-ion batteries as well.

8.2.3.1 Solid Polymer Electrolytes for Mg-Ion Batteries

Oligo (ethylene oxide) grafted polymethyl acrylate-(PMA) based solid-polymer electrolyte was the first synthesized polymer electrolyte in Mg-ion batteries [37]. This polymer matrix provides ionic conductivity of 0.4 mS cm^{-1} even at 60° C, but the discharge capacity was very low. Additives such as plasticizers are helpful for the improvement of ionic conductivity. Later, Yoshimoto et al. [38] introduced a PEO-PMA blended matrix with the addition of plasticizers, providing an insignificant increase in the electrochemical performance. Sheha et al. [39] reported complexation polymeric materials that can also upgrade the electrical and electrochemical performance of the battery. $(PVA)_{0.7}(NaBr)_{0.3}$ solid polymer electrolyte doped with sulphuric acid (SA)enhances the chemical and mechanical stability of the polymer matrix owing to the strong intra molecular proton switch mechanism. $(PVA)_{0.7}(NaBr)_{0.3}$:xM (SA) delivers highest ionic conductivity of 6 10^{-4} Scm^{-1} at 2.6M SA addition and then decreases. However specific capacity was less (~90 mAh g^{-1}) compared to their theoretical capacity (~300 mAh g^{-1}) Biodegradable polymers are environmentally benign materials, and the introduction of PVA to PVP doped with Mg nitrates offers high thermal and mechanical stability even though it contributes less ionic mobility [40]. On increasing doped salts, ionic conductivity increases to an extent and then decreases because of the formation of ion pairs, triplets, etc. (Figure 8.4a). The ionic transference number is 0.98 measured from direct current (DC) polarization technique (Figure 8.4b). Similarly, studies also report blending PVA with PVdF-co-HFP (poly(vinylidene fluoride-co-hexafluoropropene) that has had polymer applied in dye sensitized solar cells for better electrical performance [41].

8.2.3.2 Gel Polymer Electrolytes for Mg-Ion Batteries

Gel-polymer electrolytes are promising candidates for the next generation of battery electrolytes. The major advantages of gel-polymer electrolytes over solid-polymer electrolytes include their easy ion mobility, flexibility, high ionic conductivity, and safety. Gel-polymer electrolytes, which are created by incorporating Mg salts mixed with a plasticizer, such as alkyl carbonates, were introduced by Yoshimoto et al. [42]. Flexible, free-standing gel polymer electrolytes were prepared by blending PEO with PMA (Figure 8.5b) and doping salt, as magnesium imide delivers ionic conductivity of 2.8 mS cm^{-1}. Impedance spectra of (PEO/PMA)/(EC'/ DMC)/ $Mg[(CF_3SO_2)_2N]_2$ (25/5) at 60° C is given in Figure 8.5a. The prototype cell assembled with (PEO/PMA)-(EC-DMC))$Mg[(CF_3SO_2)2N]_2$ polymer gel, Mg V_2O_5/ MnO_2

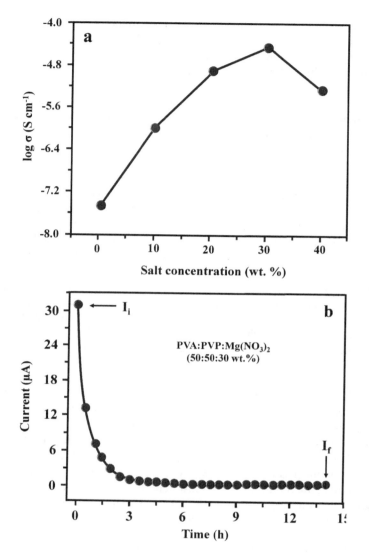

FIGURE 8.4 Properties of polyvinyl alcohol/polyvinyl pyrrolidone (PVA/PVP) (50:50) polymer blend electrolyte: (a) effect of Mg nitrate content (wt%) on the ionic conductivity, and (b) DC polarization versus current plot. Adapted and reproduced with permission from reference [40]. Copyright 2015 Elsevier.

electrodes delivers speciifc capacity of 60 mAh g[-1] where as with MgV_2O_5/ V_2O_5 exhibits specific capacity of 140 mAh g[-1] (0.1 mA cm[-1]); however, both the cells shows an open circuit voltage of 2.3 V. The rechargeablility of V_2O_5 cathode material is higher than MnO_2 and hence V_2O_5 was considered as suitable candidate for this polymer matrix.

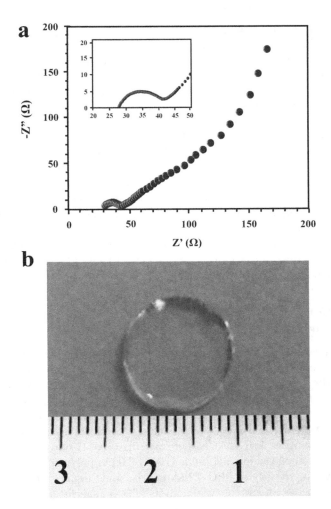

FIGURE 8.5 (a) AC-impedance of PEO/grafted polymethyl acrylate (PEO/*g*-PMA) polymer blend electrolyte, and (b) optical image depicting the transparency and physical appearance of PEO/PMA blend electrolyte with Mg triflate (Mg[(CF$_3$SO$_2$)$_2$N]$_2$) in EC/DMC at room temperature. Adapted and reproduced with permission from reference [42]. Copyright 2003 Elsevier.

8.2.3.3 Polymer Composite Electrolytes for Mg-Ion Batteries

Composite gel polymer electrolytes are materials that contain polymers, doping salt, and inorganic fillers for better structural stability, ionic conductivity, mobility, etc. A Lewis acid–base interaction takes place between the Mg^{2+} ions and hydroxyl groups in metal oxides that increases the ionic mobility. Kim et al. [43] and Yu et al. [44] reported that adding filler to PVdF-*co*-HFP-based gel polymer electrolytes enhanced the ionic conductivity to 3.2 mS cm^{-1}. Gel polymer electrolytes of 15% PVdF-*co*-HFP,

186   Ceramic and Specialty Electrolytes

73% $Mg(ClO_4)_2$–EC/PC and 15 % silica composites provide a high electrochemical stability window of 4.3 V. Silica filler reinforced the physical properties of the matrix. Pandey [45] investigated the same matrix with different silica content and found that ionic conductivity and cyclability was also improved by the addition of active filler MgO instead of passive filler silica. Ionic conductivity was increased to 8 mS cm^{-1} with good thermal and electrochemical stability. MgO facilitates the further dissociation of aggregates, undissociated particles, etc. [45]. Recently a PVA/PAN-based matrix was introduced to $Mg(ClO_4)_2$ salt [46]. Strong interaction between the blend and the salt was clearly observed by the X-Ray Diffraction (XRD) studies. Still further studies on composite gel polymer electrolytes with the addition of plasticizers, fillers, etc. have been carried out. The addition of nano size filler increases the amorphous nature of the polymer matrix, thereby increasing the ionic mobility of the material. Biodegradable nano fillers are an important area in the research field that are environmentally friendly. Sreedevi et al. [47] reported the addition of biodegradable nanosize chitin and succinonitrile (SN) to the PEO-Mg perchlorate matrix. The maximum ionic conductivity was obtained for 10 wt% $MgClO_4$ chitin nanofiber, delivering in the order of 10^{-3} S cm^{-1} at 60° C.

8.2.4 Room-Temperature Ionic Liquid-Based Electrolytes for Mg-ion Batteries

Safety is a major threat for the commercialization of Mg-ion batteries. Many measurements were taken in order to create a safer electrolyte. Room temperature ionic liquids (RTILs) are quaternary ammonium salts with an ambient temperature conduction range of 0.1 mS cm^{-1}–18 mS cm^{-1}. In batteries, ionic liquid is always associated with lithium salts or some other salts, depending on the type of cations. Thus, there will be two cations and one anion that enhance the conduction [48] and possess electrochemical stability of 4–6 V. An earlier study dissolved (1-ethyl 3-methyl) imidazolium bis(trifluromethylsulphonyl)imide (EMITFSI) in polymeric matrix and ionic salts. The system consists of PEO–PMA matrix, ionic liquid, and Mg-conducting triflate. From the thermogravimetric analysis (TGA) analysis, a shift in value suggested ionic liquid acts as a plasticizing agent, and ionic conductivity of 3.5 mS cm^{-1} was observed. An increase in viscosity with a decrease in conductivity was observed by the addition of Mg salts [49]. The same group investigated the effect of the ionic liquid on polymer electrolytes [50] consisting of ethyl magnesium bromide in THF and ionic liquid. The study obtained a maximum conductivity of 7.4 mS cm^{-1} and optimized the ratio of Mg salt and ionic liquid of quaternary ammonium salts in the ratio of 3:1 volume. In 2007, a detailed study on the reduction of ionic liquids on Mg salt found that imidazolium salt was unsuitable for the reaction; however, 1-butyl 1-methyl pyrrolidinium systems (BMP) are a suitable candidate for reduction. Out of these systems, 1-butyl 1-methyl pyrrolidinium bis-trifluro methyl sulphonyl imide ($BMPTf_2N$) has a better deposition when Grignard reagents are incorporated [38, 51]. Different ionic liquids were studied, and a single ionic liquid was used for the system. Wang et al. [52] attempted to mix two ionic liquids with conducting salt. N-methyl N-propyl piperidinium (bistrifluoromethylsulfonyl) imide (PP13-TFSI) and

Magnesium-Ion Batteries

FIGURE 8.6 FE-SEM images on surface morphology of Mg electrodeposits at different current densities (a) 0.5 mA cm^{-2} (b) 2.5 mA cm^{-2}, in which no dendrite formation is noted. Adapted and reproduced with permission from reference [55]. Copyright 2015 Elsevier.

1-*n*-butyl 3-methyl imidazolium tetrafluoroborate (BMIMBF$_4$) were optimized by a 4:1 ratio. The study shows almost 200 cycles were processed with low overpotential value and concluded that these were compatible with Mg ions. BMIMBF$_4$ was also chosen for mixing with Mg triflate, and the deposition and dissolution were studied on a silver substrate. It has been noted that deposition occurs in the pyramidal form and becomes thin and flat on dissolution, providing an electrochemical window of 4.2 V with Platinum electrode (*Vs* Pt) [53]. Different ionic liquids show different behavior in salts, and the behavior was later studied by choosing three ionic liquids and three Mg salts. The ionic liquids chosen were: N-methyl-*N*-propyl piperidinium (PP13)·Tf$_2$N, *N,N*-diethyl-*N*-methyl(2-ethoxyethyl)-ammonium (DEME$^+$) tetrafluoroborate (BF^{4-}), and 1-*n*-butyl-3-methylimidazolium (BMIM)-Tf$_2$N. The Mg salts chosen were bis(trifluoromethanesulfonyl)imide (Tf$_2$N$^-$), borohydride (BH$_4^-$) and trifluoromethanesulfonate (TfO$^-$). Mg plating is found to be quite difficult in Tf$_2$N$^-$ and BH$_4^-$ because of the dense charge density of Mg and greater coulombic attraction. Owing to these factors, these batteries always prefer the low charge density of ionic liquid cation [54]. Kitada et al. [55] synthesized halide-free ionic liquid-based electrolytes by choosing a magnesium imide. Out of the different concentrations chosen, an equimolar ratio of Mg/glymes shows good oxidative stability and was found to be safer. Field emission scanning electron microscope images (Figure 8.6) show no dendrite formation.

8.3 CONCLUSION

For the past three decades, lithium-ion batteries ruled the electrochemical world. Electrolytes are the crucial part of batteries, and researchers mainly focus on the development of safer and efficient electrolytes. However, lithium-based batteries are not the best choice because lithium metal is highly reactive, toxic, and expensive. Mg-ion batteries are an emerging type of energy storage solution owing to its availability, low cost, ease of handling, and low environmental impact. Increased research

188 Ceramic and Specialty Electrolytes

efforts on Mg-ion batteries have improved the performance of batteries' voltage, cycle life, shelf life, charge–discharge rate, etc. Mg-ion batteries are required for the future world because the cost and safety of lithium-ion batteries are a primary concern. In a battery, the cathode is the electrode from which current flows, and electrolytes are the medium through which ionic charge flows through the electrode. Electrolytes are important in the performance of a battery. The addition of fillers, plasticizers, ionic liquids, etc., to electrolytes enhance the conductivity of the battery system. Polymer electrolytes have an indispensable role in the technology world. Reports show that gel polymer electrolytes are adequate, much safer, and can work in a wide temperature range.

ACKNOWLEDGMENT

Authors Anjumole P. Thomas, Dr. Jabeen Fatima M. J., and Dr. Prasanth Raghavan, would like to acknowledge the Department of Science and Technology, India, and Kerala State Council for Science, Technology and Environment (KSCSTE), Kerala, India, for their financial assistance.

REFERENCES

1. Goodenough JB, Park KS (2013) The Li-ion rechargeable battery: A perspective. *J Am Chem Soc* 135:1167–1176. https://doi.org/10.1021/ja3091438
2. Yoshino A (2012) The birth of the lithium-ion battery. *Angew Chemie - Int Ed* 51:5798–5800. https://doi.org/10.1002/anie.201105006
3. Chen M, Liu J, He Y, et al. Study of the fire hazards of lithium-ion batteries at different pressures, *Appl. Therm Eng*, 125: 1061–1074. doi.org/10.1016/j.applthermaleng.2017. 06.131
4. Saha P, Datta MK, Velikokhatnyi OI, et al. (2014) Rechargeable magnesium battery: Current status and key challenges for the future. *Prog Mater Sci* 66:1–86. https://doi.org/ 10.1016/j.pmatsci.2014.04.001
5. Foot PJS (2015) Principles and prospects of high-energy magnesium-ion batteries. *Sci Prog* 98:264–275. https://doi.org/10.3184/003685015X14388749247375
6. Wang F, Fan X, Gao T, et al. (2017) High-voltage aqueous magnesium ion batteries. *ACS Cent Sci* 3:1121–1128. https://doi.org/10.1021/acscentsci.7b00361
7. Sources P (2014) A short review on the comparison between Li battery systems and rechargeable magnesium battery technology. 98:28–32. https://doi.org/10.1016/S0378-7753(01)00585-7
8. Yoo HD, Shterenberg I, Gofer Y, Gershinsky G, Pour N, Aurbach D (2013) Mg rechargeable batteries: An on-going challenge. *Energy Environ Sci* 6: 226–2279. https://doi.org/ 10.1039/C2EE23635D
9. Doe RE, Han R, Hwang J, et al. (2014) Novel, electrolyte solutions comprising fully inorganic salts with high anodic stability for rechargeable magnesium batteries. *Chem Commun* 50:243–245. https://doi.org/10.1039/c3cc47896c
10. Shao Y, Gu M, Li X, et al. (2014) Highly reversible Mg insertion in nanostructured Bi for Mg ion batteries. *Nano Lett* 14:255–260. https://doi.org/10.1021/nl403874y
11. Barile CJ, Spatney R, Zavadil KR, Gewirth AA (2014) Investigating the reversibility of in situ generated magnesium organohaloaluminates for magnesium deposition and dissolution. *J Phys Chem C* 118:10694–10699. https://doi.org/10.1021/jp503506c

Magnesium-Ion Batteries

12. Huie MM, Bock DC, Takeuchi ES, et al. (2015) Cathode materials for magnesium and magnesium-ion based batteries. *Coord Chem Rev* 287:15–27. https://doi.org/10.1016/j.ccr.2014.11.005

13. Erickson EM, Markevich E, Salitra G, et al. (2015) Review—development of advanced rechargeable batteries: A continuous challenge in the choice of suitable electrolyte solutions. *J Electrochem Soc* 162:A2424–A2438. https://doi.org/10.1149/2.0051514jes

14. Gregory TD (1990) Nonaqueous electrochemistry of magnesium. *J Electrochem Soc* 137:775. https://doi.org/10.1149/1.2086553

15. Aurbach D, Weissman I, Gofer Y, Levi E (2003) Nonaqueous magnesium electrochemistry and its application in secondary batteries. *Chem Rec* 3:61–73. https://doi.org/10.1002/tcr.10051

16. Aurbach D, Schechter A, Gofer Y (2000) Prototype systems for rechargeable. 407:10–14. https://doi.org/10.1038/35037553

17. Liebenow C, Yang Z, Lobitz P (2000) The electrodeposition of magnesium using solutions of organomagnesium halides, amidomagnesium halides and magnesium organoborates. *Electrochem Commun* 2:641–645. https://doi.org/10.1016/S1388-2481(00)00094-1

18. Novák P (1993) Electrochemical insertion of magnesium in metal oxides and sulfides from aprotic electrolytes. *J Electrochem Soc* 140:140. https://doi.org/10.1149/1.2056075

19. Sutto TE, Duncan TT (2012) Electrochemical and structural characterization of Mg ion intercalation into Co_3O_4 using ionic liquid electrolytes. *Electrochim Acta* 80:413–417. https://doi.org/10.1016/j.electacta.2012.07.050

20. Sutto TE, Duncan TT (2012) Electrochemercalation into Co3O4 using ionic liquid electrolytes. *Electrochim Acta* 80:413–417. https://doi.org/10.1016/j.electacta.2012.07.050

21. Mohtadi R, Matsui M, Arthur TS, Hwang SJ (2012) Magnesium borohydride: From hydrogen storage to magnesium battery. *Angew Chemie - Int Ed* 51:9780–9783. https://doi.org/10.1002/anie.201204913

22. Shao Y, Liu T, Li G, et al. (2013) Coordination chemistry in magnesium battery electrolytes: How ligands affect their performance. *Sci Rep* 3:4–10. https://doi.org/10.1038/srep03130

23. Aurbach D, Gizbar H, Schechter A, et al. (2002) Electrolyte solutions for rechargeable magnesium batteries based on organomagnesium chloroaluminate complexes. *J Electrochem Soc* 149:A115. https://doi.org/10.1149/1.1429925

24. Ram C, Sivamani S, Micha Premkumar T, Hariram V (2017) Computational study of leading edge jet impingement cooling with a conical converging hole for blade cooling. *ARPN J Eng Appl Sci* 12:6397–6406. https://doi.org/10.1039/b000000x

25. Liu T, Shao Y, Li G, et al. (2014) A facile approach using $MgCl_2$ to formulate high performance Mg^{2+} electrolytes for rechargeable Mg batteries. *J Mater Chem A* 2:3430–3438. https://doi.org/10.1039/c3ta14825d

26. Nist-Lund CA, Herb JT, Arnold CB (2017) Improving halide-containing magnesium-ion electrolyte performance via sterically hindered alkoxide ligands. *J Power Sources* 362:308–314. https://doi.org/10.1016/j.jpowsour.2017.07.045

27. Stephan AM (2006) Review on gel polymer electrolytes for lithium batteries. *Eur Polym J* 42:21–42. https://doi.org/10.1016/j.eurpolymj.2005.09.017

28. Xie H, Tang Z, Li Z, et al. (2008) PVDF-HFP composite polymer electrolyte with excellent electrochemical properties for Li-ion batteries. *J Solid State Electrochem* 12:1497–1502. https://doi.org/10.1007/s10008-008-0511-9

29. Tang C, Hackenberg K, Fu Q, et al. (2012) High ion conducting polymer nanocomposite electrolytes using hybrid nanofillers. *Nano Lett* 12:1152–1156. https://doi.org/10.1021/nl202692y

30. Liu L, Wang Z, Zhao Z, et al. (2016) PVDF/PAN /SiO$_2$ polymer electrolyte membrane prepared by combination of phase inversion and chemical reaction method for lithium ion batteries. *J Solid State Electrochem* 20: 699–712. https://doi.org/10.1007/s10008-015-3095-1

31. Lee SW, Choi SW, Jo SM, *et al.* (2006) Electrochemical properties and cycle performance of electrospun poly(vinylidene fluoride)-based fibrous membrane electrolytes for Li-ion polymer battery. *J Power Sources* 163:41–46. https://doi.org/10.1016/j.jpowsour.2005.11.102

32. Agrawal RC, Pandey GP (2008) Solid polymer electrolytes: Materials designing and all-solid-state battery applications: An overview. *J Phys D Appl Phys* 41:223001–223018. https://doi.org/10.1088/0022-3727/41/22/223001

33. Ataollahi N, Ahmad A, Hamzah H, et al. (2012) Preparation and characterization of PVDF-co-HFP/MG49 based polymer blend electrolyte. *Int J Electrochem Sci* 7:6693–6703. https://doi.org/10.1007/s11581-009-0415-4

34. Appetecchi GB, Croce F, Hassoun J, et al. (2003) Hot-pressed, dry, composite, PEO-based electrolyte membranes: I. Ionic conductivity characterization. *J Power Sources* 114:105–112. https://doi.org/10.1016/S0378-7753(02)00543-8

35. Huang X (2012) A lithium-ion battery separator prepared using a phase inversion process. *J Power Sources* 216:216–221. https://doi.org/10.1016/j.jpowsour.2012.05.019

36. Bansal D, Meyer B, Salomon M (2008) Gelled membranes for Li and Li-ion batteries prepared by electrospinning. *J Power Sources* 178:848–851. https://doi.org/10.1016/j.jpowsour.2007.07.070

37. Morita M, Yoshimoto N, Yakushiji S, Ishikawa M (2001) Rechargeable magnesium batteries using a novel polymeric solid electrolyte. *Electrochem Solid-State Lett* 4:A177. https://doi.org/10.1149/1.1403195

38. Morita M, Shirai T, Yoshimoto N, Ishikawa M (2005) Ionic conductance behavior of polymeric gel electrolyte containing ionic liquid mixed with magnesium salt. *J Power Sources* 139:351–355. https://doi.org/10.1016/j.jpowsour.2004.07.028

39. Sheha E, El-Mansy MK (2008) A high voltage magnesium battery based on H2SO4-doped (PVA)0.7(NaBr)0.3solid polymer electrolyte. *J Power Sources* 185:1509–1513. https://doi.org/10.1016/j.jpowsour.2008.09.046

40. Polu AR, Kumar R, Rhee HW (2015) Magnesium ion conducting solid polymer blend electrolyte based on biodegradable polymers and application in solid-state batteries. *Ionics (Kiel)* 21:125–132. https://doi.org/10.1007/s11581-014-1174-4

41. Tiautit N, Puratane C, Panpinit S, Saengsuwan S (2014) Effect of SiO 2 and TiO 2 nanoparticles on the performance of dye- sensitized solar cells using PVDF-HFP / PVA gel electrolytes. *Energy Procedia* 56:378–385. https://doi.org/10.1016/j.egypro.2014.07.170

42. Yoshimoto N, Yakushiji S, Ishikawa M, Morita M (2003) Rechargeable magnesium batteries with polymeric gel electrolytes containing magnesium salts. *Electrochim Acta* 48:2317–2322. https://doi.org/10.1016/S0013-4686(03)00221-4

43. Oh JS, Ko JM, Kim DW (2004) Preparation and characterization of gel polymer electrolytes for solid state magnesium batteries. *Electrochim Acta* 50:903–906. https://doi.org/10.1016/j.electacta.2004.01.099

44. Houghton T, Eltohamy G, Yu H (2017) An experimental magnesium ion battery cell made of flexible materials. In: *Proceedings - Electronic Components and Technology Conference*. Orlando, USA, 30 May – 2 June, pp 206–211.

45. Pandey GP, Agrawal RC, Hashmi SA (2009) Magnesium ion-conducting gel polymer electrolytes dispersed with nanosized magnesium oxide. *J Power Sources* 190:563–572. https://doi.org/10.1016/j.jpowsour.2009.01.057

46. Manjuladevi R, Thamilselvan M, Selvasekarapandian S, et al. (2017) Mg-ion conducting polymer blend electrolyte based on poly(vinyl alcohol)-poly (acrylonitrile) with magnesium perchlorate. *Solid State Ionics* 308:90–100. https://doi.org/10.1016/j.ssi.2017.06.002

47. Sridevi NA, Karuppasamy K, Balakumar S, Shajan XS (2012) Structural and ionic conductivity studies on nanochitosan incorporated polymer electrolytes for rechargeable magnesium batteries. *Chem Sci Trans* 1:311–316. https://doi.org/10.7598/cst2012.198

48. Oehme A, Leitner R, Wittbrodt N (2013) Challenges of multiple airport control. *Aviat Psychol Appl Hum Factors* 3:1–8. https://doi.org/10.1016/j.jpowsour.2009.06.089

49. Yoshimoto N, Shirai T, Morita M (2005) A novel polymeric gel electrolyte systems containing magnesium salt with ionic liquid. *Electrochim Acta* 50:3866–3871. https://doi.org/10.1016/j.electacta.2005.02.036

50. Yoshimoto N, Matsumoto M, Egashia M, Morita M (2010) Mixed electrolyte consisting of ethylmagnesiumbromide with ionic liquid for rechargeable magnesium electrode. *J Power Sources* 195:2096–2098. https://doi.org/10.1016/j.jpowsour.2009.10.073

51. Cheek GT, O'Grady WE, El Abedin SZ, et al. (2008) Studies on the electrodeposition of magnesium in ionic liquids. *J Electrochem Soc* 155:D91. https://doi.org/10.1149/1.2804763

52. Wang P, Nu LY, Yang J, Feng Z (2006) Mixed ionic liquids as electrolyte for reversible deposition and dissolution of magnesium. *Surf Coatings Technol* 201:3783–3787. https://doi.org/10.1016/j.surfcoat.2006.03.020

53. Nu LY, Yang J, Wu R (2005) Reversible deposition and dissolution of magnesium from BMIMBF4ionic liquid. *Electrochem Commun* 7:1105–1110. https://doi.org/10.1016/j.elecom.2005.07.013

54. Vardar G, Sleightholme AES, Naruse J, et al. (2014) Electrochemistry of Magnesium Electrolytes in Ionic Liquids for Secondary Batteries, *ACS Appl. Mater. Interfaces* 20: 18033–18039. https://doi.org/10.1021/am5049064

55. Kitada A, Kang Y, Matsumoto K, Fukami K (2015) Room temperature magnesium electrodeposition from glyme-coordinated ammonium amide electrolytes. *J Electrochem Soc* 162:389–396. https://doi.org/10.1149/2.0731508jes

9 Aqueous Electrolytes for Lithium- and Sodium-Ion Batteries

Saurabh S. Soni and Jyoti Prasad

CONTENTS

9.1 Introduction 194
9.2 Why Aqueous Electrolytes for Alkaline Metal-Ion Batteries? 195
    9.2.1 Cost Effective 195
    9.2.2 Safety Concerns 195
    9.2.3 Ionic Conductivity 195
    9.2.4 Rate Capability 196
9.3 Aqueous Rechargeable Lithium-Ion Batteries (ARLIB) 196
    9.3.1 Electrode Materials for ARLIBs 196
    9.3.2 Design and Structure of Electrode Materials for ARLIBs 197
    9.3.3 Aqueous Electrolytes for ARLIBs 199
        9.3.3.1 Effect of pH 199
        9.3.3.2 Effect of Dissolved Oxygen and Additives in Electrolytes 200
        9.3.3.3 Effect of Concentration of Electrolytes 201
        9.3.3.4 "Water in Salt" Properties in Aqueous Electrolytes 201
        9.3.3.5 Aqueous Gel Polymer Electrolytes for ARLIBs 203
9.4 Aqueous Rechargeable Sodium-Ion Batteries (ARNIBs) 204
    9.4.1 Electrode Material for ARNIBs 205
    9.4.2 Aqueous Electrolytes for ARNIBs 207
        9.4.2.1 High Concentration Aqueous Electrolytes for ARNIBs 207
        9.4.2.2 Aqueous Gel Polymer Electrolytes for Sodium-Ion
                    Batteries 208
        9.4.2.3 Other Factors of Aqueous Electrolytes Affect the
                    Electrochemical Properties of ARNIBs 210
9.5 Challenges and Further Perspectives of ARLIBs/ARNIBs 210
    9.5.1 Electrolyte Decomposition with H_2 and O_2 Evolution 210
    9.5.2 Evolution of H_2 and O_2 from Electrolyte Decomposition 211
    9.5.3 Dissolution of Electrode Material in Aqueous Electrolytes 211
    9.5.4 Coinsertion of H^+ with Guest Ions 211
9.6 Conclusion and Future Outlook 212
Acknowledgment 212
References 213

9.1 INTRODUCTION

In recent years, the rapid growth of the global economy has significantly increased the use of fossil fuels that leads to the depletion of existing reserved fossil fuels and environmental problems due to the extensive emissions of greenhouse gases. Therefore, human beings have gradually realized that there is an urgent need to develop environmentally friendly, clean, renewable energy and safe energy storage devices [1]. In response to these concerns scientists need to develop a superior device or source that could fulfill the human economic demand by coding with "Three E" criteria, which include energy (high energy content with respect to unit weight and volume), economics (low manufacturing costs and long cycling life), and environmental (safe, non-toxic, and high reliability) [1–5]. Hence, as it was well known that organic-based lithium-ion- (Li-ion) and sodium-ion (Na-ion) batteries can be harmful for the human society which includes less concerns in the field of safety and expensive fabrication process based on large scale energy storage systems. To avoid such hazardous effect scientist started focusing on essential criteria and concepts that include promising approach by designing reliable aqueous-based lithium and sodium ion batteries that could acquire high safety route with long cycling life and low cost fabrication.

The low cost fabrication with less hazardous effect is an important step for battery types to use in electrical vehicles (EVs), and EV technology should be cost effective, safe with reliable features. To date, a rechargeable battery with high energy is a prime requirement of EV system. To be considered acceptable, an EV battery must meet the following criteria: (i) long life cycle, (ii) low cost, (iii) high power density with good rate capability, and (iv) better safety. Only few battery types meet these stated characteristics in which Li-ion batteries (LIBs) and Sodium ion batteries(NIBs) are two of them with stated characteristics. Because LIBs and NIBs exhibit a high power/energy density potential window, over the past two decades, Li-ion/Sodium ion intercalation material or the electrodes and nonaqueous organic solvents as electrolytes have been widely explored [2]. Because it is well established that the presence of organic electrolytes might cause severe safety problems, and controlling them in the assembly environment is expensive, aqueous rechargeable LIBs and NIBs are found to be more reliable in many aspects, as they are more suitable for replacement of flammable organic solvents. Therefore, making selected changes to electrode and electrolyte material in aqueous based LIBs and NIBs present a wide exploration in these revolutionary battery systems.

Due to the aforementioned drawbacks, the wide utility of non-aqueous batteries in energy devices is hindered. The problems with LIBs and NIBs can be eliminated by developing a new type of less expensive and environmentally benign battery material and devices by optimizing the technical characterization of these batteries. As such, aqueous media can be proven to be an ideal electrolyte solvent due to its neutral nature and friendliness behavior.

9.2 WHY AQUEOUS ELECTROLYTES FOR ALKALINE METAL-ION BATTERIES?

From the above discussion it is clear that electrolytes are key components in the safety of LIBs and NIBs. Aqueous electrolytes for LIBs and NIBs have been found to be more compatible than organic electrolytes. Some of the reasons to use aqueous electrolytes for the manufacturing of batteries on a large scale include cost-effectiveness, safety, and ionic conductivity.

9.2.1 COST EFFECTIVE

- Aqueous batteries can be prepared under ambient conditions, eliminating the need to use a glove box.
- With the easy diffusion of ions from water-based electrolytes, replacing expensive cathode/anode separators with a cheap separator has been found to be suitable.
- For effective dissolution of Li^+/Na^+, an expensive hydrophobic trifluoro-methanesulfonate and bis(trifluoromethane)sulfonamide-based salts are used as organic electrolytes. This can be replaced with cheaper salts such as $LiNO_3$, $LiSO_4$, Na_2SO_4, $LiOH$, etc., which are easily soluble in water.

9.2.2 SAFETY CONCERNS

It is now well known that Li/Na metal and organic electrolytes possess high volatility, which causes explosions and fire because of the high rate of overcharging in mobile phones and electrical vehicles. [6] It has been observed that in LIBs/NIBs, the flammability of the organic solvent used is the main cause of explosions, which may happen due to a short circuit during excess charging. The use of aqueous electrolytes with low volatility can easily absorb heat due to short circuiting that ultimately eliminates accidents caused due to thermal abuse.

9.2.3 IONIC CONDUCTIVITY

Along with thermal stability, high ionic conductivity is essential for LIBs and NIBs, and high mobility with smooth diffusion is required. High ionic conductivity is majorly governed by high concentration of metal salts that ultimately enhance the high rate of capability and good reversibility in batteries. The normal conductivity of aqueous electrolytes is about 10^{-1} S cm^{-1}, which is far better than other types of electrolytes, including organic electrolytes (10^{-3}–10^{-2} S cm^{-1}), polymer electrolytes (10^{-7}–10^{-3} S cm^{-1}), and inorganic solid electrolytes (10^{-7}–10^{-2} S cm^{-1}) [3]. The ionic mobility rate of aqueous electrolytes is found to be much greater than organic electrolytes because aqueous electrolytes do not form a solid electrode interface (SEI), which eliminates the cause of resistance and thus exhibits high ionic conductivity. Also, water in salt electrolytes are the best medium to cause high ionic mobility at room temperature (25° C) to lower temperatures around -90° C with negligible

196 Ceramic and Specialty Electrolytes

crystallization of salt causing conductivity ~10 mS cm^{-1}, which is comparable to that of typical organic electrolytes (9.0 mS cm^{-1}).

9.2.4 RATE CAPABILITY

Researchers found that the rate capability for aqueous electrolytes is more stable than organic electrolytes, which depends on smooth intercalation and de-intercalation properties at high rate current density through anodes. Comparatively this results aqueous electrolytes into better rate capacity than organic electrolytes.

From the aforementioned discussion, it is clear that aqueous rechargeable alkali–metal ion (Li^+/Na^+) batteries are a better alternative to organic electrolytes for large scale application, as they are based on the environmentally benign aqueous electrolyte. The only concern with aqueous electrolytes is their limited cell voltage of up to 1.23 V in normal cases, which is lower than organic electrolytes (> 3 V). Therefore, the various aspects of aqueous electrolyte-based alkali metal ion batteries for future perspectives in energy storage devices are worth discussing.

9.3 AQUEOUS RECHARGEABLE LITHIUM-ION BATTERIES (ARLIB)

Aqueous rechargeable LIB (ARLIBs) have received the attention of researchers since the mid-1990s [4]. In 1994, the first aqueous LIB was reported with an intercalation compound VO_2 (B) as cathode, $LiMn_2O_4$ as anode, and $LiNO_3$ as an electrolyte [7]. Since then, there have been a good numbers of reports available on aqueous LIBs that are environmentally benign, but H_2 and O_2 evolution limits results in a lower potential window (~ 1.23 V), which is much lower than (> 3V) organic electrolytes. As a result, a decrease in energy density is observed, but it is comparable with Ni-Cd batteries and lead-acid batteries [8].

9.3.1 ELECTRODE MATERIALS FOR ARLIBs

The mechanism of aqueous LIBs involves the intercalation of Li^+-ion into/from the host electrode material in water. A schematic diagram of this phenomenon in ARLIBs is given in Figure 9.1.

From the mechanism, it is clear that the selection of suitable material for intercalation of Li^+-ions is crucial to avoid the decomposition of water, as, later, it has a lower electrochemical stability window [9]. Therefore, the nature and type of electrode material has a marked effect on the cell capacity and the recycling efficiency of ARLIBs. A simple potential diagram in Figure 9.2 shows the electrochemical stability range of water and redox potential (vs. Standard Hydrogen Electrode (SHE)) for various types of electrode materials.

From Figure 9.2, the working feasibility of the electrode material used for the aqueous system can be determined in such a way that electrolysis can be controlled. A detailed list of widely used anode and cathode materials along with capacity is given in Table 9.1. As shown in Figure 9.2 and Table 9.1, the anode and cathode material for ARLIBs can be broadly classified into metal oxides, polyanionic compounds, and Prussian-blue-type analog compounds.

Aqueous Electrolytes for LIBs and SIBs

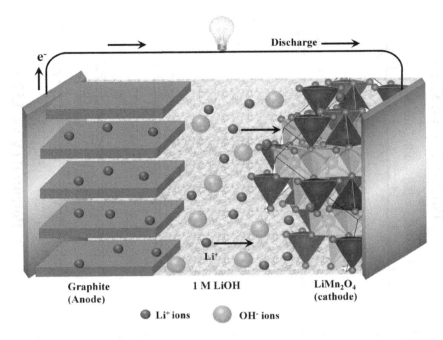

FIGURE 9.1 Schematic illustration of the cell configuration and working principle of ARLIBs.

9.3.2 Design and Structure of Electrode Materials for ARLIBs

An ARLIB with excellent electrochemical performance requires an electrode material with optimized composition, morphology, and geometrical/microstructure. To achieve better intercalation of Li$^+$-ion, the electrode materials should possess properties such as high surface area, high conductivity, and better diffusion path of Li$^+$-ions [10, 11]. To achieve these desired properties of electrode material, synthesis and material processing plays a vital role.

Methods such as gel combustion, sol-gel, solid-state synthesis, hydrothermal, etc. are used for synthesis of various electrode materials. Among all these reported methods, wet processes, such as sol-gel, are viewed as more promising methods over dry processes, such as solid-state method, because the method later leads to agglomeration and polydisperse particles, while the former method gives homogeneous mixing of metal atoms. The electrochemical performance, such as reversible capacity, is better in material prepared by sol-gel compared to those prepared with solid-state methods [14]. Furthermore, the crystal structure of electrode materials has attracted more attention, as it affects the intercalation of Li$^+$-ions along with other cations. The electrode materials reported so far for ARLIBs are broadly classified into three types of structures: layered (e.g., Li$_2$MnO$_3$, LiCoO$_2$), olivine (e.g., LiFePO$_4$) and spinel (e.g., LiMn$_2$O$_4$, LiV$_3$O$_8$). In ARLIBs, the co-insertion of small cation H$^+$ along with Li$^+$-ions affects the overall electrochemical performance [24], as high numbers of H$^+$-ions aligned in cathode materials act as a barrier for diffusion process of Li$^+$-ions. In view of this, crystal structures that control the co-insertion process of H$^+$-ion

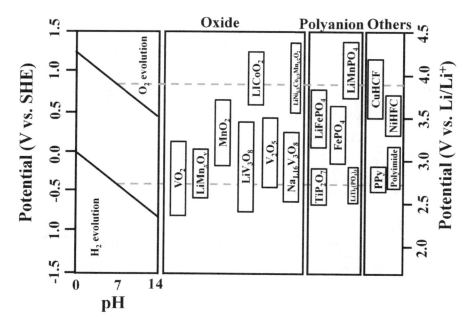

FIGURE 9.2 Electrochemical stability range of water and redox potential for different electrode materials employed in ARLIBs.

in the cathode is preferable. In the layered structure (Figure 9.3), this process of co-insertion is favored over a closed, packed olivine structure.

In addition to the crystal structure, geometry of material is also a key parameter for selection of electrode material. Nanostructures, such as nanosheet, nanoplatelets, nanowires, hollow tube, flower-shaped, etc., are the materials of choice because they can provide a large surface area, short diffusion length, and better conductivity, which promotes intercalation in the host crystal structure that leads to high cycling stability and rate capability [11].

From the aforementioned discussion, it is clear that the following points can be kept in center while selecting electrode materials:

- The synthesis process that offers homogeneous, uniform, small particle size is preferable.
- Close, packed olivine structures that control co-intercalation of H^+-ions are desirable over an open, layered structure.
- Nanostructure electrode material is important, as it gives high capacity and cyclability due to high ionic conductivity, large surface area, and short diffusion length.
- A porous structure of electrode material facilitates effective penetration of aqueous electrolytes and controls the volume expansion effect during the charging/discharging process.

Aqueous Electrolytes for LIBs and SIBs

TABLE 9.1

Cell Performance of ARLIBs Comprising Different Cathodic and Anodic Materials with Various Aqueous Electrolytes

Cathode	Anode	Electrolyte	Capacity mAh g^{-1}	Ref.
VO_2	$LiMn_2O_4$	5 mol L^{-1} $LiNO_3$	10	[12]
$LiTi_2(PO_4)_3$	$LiFePO_4$	1 mol L^{-1} Li_2SO_4 pH=13	55	[13]
$LiFePO_4$/C	VO_2	Saturated $LiNO_3$	106	[14]
$LiFePO_4$/C	LiV_3O_8	$LiNO_3$	90	[15]
$LiFePO_4$	Activated carbon	Li_2SO_4	124	[16]
$LiMn_{0.05}Ni_{0.05}Fe_{0.9}PO_4$	$LiT_2(PO_4)_3$	Saturated Li_2SO_4	87	[17]
$LiFePO_4$	$LiFePO_4OH$	Saturated $LiOH$	140	[18]
$LiVPO_4F$	$LiVPO_4F$	LiTFSI in 10% PVA (water in salt)	141 Wh kg^{-1}	[19]
$LiMn_2O_4$	$LiTi_2(PO_4)_3$	5 M $LiNO_3$	45	[20]
$Li_{0.75}CoO_2$	$LiCoO_2$	LiCl, $LiNO_3$, Li_2SO_4	-	[21]
$Li_4Ti_5O_{12}$	$LiCoO_2$	$(PTFSI)_{0.6}(TFSI)_{0.4}$(1 H_2O)		[22]
$Li_4Ti_5O_{12}$	$LiMn_2O_4$	MSM: $LiClO_4$: H_2O	160 Wh kg^{-1}	[23]
$LiMn_2O_4$	$LiTi_2(PO_4)_3$	1 M Li_2SO_4	40	[24]
$LiCoO_2$	LiV_3O_8	Saturated $LiNO_3$	53	[25]
$LiCoO_2$	Polyimide	5 M $LiNO_3$	70	[26]

9.3.3 AQUEOUS ELECTROLYTES FOR ARLIBs

In batteries, an electrolyte is the medium of ion conductors between anode and cathode. For better performance of the battery, it should possess good mobility of ions so that they can diffuse effectively in the active electrode material. As discussed in Section 9.2, due to silent features such as low environmental impact, safety, low cost, high specific capacity, rate capacity, etc., aqueous electrolytes are seen to be the right choice over organic electrolytes. These mentioned properties of aqueous electrolytes are also crucial along with electrode material, as they synergistically enhance the electrochemical and stability performance of aqueous battery systems. As mentioned in Table 9.1, cost effective salts, such as $LiNO_3$, $LiClO_4$, $LiOH$ etc., have been used extensively in ARLIBs; however, properties such as concentration and pH of electrolyte, concentration of dissolved oxygen, and additives in electrolytes have been considered for optimization of electrochemical performance of ARLIBs.

9.3.3.1 Effect of pH

The nature or pH of the aqueous electrolyte solution and its effect on the capacity of ARLIBs has been studied and documented in detail [27]. The change in pH value of aqueous electrolytes has a marked effect on device performance, as it enhances the solubility of ions. Extremely acidic or basic conditions lead to an increase in the extent of dissolved ions. In the case of $LiFePO_4$, Li$^+$-ions dissolved into the aqueous

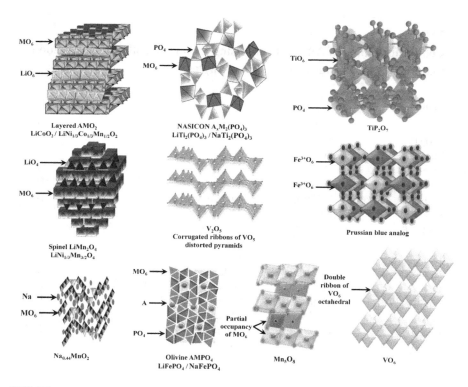

FIGURE 9.3 Crystal structures of some of the important inorganic metal oxides used as positive and negative electrodes in ARLIBs.

electrolyte under highly acidic conditions, while PO_4^{3-} dissolved more in very high basic conditions; therefore, the stability of electrode material can be controlled by adjusting the pH value of an aqueous electrolyte. It has also been found that both the cathode and anode have different cyclic stability even with same pH value of aqueous electrolyte. However, the electrochemical performance may be different for various types of electrolytes. For example, $LiNi_{1/3}Co_{1/3}Mn_{1/3}O_2$ in Li_2SO_4 with pH 13 exhibited better electrochemical performance as compared with Li_2SO_4 with pH 11 [25], but the same material in 5 M $LiNO_3$ at pH 11 is highly stable. Similarly, pH ranging from 7 to 12 has a marked effect on the electrochemical performance of $Na_2V_6O_{16}·0.14H_2O$ in aqueous solution of Li_2SO_4 [15]. On the contrary, as per a Pourbaix diagram, it is well established that an increase of pH will limit the electrochemical window of the electrolyte, which deteriorates the reversibility capacity of the system. Therefore, the optimum value of pH should be selected so that it controls the dissolution of ions in the electrolyte and maintains good reversible capacity.

9.3.3.2 Effect of Dissolved Oxygen and Additives in Electrolytes

Several researchers have demonstrated that inferior capacity fading in ARLIBs is due to the presence of dissolved O_2 and OH^- in the electrolyte [15]. Recent studies

Aqueous Electrolytes for LIBs and SIBs

have noted that the coulombic efficiency and discharge capacity can be improved by removing the dissolved oxygen from aqueous electrolytes just by bubbling the highly pure nitrogen gas into electrolytes for about 8 hours [16]. Moreover, this measurement has also been carried out under nitrogen atmosphere. The potential difference between the redox peaks of $LiFePO_4$ without dissolved oxygen containing electrolyte was smaller than the electrolyte with dissolved oxygen. These observations confirmed that ARLIBs without dissolved oxygen will exhibit less polarizability and low chemical resistance, which highly improves capacity and cycling behavior of ARLIBs. The presence of additives improves the behavior of intercalation process of Li^+-ions in aqueous solution. There are very few reports available on studies based on the effect of the presence of additives in aqueous electrolyte solutions on the performance of ARLIBs. Stojkovic et al. [28] demonstrated that presence of 1% (w/w) of vinylene carbonate (VC) in an aqueous electrolyte solution improved the discharge capacity compared to aqueous electrolytes without additives.

9.3.3.3 Effect of Concentration of Electrolytes

In principle, the ionic conductivity of electrolytes is a key factor for the performance of ARLIBs, and the concentration of the electrolytes also work in parallel to ionic conductivity. In aqueous rechargeable batteries, the concentration of an electrolyte has an effect on the voltage plateau as well as polarization, as both increase with the concentration of an electrolyte. A study using a $LiMn_2O_4$ electrode in 2 M Li_2SO_4 and 3, 5, and 9 M $LiNO_3$ aqueous solution found that 5 M $LiNO_3$ electrolyte outperforms all the concentrations considered in the study [29]. The electrochemical performance of $LiFePO_4$ in $LiNO_3$ solution with different concentrations of 2, 5, and 9 M was studied, and researchers concluded that they have little effect on specific capacity, rate capability, and charging–discharging cycle [15]. However, from the variety of available literature on the effect of concentration on ARLIBs, it has been concluded that there should be an optimum concentration required (not higher or lower) for better electrochemical performance of ARLIBs.

In terms of mechanism based on Kohlrausch's law of independent migration of ions in an aqueous electrolyte, ions are responsible for conductivity of an electrolyte, i.e., a higher number of ions enhances conductivity and electricity [30]. However, at very high salt concentration, the ionic conductivity decreases when the concentration of an electrolyte increases. At very high concentration of salts, the electricity flow will be hindered and thus decreases in the conductivity. As compared with the conductivity of the organic electrolyte, aqueous electrolytes' conductivity is 17 times higher, which can be proved by simple Arrhenius activation energy. Simply put, if the concentration of the electrolyte in aqueous and organic phase is the same (1 M), then the aqueous electrolyte will show 5 times lower viscosity than the organic electrolyte. Thus, it is essential to select the optimum concentration of an electrolyte to achieve high electrochemical performance in ARLIBs.

9.3.3.4 "Water in Salt" Properties in Aqueous Electrolytes

In conventional aqueous electrolytes, production of H_2, O_2, and OH^- upon decomposition cannot deposit on the surface of the negative electrode to form a solid electrolyte interface (SEI). This results into relatively low voltage and energy density in aqueous rechargeable batteries. To overcome this problem, a new class of aqueous electrolyte, the "water in salt" electrolyte (WISE), was introduced, which forms a type of interphase at the electrode surface and results in control of production of H_2 and O_2 at the electrode surface and thus enhances the potential window up to about 3 V [31].

WISE is nothing but the concentrated electrolyte (molarity over 5) that contains a high mole concentration of salt than that of water. Because of this, fewer free water molecules are available to control evolution of H_2 or O_2, and, consequently, the electrochemical stability window of aqueous electrolytes is wider than thermodynamic value up to 1.23 V. To obtain concentrated electrolytes (molarity of about 20 mol.lit^{-1} at 25 °C), a salt with high solubility and better hydrolysis stability, lithium bis (trifluoro methane sulphonyl) LiTFSI, was introduced [32].

At this much high concentration of salt, there is a presence of an anion-containing Li$^+$-ion solvation sheath that contributes to the formation of SEI. A schematic representation of solvation of anion in conventional diluted aqueous electrolyte (salt-in-water) and WISE is given in Figure 9.4 [33]. From the figure, it is clear that in the primary sheath of Li$^+$ is mixed with an average of two water molecules and two organic TFSI anions. Based on this, the mechanism behind the enhancement in the stability window is given in Figure 9.5 [34].

Accordingly, the reduction in water produces OH$^-$ ions that catalyzed the decomposition of TFSI anions through nucleophilic attack. This process results in the generation of SEI layers that are rich in hydroxides and fluorinated species that prevent the decomposition of the aqueous electrolyte. Furthermore, it was also documented that this mechanism of catalytic degradation of anion of salts at the negative electrode in presence of water could be not only restricted with TFSI anion but also extended to other electrolyte systems. Thus, the new ARLIBs with WISE retain high

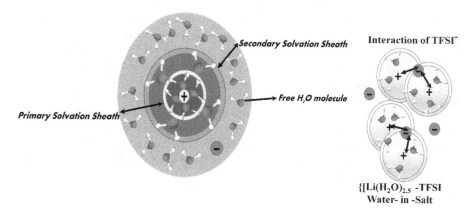

FIGURE 9.4 The effect of LiTFSI concentration on ion–solvent and ion–ion interaction and the electrochemical stability window of LiTFSI-H$_2$O electrolyte on nonactive electrodes. Evolution of the Li$^+$ primary solvation sheath in diluted and water in salt solution.

Aqueous Electrolytes for LIBs and SIBs

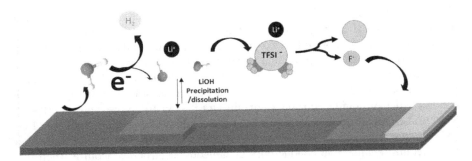

FIGURE 9.5 Schematic illustration of the formation of the solid electrolyte interface (SEI) following a water reduction mediated mechanism occurring in 20 M LITFSI WISE.

stability along with high voltage and energy density, which is not the case with other aqueous systems that retain stability by sacrificing their voltage and energy density.

9.3.3.5 Aqueous Gel Polymer Electrolytes for ARLIBs

Conventional LIBs mainly suffer from various critical properties such as ionic conductivity, cationic transfer number, electrochemical stability, chemical and thermal stability, mechanical properties, porosity, and electrolyte uptake [35]. It has been observed that the breakage within the LIB causes serious safety issues, as they release toxic gases from the electrolytes due to leakage, which finally results in instability of the device. Further, many reports came with a development of aqueous electrolyte by introducing polymer electrolyte in gel phase called gel polymer electrolyte (GPE). Till now many polymer matrices, such as poly(ethylene oxide) (PEO), polyacrylonitrile (PAN), poly (vinylidene fluoride) (PVdF), poly(methyl methacrylate) (PMMA), etc., have been investigated for liquid polymer gel electrolyte (PGE) [33]. The majority of these are used in rechargeable LIBs, as they are composite polymers rather than single polymer chains that significantly enhance the thermal stability of GPE. Generally, GPEs are obtained by incorporating a certain amount of liquid plasticizers or solvent in polymer salt. GPEs have two classes: physical and chemical gels [37]. The physical gel is comprised of liquid electrolytes, which is incorporated within a polymer matrix without any bond formation between the polymer and liquid medium. Secondly, the chemical gels which are comprised of cross-linkers that lead to the formation of chemical bonding between the functional group of the polymer and the cross-linking agent. Due to electrochemical properties of PGE, they function both in supporting the device mechanically and transportation of diffused Li$^+$-ions through the matrix to the opposite electrode. Many researchers consider that Li$^+$ motion transport completely independent from the polymeric segmental relaxation. The host polymer remains semi viscous because of the presence of plasticizers/solvents, thus its microscale of Li$^+$ is similar to that of the liquid environment inside the GPE. Researchers have reported that coating of the lithium metal with gel polymer and lithium superionic conductor (LISICON) film inhibits the formation of dendrites [38]. Due to its higher viscosity than those of the organic liquid electrolytes, the Li^+-ion dendrites are restricted on the surface of the electrodes, and, because of this, the cycling property of the device is not inherited on the Li^+-metal anode. Researchers reported that Polymer gel electrolyte (PGE) functions as a best separator between the electrode and electrolyte. Thus, the use of aqueous electrolytes within the polymer matrix was found to facilitate the ionic (Li^+) transport and inhibit the self-discharge of the cathode or anode material [39]. Actually, the ionic conductivities of liquid electrolytes containing Li^+ salts are in the range of 10^{-3}–10^{-2} S cm^{-1}. Therefore, to enhance uniformity in the conductivity within the aqueous PGE (APGE), the conductivity of the ions must be in a particular path or sequence and must acquire comparable conductivity as aqueous electrolytes acquire when they are in liquid form. The most prominent property for the aqueous gel polymer is the transfer number that is generated because of the actively mobilized cations for the anion in single salt of GPEs. Therefore, a system must acquire the phenomenon of well-defined charging–discharging only when there is low concentration of mobile ions (Li^+) so that it can result in easy ion diffusion and mobility, which should be very near to unity ($T \approx 1$) in the electrolytic system, that is very close to the liquid aqueous electrolyte [39–41]. In 2016, the ARLIB with APGE was designed, in which carbon nanotubes were loaded with $LiMn_2O_4$ (LMO) and $LiTi_2(PO_4)_2$ (LTP) on a self-healing polymer substrate as electrode and aqueous lithium sulphate/sodium carboxymethylcelluslose ($LiSO_4$/CMC) as gel electrolyte, which worked as a separator and a better interface between the two electrodes [42]. Thus, it assured that AGPEs are the key to regain the lost electrochemical capacity. Several other factors are also helpful in supporting the aqueous electrolyte for LIBs in cooperation with gel polymer, which are good for the thermal and chemical stability of the device. As it is well known that aqueous electrolytes can absorb excess heat, their self-cooling properties contribute to high thermal capacitance. However, if there is some kind of external force applied on the battery, and the electrode has been protected or coated with gel polymer and LISICON film, it retards the evolution of hydrogen gas, causing a smooth diffusion within the aqueous medium allowing it to self-cool before it explodes. An ARLIB was designed using coated lithium metal as anode covered with GPE, whose ionic conductivity was about 0.2 mS cm^{-1} at room temperature, has been developed. They used polymers as gel electrolytes, PVdF/PMMA/PVdF and $LiMn_2O_4$ as cathodes were dipped in an $LiSO_4$ electrolytic system. Due to the cross over effect, Li^+-ions in the coating of this ARLIB delivered an output voltage of about 4.0 V, with a coulombic efficiency and energy density around 446 Wh kg^{-1}. Based on these studies, it is clear that APGE has proven itself as the potent candidate to correct vulnerabilities in terms of mechanical strength, ionic conductivity, safety, risk, and leakage.

9.4 AQUEOUS RECHARGEABLE SODIUM-ION BATTERIES (ARNIBS)

Na metal is the sixth most abundant metal element, making it a low cost element compared to Li. However, as both the elements fall in the same group of alkali metals, Na has similar electrochemical properties as Li because of a similar ionic

Aqueous Electrolytes for LIBs and SIBs

radius. All these aforementioned silent features favor the large-scale application of NIBs and LIBs. As an important component, aqueous electrolyte-based NIBs have several benefits, including high sodium ion conductivity, good wettability, relatively high thermal stability, non-flammability, etc., over organic solvent-based electrolytes [43]. In practice, aqueous rechargeable NIBs (ARNIBs) can be more cost-effective because salts, such as $NaNO_3$, NaCl, Na_2SO_4, etc., used in aqueous systems are cheaper than Li salts. As discussed earlier, ARNIBs behave similarly to ARLIBs. They also show similar properties in aqueous electrolytes and active electrode materials, which also plays a vital role. However, the working principle and detailed mechanism are similar to ARLIBs, as shown in Figure 9.1.

9.4.1 Electrode Material for ARNIBs

Electrode materials were categorized as oxide compounds, polyanionic compounds, and other compounds. The electrode material to be used in ARNIBs should possess the following minimum conditions:

- The electrode redox potential should be in between 2.297 and 3.527 V vs. Na^+/Na at neutral pH so that evaluation O_2 and H_2 due to water splitting can be avoided [7, 24]. As this stated potential range is dependent on pH of the electrolyte, Figure 9.6 covers the various electrode materials along with their potential vs. SHE and Na^+/Na.

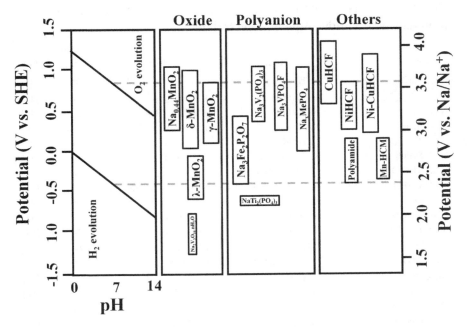

FIGURE 9.6 Electrochemical stability range of water and redox potential for different electrode materials employed in aqueous rechargeable sodium-ion batteries.

206 Ceramic and Specialty Electrolytes

- The electrode material should be chemically stable within the entire operating pH range of an aqueous electrolyte. Moreover, dissolution of electrode materials in aqueous electrolytes in the presence of O_2 or H_2 should not occur.
- Preferably, the cathode materials should contain Na in ARNIBs. If cathode materials without Na elements must be used, then anode materials should be presodiated, otherwise the ARNIBs do not work efficiently.
- For an effective intercalation process and resistance in volume during this process, electrode materials with open structures are preferable.

Since the first report on ARNIBs, many electrode materials have been evaluated. The anode and cathode material used, along with various aqueous electrolytes and their detailed electrochemical activity in ARNIBs, are given in Table 9.2.

As shown in table, Na_xMnO_2 has been widely in use and investigated in detail as an electrode that undergoes insertion/deinsertion process in ARNIBs. Various amounts of $Na(x)$ have been doped in MnO_2, and the optimized value of $x = 0.44$ for aqueous electrolytes [44]. The electrochemical activity of aqueous Na-ion full cell using $NaTi_2(PO_4)_3$ as a counter electrode exhibited a remarkably high rate of performance with much higher density and capacity retention even after 700 cycles [45].

TABLE 9.2

Cell Performance of ARNIBs Comprising Different Cathodic and Anodic Materials with Various Aqueous Electrolytes

Cathode	Anode	Electrolyte	Capacity mAh g^{-1}	Ref.
$Na_{0.44}MnO_2$	$NaTi_2(PO_4)_3$	1 M Na_2SO_4	95	[45]
$Na_{0.66}[Mn_{0.66}Ti_{0.34}]O_2$	$NaTi_2(PO_4)_3$	1 M Na_2SO_4	76	[47]
$NaMnO_2$	$NaTi_2(PO_4)_3$	2 M CH_3COONa	27	[48]
$K_{0.27}MnO_2$	$NaTi_2(PO_4)_3$	1 M Na_2SO_4	68.5	[49]
$Na_3V_2(PO_4)_3$	$NaTi_2(PO_4)_3$	1 M Na_2SO_4	58	[50]
$Na_2VTi(PO_4)_3$	$Na_2VTi(PO_4)_3$	1 M Na_2SO_4	40.6	[51]
$Na_3MnTi(PO_4)_3$	$Na_3MnTi(PO_4)_3$	1 M Na_2SO_4	56.5	[52]
$Na_3V_2O_2(PO_4)F$-MWCNT	$NaTi_2(PO_4)_3$·MWCNT	10 M $NaClO_4$ + 2% VC	54.3	[53]
$NaVPO_4F$	Polyimide	5 M $NaNO_3$	54	[26]
$Na_2CuFe(CN)_6$	$NaTi_2(PO_4)_3$	1 M Na_2SO_4	86	[52]
$Na_2NiFe(CN)_6$	$NaTi_2(PO_4)_3$	1 M Na_2SO_4	79	[54]
$Na_{0.44}MnO_2$	Polyimide-MWCNT	1 M Na_2SO_4	60	[55]
$Na_{0.44}MnO_2$	$Na_2V_6O_{16}.nH_2O$	1 M Na_2SO_4	30	[56]
$Na_{0.44}MnO_2$	$NaV_3(PO_4)_3$@ C	1 M Na_2SO_4	100	[57]
$Na_{0.35}MnO_2$	PPy@MoO_3	0.5 M Na_2SO_4	25	[58]
Cu^{II}- NC-Fe$^{III/II}$	Mn^{II}-NC – $Mn^{III/II}$	10 M $NaClO_4$	22	[59]
$Na_3(VOPO_4)_2F$	$NaTi_2(PO_4)_3$	35 M NaFSI	-	[57]

Aqueous Electrolytes for LIBs and SIBs

Apart from Na_xMnO_2, pure manganese dioxide (MnO_2) with different crystalline geometry has also been used extensively in aqueous-based electrolytes. The ARNIBs with MnO_2 and activated carbon gives almost similar results to ARLIBs in which $LiMn_2O_4$ was used instead of MnO_2. Similarly, 1 M Li_2SO_4 was substituted with a 1M Na_2SO_4 aqueous electrolyte system, but the main concern is the source of Na, as neither λ-MnO_2 nor activated carbon contains Na [46]. The detailed crystallographic structure is shown in Figure 9.3. In addition to Na-doped and undoped MnO_2, poly-anionic compounds (e.g., $Na_2FeP_2O_7$), sodium superionic conductor (NASICON) type (e.g., $Na_3V_2(PO_4)_3$ and $NaVPO_4F$), maricite (e.g., Na $Co_{1/3}Ni_{1/3}Mn_{1/3}PO_4$), olivine (e.g., $Li_xMn_2PO_4$), and Prussian-blue analogues with different aqueous electrolytes have been used as cathode material.

Similar to cathode, NASICON type, $NaTi_2(PO_4)_3$, Prussian-blue analogues, and (Manganese hexaxyano manganate) oxides like $V_2O_5.xH_2O$, organic compounds are also introduced successfully in ARNIBs. Among all these, NASICON type $NaTi_2(PO_4)_3$ anode material has been studied intensively and has shown a high specific capacity of ~133 mAh g^{-1} with a flat potent at about -0.6 V (vs. SHE); however, they suffer with poor electronic conductivity. The mechanism and effect of the crystal structure of cathode material is almost similar to Li-based batteries, hence it is not discussed here in detail.

9.4.2 Aqueous Electrolytes for ARNIBs

Similar to aqueous lithium-ion batteries, NIBs can also use cheaper salts with anions, such as sulphate (SO_4^{2-}), nitrate (NO_3^{-}), perchlorate (ClO_4^{-}), etc., and have been used initially and later for better Na^+-ion transport, and salts with bigger anions, such as $NaCF_3SO_3$, $NaPO_4$, etc., have been used as aqueous electrolytes. However, due to the abundance of Na over Li, the cost of these salts and thus overall cost of ARNIBs is lower than ARLIBs. As discussed in Section 9.3.3, various factors such as pH, dissolved oxygen, and additives in electrolytes, concentration of electrolytes, etc. govern the electrochemical performance of ARNIBs.

9.4.2.1 High Concentration Aqueous Electrolytes for ARNIBs

Broadening the stability window by controlling the evolution of H_2 and O_2 in aqueous-based electrolytes is the main goal for large-scale application of aqueous LIBs and NIBs. As discussed in Section 9.3.3, WISE or "hydrated melt" has proven to be better than conventional aqueous electrolyte systems by suppressing water activity, changing solvation structure with ion aggregation. These approaches expand the electrochemical stability window with suppressed oxygen and hydrogen evolution. However, generally it requires super concentration of expensive organic anion–as solutes in aqueous electrolyte which becomes another major obstacle.

To make aqueous NIBs one step closer to being high voltage, safe, and low-cost rechargeable batteries, the use of high concentration electrolytes consisting of low cost solutes, such as sodium salts of sulphate (SO_4^{2-}), nitrate (NO_3^{-}), and perchlorate (ClO_4^{-}), has been introduced recently [46].

TABLE 9.3
The Solubility of Different Sodium Salts at 20° C

Electrolyte	Solubility (g/100g H$_2$O)	Molality (mol kg^{-1})
CH$_3$COONa	46.4	5.7
NaCl	35.9	6.1
NaNO$_3$	87.6	10.3
Na$_2$SO$_4$	19.5	1.4
NaClO$_4$	201	16.5

Adapted and reproduced from [43].

The following criteria are considered when selecting salts for high concentrated aqueous electrolytes:

- To eliminate free water, the cation/water ratio > 0.3 is required for high intrinsic solubility.
- Should be easily available with low cost.
- Should have the ability to destabilize the water structure and to form an ion-aggregated structure that leads to low water activity.
- Application of the Hofmeister series.

Based on the Hofmeister series, it was confirmed that inorganic salts follow this order: $SO_4^{2-} < NO_3^- < ClO_4^-$, which has the capability to destabilize the bulk water structure. The order says that ClO_4^- anions-based salts have a better capacity to break the water structure by changing the solvation structure with ion aggregates. The solubility for several commonly used Na salts at 20° C can be seen in Table 9.3, which were calculated on the basis of solubility.

It was also observed that solubility of the inorganic electrolytes or salts also followed the order of water-structure-breaking strength for all these salts (i.e., $SO_4^{2-} < NO_3^- < ClO_4^-$) from which (as shown in Table 9.4) ClO_4^- acquires higher conductivity in an aqueous medium in comparison to a conventional, organic medium. Moreover, it was also confirmed from Raman spectroscopy that NaClO$_4$ exhibits a unique hydration characteristic among those other conventional electrolytes, but is surprisingly similar to those of NaCF$_3$SO$_3$ and LiTFSI. The ARNIB was fabricated by using these aqueous electrolytes with Na$_4$Fe$_3$(PO$_4$)$_2$ (P$_2$O$_7$) / NaTi (PO$_4$)$_3$ electrodes that were found with better retention of coulombic efficiency (up to 99%) even after 200 cycles. Apart from this, the introduction of high concentration aqueous electrolytes enhances the stability window from 1.23 to 2.7 V by suppressing water decomposition. Therefore, this new class of aqueous electrolyte system is a step toward realizing low cost, high voltage aqueous batteries.

9.4.2.2 Aqueous Gel Polymer Electrolytes for Sodium-Ion Batteries

Alike AGPE for lithium, there were also some promising candidates for the ARNIB that provided high safety, low cost, and environment friendliness. It was observed that

Aqueous Electrolytes for LIBs and SIBs

TABLE 9.4

Comparison on the Properties of 1 M LiPF$_6$ (the Nonaqueous Electrolyte) vs. Aqueous Electrolyte with Different Salts. (The Cost from Sigma-Aldrich with an Assay above 99% was Used. The Ionic Conductivity was Measured at 25° C)

Salt	Max. Conc. (m)	Na$^+$(Li$^+$)/Water Molar Ratio	Ionic Conductivity (mS cm^{-1})	Cost ($ g^{-1})	Electrolyte Cost ($ L^{-1})
LiPF$_6$	-			16.06	1M = 2,439.7
LiTFSI	21	0.38:1	~ 10	7.18	21m = 43,287.4
Li$_2$SO$_4$	3.1	0.06:1	69.2	0.35	3.1 m = 119.3
LiNO$_3$	7.5	0.14:1	80.6	0.582	7.5 m = 400
LiClO$_4$	5.6	0.10:1	75	1.48	5.6 m = 881.8
Na$_2$SO$_4$	1.3	0.02:1	118	0.197	1.3 m = 36.4
NaNO$_3$	10.7	0.19:1	190	0.204	10.7 m = 185.5
NaCF$_3$SO$_3$	9.26	0.17:1	50	7.68	9.26 m = 12,235.6
NaClO$_4$	17	0.31:1	108	0.49	17 m = 1,020.1

Adapted and reproduced from [60].

liquid organic electrolytes cause safety concerns because of high flammability and toxicity [51]. To correct the problems found with organic liquid electrolytes, scientists introduced aqueous electrolytes with many features that address safety and low toxicity and are adaptable to all types of criteria required for electrochemical devices either by converting into hybrid material or by adding additives. Sodium is a metal being used to make energy storage devices, and researchers are still developing new ideas for the ARNIBs with aqueous electrolytes. Until now, many anions of the electrolytes, mixing of some analogue and different doped and undoped matters with sodium ion have resulted in anode and cathode structure material that enhance the stability window from 1.23 to 2.7 V [46]. Further, to increase its ability in terms of ionic conductivity and stability factor with no leakage and easy diffusion of sodium ions within the aqueous electrolyte, researchers introduced the concept of a polymer matrix within the aqueous medium in a new phase, known as gel or hydrogel polymer electrolytes (GPE). GPEs, in the aqueous phase, favor high ionic conductivity and energy density and stability for ARNIBs. PAN and PVDF were first introduced by Feuillade and Perche in 1975 to enhance the ionic conductivity of the energy storage system at room temperature [62]. It has been reported that GPE serves in many aspects, as they have good mechanical strength and high ionic conductivity and function as good media for conducting electricity and as a separator, and they are easy to use for the fabrication and design of batteries. Researchers took this concept of the aqueous sodium-ion GPE battery system to minimize the issue of flammability while achieving high ionic conductivity. They used PAN-based GPE through electro spinning at high voltage that converted into a polymer solution with slender nanofiber [63]. These nanofibers were immersed in aqueous electrolytes (1 M Na$_2$SO$_4$/0.5 M ZnSO$_4$) that had the ability to absorb liquid electrolytes exceeding 65 wt%, which provides low modulus and large elongation to the electrolytic ions to pass, which is the most important part for battery to run smoothly. Further, a group investigated aqueous NIBs with polyacrylamide hydrogel as the electrolyte and alloxazine (ALO) encapsulated in (conductive carbon material) CMK-3 anode. The polyacrylamide as hydrogel was found in a cross-linked structure that easily reserves the water molecule within the matrix. The hydrogel with 60% solid content had effective potential to solubilize the sodiated ALO. In this case, they measured excess capacity of 160 mAhg^{-1}. The battery was carrying $Na_3V_2 (PO_4)_3$ as cathode and ALO/CMK-3 as anode with polyacrylamide hydrogel containing the aqueous electrolyte $NaCF_3SO_3$ (1 M), which exhibited a capacity retention of 90% after 100 cycles at 2C. The hydrogel contained the solid particle trapped between the matrix, meaning that the salt of sodium within the system caused high rate capability of 146 mAh^{-1} at 10C (1C = 250 mA g^{-1}) [64]. Polyacrylamide hydrogel is composed of cross-linked polymer chains, $NaCF_3SO_3$ and H_2O, and its cross-linked structure is beneficial for water retention, thus enhancing the mechanical strength. Due to this successful system, the elements present within the salt of $NaCF_3SO_3$ get easily distributed homogeneously. The electrochemical stability was observed around 4.3 V for 1 M $NaCF_3SO_3$. Hydrogels are three dimensional networks with water-swelling-type material that exhibit superior water retention ability.

9.4.2.3 Other Factors of Aqueous Electrolytes Affect the Electrochemical Properties of ARNIBs

As discussed in section 9.3.3, it was carrying same concept for the ARNIBs. Still, there were reports that covered the application of these electrolytes in the form of changes in concentration, temperature, and pH as well as the use of water-in-salt in battery systems resulted in promising ARNIBs for large-scale electric energy storage application. Moreover, some of the researchers applied changes in electrode material to enhance the results with the intercalation mechanism with a wide electrochemical window. To qualify for further application in rechargeable gadgets and EVs, additional research needs to explore the voltage window and ways to increase the energy density of ARNIBs.

9.5 CHALLENGES AND FURTHER PERSPECTIVES OF ARLIBS/ARNIBS

As discussed earlier, the role of electrode material is crucial in LIBs and NIBs. From the available literature, it is clear that aqueous alkaline metal-ion batteries suffer from inferior cycle stability in the solutions, and various side reactions are involved in the electrode reactions of insertion compounds. The following sections discuss the different side reactions that need to be addressed to improve the reversibility of LIBs and NIBs [44].

9.5.1 ELECTROLYTE DECOMPOSITION WITH H_2 AND O_2 EVOLUTION

In an aqueous electrolyte system, the stability of intercalated Li in the host electrode is an important issue. The cycle stability is affected by dendrite formation due to side

Aqueous Electrolytes for LIBs and SIBs

reactions occurring between intercalated Li and H_2O. Equations 9.1 and 9.2 represent the reactions occurring between intercalated Li with H_2O and O_2.

$$Li(intercalated) + H_2O \rightarrow Li^+ + OH^- + 0.5H_2 \tag{9.1}$$

$$Li(intercalated) + 0.25O_2 + 0.5H_2O \rightarrow Li^+ + OH^- \tag{9.2}$$

As both the reactions produce LiOH in an aqueous medium, materials that are stable at pH greater than 8, can be used as electrode material; for example, $LiMn_2O_4$ (~ 2.97 V Vs Li^+/ Li) is stable in aqueous LiOH solution at pH value above 8. Thus, for the stable operation of aqueous batteries, control of cut off voltage at a certain pH and elimination of O_2 in the electrolyte are highly essential. The electrode side reactions can be controlled by coating electrodes with carbon or additive-induced surface modification of the electrode. From the available reports, it is clear that only a few electrode materials are chemically stable without surface treatment. Therefore, the identification of electrode materials with appropriate redox material is the key point for chemical stability during battery operation.

9.5.2 Evolution of H_2 and O_2 from Electrolyte Decomposition

The stability potential window for aqueous electrolytes is relatively narrow (~ 1.23 V) compared to organic electrolytes (> 4.0 V). Beyond this potential, aqueous electrolytes decompose and the evolution of H_2 and O_2 gases occurs. Unlike organic electrolytes, the decomposition of aqueous electrolytes does not make any protective layer or film on the electrode surface. Therefore, for long-term cycle life of aqueous LIBs and NIBs, control of operational potential for anode and cathode in aqueous rechargeable batteries is important.

9.5.3 Dissolution of Electrode Material in Aqueous Electrolytes

Long-term cyclability is limited due to electrode dissolution in water-based electrolytes. Studies have found that the pH of aqueous electrolytes plays a crucial role in dissolution of electrode material. For example, $LiFePO_4$ decomposes into Fe_3O_4 at very high pH $\approx$ 10; similarly, Prussian blue is highly unstable at pH $\approx$7 [65, 66]. Moreover, size of electrode material also plays a vital role. For example, due to large surface area, nanostructure electrode material accelerated dissolution or decomposition in the presence of aqueous electrolytes. Therefore, protection of the electrode surface can control the dissolution process during long-term cycling of the battery.

9.5.4 Coinsertion of H^+ with Guest Ions

Proton (H^+) insertion into the host electrode along with guest ions has been found in ARLIBs and ARNIBS. A recent study confirms that substitutional protons block the diffusion path of Li^+ that reduces the cyclability of layered-type electrodes in an aqueous solution [67]. The process of proton co-insertion can be controlled by controlling pH. Alkaline pH (>8) may effectively restrict the proton co-insertion process, but, as mentioned in dissolution, a of pH ≈ 7 (neutral aqueous electrolyte) is advantageous in aqueous metal-ion batteries. Moreover, development of novel electrode materials with minimum proton insertion is also highly essential.

In summary, the utilization of aqueous electrolytes in LIBs and NIBs is the safe and cost effective route that helps in meeting essential criteria for large-scale production of energy storage devices for electrical vehicles and wearable electronics. Additionally, they possess properties such as high energy density and high round-trip efficiency that can be tailored to meet specific requirements of society. Further, improvement in cycle stability and capacity retention in alkali- metal-ion batteries are required for stable operation. Future study should be focused on new types of electrode material that are capable of improving reversibility by taking and releasing guest ions in their flexible structures.

9.6 CONCLUSION AND FUTURE OUTLOOK

The electrolyte plays a potent role, acting as an electrochemical source for ion regeneration. The force that enhances the redox behavior between the two opposite electrodes is favored by external circuit behavior through charging–discharging of the battery. Therefore, a battery consists of three main components: cathode, anode, and electrolyte. As from the above discussed criteria, the development of electrolyte and electrode material is essential in all aspects. Rather than switching to the nonaqueous electrolyte, it is better to choose an alternative source of electrolyte in aqueous medium for Li^+- and Na^+-ion batteries. In comparison to organic-based (nonaqueous) electrolytes, the compatible features that favor aqueous electrolytes is easy ion mobility that causes high conductivity with smooth diffusion in the medium. Use of aqueous electrolyte with these metal-ion-based batteries proves to be less hazardous, which excludes leakage and other gas evolution problems. Also, in terms of cost, it is less expensive than costly salts, such as LiPF6 and DMSO; ether electrolytes; and solvent-based salts, such as dimethyl carbonate (DMC), ethylene carbonate (EC), that are generally used in Li^+- and Na^+-ion batteries with $LiNO_3$, $LiOH$, $NaOH$, etc.

In terms of future perspective, it is better to design metal-ion batteries with sustainable materials and safety features that can operate with a high voltage output that can work with the potential for improved thermal and chemical stability against abuse or with ambient environment. Therefore, using aqueous electrolytes, along with designing electrode material that can resist corrosion and leakage, is a step toward discovering new viable options that can achieve high voltage output with high mobility based on low concentration that can support the existing technology.

ACKNOWLEDGMENT

The authors thank UGC-DAE, Mumbai, India, and UGC-CAS (Phase – II), New Delhi, India, programs for their financial support.

REFERENCES

1. Zhong C, Deng Y, Hu W, Qia J, et al. (2015) A review of electrolyte materials and compositions for electrochemical super capacitors. *Chem Soc Rev* 44:7484–7539. https://doi.org/10.1039/C5CS00303B
2. Zhang SS (2006) A review on electrolyte additives for lithium-ion batteries. *J Power Sources* 162:1379–1394. https://doi.org/10.1016/j.jpowsour.2006.07.074
3. Aurbach D, Talyosef Y, Markovsky B, Markevich E, et al. (2004) Design of electrolyte solutions for Li and Li-ion batteries: A review. *Electrochim Acta* 50:247–254. https://doi.org/10.1016/j.electacta.2004.01.090
4. Alias N, Mohamad AA (2015) Advances of aqueous rechargeable lithium-ion battery: A review. *J Power Sources* 274:237–251. https://doi.org/10.1016/j.jpowsour.2014.10.009
5. Aifantis KE, Hackney SA, et al. (2010) High energy density lithium batteries. *Mater Eng Appl* 81–101. Wiley-VCH. https://doi.org/10.1002/9783527630011
6. Cakan RD, Palacin MR, et al. (2019) Rechargeable aqueous electrolyte batteries: From univalent to multivalent cation chemistry. *J Mater Chem A* 7:20519–20539. https://doi.org/10.1039/C9TA04735B
7. Li W, Dahn JR, et al. (1994) Rechargeable lithium batteries with aqueous electrolytes science. 264:1115–1118. https://doi.org/10.1126/science.264.5162.1115
8. Wang G, Fu L, et al. (2007) An aqueous rechargeable lithium battery with good cycling performance. *Angew Chem Int Ed* 46:295–297. https://doi.org/10.1002/anie.200603699
9. Kim H, Hong J, Park KY, et al. (2014) Aqueous rechargeable Li and Na ion batteries. *Chem Rev* 114:11788–11827. https://doi.org/10.1021/cr500232y
10. Wang Y, Cao G (2008) Developments in nanostructured cathode materials for high-performance lithium-ion batteries. *Adv Mater* 20:2251–2269. https://doi.org/10.1002/adma.200702242
11. Wang Y, Li H, et al. (2010) Nano active materials for lithium-ion batteries. *Nanoscale* 2:1294–1305. doi:10.1039/C0NR00068J
12. Li W, Dahn JR (1995) Lithium-ion cells with aqueous electrolytes. *J Electrochem Soc* 142:1742–1746. https://doi.org/10.1149/1.2044187
13. Yutao L, Bin X, et al. (2012) Parameter identification and SOC estimation of electric vehicle lithium ion battery pack. *J South China Univ Technol (Nat Sci)* 40(12):79–85. doi.10.3969/j.issn.1000-565X.2012.12.014
14. Vujkovic M, Stojkovic I, et al. (2013) Gel-combustion synthesis of $LiFePO_4$/C composite with improved capacity retention in aerated aqueous electrolyte solution. *Electrochimica Acta* 92:248–256. https://doi.org/10.1016/j.electacta.2013.01.030
15. Zhao M, Zhang B, Huang G, Zhang H, et al. (2013) Excellent rate capabilities of $(LiFePO_4/C)//LiV_3O_8$ in an optimized aqueous solution electrolyte. *J Power Sources* 232:181–186. https://doi.org/10.1016/j.jpowsour.2013.01.026
16. He P, Liu JL, et al. (2011) Investigation on capacity fading of $LiFePO_4$ in aqueous electrolyte. *Electrochim Acta* 56:2351–2357. https://doi.org/10.1016/j.electacta.2010.11.027
17. Liu XH, Saito T, et al. (2009) Electrochemical properties of rechargeable aqueous lithium ion batteries with an olivine-type cathode and a Nasicon-type anode. *J Power Sources* 189:706–710. https://doi.org/10.1016/j.jpowsour.2008.08.050
18. Sharma L, Nakamoto K, et al. (2019) Tavorite $LiFePO_4OH$ hydroxyphosphate as an anode for aqueous lithium-ionbatteries. *J Power Sources* 429:17–21. https://doi.org/10.1016/j.jpowsour.2019.04.110
19. Yang C, Ji X, Fan X, Gao T, et al. (2017) Flexible aqueous Li-ion battery with high energy and power densities. *Adv Mater* 29:1701972. https://doi.org/10.1002/adma.201701972

20. Wang H, Huang K, Zeng Y, et al. (2007) Electrochemical properties of TiP_2O_7 and $LiTi_2(PO_4)(3)$ as anode material for lithium ion battery with aqueous solution electrolyte. *Electrochimica Acta* 52:3280–3285. https://doi.org/10.1016/j.electacta.2006.10.010

21. Ramanujapuram A, Yushin G (2018) Understanding the exceptional performance of lithium-Ion battery cathodes in aqueous electrolytes at subzero temperatures. *Adv Energy Mater* 8:1802624. https://doi.org/10.1002/aenm.201802624

22. Ko S, Yamada Y, Miyazaki K, et al. (2019) Lithium-salt monohydrate melt: A stable electrolyte for aqueous lithium-ion batteries. *Electrochem Commun* 104:106488. https://doi.org/10.1016/j.elecom.2019.106488

23. Jiang P, Yan X, Chen L, Liang X, et al. (2019) Methylsulfonylmethane-based deep eutectic solvent as a new type of green electrolyte for a high-energy-density aqueous lithium-ion battery. *ACS Energy Lett* 4:1419–1426. doi:10.1021/acsenergylett.9b00968

24. Luo JY, Xia YY, et al. (2007) Aqueous lithium-ion battery $LiTi_2(PO_4)_3/LiMn_2O_4$ with high power and energy densities as well as superior cycling stability. *Adv Funct Mater* 17:3877–3884.https://doi.org/10.1002/adfm.200700638

25. Wang H, Huang K, Zeng Y, et al. (2007) Stabilizing cyclability of an aqueous lithium-ion battery $LiNi_{1/3}Mn_{1/3}Co_{1/3}O_2 / Li_xV_2O_5$ by polyaniline coating on the anode. *Electrochem Solid State Lett* 10:A199–A203. https://doi.org/10.1149/1.2748637

26. Qin H, Song ZP, et al. (2014) Aqueous rechargeable alkali-ion batteries with polyimide anode. *J Power Sources* 249:367–372. https://doi.org/10.1016/j.jpowsour.2013.10.091

27. He P, Wang Y, et al. (2011) The effect of alkalinity and temperature on the performance of lithium-air fuel cell with hybrid electrolytes. *J Power Sources* 196:5611–5616. https://doi.org/10.1016/j.jpowsour.2011.02.071

28. Stojkovic IB, Cvjetićanin ND, et al. (2010) The improvement of the Li-ion insertion behaviour of $Li_{1.05}Cr_{0.10}Mn_{1.85}O_4$ in an aqueous medium upon addition of vinylene carbonate. *Electrochem Commun* 12:371–373. DOI10.1016/j.elecom.2009.12.037

29. Tian L, Yuan A, et al. (2009) Electrochemical performance of nanostructured spinel $LiMn_2O_4$ in different aqueous electrolytes. *J Power Sources* 192:693–697. https://doi.org/10.1016/j.jpowsour.2009.03.002

30. Ruffo RF, Mantia FL, et al. (2011) Electrochemical characterization of $LiCoO_2$ as rechargeable electrode in aqueous $LiNO_3$ electrolyte. *Solid State Ionics* 192:289–292. https://doi.org/10.1016/j.ssi.2010.05.043

31. Suo L, Borodin O, Gao T, et al. (2015) "Water-in-salt" electrolyte enables high-voltage aqueous lithium-ion chemistries. *Science* 350:938–943. doi:10.1126/science.aab1595

32. Lux SF, Terborg L, Hachmoller O, et al. (2013) LiTFSI stability in water and its possible use in aqueous lithium-ion batteries: pH dependency, electrochemical window and temperature stability. *J Electrochem Soc* 160:A1694–A1700. https://doi.org/10.1149/2.039310jes

33. Suo L, Han F, Fan X, et al. (2016) "Water-in-salt" electrolytes enable green and safe Li-ion batteries for large-scale electric energy storage applications. *J Mater Chem* 4:6639–6644. https://doi.org/10.1039/C6TA00451B

34. Dubouis N, Lemaire P, Mirvaux B et al. (2018) The role of the hydrogen evolution reaction in the solid–electrolyte interphase formation mechanism for "water-in-salt" electrolytes, *Energy Environ Sci* 11:3491–3499. https://doi.org/10.1039/C8EE02456A

35. Baskoro F, Wong HQ, Yen HJ (2019) Strategic structural design of a gel polymer electrolyte toward a high efficiency lithium-ion battery. *ACS Appl Energy Mater* 26:3937–3971. https://doi.org/10.1021/acsaem.9b00295

36. Song JY, Wang YY, Wan CC (1999) Review of gel-type polymer electrolytes for lithium-ion batteries. *J Power Sources* 77:183–197. https://doi.org/10.1016/S0378-7753(98)00193-1

37. Arya A, Sharma AL (2017) Polymer electrolytes for lithium ion batteries: A critical study. *Ionics* 23:497–540. https://doi.org/10.1007/s11581-016-1908-6

Aqueous Electrolytes for LIBs and SIBs

38. Chen YH, Freunberger SA, Peng, Z, et al. (2012) Li–O_2 battery with a dimethylformamide electrolyte. *J Am Chem Soc*134:7952–7957. https://doi.org/10.1021/ja302178w
39. Long L, Wang S, Xiao M, Meng Y (2016) Polymer electrolytes for lithium polymer batteries. *J Mater Chem A* 4:10038–10069. https://doi.org/10.1039/C6TA02621D
40. Dias FB, Plomp L, Veldhuis JB (2000) Trends in polymer electrolytes for secondary lithium batteries. *J Power Sources* 88:169–191. https://doi.org/10.1016/S0378-7753(99)00529-7
41. Zhu YS, Wang XJ, Hou YY, et al. (2013) A new single-ion polymer electrolyte based on polyvinyl alcohol for lithium ion batteries. *Electrochim Acta* 87:113–118. https://doi.org/10.1016/j.electacta.2012.08.114
42. Zhao Y, Zhang Y, Sun H, et al. (2016) A self-healing aqueous lithium-ion battery. *Angew Chem Int Ed* 55:14384–14388. https://doi.org/10.1002/anie.201607951
43. Bin D, Wang F, Tamirat AG, et al. (2018) Progress in aqueous rechargeable sodium-ion batteries. *Adv Energy Mater* 8:1703008. https://doi.org/10.1002/aenm.201703008
44. Tevar AD, Whitacre JF (2010) Relating synthesis conditions and electrochemical performance for the sodium intercalation compound $Na_4Mn_9O_{18}$ in aqueous electrolyte. *J Electrochem Soc* 157:A870–A875. https://doi.org/10.1149/1.3428667
45. Li Z, Young D, Xia K, Carter WC, Chiang YM (2013) Towards high power high energy aqueous sodium-ion batteries: The $NaTi_2(PO_4)_3/Na_{0.44}MnO_2$ system. *Adv Energy Mater* 3:290–294. https://doi.org/10.1002/aenm.201200598
46. Kim H, Hong J, Park KY, Kim H, et al. (2014) Aqueous rechargeable Li and Na ion batteries. *Chem Rev*114:11788–11827. https://doi.org/10.1021/cr500232y
47. Wang Y, Mu L, Liu J, Yang Z, et al. (2015) A novel high capacity positive electrode material with tunnel-type structure for aqueous sodium-ion batteries. *Adv Energy Mater* 5:1501005. https://doi.org/10.1002/aenm.201501005
48. Hou Z, Li X, Liang J, et al. (2015) An aqueous rechargeable sodium ion battery based on a $NaMnO_2$–$NaTi_2(PO_4)_3$ hybrid system for stationary energy storage. *J Mater Chem A* 3:1400–1404. https://doi.org/10.1039/C4TA06018K
49. Liu Y, Qiao Y, Zhang W, Xu H, et al. (2014) High-performance aqueous sodium-ion batteries with $K_{0.27}MnO_2$ cathode and their sodium storage mechanism. *Nano Energy* 5:97–104. https://doi.org/10.1016/j.nanoen.2014.02.010
50. Zhang Q, Liao C, Zha T, Li H (2016) A high rate 1.2V aqueous sodium-ion battery based on all NASICON structured $NaTi_2(PO_4)_3$ and $Na_3V_2(PO_4)_3$. *Electrochim Acta* 196:470–478. https://doi.org/10.1016/j.electacta.2016.03.007
51. Wang H, Zhang T, Chen C, et al. (2018) High-performance aqueous symmetric sodium-ion battery using NASICON-structured $Na_2VTi(PO_4)_3$. *Nano Res* 11:490–498. https://doi.org/10.1007/s12274-017-1657-5
52. Wu E, Sun M, Shen Y, et al. (2014) Energetic aqueous rechargeable sodium-ion battery based on $Na_2CuFe(CN)_6$-$NaTi_2(PO_4)_3$ intercalation chemistry. *ChemSusChem* 7:407–411. https://doi.org/10.1002/cssc.201301036
53. Kumar PR, Jung YH, Wang JE, Kim DK (2016) $Na_3V_2O_2(PO_4)_2$F-MWCNT nanocomposites as a stable and high rate cathode for aqueous and non-aqueous sodium-ion batteries. *J Power Sources* 324:421–427. https://doi.org/10.1016/j.jpowsour.2016.05.096
54. Wu X, Cao Y, Ai X, Qian J, Yang H (2013) A low-cost and environmentally benign aqueous rechargeable sodium-ion battery based on $NaTi_2 (PO_4)_3Na_2NiFe (CN)_6$ intercalation chemistry. *Electrochem Commun* 31:145–148. https://doi.org/10.1016/j.elecom.2013.03.013
55. Gu T, Zhou M, Liu W, Cheng MK, et al. (2016) A polyimide–MWCNTs composite as high performance anode for aqueous Na-ion batteries. *RSC Adv* 6:53319–53323. https://doi.org/10.1039/C6RA09075C
56. Deng C, Zhang S, Dong Z, Shang Y (2014) 1D nanostructured sodium vanadium oxide as a novel anode material for aqueous sodium ion batteries. *Nano Energy* 4:49–55. https://doi.org/10.1016/j.nanoen.2013.12.014

57. Ke L, Dong J, Lin B, Yu T, et al. (2017) A $NaV_3(PO_4)_3$@C hierarchical nanofiber in high alignment: Exploring a novel high-performance anode for aqueous rechargeable sodium batteries. *Nanoscale* 9:4183–4190. https://doi.org/10.1039/C7NR00793K

58. Liu Y, Zhang BH, Xiao SY, Liu LL, et al. (2014) A nanocomposite of MoO_3 coated with PPy as an anode material for aqueous sodium rechargeable batteries with excellent electrochemical performance. *Electrochim Acta* 116:512–517. https://doi.org/10.1016/j.electacta.2013.11.077

59. Pasta M, Wessells CD, Liu N, Nelson J, et al. (2014) Full open-framework batteries for stationary energy storage. *Nat Commun* 5:3007. https://doi.org/10.1038/ncomms4007

60. Lee MH, Kim SJ, Chang D, et al. (2019) Toward a low-cost high-voltage sodium aqueous rechargeable battery. *Mater Today* 29:26–36. https://doi.org/10.1016/j.mattod.2019.02.004

61. Kuhnel RS, Reber OD, Battaglia C (2017) A high-voltage aqueous electrolyte for sodium-ion batteries. *ACS Energy Lett* 2:2005–2006. https://doi.org/10.1021/acsenergylett.7b00623

62. Feuillade G, Perche PJ (1975) Ion-conductive macromolecular gels and membranes for solid lithium cells. *Appl Electrochem* 5:63–69. https://doi.org/10.1007/BF00625960

63. Zhang Y, Tan ZT, Huang J (2018) Polyacrylonitrile-nanofiber based gel polymer electrolyte for novel aqueous sodium-ion battery based on a $Na_4Mn_9O_{18}$ cathode and Zn metal anode. *Polymers* 10(853):1–10. https://doi.org/10.3390/polym10080853

64. Zhong L, Lu Y, Li H, Tao Z, Chen J (2018) High-performance aqueous sodium-ion batteries with hydrogel electrolyte and alloxazine/CMK-3 anode. *ACS Sustainable Chem Eng* 6:7761–7768. https://doi.org/10.1021/acssuschemeng.8b00663

65. Manickam M, Singh P, Thurgate S, Prince KJ (2006) Redox behavior and surface characterization of $LiFePO_4$ in lithium hydroxide electrolyte. *J Power Sources* 158:646–649. https://doi.org/10.1016/j.jpowsour.2005.08.059

66. Wessells CD, Peddada SV, Matthew T, et al. (2011) The effect of insertion species on nanostructured open framework hexacyanoferrate battery electrodes. *J Electrochem Soc* 159:A98–A103. https://doi.org/10.1149/2.060202jes

67. Gu X, Liu JL, Yang JH, Xiang HJ, et al. (2011) First-principles study of H^+ intercalation in layer structured $LiCoO_2$. *J Phys Chem C* 115:12672–12676. doi:10.1021/jp202846p

10 Transparent Electrolytes
A Promising Pathway for Transparent Energy Storage Devices in Next Generation Optoelectronics

Anjumole P. Thomas, Akhila Das, Neethu T.M. Balakrishnan, Sajan Chinnan, Jou-Hyeon Ahn, Jabeen Fatima M. J., Prasanth Raghavan

CONTENTS

10.1 Introduction 217
10.2 Transparent Electrolyte for Li$^+$-ion Batteries 220
10.3 TSSEs for Supercapacitors 226
    10.3.1 IL-Based Transparent Electrolytes 230
10.4 Transparent Electrolytes for Fuel Cells 232
10.5 Conclusions and Perspectives 233
Acknowledgments 234
References 234

10.1 INTRODUCTION

To address the energy crisis, the scientific world is exploring renewable energy resources such as wind energy, hydro energy, solar energy, tidal energy etc., as well as materials with high performance at a low cost. As green energy, the advantages of lithium-ion batteries (LIBs) [1, 2] and supercapacitors [3] include large energy density, power density, long service life, and no environmental pollution. But most of the energy storage devices are rigid and do not meet today's stringent requirements; therefore, flexible and transparent energy storage systems have been increasingly used for portable wearable devices, light emitting diodes [4], transistors [5], energy storage smart windows [3], gas sensors [6], and so on.

Transparent electronics are an emerging and promising technology that recently have gained more attention in various applications, such as in touch screens, TV displays, and solar cells [7]. All these electronic devices are inseparable from the support of energy storage devices, such as batteries and supercapacitors [8]. Typically,

217

an energy storage device consists of electrodes, electrolytes, current collectors, separators, and packaging [9]. In order to make the whole device transparent, the first step is to make or use a transparent electrolyte, which is the major component of any energy storage device [7]. None of the other components are transparent, so a fully integrated energy storage device cannot be visualized without reducing the size of the active materials. Small devices possess a low voltage window that may not be practical for the above-mentioned applications [8]. For the successful use of transparent electrolytes, it is possible to use a series of energy storage devices to scale up the charge density and that can be used in modern applications [9].

Transparent electronic devices appear in a substantial number of applications including portable electronic devices and solar cells [10]. The concept of a fully transparent cell phone has attracted great attention recently. Transparent screens also have experienced rapid development in modern technological gadgets; however, the key to developing a transparent cell phone is to overcome the problem of a fully transparent battery. However, the research and development of transparent LIBs are still at an infant stage. The typical method to make a transparent device is to decrease the thickness of the battery. A commonly used method for making transparent devices is to reduce the thickness of active materials as demonstrated in carbon nanotubes [11, 12], graphene, and organic semiconductors. Low cost, safety, and high energy density are important factors in the development of energy storage devices. Solid-state lithium batteries are expected to be safe for rigorous use applications because a nonflammable solid-state electrolyte (SSE) is used instead of the flammable organic liquid electrolytes used in conventional LIBs [13]. This solid-state electrolytes can be either ceramic-based (solid ceramic electrolytes, SCEs) or polymer-based (solid polymer electrolyte, SPE) electrolytes

Suzuki et al. [13] reported that a Garnet-type $Li_7La_3Zr_2O_{12}$ (LLZ) is a better transparent electrolyte candidate material for the LIBs because of its high stability and high lithium-ion (Li^+-ion) conductivity at room temperature. LLZ is stable in contact with lithium metal and has an excellent electrical conductivity at room temperature [14]. Transparent 1.0 wt% Al_2O_3-doped LLZ (A-LLZ) was prepared using hot isostatic pressing (HIP) treatment. Through HIP treatment, the relative density of the LLZ pellet was increased from 91.5% to 99.1%. The HIP-treated samples have both white and transparent areas, showing electrical conductivity of 9.9×10^{-4} S cm^{-1} at 25° C. LLZ is an attractive material for future LIBs because of its high stability and Li^+-ion conductivity at room temperature [15]. Puthirath et al. [16] reported a novel transparent flexible Li^+-ion conducting solid polymer electrolyte (SPE) based on poly-dimethyl siloxane (PDMS) and polyethylene oxide (PEO) polymer blend. Advantages of atomically smooth PDMS and flexible high solvation matrix PEO for Li^+-ion is considered for material selection in developing SSEs [17, 18]. PDMS holds the SSE as a laminated surface and provides high hydrophobicity to the Li^+-ion conducting medium [16]. A synergistic effect, a down shift in percentage crystallinity and crystalline melting point of matrix polymer of SSE upon the addition of lithium salt such as $LiPF_6$, $LiClO_4$, or LiBOB, is observed, which is due to the salting-in phenomenon. This improved the ionic conductivity and electrochemical performance of the SSE without affecting lithium transference number. Because of the 3D network

Transparent Electrolytes

structure formed by the cross-linking reaction, PDMS holds the SSE as a laminated surface by providing high water contact angle (WCA), ensuring the durability of SSEs for ambient conditions. A completely transparent and flexible supercapacitor can be realized from this SSE.

Pan et al. [19] reported a gel type LIB with a long cycle enabled by a dense transparent polymeric single-ion conductor. Polymer electrolytes were synthesized using the side-chain grafting method with 4-amino-4'trifuorolmethyl bis(benzene sulphonyl)imide grafted on side chains of poly(ethylene-alt-maleic anhydride) with a grafting ratio of 50%. Blending lithiated side-grafted poly(ethylene-alt-maleic anhydride) with poly(vinylidene fluoride-*co*-hexafluoropropylene) (PVdF-*co*-HFP) via the solution cast method results in dense transparent film. The fabricated polymer-blend-electrolyte film has the ionic conductivity of 0.104 mS cm^{-1} at room temperature, a tensile strength of 15.5 MPa, and percentage elongation at break of 5%. A gel type single-ion conductive polymeric LIB was assembled using the blended film as the separator as well as the electrolyte, LiFePO$_4$/C mixed with ionomers as the cathode, and a lithium foil as the anode. The battery delivers a reversible discharge capacity of 100 mAhg^{-1} at 1 C under room temperature for 1,000 cycles. The stable cyclic imide and comb-like structure are responsible for the excellent battery performance. Side-chain grafted single-ion conducting polymer electrolytes are well suited for large-scale production.

Fuentes et al. [20] reported that transparent conducting polymer electrolyte films were prepared by adding LiClO$_4$ to a mixture of chitosane and poly(amino propyl siloxane) in a molar ratio of 0.6:1 by sol-gel method. Molecular and morphological studies carried out by Fourier-transform infrared spectroscopy (FTIR) and scanning electron microscopy (SEM) depend on the lithium concentration. About 0.8 mol lithium salt per chitosan can be added before the product lost transparence and molecular compatibility of the pristine chitosan/poly(amino propyl siloxane) polymer complex. When lithium salt exceeds the concentration limit, anisotropically oriented patterns were observed in the film. Self-supporting films obtained have transmittance of 80% in the visible spectral range. Transparency and ionic conductivity of the product is due to the layered nature of the nanocomposite.

Supercapacitors or electrochemical capacitors gained increasing attention as compared to traditional capacitors because of their large capacity, specific energy, wider working range, and longer service life [21]. With the development of modern electronic device demands, supercapacitors must be transparent, flexible, and foldable [22, 23]. In order to make fully transparent supercapacitors, each component (electrode, separator, current collector, and electrolyte) must be transparent. Many researchers are working to make completely transparent and flexible supercapacitors for optoelectronics. Rodriguez et al. [24] developed a transparent PVP-LiClO$_4$ SSE using the dip-coating method, and its temperature dependence, aging time, lithium-salt concentrations, etc. are studied. Of all the types of conjugated polymers, PVP has attracted special attention because of its good environmental stability, easy processing, and excellent transparency. This electrolyte was used in the fabrication of electrochemical supercapacitors (PEDOT/PVP-LiClO$_4$/PEDOT). Ionic conductivity increases with temperature reaching a value of 3.34×10^{-3} S cm^{-1} at 60° C for a

LiClO$_4$/PVP weight ratio equal to 1.2. At higher LiClO$_4$/PVP ratios, conductivity decreases.

Wei et al. [25] reported a transparent, flexible, and solid-state supercapacitor based on room temperature ionic liquid (RTIL) gel and indium tin oxide (ITO) electrodes coated in a transparent polymer substrate without a separator, which enables the roll-to-roll technique for fabrication of supercapacitors used as printable devices. This was the first type of transparent electrochemical double layer capacitor (EDLC) based on ionic liquid gel, which introduced an environmentally friendly, safe, transparent electrolyte based on RTIL gel that is made of 1-butyl-3-methylimidazolium chloride [BMIM][Cl] and cellulose. RTILs are molten salts with a melting point close to or below room temperature. They are composed of ions of opposite charges that only loosely fit together. The supercapacitor reported in this paper using [BMIM][Cl] and cellulose gel composite is a completely transparent and flexible electrochemical device that can be bent and twisted.

Jung et al. [26] reported creating transparent, flexible supercapacitors by assembling nanoengineered carbon electrodes, prepared in porous templates, with morphology of interconnected arrays of complex shape and porosity. Highly textured graphitic films act as electrodes and integrate with polymer electrolytes that act as a thin film supercapacitor. Solid polymer electrolytes with conformal electrolyte packing provide excellent mechanical stability and optical transparency to the supercapacitor. The design of the devices allows for mechanically flexible energy storage devices that could be integrated into unique applications that require high form factor and optical transparency, such as roll-up displays, wearable devices, and organic solar platforms.

High-performance SSEs are a major challenge for some applications in batteries, solar cells, fuel cells, etc. [27]. In the case of fuel cells, the electrolytic membrane should possess a medium-range operating temperature for many applications [28]. Vioux et al. [29] reported a versatile heat-resistant polymer electrolyte in which room temperature ionic liquids (RTILs) are confined in a porous silica matrix prepared using one-step nonhydrolytic sol-gel route. Ionogels are prepared from a mixture of tetramethoxysilane (TMOS), formic acid (FA) and RTIL. Ionogels are a versatile family of transparent, temperature-resistant SSEs and can operate in a wide range of temperatures.[30]. A protonic conductive membrane is a very important element for polymer electrolyte fuel cells (PEFCs), while it is also applicable for proton sensor, separation, acidic catalyst, and so on. Honma et al. [31] and Advani et al. [32] reported transparent proton conducting hybrid SSE for proton exchange membrane (PEM) fuel cell (PEMFC). This chapter focuses on the preparation and properties of transparent electrolytes for different energy storage devices such as LIBs, super capacitors (SCs) and fuel cells (FCs).

10.2 TRANSPARENT ELECTROLYTE FOR Li$^+$-ion BATTERIES

LIBs are largely used energy storage devices in the electronics market, expanding its horizons from consumer electronics to advanced areas such as aerospace and military applications [33]. In LIBs, high performance smart SSEs replace the conventional liquid electrolyte due to safety threats in advanced applications. Solid-state electrolyte-based batteries have better stability and safety measures as compared to liquid electrolyte-based batteries [34]. The safety threats reported for liquid electrolyte-based conventional LIBs limit their future use and there is a need to develop high performance smart SSEs. Batteries employing SSEs, collectively called solid-state batteries (SSBs), with high energy and power densities are alternatives to the conventional liquid electrolyte-based ones with much improvement in all-round stability and safety measures [34]. Poor ion-kinetics at room temperature leading to poor ionic conductivity is an "Achilles heel" in the development of SSE-based energy storage devices [35].

Puthirath et al. [16] reported a polymer-based transparent flexible Li$^+$-ion conducting SSE. A novel organic–inorganic hybrid SSE based on PDMS, PEO, and LiClO$_4$ was demonstrated for its high Li$^+$-ion conductivity at room temperature. PDMs is attracted for the preparation of transparent electrolytes is due to a wide and varied set of advantages that include low cost, chemical inertness, non-toxicity, and the ability to translate features in the micrometer range. In addition, it is optically transparent, easy to process and permeable to gases. It is an elastic and physically robust material that is reversibly deformable, which is beneficial for development of flexible and stretchable SSE for the fabrication of flexible batteries and super capacitors. Because of the presence of Si atoms in the polymer back bone, PDMS, is a highly hydrophobic material (water contact angle >100°). PDMS also known as dimethicone, belongs to a group of polymeric organosilicon compounds that are the most widely used silicon-based organic polymer used for the preparation of transparent electrolytes in LIBs [17,18]. PDMS holds the SSE as a laminated surface and provides high hydrophobicity to the Li$^+$-ion conducting medium. The PDMS/PEO organic-inorganic hybrid electrolyte showed visible light transparency of more than 80% and can be used as an SSE in transparent and flexible energy storage devices.

In this study, sample preparation started with dissolving the LiClO$_4$ in ethanol, then mortaring it with 0.1 g of PEO with different concentrations. Later, the compound was mixed with 1 ml of PDMS followed by the addition of a curing agent, and finally curing of the mix after smearing the viscous fluid onto a quartz substrate, at 80° C for 3 hours. Schematic representation of the preparation of transparent SSEs (TSSEs) is shown in Figure 10.1. The products formed are named as pristine PDMS, PEO-PDMS, LiPEOP 1–4, respectively. Li$^+$-ion half-cells were assembled with Li

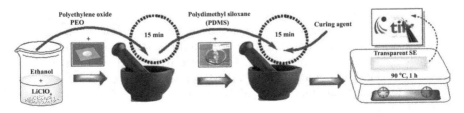

FIGURE 10.1 Synthesis sequences involved in the development of transparent and flexible SEs based on polyethylene oxide (PEO) and polydimethyl siloxane (PDMS). Adapted and reproduced with permission from reference [16]. Copyright 2017 Royal Society of Chemistry.

metal as the anode, LiFePO$_4$ as the cathode, and TSSE as the electrolyte. The electrochemical characterizations are carried out to ensure quality and performance efficiency. Cyclic voltammetry (CV) characterization, transport number calculation, and electrochemical impedance spectroscopy (EIS) measurements of the samples were carried out. Direct current (DC) polarization and alternating current (AC) impedance measurements were carried out with a DC voltage of 10 MV applied across each sample in a metal electrode-sample-metal (Li/SSE/Li) configuration. From the results, it is clear that by increasing the LiClO$_4$ concentrations, the Li$^+$-ion transport number increased to 0.69 for LiPEOP$_4$. The combined synergic effect of PDMS and PEO matrices is the reason behind the high Li$^+$-ion transfer number observed in LiPEOP$_4$. CVs were obtained by sandwiching TSSE between Li electrodes and stainless steel over 2–5 V using a potentiostat. On moving from pristine PDMS to LiPEOP$_4$, no faradaic current is found in the potential window, irrespective of the improvement in ionic conductivity. TSSE film of LiPEOP$_4$ based on PEO, LiClO$_4$, and PDMS shows high Li$^+$-ionic conductivity and high Li$^+$-ion transport number. This SSE possesses Young's modulus of approximately 0.98 MPa and optical transparency of 85% in visible light. The multifunctional TSSE showed room temperature ionic conductivity of ~0.03 mS cm^{-1} endowed with other exotic properties such as large electrochemical window (2–5 V), high mechanical robustness and flexibility, and hydrophobicity (contact angle >100°).

Solid-state LIBs are considered as a better candidate for rigorous use applications rather than organic-liquid electrolytes used in conventional LIBs [13]. Various solid Li$^+$-ion conducting electrolytes have been reported, such as layered Li$_3$N [36] type, Li$_2$S-based glass, LISICON-type Li$_{14}$Zn(GeO$_4$)$_4$ [37], etc. Garnet-type LLZ [38] is an SSE that possesses high Li$^+$-ion conductivity and is quite stable at room temperature. Suzuki et al. [13] reported a transparent garnet-type Li$^+$-ion conducting SSE of 1.0 wt% A-LLZ was prepared using hot isotactic pressing (HIP). Developed LLZ was a grain boundary-free high-density electrolyte that was free of dendritic growth and less ionic diffusion. LLZ precursor was prepared by solid-state reaction using Li$_2$CO$_3$, La$_2$O$_3$, and ZrO$_2$. The molar ratio of Li:La:Zr was controlled to 7.7:3:2. Starting materials were ball milled with a zirconia vessel and balls using a high-energy mechanical mill. Later, the sample powder was isotatically pressed into pellets at 150 MPa and then calcined at 900° C for 5 h. Calcined pellets were ball milled with γ-Al$_2$O$_3$ and pressed into pellets that were then placed in alumina crucibles.

The obtained A-LLZ pellets were subjected to the HIP treatment of 127 MPa at 1160° C in an argon atmosphere for 2 h using zirconia crucibles. In HIP treatment, a crucible with a sample is put into a chamber, and the chamber is subjected to high temperature and high pressure. The electrical conductivities of the sintered samples (10 mm diameter and 0.8–0.5 mm thick) with sputtered copper electrodes were measured using an impedance gain-phase analyzer in the frequency range of 0.1 Hz–1 MHz with a voltage amplitude at 10 mV. Z View software was employed for data analysis and presentation of the impedance results. Direct current measurements of the Li/LLZ/Li cells were performed using a multichannel potentiostat/galvanostat. Light transmittance measurements were also conducted.

Transparent Electrolytes

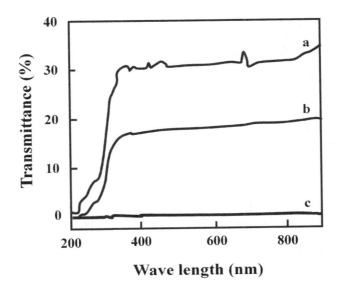

FIGURE 10.2 UV spectra on transmittance vs. wavelength curves for (a) the transparent area of the membrane, (b) the entire area of 1.0 wt% A-LLZ membrane after HIP treatment, and (c) 1.0 wt% A-LLZ membrane before HIP treatment. Adapted and reproduced with permission from reference [13]. Copyright 2015 Elsevier.

The light transmittance of the transparent parts and the entire A-LLZ are shown in Figure 10.2. Raman scattering measurements confirmed that the white parts of the sample contained Li_2CO_3 and LiOH. LiOH reacts with CO_2 in ambient air to produce Li_2CO_3. The Li_2CO_3 and LiOH observed in A-LLZ may be due to contamination by water and CO_2 in the air. The cell with HIP-treated transparent A-LLZ that did not contain any white areas showed no sudden voltage drop, instead of cell voltage increases gradually during the polarization period. LLZ is an attractive material for future LIBs because of its high stability and Li^+-ion conductivity at room temperature. To perform as a better electrolyte, the dendritic formation of lithium during high current density should be suppressed. HIP-treated LLZ showed white and transparent areas, whereas the HIP-treated LLZ was as high as 9.9×10^{-4} S cm^{-1} at 25° C. The LLZ electrolyte that included white areas was short-circuited after 250 s polarization at 0.5 mA cm^{-2} due to lithium dendrite formation, whereas the transparent LLZ without white areas was not short-circuited. This result suggests that the grain boundary in LLZ may play an important role in lithium dendrite formation during the lithium deposition process.

Pan et al. [19] reported a dense transparent polymeric single-ion conductor for LIBs. Synthesis of a single-ion conductor made of the commercially available poly(ethylene-alt-maleic anhydride) as the polymer backbone with maleic anhydrides providing the reaction sites for grafting with functional side chains is reported in this paper. The flexible alkyl main chain ensures the mechanical stability. An asymmetric bis(benzene sulfonyl)imide molecule, i.e., 4-amino-4'-trifluoromethyl bis(benzene sulfonyl)imide is designed and synthesized as a selected anion on side chains. The 4-amino-4'-trifluoromethyl bis(benzene sulfonyl)imide is grafted on the side chains of the polymer backbone via cyclic imides to obtain a comb-like polymer. The polar chemical bonds of imide and anhydride in the side chains are more compatible with the polar solvents, which is beneficial for film swelling and lithium ionization. Blending the lithiated side-grafted poly(ethylene-alt-maleic anhydride) with polyvinylidene fluoride-co-hexafluoropropylene (PVdF-co-HFP) via a solution cast method results in a dense transparent film.

Synthesis of 4-amino-4'-trifluoromethyl bis(benzene sulfonyl) imide is achieved by dissolving 0.05 mol of 4-nitrobenzene sulphonamide in sodium hydroxide solution to form a homogeneous solution. While stirring, 0.025 mol of 4-(trifluoromethyl) benzene-1-sulfonyl chloride was added stepwise for 1 hr. On cooling, the suspension was filtered, and the filtrate was collected. Concentrated hydrochloric acid was added to the filtrate to precipitate completely. The precipitate was washed and recrystallized in water. The yield was 40%. 0.4 mol of tin dichloride dehydrate was dissolved in 20 ml methanol with an addition of hydrochloric acid. Additionally, 3.2 mol 4-4'-trifluoromethyl bis(benzene sulfonyl)imide dissolved in 80 ml of dichloromethane solution. The reaction mixture heated under 40° C for 4 h. The precipitate obtained was washed and collected. Side-chain grafting 4-amino-4'-trifluoromethyl bis(benzene sulfonyl)imide on poly(ethylene-alt-maleic anhydride) was completed by the following procedures. Poly(ethylene-alt-maleic anhydride), 4-amino4'-trifluoromethyl bis (benzene sulphonyl)imide, 30 ml of m-cresol and five drops of isoquinoline were transferred into a 50 ml two-neck flask. Heated the above reactants at 120° C in an argon atmosphere. After cooling, the reaction mixture was poured into toluene to precipitate the product. The precipitate was collected by filtration followed by washing with methanol. The electrochemical characterization of the electrolyte film was carried out. A Li^+-ion transference number of 0.92 was derived from chronoamperometry and electrochemical impedance spectroscopic calculations. This depicts that the formed electrolyte is a single-ion conductor. The electrolyte film exhibits good tensile strength and high ionic conductivity at room temperature. Side-chain grafting imparts lithium ionization and, therefore, high ionic mobility. Batteries equipped with this electrolyte film display outstanding long-term cycle performance.

A conventional battery device usually uses PVdF as a binder; instead of this, a lithiated side-chain grafted polymer was used as a binder, which helps to construct a well-connected ion transport network as well as adhesion effect between active materials. The cycle performance of the battery at various C-rates was examined at room temperature and is shown in Figure 10.3. The charge–discharge curve at each C-rate is shown in Figure 10.3a. The device is capable of delivering 123 mAh g^{-1} at 0.2 C, 114 mAh g^{-1} at 0.4 C, 107 mAh g^{-1} at 0.6 C, 103 mAh g^{-1} at 0.8 C, 100 mAh g^{-1} at 1.0 C, 86 mAh g^{-1} at 2.0 C, 77 mAh g^{-1} at 3.0 C, 71 mAh g^{-1} at 4.0 C, and 65 mAh g^{-1} at 5.0 C (Figure 10.3 b). The specific capacities at low C-rates are generally lower than the values of the batteries using the linear single-ion conducting polymer electrolyte. Nevertheless, the capacities at high C-rates are higher than the

Transparent Electrolytes 225

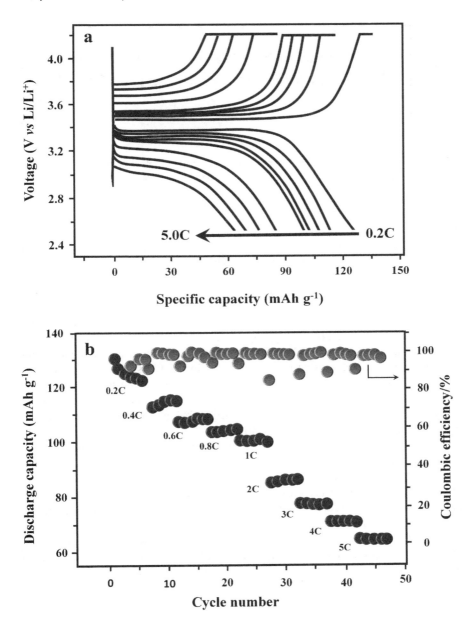

FIGURE 10.3 Cell performance (rate capability) of LiFePO$_4$/Li cell comprising polymer blend single-ion conductor electrolyte cycled between 2.5–4.2 V at room temperature, at different C-rate from 0.2C to 5C. (a) Charge–discharge profiles and (b) discharge capacity. Adapted and reproduced with permission from reference [19]. Copyright 2016 Elsevier.

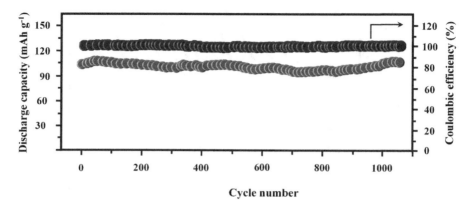

FIGURE 10.4 Cell performance (cycling stability) of LiFePO$_4$/Li cell comprising polymer blend single-ion conductor electrolyte cycled between 2.5–4.2 V at room temperature, at 1C. Adapted and reproduced with permission from reference [19]. Copyright 2016 Elsevier.

values with the linear single-ion conducting polymer electrolyte, which reflects the better ion transport network with the side-chain grafted polymer. The device was operated continuously for more than 1000 cycles at 1 C without decay, demonstrating its excellent stability and reliability (Figure 10.4). It is also noteworthy that both the discharge capacity and the coulombic efficiency remain steady across the test range. It is an important step toward practical application of LIBs with a single-ion conducting polymer electrolyte membrane. The excellent device performance is chiefly attributed to the side-chain grafted comb-like single ion conducting polymer electrolyte that enables the battery to operate with high Li$^+$-ion mobility, low concentration polarization, and good mechanical stability.

Fuentus et al. [20] reported a transparent conducting polymer electrolyte by adding lithium to the molecular complex chitosane-polyamino propyl siloxane. In this study, electrochemical characteristics of lithium-incorporated chitosan (CHI)/polyamino propyl siloxane (pAPS) was described. CHI and pAPS solutions in the appropriate ratios were stirred for about 24 h at room temperature. Anhydrous LiClO$_4$ was added as a 1 M solution in absolute ethanol. Films of 0.07–1.5 mm thick were prepared by solution casting on a polyethylene film and then dried by evaporation at room temperature. Self-supporting films obtained have a transmittance of 80% in the visible spectral range. Transparency and ionic conductivity of the product is due to the layered nature of the nanocomposite.

10.3 TSSEs FOR SUPERCAPACITORS

The advent of electronic portable devices and electric vehicles energizes the demand for energy storage devices. Researchers have expressed interest in supercapacitors, also called electrochemical capacitors, because of their high power density, low maintenance cost, and long durability [39]. They are often connected with batteries or fuel cells to deliver high power in electrical energy. Next generations of portable

Transparent Electrolytes

devices require solid-state supercapacitors with high power density, flexibility, and transparency to meet various requirements.

In the past, solid-polymer electrolytes gained great attention in electrochemical devices and rechargeable batteries. Solid-polymer electrolytes are formed from the dissolution of salts into polar and high molecular weight macromolecules. In order to forge an inexpensive and durable storage device, it is essential to use a solid-polymer electrolyte with good stability and performance. Rodriguez et al. [24] developed a transparent PVP-LiClO$_4$ SSE using the dip-coating method, and its temperature dependence, aging time, lithium salt concentrations, etc., were studied. This electrolyte was used in the fabrication of electrochemical supercapacitor (PEDOT/PVP-LiClO$_4$/PEDOT). Solutions of PVP-LiClO$_4$ were prepared by dissolving desired amounts of PVP and lithium salt in ethanol. Immediately after continuous stirring for 30 minutes, the solution was cast into a film using the dip-coating technique. In order to evaluate the performance of the PVP-LiClO$_4$ SSE, symmetrically structured EDLCs (glass/ITO/PEDOT/PVP-LiClO$_4$/PEDOT/ITO/ glass) were fabricated. Thin Poly(3,4-ethylene dioxythiophene) films were grown by electropolymerization of 3,4 Ethylenedioxythiophene (EDOT) over commercial ITO/glass substrates. In this, a typical three-electrode electrochemical cell geometry was used comprising an ITO-coated glass substrate (2.0 cm^2), a platinum wire, and a saturated calomel electrode (SCE).

The effect of LiClO$_4$ content on ionic conductivity of PVP-LiClO$_4$ samples was studied. The results showed that ionic conductivity increases as the amount of LiClO$_4$ increases, reaching a maximum of ionic conductivity as the LiClO$_4$/PVP weight ratio attains a value of 1.2. Beyond this point, ionic conductivity decreases with an increase in LiClO$_4$ content. A maximum value of ionic conductivity was observed when the LiClO$_4$ content is 14%. This increase is due to the increase in charge carrier numbers in polymer electrolytes.

On the other hand, the decrease in ionic conductivity due to an increase in the amount of LiClO$_4$ is because the excess ions trapped in the polymer cages hinder the ionic motion. Also, at high lithium salt concentration ranges, the decreasing conductivity could be due to emerging salt crystallites as a result of having exceeded the local solubility of the lithium salt in the polymer. Excessive cations and anions could aggregate and form crystalline phases that block the movement of the charge carrier, which would result in a decrease in the ionic conductivity of the polymer electrolyte. Figure 10.5 shows the variation of ionic conductivity with the amount of LiClO$_4$ at room temperature.

Figure 10.6 shows the CV curves for four different PVP-LiClO$_4$ solid-polymer electrolyte layers (different layers are achieved by dip-coating method). It was found that the electrochemical performance of the supercapacitor depends on the PVP-LiClO$_4$ thickness. Figure 10.6 shows the resulting CV curves (scan rate of 75 mV s^{-1}) for four different PVP-LiClO$_4$ electrode layer numbers (1–4 dip cycles). All the CV curves shown in Figure 10.6a have a nearly rectangular shape, indicating a nearly ideal response. Moreover, it can be seen that the specific electrode capacitance reaches a maximum of mass-specific capacitance (15 F g^{-1}) when the number of layers is two. Figure 10.6b shows a comparison of the characteristic CV curves for

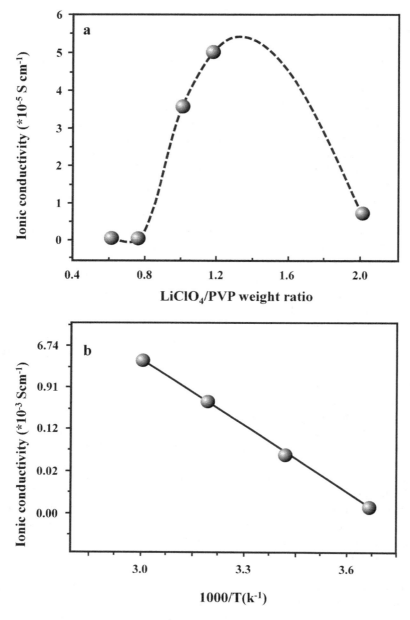

FIGURE 10.5 Transport properties of PVP/LiClO$_4$ solid polymer transparent electrolyte. (a) Ionic conductivity as a function of the LiClO$_4$ content in a typical PVP/LiClO$_4$ sample measured at room temperature (solid line), and (b) plot of the temperature dependence of ionic conductivity for a sample with a LiClO$_4$/PVP weight ratio of 1.2, where the linear fitting is indicated by a dashed line. Adapted and reproduced with permission from reference [24]. Copyright 2013 Elsevier.

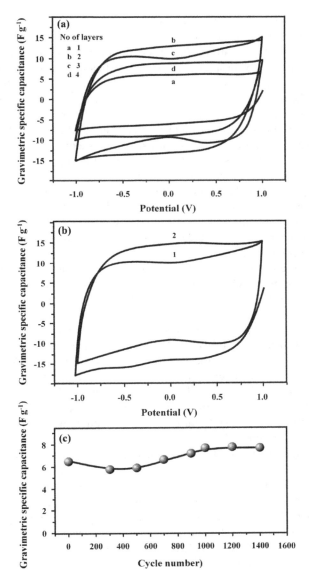

FIGURE 10.6 Electrochemical performance of the symmetrical structured EDLCs (glass/ITO/PEDOT/PVP-LiClO$_4$/PEDOT/ITO/glass). (a) Cyclic voltammograms for PVP-LiClO$_4$ solid polymer transparent electrolytes with a different number of layers; (b) cyclic voltammograms of a capacitor as depicted in (a), with two PVP-LiClO$_4$ solid polymer electrolyte layers, recorded just after the device has been prepared (Curve 1), and recorded after an aging time of 9 months (Curve 2); and (c) mass specific capacitance over 1400 cycles of CV for a 9-month aged supercapacitor assayed in (b) (the solid line is a guide for the eye). In all cases, the LiClO$_4$/PVP weight ratio was 1, and the CV scan rate was 100 mV s^{-1}. PEDOT: poly(3,4-ethylenedioxythiophene). Adapted and reproduced with permission from reference [24]. Copyright 2013 Elsevier.

a supercapacitor device (with two layers of PVP-LiClO$_4$) taken just after the device has been prepared and after the device has been stored under air atmosphere conditions and at room temperature after 9 months of aging time. Very little difference between the two CV profiles can be seen, indicating a very small decrease in the mass-specific capacitance from 15 g^{-1} to 10 F g^{-1} after a 9-month aging time. Figure 10.6c shows the cyclability study carried out by CV of the supercapacitor device with four layers (four dip cycles) after 9 months' storage in an air atmosphere, a decrease of 10% of specific capacitance was found at the early 500 cycles stage (scan rate 100 mV s^{-1}). After the 500 cycles stage, the specific capacitance increases significantly with the increasing cycle number until the capacitance reaches a plateau, and the values before aging are recovered.

Jung et al. [26] reported on transparent, flexible supercapacitors from nanoengineered carbon nanofilms. In this paper, mechanically flexible and optically transparent thin-film solid-state supercapacitors are developed by assembling nanoengineered carbon electrodes and transparent electrolyte films. Solid-polymer electrolytes with conformal electrolyte packing provides excellent mechanical stability and optical transparency to the supercapacitor. The fabrication process for thin branched carbon nanocup (CNC) polymer electrolyte film is as follows. In the first step, prepared nanocup films prepared are transferred to a PDMS matrix and released by dissolving an anodic aluminum oxide (AAO) templates in a copper chloride and hydrochloric acid mixture solution to produce transparent graphitic carbon electrodes. The CNC films are then utilized as dual function layers in supercapacitor devices in which an inner graphitic layer exposed to the electrolyte acts as active electrodes and an outer graphitic layer works as current collectors. For the ionic electrolyte/separator, the polyvinyl alcohol-phosphoric acid (PVA-H$_3$PO$_4$) gel electrolyte is then sandwiched between two separate CNC electrode films. For this, PVA-H$_3$PO$_4$ polymer solution is poured over the CNC film and spin-coated at 500 rpm to obtain the effective electrolyte thickness (12 mm). CNC films are transparent with transmittance of 71% at 550 nm wavelength; therefore the fabricated solid-state thin film CNC supercapacitor devices are optically transparent, as shown in Figure 10.7.

This developed supercapacitor possesses morphological and structural features because the films enable an excellent conformal filling of polymer electrolyte and maximize active electrochemical surface area, leading to high energy density. The design of the devices allows for mechanically flexible energy storage devices that could be integrated into unique applications that require high form factor and optical transparency, such as roll-up displays, wearable devices, and organic solar cell platforms.

10.3.1 IL-Based Transparent Electrolytes

The next generation devices require environmental friendly, safe, flexible, and transparent electrolytes. RTILs have all these features and are suitable for electrolytes in advanced energy storage devices, making them the best candidate. RTILs are molten state salts and their melting points are always close to room temperature. IL is made of

Transparent Electrolytes 231

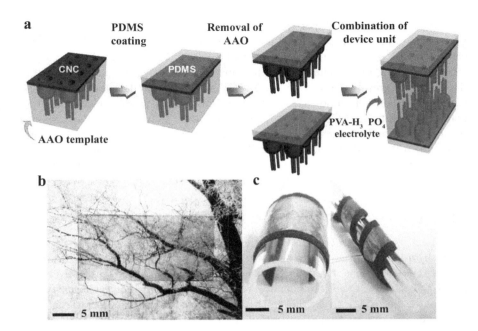

FIGURE 10.7 Schematics of the fabrication process of a branched carbon nanocup (CNC) polymer electrolyte-based supercapacitor and its optical images. (a) First the CNC films are transferred to PDMS and released by dissolving anodic aluminum oxide (AAO) templates. Then the gel-electrolyte (as electrolyte-separator) is sandwiched between two CNC electrodes (as electrode-current collector) of 12 mm thickness that solidifies after evaporation of water. Optical pictures demonstrating (b) transparent and (c) flexible natures of CNCs supercapacitor devices. Adapted and reproduced with permission from reference [26]. Copyright 2012 Springer Nature.

smaller anions loosely held to bulky organic cations. RTILs possess high conductivity, nonvolatility, low toxicity, large electrochemical window, and high electrochemical stability [40]. Wei et al. [25] reported transparent, flexible, and solid-state supercapacitors based on RTIL gel. This paper introduced an environmentally friendly, safe, transparent electrolyte based on RTIL gel composed of 1-butyl-3-methylimidazolium chloride and cellulose. The supercapacitor reported in this paper that used 1-butyl-3-methylimidazolium chloride and cellulose gel composite is a completely transparent and flexible electrochemical device. Solutions containing up to 25 wt% cellulose can be formed as viscous pastes in chloride containing RTILs. The viscous solution obtained was optically anisotropic and showed excellent mechanical properties as well as durability. The supercapacitor electrodes were made by coating a flexible polymeric substrate, polyethylene naphthalate (PEN), with ITO. The RTIL gel electrolyte, [BMIM][Cl] composing of 6 wt% cellulose was used, which forms a totally transparent electrolyte when dried. Cellulose was evenly distributed in the gel, as it can function as a separator in the supercapacitor simultaneously.

232   Ceramic and Specialty Electrolytes

The electrochemical properties of the supercapacitors were studied by CV and galvanostatic measurements. Near rectangular shaped CV curves indicated good capacitive characteristics of the device. Galvanostatic charge–discharge measurements were used to evaluate the specific capacitance and the internal resistance of the device. The results showed that the RTIL electrolyte can reduce the contact resistance more than conventional SSEs by providing adhesive contacts with charge-collecting electrodes. Conventional supercapacitors feature neither mechanical flexibility nor optical transparency for long duration; however, this supercapacitor fabricated using RTIL gel electrolyte and the ITO electrodes coated on PEN showed excellent flexibility and transparency owing to potential application. This approach may be able to work as a platform for future transparent and flexible devices.

10.4 TRANSPARENT ELECTROLYTES FOR FUEL CELLS

A fuel cell is an electrochemical cell that converts the chemical energy of a fuel (often hydrogen) and an oxidizing agent (often oxygen) into electricity through a pair of redox reactions. Every fuel cell has two electrodes called, respectively, the anode and cathode. The electrochemical redox reactions that produce electricity take place at the electrodes. Every fuel cell also has an electrolyte, which carries electrically charged particles from one electrode to the other, and a catalyst, which speeds the reactions at the electrodes. Because of the high thermal stability, RTILs have attracted attention for a long time as effective electrolytes in fuel cells, batteries, and supercapacitors [29]. RTILs exhibit high ionic conductivity, wide electrochemical stability window, nonvolatility, high thermal stability, and nonflammability [40]. Ionogels represent the other effective electrolyte in which the structure resembles ILs trapped inside the thermally stable inorganic skeleton. Viox et al. [29] reported ionogels through a nonhydrolytic sol-gel process using a mixture of TMOS, FA, and IL. Various ionogels made of three different RTILs: 1-butyl-3-methylimidazolium bis(trifluoromethylsulphonylimide) [BMI][TFSI], butylpyridinium bis(triflouromethylsulphonylimide) [BPy][TFSI], and 1-butyl-3-methylimidazolium tetrafluoroborate [BMI][BF$_4$]. In each case, gelation occurred after about 1.5 h, and the gels were aged for a few days at room temperature or for a few hours upon exposure to ultrasounds. The ionogels were obtained as transparent pellets and rods.

The properties of ionogels are dependent on those of RTILs as well as on their relative amount. Ionogels represent a significant advancement in electrolyte membranes for fuel cells by working under anhydrous conditions and operating temperatures from 400 to at least 520 K [30]. Operating at higher temperatures should be extremely beneficial for the efficiency of fuel cells. By tuning the properties of ionogels by changing the sol-gel precursor and method, numerous applications could be achieved.

A protonic conductive membrane is an important factor in polymer electrolyte membrane fuel cells, as it is applicable for proton sensors, separation, acidic catalysts, and so on. Incorporation of inorganic solid acids in polymers has been attempted for ionic conductive materials [41]. Honma et al. [31] reported a transparent proton-conducting/inorganic hybrid-SSE for intermediate temperature fuel cells. The SSE

Transparent Electrolytes

membrane is prepared by sol-gel method which involved stabilization of metastable inorganic acidic clusters (acidic tungsten oxide clusters) present in the polymer composite membrane. Investigating the protonic conductivity at room temperature to 160° C, a freestanding, flexible, pale yellowish, transparent membrane was formed from tungsten acidic homogeneous solution by sol-gel condensation with alkoxysilylated polyethylene oxide (PEO). The membrane showed a very high protonic conductivity of 10^{-2} –10^{-3} S cm^{-1} from room temperature to 120° C. The protonic conductivity at 80° C was found to be 1.4×10^{-2} S cm^{-1}. The structure of tungsten cluster moieties was neither peroxo complex nor $WO_3.2H_2O$. It is suggested that nanosize clusters are dispersed homogeneously in polymer matrix without long-range ordering. Thermal and ionic transport properties could be controlled by organic derivatives, such as malonic acid, to clusters. It was shown that the tungstic acidic cluster has been stabilized in the polymer matrix and the resulting membrane has good protonic conductivity, even at 140° C it has 10^{-4} S cm^{-1}. Honna et al. [31] also have investigated the effect of different carboxylato ligands for protonic conduction among oxalic acid, citric acid, malonic acid, and dimethylmalonic acid. The results of conductivity revealed that malonic acid have great influence on the conductivity than the other, suggesting these kinds of ligand were effective for protonic conduction.

Advani et al. [32] carried out an experimental investigation of liquid water formation and transport in a transparent single-serpentine PEM fuel cell. Liquid water formation and transport were investigated by direct experimental visualization in an operational transparent single-serpentine PEM fuel cell. In this paper, the effectiveness of various GDL materials in removing water away from the cathode and through the flow field over a range of operating conditions were also studied. The level of cathode flow-field flooding, under the same operating conditions and cell current, was recognized as a criterion for the water removal capacity of the gas GDL materials. When compared at the same current density (i.e. water production rate), a higher amount of liquid water in the cathode channel indicated that water had been efficiently removed from the catalyst layer. Visualization of the anode channel was used to investigate the influence of the microporous layer (MPL) on water transport. No liquid water was observed in the anode flow field unless cathode GDLs had an MPL.

This work examines the two-phase flow inside a single-serpentine PEMFC by direct experimental visualization. The study investigated the flooding phenomena under realistic operating conditions at high water-production rates (up to almost an order of magnitude higher), with cell performance comparable to conventional fuel cells. The study also demonstrated that single serpentine cell with transparent proton conducting SPE was able to operate with high liquid water content in the flow field over time, attributed to the efficient water removal through the flow field, without prolonged channel blockage.

10.5 CONCLUSIONS AND PERSPECTIVES

Transparent electronics is an emerging and promising technology that recently gained more attention in various applications, such as touch screens, TV displays, and solar cells. All these electronic devices are inseparable from the support of energy storage devices, such as batteries supercapacitors, and fuel cells. The development of transparent electrolytes has been a major research concern in the field of transparent electronics. Currently, researchers are carrying out many studies to develop transparent LIBs, supercapacitors, and fuel cells. LIBs are largely used energy storage devices in the electronics market, where high performance smart SSEs are replacing the conventional liquid electrolyte due to safety threats in advanced applications. Many polymer-based electrolytes, such as organic–inorganic hybrid SSEs based on PDMS-, PEO-, and $LiClO_4$-based electrolytes, are used in LIBs. A-LLZ electrolytes and transparent polymeric single-ion conductor electrolytes were also reported. All these new developments in electrolytes give an advanced path for LIBs in the next generation of optoelectronics. Great interest in supercapacitors in the transparent electronics research arena has also been seen because of their high power density, low maintenance cost, and long durability. They are often connected with batteries or fuel cells to deliver high power in electrical energy. Transparent PVP-$LiClO_4$ SSEs, RTIL-based composite electrolytes (1-butyl-3-methylimidazolium chloride and cellulose gel composite), and polymer-based electrolytes (PDMS) were developed. These show excellent mechanical stability as well as performance and are considered as future candidates for transparent optoelectronics. In the case of fuel cells, the electrolytic membrane should possess medium-range operating temperatures for many applications. RTILs have attracted attention for a long time as effective electrolytes in the case of fuel cells. Ionogel-based electrolytes and advanced proton-conducting transparent electrolytes were reported. All these transparent electrolytes are leading a prominent path for the future of the electronics market, and advanced research in these areas have developed new academic interest as well.

ACKNOWLEDGMENTS

Authors Anjumole P. Thomas, Dr. Jabeen Fatima M. J., and Dr. Prasanth Raghavan would like to acknowledge the Department of Science and Technology (DST), India, and Kerala State Council for Science, Technology and Environment (KSCSTE), Kerala, India, for their financial assistance.

REFERENCES

1. Kim JS, Lee YH, Lee I, et al. (2014) Large area multi-stacked lithium-ion batteries for flexible and rollable applications. *J Mater Chem A* 2:10862–10868. https://doi.org/10.1039/c4ta00551a
2. Wu Y, Wu H, Luo S, et al. (2014) Entrapping electrode materials within ultrathin carbon nanotube network for flexible thin film lithium ion batteries. *RSC Adv* 4:20010–20016. https://doi.org/10.1039/c4ra01876a
3. Wang K, Wu H, Meng Y, et al. (2012) Integrated energy storage and electrochromic function in one flexible device: An energy storage smart window. *Energy Environ Sci* 5:8384–8389. https://doi.org/10.1039/c2ee21643d
4. Ju S, Li J, Liu J, et al. (2008) Transparent active matrix organic light-emitting diode displays driven by nanowire transistor circuitry. *Nano Lett* 8:997–1004. https://doi.org/10.1021/nl072538+

Transparent Electrolytes

5. Wang L, Yoon MH, Lu G, et al. (2006) High-performance transparent inorganic-organic hybrid thin-film n-type transistors. *Nat Mater* 5:893–900. https://doi.org/10.1038/nmat1755

6. Wang T, Guo Y, Wan P, et al. (2016) Flexible transparent electronic gas sensors. *Small* 12:3748–3756. https://doi.org/10.1002/smll.201601049

7. Yang Y, Jeong S, Hu L, et al. (2011) Transparent lithium-ion batteries. *Proc Natl Acad Sci U S A* 108:13013–13018. https://doi.org/10.1073/pnas.1102873108

8. Li J, Jiang Q, Yuan N, Tang J (2018) A review on flexible and transparent energy storage system. *Materials (Basel)* 11: 2280. https://doi.org/10.3390/ma11112280

9. Armand MJ-MT (2001) Issues and challenges facing rechargeable lithium batteries. *Nat Commun* 414:359–367.

10. Yoon J, Baca AJ, Park S, et al. Ultrathin silicon solar microcells for semitransparent, mechanically flexible and microconcentrator module designs, *Nature Materials*. 7: 907–915. https://doi.org/10.1038/nmat2287

11. Hu L, Hecht DS, Gruner G (2004) Percolation in transparent and conducting carbon nanotube networks. *Nano Lett* 4:2513–2517. https://doi.org/10.1021/nl048435y

12. Taylor RL (1950) Conductive, carbon nanotube films. *J Clin Endocrinol Metab* 10:1361–1362. https://doi.org/10.1210/jcem-10-10-1361

13. Suzuki Y, Kami K, Watanabe K, et al. (2015) Transparent cubic garnet-type solid electrolyte of Al2O3-doped Li7La3Zr2O12. *Solid State Ionics* 278:172–176. https://doi.org/10.1016/j.ssi.2015.06.009

14. Murugan R, Thangadurai V, Weppner W (2007) Fast lithium ion conduction in garnet-type Li7La 3Zr2O12. *Angew Chemie - Int Ed* 46:7778–7781. https://doi.org/10.1002/anie.200701144

15. Awaka J, Kijima N, Hayakawa H, Akimoto J (2009) Synthesis and structure analysis of tetragonal Li7La3Zr2O12 with the garnet-related type structure. *J Solid State Chem* 182:2046–2052. https://doi.org/10.1016/j.jssc.2009.05.020

16. Puthirath AB, Patra S, Pal S, et al. (2017) Transparent flexible lithium ion conducting solid polymer electrolyte. *J Mater Chem A* 5:11152–11162. https://doi.org/10.1039/c7ta02182h

17. Lötters JC, Olthuis W, Veltink PH, Bergveld P (1997) The mechanical properties of the rubber elastic polymer polydimethylsiloxane for sensor applications. *J Micromechanics Microengineering* 7:145–147. https://doi.org/10.1088/0960-1317/7/3/017

18. Yang P, Wirnsberger G, Huang HC, et al. (2000) Mirrorless lasing from mesostructured waveguides patterned by soft lithography. *Science* 287:465–467. https://doi.org/10.1126/science.287.5452.465

19. Pan Q, Chen Y, Zhang Y, et al. (2016) A dense transparent polymeric single ion conductor for lithium ion batteries with remarkable long-term stability. *J Power Sources* 336:75–82. https://doi.org/10.1016/j.jpowsour.2016.10.033

20. Fuentes S, Retuert PJ, González G (2003) Transparent conducting polymer electrolyte by addition of lithium to the molecular complex chitosane-poly(aminopropyl siloxane). *Electrochim Acta* 48:2015–2019. https://doi.org/10.1016/S0013-4686(03)00180-4

21. Niu Z, Luan P, Shao Q, et al. (2012) A "skeleton/skin" strategy for preparing ultrathin free-standing single-walled carbon nanotube/polyaniline films for high performance supercapacitor electrodes. *Energy Environ Sci* 5:8726–8733. https://doi.org/10.1039/c2ee22042c

22. Cong HP, Ren XC, Wang P, Yu SH (2013) Flexible graphene-polyaniline composite paper for high-performance supercapacitor. *Energy Environ Sci* 6:1185–1191. https://doi.org/10.1039/c2ee24203f

23. Liu L, Niu Z, Zhang L, et al. (2014) Nanostructured graphene composite papers for highly flexible and foldable supercapacitors. *Adv Mater* 26:4855–4862. https://doi.org/10.1002/adma.201401513

24. Rodríguez J, Navarrete E, Dalchiele EA, et al. (2013) Polyvinylpyrrolidone e LiClO 4 solid polymer electrolyte and its application in transparent thin film supercapacitors. 237:270–276. https://doi.org/10.1016/j.jpowsour.2013.03.043
25. Wei D, Wakeham SJ, Ng TW, et al. (2009) Transparent, flexible and solid-state supercapacitors based on room temperature ionic liquid gel. *Electrochem Commun* 11:2285–2287. https://doi.org/10.1016/j.elecom.2009.10.011
26. Jung HY, Karimi MB, Hahm MG, et al. (2012) Transparent, flexible supercapacitors from nano-engineered carbon films. *Sci Rep* 2:1–5. https://doi.org/10.1038/srep00773
27. Dillon R, Srinivasan S, Aricò AS, Antonucci V (2004) International activities in DMFC R&D: Status of technologies and potential applications. *J Power Sources* 127:112–126. https://doi.org/10.1016/j.jpowsour.2003.09.032
28. Li Q, He R, Jensen JO, Bjerrum NJ (2003) Approaches and recent development of polymer electrolyte membranes for fuel cells operating above 100 °C. *Chem Mater* 15:4896–4915. https://doi.org/10.1021/cm0310519
29. Neóuze M-A, Bideau J Le, Vioux A (2005) Versatile heat resistant solid electrolytes with performances of liquid electrolytes. *Prog Solid State Chem* 33:217–222. https://doi.org/10.1016/j.progsolidstchem.2005.11.049
30. Tsuzuki S, Shinoda W, Miran S, et al. (2014) Interactions in ion pairs of protic ionic liquids: Comparison with aprotic ionic liquids, *J Chem Phys*. 139: 174504. https://doi.org/10.1063/1.4827519
31. Nakajima H, Honma I (2002) Proton-conducting hybrid solid electrolytes for intermediate temperature fuel cells. *Solid State Ionics* 148:607–610. https://doi.org/10.1016/S0167-2738(02)00127-3
32. Spernjak D, Prasad A K, Advani SG (2007) Experimental investigation of liquid water formation and transport in a transparent single-serpentine PEM fuel cell. *J Power Sources* 170:334–344. https://doi.org/10.1016/j.jpowsour.2007.04.020
33. Goodenough JB, Park KS (2013) The Li-ion rechargeable battery: A perspective. *J Am Chem Soc* 135:1167–1176. https://doi.org/10.1021/ja3091438
34. Robinson AL, Janek J (2014) Solid-state batteries enter EV fray. *MRS Bull* 39:1046–1047. https://doi.org/10.1557/mrs.2014.285
35. Kato Y, Hori S, Saito T, et al. (2016) High-power all-solid-state batteries using sulfide superionic conductors. *Nat Energy* 1:1–7. https://doi.org/10.1038/nenergy.2016.30
36. Alpen U V., Rabenau A, Talat GH (1977) Ionic conductivity in Li3N single crystals. *Appl Phys Lett* 30:621–623. https://doi.org/10.1063/1.89283
37. Hong Y-P, Kafalas JA (1978) High Na +ion conductivity in Na5Y Si 4O12. 2:377–389.
38. Murugan R, Thangadurai V, Weppner W (2007) Fast lithium ion conduction in garnet-type $Li_7La_3Zr_2O_{12}$. *Angew Chemie - Int Ed* 46:7778–7781. https://doi.org/10.1002/anie.200701144
39. Kötz R, Carlen M (2000) Principles and applications of electrochemical capacitors. *Electrochim Acta* 45:2483–2498. https://doi.org/10.1016/S0013-4686(00)00354-6
40. Picquet M, Tkatchenko I, Tommasi I, et al. (2003) Ionic liquids, 3. Synthesis and utilisation of protic imidazolium salts in homogeneous catalysis. *Adv Synth Catal* 345:959–962. https://doi.org/10.1002/adsc.200303025
41. Thampan T, Malhotra S, Tang H, Datta R (2000) Modeling of conductive transport in proton-exchange membranes for fuel cells. *J Electrochem Soc* 147:3242. https://doi.org/10.1149/1.1393890

11 Recent Advances in Non-Platinum-Based Cathode Electrocatalysts for Direct Methanol Fuel Cells

Bhagyalakhi Baruah and Ashok Kumar

CONTENTS

11.1 Introduction 237
11.2 Working Principles of DMFCs 238
11.3 ORR Mechanism 239
11.4 Synthesis Techniques of Non-Pt-Based Cathode Catalysts for DMFC 240
    11.4.1 Electrochemical Deposition 240
    11.4.2 Chemical Reduction 241
    11.4.3 Hydrothermal/Solvothermal Method 241
    11.4.4 Sol-Gel Method 242
    11.4.5 Microwave-Assisted Synthesis 242
    11.4.6 Template-Guided Synthesis 243
11.5 Non-Pt Cathode Electrocatalysts 244
    11.5.1 Transition Metal-Based Electrocatalysts 245
    11.5.2 Metal Oxide-Based Electrocatalysts 246
    11.5.3 Transition Metal-Nitrogen (M-N$_x$) Macrocycle-Based
          Electrocatalysts 247
    11.5.4 Metal-Free Nanocarbon-Based Electrocatalyst 251
11.6 Conclusion and Future Outlook 253
References 254

11.1 INTRODUCTION

Development of alternative energy sources over the traditional ones is an urgent need because of the continuous depletion of fossil fuels. Currently, people have grown interest in fuel-based technologies because of their high efficiency, very low emission and noise, modular design, and low maintenance cost of the fuel cells [1]. Among several fuel-cell-based technologies, direct methanol fuel cells (DMFCs) have been considered a promising energy conversion system because they have high conversion efficiency and are environmentally benign. DMFC is a low temperature (60° C–120° C) proton exchange membrane fuel cell (PEMFC) with high energy density

(5.04 kWh L^{-1}), simple configuration, easy portability, and light weight; however, DMFC has some serious issues that limit its wide-scale commercialization. Platinum (Pt) has long been known as the most effective cathode catalyst in DMFC to reduce high overpotential of oxygen reduction reaction (ORR), however, the high cost of Pt inhibits the large-scale use of DMFC. Methanol crossover from the anode to the cathode side of the cell is the major drawback of DMFC. Therefore, intense research efforts have been made recently to develop non-Pt-based methanol-tolerant cathode catalysts at a low cost. Recently, many Pt-free cathode catalysts have been designed using carbon-based compounds, transition metals, macrocycle-based materials, etc.; however, these cathode catalysts may not show much improved ORR in comparison to Pt-based compounds, although these can reduce the crossover loss than that of many Pt-based materials.

The present chapter initially discusses the basic working principles and ORR mechanism in DMFC. The main purpose of this chapter is to present a brief review of the recent developments of non-Pt-based cathode catalysts, including transition metal-based metal oxides, transition metal-nitrogen-based, and metal-free nanocarbons. The synthesis procedures of the catalysts are elaborated in the chapter. Finally the conclusions drawn from the chapter and future outlook are discussed.

11.2 WORKING PRINCIPLES OF DMFCS

The main components of DMFC are the two electrodes, anode and cathode, that are separated by an electrolyte. Figure 11.1 displays the schematic illustration of DMFC

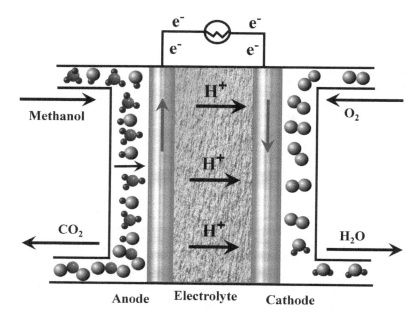

FIGURE 11.1 Schematic illustration of the structure and working principle of DMFC.

Direct Methanol Fuel Cells

system, showing the basic working principles of DMFC with reactant and exhaust components and directions of ions and electrons. In DMFC, methanol is oxidized to CO_2 and H_2O and thus chemical energy is converted into electrical energy. At the anode side, methanol units react with H_2O molecules and generates CO_2, six protons that flow through the electrolyte toward the cathode side, and six electrons that flow toward the cathode through the external circuit. The produced CO_2 gas is exhausted by the electrolyte. The protons flowing through the electrolyte solution and the electrons migrating via the external circuit reach the cathode side, and the O_2 is reduced forming the H_2O molecules [2].

The electric potential generated between the anode and cathode due to excess electrons produced at the anode in comparison to the cathode, generates a current through the external circuit and thus the fuel cell can act as a power source. The theoretical voltage of DMFC due to overall reaction is 1.18 V with maximum theoretical efficiency of 96.5%, but, practically, this voltage and efficiency are not attainable owing to the slow electrooxidation kinetics due to CO poisoning and different types of losses, such as activation loss, ohmic loss, and concentration loss as well as methanol crossover in the electrolyte [3, 4]. The electrochemical reactions at the electrodes are [5] shown in Equations 11.1, 11.2, and 11.3.

$$\text{At anode:} CH_3OH + H_2O \rightarrow CO_2 + 6H^+ + 6e^- \tag{11.1}$$

$$E_{anode} = 0.046V\left(\text{oxidation}\right)$$

$$\text{At Cathode:} 3/2O_2 + 6H^+ + 6e^- \rightarrow 3H_2O \tag{11.2}$$

$$E_{Cathode} = 1.23V\left(\text{reduction}\right)$$

$$\text{Overall reaction:} CH_3OH + 3/2O_2 \rightarrow 2H_2O + CO_2 \tag{11.3}$$

$$E_{cell} = 1.18V\left(\text{Cell terminal voltage}\right)$$

11.3 ORR MECHANISM

Another important electrochemical process in energy conversion systems is ORR. The ORR process is complicated with many intermediate steps. Moreover, nature of the cathode catalyst and electrolyte is highly important in ORR mechanism. The ORR mechanism in both acidic and alkaline media is the same. There are two paths, i.e. direct (four electrons transfer) and indirect (two electrons transfer), through which O_2 reduction reaction can take place in both media. Both these reduction paths are shown in Figure 11.2 [4, 6]. In acidic medium, the final product is water in the direct pathway, whereas, in the indirect pathway, hydrogen peroxide is the final product. In alkaline media, hydroxide anions are formed in the direct pathway, while peroxide are generated in the indirect pathway. The ORR must follow four electron pathways to attain maximum energy capacity. Thus, the four electron path for ORR is used in fuel cells and the two electron path is used in case of peroxide formation.

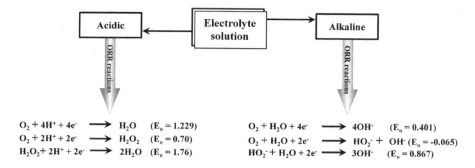

FIGURE 11.2 Schematic illustration of the ORR in fuel cells. Adapted and reproduced with permission from reference [4]. Copyright 2013 Elsevier.

11.4 SYNTHESIS TECHNIQUES OF NON-Pt-BASED CATHODE CATALYSTS FOR DMFC

The electrocatalytic performance of the catalysts depends upon composition, structure, morphology, surface area, and size of the catalyst. Non-Pt cathode catalysts, including transition metal, nonprecious metal, transition metal-nitrogen macrocycle, and carbon-based catalysts, have been used for ORR. The main synthesis procedures are electrodeposition, chemical reduction, hydrothermal method, sol-gel method, microwave irradiation, template-directed synthesis, etc. The details of these synthesis procedures have been described below.

11.4.1 Electrochemical Deposition

Electrochemical deposition is a facile method to deposit metal nanoparticles (NPs) onto a conductive substrate such as indium tin oxide (ITO), fluorine-doped tin oxide (FTO), glassy carbon electrode (GCE), and carbon paste electrode (CPE). Monometallic catalysts or deposition of more than one metal alloy is done by electrochemical deposition or electrodeposition technique. Cyclic voltammetry (CV) and chronoamperometry (CA) are the electrochemical techniques through which electrodeposition can be performed. In this synthesis method, a three electrode cell is used in which working, reference, and counter electrodes are immersed into an electrolyte solution. The desired voltage is supplied at the working electrode to provide electrons to the electrolyte during reduction while extracting electrons from the electrolyte during oxidation [7]. The reference electrode is used to determine voltage of the working electrode, and the counter electrode maintains flow of current. Finally, the film of the catalyst material is deposited over the working electrode. In this method, the size, shape, and structure of the catalysts can be tuned by optimizing the experimental conditions, such as deposition time, applied potential, concentration of the precursor solution, etc. [8]. Moreover, surfactant or capping agents are not required in this method; however, the major drawback of electrochemical deposition is that

Direct Methanol Fuel Cells

poor distribution and formation of large NPs within the size range of 10 nm–100 nm, which is not very useful for electrocatalytic activity.

11.4.2 CHEMICAL REDUCTION

The chemical reduction method is used to synthesize monometallic, bimetallic, or ternary materials for the use as an electrocatalyst. This method is facile, low cost, and efficient, and the metal nanostructures of appropriate size and shape can be obtained by proper optimization of experimental conditions, which includes the molar ratios of surfactant and reducing agent to the metal salt [9]. The metal nanostructures of desired morphology can be obtained by controlling the growth using a suitable reducing agent. In this particular method, different reducing agents, including ammonia, hydrazine hydrate, poly(vinyl pyrrolidone) (PVP), sodium borohydride, ethylene glycol, glycerol, and ascorbic acid, have been used to reduce metallic components from metal precursors. In this technique, the concentrations of reactants and reducing agents can be varied in order to tune the shape, size, and distribution of metal nanostructures. Because nature and concentration of the reducing agents determine the morphology, size, and distribution of metal nanostructures, choosing the appropriate reducing agent is an important factor. In this technique, when the rate of reaction is very fast, a considerable amount of metal nuclei are formed suddenly, resulting in small particles [10]. However, a slow reaction rate causes agglomeration of particles. Moreover, the stability, dispersibility, chemical reactivity, and morphology of the nanostructures depend on the surfactant; therefore, choice of proper surfactant is another important factor in the chemical reduction process. Usually, metallic components are dispersed over the supporting materials, such as conducting polymer, carbon black, graphene, CNT, transition metal carbides, etc., for electrocatalytic applications.

11.4.3 HYDROTHERMAL/SOLVOTHERMAL METHOD

Hydrothermal/solvothermal methods are frequently used synthesis procedures owing to their characteristics, such as fast, simple, environmentally friendly, low cost, and controlled morphology with homogeneous reaction conditions. In the hydrothermal or solvothermal process, the chemical reactions of the components in aqueous or nonaqueous solutions occur inside a sealed container known as an autoclave and heated to a high temperature of up to $1000°$ C and pressure up to 100 MPa [11]. The term solvothermal is applied when the reaction occurs in organic nonaqueous solvents. At the optimized reaction conditions, the solubility of precursor materials increases, and the reaction rate is also enhanced. In this typical method, the reactants are mixed in certain molar ratios into an autoclave and then kept inside an oven at a fixed temperature for a specific time period. Then the prepared sample is centrifuged and cleaned using deionized (DI) water and alcohols to eliminate the unused part and then vacuum dried in an oven to obtain the final product. The main benefit of this method is that by increasing temperature and pressure above a critical limit, any material can be made soluble in solvent. In hydrothermal/solvothermal processes, direct crystallization occurs from solutions involving two main steps [12]: nucleation of the crystal and subsequent growth. The nanostructures of desired size and shape can be obtained by controlling many factors, such as reaction temperature, molar concentration of the reactants, and pH of the solution. The first step, nucleation of the crystals, occurs when the dissolved solute surpasses the critical limit in the solution. This reaction is irreversible, as the clusters of the crystals are precipitated out and increase in size. Gradually, the size of the crystals increases because of the sequence of processes, including the addition of crystal units of the same constituents as the crystal but having different structures.

11.4.4 Sol-Gel Method

Sol-gel is a common method that is used mostly to synthesize small metal oxide particles and mixed oxide-based composites. The sol-gel process is inexpensive, has a low reaction temperature process, and can control the amount of product obtained. The sol-gel method involves mainly three steps: hydrolysis, condensation, and drying process to produce metal oxide nanostructures. In this method, the starting materials are converted into a colloidal solution (sol), which is used as precursor material in further reactions to form a gel. The precursor materials are dissolved and reacted with water and then polycondensed to form three-dimensional (3D) gels. The obtained gel is then dried and converted to Xerogel or Aerogel based on the drying process. Based on the nature of the solvents, the sol-gel process is classified into two parts, i.e. aqueous and nonaqueous sol-gel processes [13]. In the aqueous sol-gel process, water is the reaction media, whereas organic solvent is used as reaction media in the nonaqueous sol-gel method. Figure 11.3 illustrates the schematic diagram of the sol-gel process [13]. In this method, the parameters, such as molar concentration of the reactants (e.g., precursors and additives), pH of the solution, heat treatment, and the type of solvent used, can be controlled to vary the morphology and size of the nanostructures [14]. The size and shape of the nanostructures formed in this process are uniform and, therefore, the electrical, optical, and magnetic properties are enhanced. The materials obtained from the sol-gel method possess a large surface to volume ratio, therefore, these can be used in catalytic applications. Moreover, the low reaction temperature causes fewer defects and disorders in the synthesized system.

11.4.5 Microwave-Assisted Synthesis

Conventional heating processes has some major limitations, such as high thermal gradient, inefficient and slow reaction kinetics, lack of homogeneity, low crystallization, and unwanted reaction conditions that have tremendous negative impact on the nucleation and size distribution of the nanostructures [15]. Microwave-assisted synthesis is considered as a promising and eco-friendly process to prepare the metal nanostructures and metal oxides of different sizes and shapes. This process has several benefits, such as cost effectiveness, high yield of product, fast reaction, and

Direct Methanol Fuel Cells

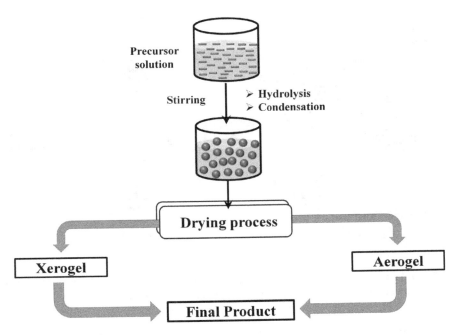

FIGURE 11.3 Schematic illustration of sol-gel process. Adapted and reproduced with permission from reference [13]. Copyright 2017 Elsevier.

homogeneous heat treatment in the reaction solution. From this perspective, the microwave-assisted synthesis process is introduced as an alternative to the conventional heating system to remove the drawbacks related to conventional heating processes. Microwaves use electromagnetic radiation with a frequency range within 300 MHz–300 GHz [13]. During the reaction, the microwaves interact with materials via two mechanisms: interaction of dipole and conduction of ions. These mechanisms are valid only when the target material and the electric field of microwave irradiation interact with each other. Figure 11.4 illustrates the generation of thermal energy due to microwave irradiation on water molecules [16]. In this system, the water molecules try to align along the electric field, while the polar ends try to realign along the alternating electric field, causing a loss of energy in the form of heat. The rate of change of polarity of the alternating electric field is faster than the alignment of the water molecules around the dipole, causing a shift in phase and absorption of energy from the electric field [17].

11.4.6 Template-Guided Synthesis

The template-guided method is used to synthesize high-grade nanostructures with controlled morphology using an appropriate template. The important parameters of nanostructures, such as composition of phase, size of the pore, grain morphology, and shape of the nanomaterial can be tuned with the use of a suitable template

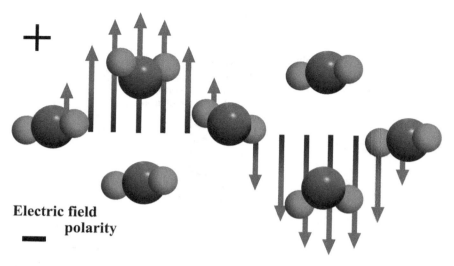

FIGURE 11.4 The effect of microwave irradiation on water molecules. Adapted and reproduced with permission from reference [16]. Copyright 2009 Elsevier.

[13]. In this process, the resultant solid material is formed over the template through the reaction between solid and liquid interfaces [18]. The template provides desired morphology to the nanomaterial, which is similar to that of template morphology. In addition, the template-directed process is beneficial because it does not require external energy sources and it has a reduced reaction time, low reaction temperature, and low toxicity of the precursors [13]. Nanostructures are formed within the template and completely removed by certain routes, which include chemical etching and calcinations. Based on the structure, the template-directed synthesis process can be classified into two routes: hard- and soft-template methods. Hard templates include porous anodic alumina, porous carbon, porous silica, carbon NPs, metal oxides, polystyrene beads, and block polymers, whereas the soft templates are polymer vesicles, droplets, bubbles, amphiphilic surfactants, and micelles. However, the template method has a major limitation that complete removal of the template might affect the structure and purity of the synthesized nanostructures.

11.5 NON-Pt CATHODE ELECTROCATALYSTS

The sluggish kinetics of ORR are related to various factors, such as pH of the electrolyte, reaction temperature, etc. The alkaline media is preferred over an acidic one for the use of nonnoble metal catalysts because of their less-corrosive nature. The methanol crossover from the anode to cathode in DMFC may cause internal short circuit and thereby reducing the efficiency of DMFC. Therefore, cathode catalysts should be highly selective to ORR and should be methanol tolerant. In this section, recent findings of Pt-free cathode catalysts for ORR mechanisms are reviewed. The various non-Pt catalysts for ORR in alkaline electrolytes are transition metal-based

Direct Methanol Fuel Cells

compounds, nonprecious metal oxides, macrocycle-based catalysts, and carbon-based catalysts.

11.5.1 Transition Metal-Based Electrocatalysts

The transition metals alloyed with precious metals show excellent electrocatalytic activity toward ORR. The transition metal alloys have many advantages over mono-metallic forms, such as synergistic effects of more than one component, variations in the structure and morphology of the surface, concentration of electrons, and disorder of the lattice structure [19]. Many transition metal alloys, such as CuFe NPs/N-rGO [20], Pd_3Fe NPs/CB, Pd_3Co NPs/CB, Pd_3Ni NPs/CB [21], Ir-Pd/C [22], NiPd NPs/N-GR [23], and Au-Pd_6CoCu/C [24], have been reported as cathode catalysts for ORR. The activation energy of Pt/C is 48 kJ mol^{-1}, whereas, for Pd/C, it is 39 kJ mol^{-1} with an overvoltage of 300 mV. Therefore, the ORR performance of palladium (Pd)-based transition metals in alkaline electrolytes is more favorable on Pd/C catalyst than that of Pt/C [25].

Transition metal chalcogenides (TMC) have already been used as a cathode catalyst in acidic medium; however, TMCs have recently been employed in alkaline media. Mutyala et al. [26] reported phosphorus-doped and MoS_2 encapsulated, interconnected, porous, carbon (MoS_2/P-ICPC) catalyst for ORR. The ORR activity (onset voltage and current density) of the catalyst is comparable to commercial Pt/C catalyst. Moreover, MoS_2/P-ICPC catalyst exhibits high tolerance to methanol crossover and good durability. Recently, Masud et al. [27] confirmed that electrodeposited Co_7Se_8 nanostructures on GCE exhibit high performance for ORR with a higher tolerance to methanol crossover than that of Pt catalysts. The onset voltage at Pt/glassy carbon (GC) is negatively shifted to 0.801 V vs. reversible hydrogen electrode (RHE) from 0.931 V vs. RHE in the presence of methanol due to poisoning of the electrode surface. However, the presence or absence of methanol does not affect the onset voltage of Co_7Se_8/GC electrode (0.811 V vs. RHE). The Co_7Se_8/GC electrode also exhibits high stability after 1000 linear sweep voltammetry (LSV) cycles and reproducibility in presence of 0.5 M methanol solution. The enhanced performance of Co_7Se_8 is due to the presence of Se in the lattice, which can easily modify the electronic structure of the active site (Co) of catalyst along with conduction and valence band positions with respect to water oxidation bands. It is noticed that change in transition-metal oxide to transition-metal selenide increases the conduction and valence band edges, as a result water oxidation and reduction levels become closer. The charge transfer between the catalyst and the electrolyte is enhanced because of the closeness of the band positions. Yu et al. [28] reported co-doping of iron (Fe) and nickel on a $CoSe_2$ catalyst that was obtained via the solvothermal route. $Co_{0.7}Fe_{0.3}Se_2$ shows cathodic peak voltage of 0.564 V and onset voltage of 0.759 V, while $Co_{0.7}Ni_{0.3}Se_2$ exhibits cathodic peak voltage of 0.558 V and onset voltage of 0.741 V, indicating that $Co_{0.7}Fe_{0.3}Se_2$ is a better cathode catalyst than that of $Co_{0.7}Ni_{0.3}Se_2$. Moreover, the $Co_{0.7}Fe_{0.3}Se_2$ catalyst is more stable and tolerant toward the crossover of methanol, ethanol, and ethylene glycol in comparison to that of commercial Pt/C. As reported by the authors, the improved activity of $Co_{0.7}Fe_{0.3}Se_2$ catalyst is due to Fe doping

11.5.2 Metal Oxide-Based Electrocatalysts

Many nonprecious metal oxides have been reported as cathode catalysts for ORR, such as CoPc/C-W$_{18}$O$_{49}$ [29], Au-MnO$_2$/MWNT, Au-ZnO/MWNT [30], CoO@ NS-CSs [31], Mn-CeO$_2$/rGO [32], Ti$_2$O$_3$/rGO [33], Co/CoO$_x$@NC-CNTs [34], CoO/ MnO$_2$/RGO [35], MnO$_x$- Co$_3$O$_4$/C [36], CoO@Co/N-C [37], CeO$_2$/rGO [38], RGO/ ZnWO$_4$/Fe$_3$O$_4$ [39], Fe-MFC60-T [40], RGO@Co$_3$O$_4$ [41], and different spinel oxide-based materials, such as 3D dandelion-like NiCo$_2$O$_4$, flower-like NiCo$_2$O$_4$ [42], rGO/ CoFe$_2$O$_4$ [43], hexagonal spinel-type Mn$_2$AlO$_4$ nanosheets [44], and 3D macroporous NiCo$_2$O$_4$ sheet [45]. Many studies have been conducted on Mn$_x$O$_y$-based cathode catalysts because of their rich redox chemistry and abundance as well as the environmentally friendly nature of manganese [46–48]. Lee et al. [49] reported that rGO/ MnO$_2$/Ag exhibits enhanced current density and electron transfer rate per O$_2$ at a voltage of 0.3 V compared to 20 wt% Pt/C. In addition, the results of kinetic analysis confirm that O$_2$ has been directly reduced to H$_2$O via a four-electron pathway with strong resistance to fuel crossover in comparison to that of commercial 20 wt% Pt/C. In 2015, Chen et al. [50] investigated the electrocatalytic activity of 3D nitrogen-doped graphene/MnO (3D-N-RGO/MnO) toward ORR. The as-synthesized catalyst exhibited enhanced catalytic activity and more positive potential, high tolerance to methanol crossover, and long-term stability because of the synergistic effects of 3D nitrogen-doped RGO and MnO. Therefore, graphene/metal oxide catalysts have been widely used in batteries, fuel cells, supercapacitors, and biosensors [51–54]. Zuo et al. [55] synthesized porous MnO$_2$ by facile sonochemical method (SC-PMO) and studied ORR activity. In Figure 11.5, all the transmission electron microscope (TEM) images at different magnifications (Figure 11.5a and b) and the scanning electron microscope (SEM) image (Figure 11.5c) confirm the porous structure of SC-PMO. The as-synthesized porous SC-PMO shows improved electrocatalytic activity, better stability, and higher methanol tolerance than that of commercial Pt/C catalyst in a basic medium. All the electrochemical analysis confirms that the enhancement in ORR activity at porous SC-PMO catalyst is ascribed to the porosity and well dispersity, which further increases the kinetics of the ion and electron transport mechanism.

Yu et al. [56] investigated the performance of MnO$_2$ nanofilms directly grown over nitrogen-doped hollow graphene spheres (MnO$_2$/N-HGSs) as an ORR catalyst in Zn-air batteries. As shown in Figure 11.6a, MnO$_2$/N-HGSs exhibit maximum power density of 82 mW cm^{-2} at an open-circuit voltage of 1.48 V, which is almost comparable to that of commercial Pt/C catalysts (power density 94 mW cm^{-2} at an open circuit voltage of 1.49 V). The long-term stability of MnO$_2$/N-HGSs toward ORR is confirmed from the galvanostatic discharge curves shown in Figure 11.6b. Moreover, the specific capacity of MnO$_2$/N-HGSs (744 mAh g^{-1}) is also comparable to that of a commercial Pt/C cathode (757 mAh g^{-1}) at a current density of 10 mA cm^{-2}.

Direct Methanol Fuel Cells

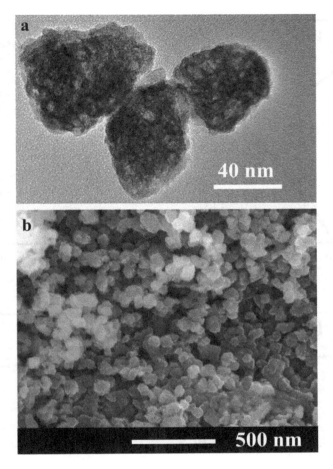

FIGURE 11.5 Morphology of porous MnO$_2$ prepared by SC-PMO. (a) TEM micrograph, and (b) FE-SEM image. Adapted and reproduced with permission from reference [55]. Copyright 2017 Elsevier.

11.5.3 TRANSITION METAL-NITROGEN (M-N$_x$) MACROCYCLE-BASED ELECTROCATALYSTS

Macrocyclic compounds are polydentate ligands, in which the donor atoms are either incorporated or attached to a cyclic backbone [57]. Macrocycles are the large molecules that have a minimum of one large ring with nine or more atoms, among which three are donor atoms [58]. Macrocyclic materials have attained much attention due to some remarkable properties, including [57] their ability to differentiate among the same group of metal ions depending upon the ring size and the enhanced stability exhibited by optimally fitted macrocyclic ligands (macrocyclic effect). In 1934, iron phthalocyanine (FePc), the first transition metal N$_4$ (MN$_4$) macrocycle was discovered by Linstead [59]. Among the various macrocyclics, phthalocyanines (Pc),

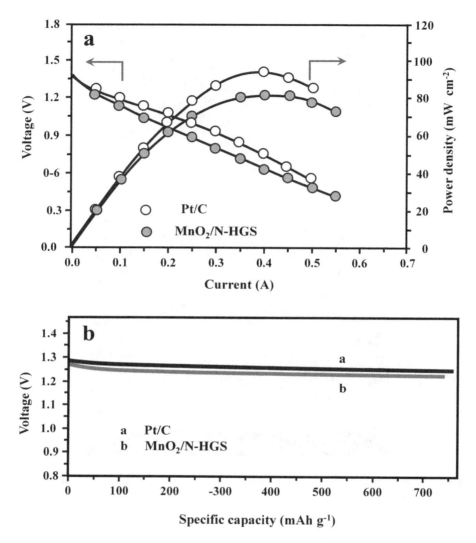

FIGURE 11.6 Performance properties of MnO$_2$/N-HGS vs. commercial Pt/C catalysts. (a) Polarization and power density plots, and (b) galvanostatic discharge curves of MnO$_2$/N-HGS and commercial Pt/C catalysts at a discharging current 10 mA cm^{-2}. N-HGS: nitrogen-doped hollow graphene spheres. Adapted and reproduced with permission from reference [56]. Copyright 2016 American Chemical Society.

combined with different transition metals, such as nickel, iron, manganese, zinc, cobalt, and copper, have been extensively studied as cathode electrocatalyst in fuel cells [29, 60, 61, 62]. The cobalt- and copper-based macrocyclic complexes are the most stable, whereas iron- and cobalt-based complexes exhibit good catalytic activity as well as stability [63]. As shown in Figure 11.7, oxygen molecules can interact with

Direct Methanol Fuel Cells 249

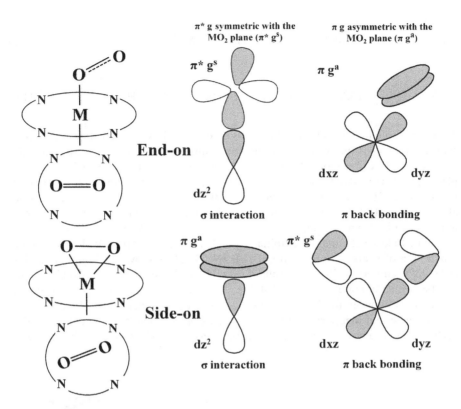

FIGURE 11.7 Orbital representation of end on and side on configurations during interaction of O_2 molecule with the metal center of nitrogen macrocycle. Adapted and reproduced with permission from reference [57]. Copyright 2020 Elsevier.

the MN_4 macrocycle-based catalyst, "end-on" or "side-on" mode, depending on the available coordination sites and energy of d-orbitals of the metal's center. Moreover, oxygen molecules can interact through the "bridge-cis" and "bridge-trans" configurations, where two metal sites are involved [57]. The binding of oxygen molecules to the catalysts depends on the binding of the d-orbitals in the central metal ion of the macrocycle [64].

Metal phthalocyanine- (MPc) based catalyst shows high ORR activity when d-orbitals are half filled in the central metal atom. These interaction mechanisms reduce the bond energy of oxygen molecules and finally lead to its rupture. Beck et al. [65] proposed the ORR mechanism of transition metal-N_4- (MN_4) based catalyst, known as "redox catalysis." Initially, the oxygen is adsorbed on the metal center of the catalyst and forms oxygen-catalyst adduct, after that, the electron is transferred from the metal center to bound oxygen molecule, and then the reduced MN_4 is regenerated as shown in Equations 11.4–11.6 [65]:

$$XMe^{II} + O_2 \rightleftarrows \left(XMe^{\delta+} \ldots O_2^{\delta+} \right) \quad (11.4)$$

$$\left(XMe^{\delta+} \quad \ldots O_2^{\delta+}\right) + H^+ \rightarrow \left(XMe^{III} \quad \ldots O_2H\right)^+ \quad (11.5)$$

$$\left(XMe^{III} \quad \ldots O_2H\right)^+ + H^+ + 2e^- \rightarrow XMe + H_2O_2 \quad (11.6)$$

There are three major routes of ORR activity exhibited by the transition metal macrocycle complexes [66, 67]: (i) two electron transfer routes for production of H_2O_2 (cobalt complexes); (ii) four electron transfer routes for production of H_2O (iron complexes); and (iii) mixed route for both two and four electron transfers for production of mixed H_2O_2 and H_2O. In some cases, these macrocycle-based complexes can also act as catalyst in the one-electron O_2 reduction process and generate superoxide ions. Recently, Komba et al. [68] reported a study on FePc immobilized on nitrogen-doped electrochemically exfoliated graphene (FePc/N-GP950). The schematic illustration of synthesis procedure of FePc/N-GP950 is shown in Figure 11.8. The FePc-33/N-GP950 exhibits a current density (5.0 mA cm^{-2} at 0.8 V), which is comparable to that of commercial Pt/C (4.0 mA cm^{-2}) in a basic medium. The strong π-π interactions between the FePc and N-doped graphene contribute to the high ORR performance and long-term durability of the as-prepared sample. Therefore, FePc-33/N-GP950 is a cost-effective and suitable alternative to Pt-based catalyst for ORR activity.

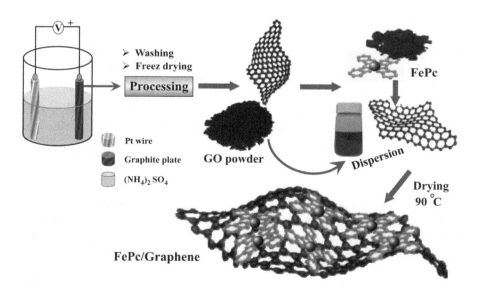

FIGURE 11.8 Synthesis strategies on electrochemical exfoliation and FePc mobilization onto graphene nanosheets. Electrochemical set-up for exfoliation of graphite, and FePc immobilization onto the pristine graphene and N-doped graphene nanosheets. Adapted and reproduced with permission from reference [68] Copyright 2019 Elsevier.

Direct Methanol Fuel Cells 251

FIGURE 11.9 FE-SEM micrographs on the surface morphology of one dimensional MnPc microstructures in different magnifications.: (a) 1 μm, and (b) 400 nm. Adapted and reproduced with permission from reference [64]. Copyright 2019 Elsevier.

Mukherjee et al. [64] reported the solvothermal synthesis of one dimensional microstructure of manganese phthalocyanine (MnPc) (Figure 11.9) and the catalytic performance toward ORR in a basic medium. The experimental results and theoretical calculations using density functional theory show that the onset and half-wave potential of MnPc are almost comparable to that of Pt/C. Moreover, the theoretical calculations confirm that the ORR mechanism occurs via a four-electron path at the MnPc catalyst. In this system, *OOH formation is the rate determining step among all the intermediates that formed in four-electron transfer path. Therefore, in this work, both theoretical and experimental results confirm the potential of MnPc as a promising alternative to Pt in fuel cells.

11.5.4 Metal-Free Nanocarbon-Based Electrocatalyst

Recently, metal-free nanocarbon- (MFNC) based materials have drawn much research interest as an ORR catalyst because of their unique characteristics such

252 Ceramic and Specialty Electrolytes

as oxygen-absorption ability, desorption of reduction products, high surface area, and electrical conductivity. Therefore, MFNC-based materials can serve as excellent electron-transfer media and also possess high electrochemical stability at large pH [19]. The MFNCs that have gained attention are boron-doped CNTs [69], defect-rich N-doped nanocarbon shells [70], nitrogen-doped carbon nanocages [71], edge-selectively sulphurized graphene nanoplatelets [72], nitrogen-doped magnetic carbon [73], nitrogen-doped single-walled CNTs [74], boron and nitrogen co-doped graphene [75], hybrid composite of rGO and polyelectrolyte functionalized MWCNTs [76], 3D N-doped graphene [77], CNTs/heteroatom-doped carbon core-sheath [78], nitrogen and phosphorus co-doped nanocarbon foam [79], sulphur-doped graphene [80, 81], polyelectrolyte functionalize CNT [82], and nitrogen-doped carbon nanosheets [83]. These MFNC-based catalysts show improved ORR activity and long-term durability than that of a commercial Pt/C in an alkaline media. The ORR activity depends on the opened structures of MFNCs, which increases exposure of the active sites to attach the heteroatoms [19]. Li et al. [84] reported single-wall carbon nanotube (SWCNT) embedded in nitrogen and phosphorus co-doped carbon (SWCNT@NPC) as an oxygen reduction electrocatalyst. The SWCNT@NPC exhibits high ORR activity with half-wave voltage of oxygen reduction 0.85 V at 10 mA cm^{-2} of current density. The reason behind the high ORR performance is the synergistic effects of both N and P doping. The excellent performance of SWCNT@NPC for ORR activity is due to three reasons: (i) N doping can enhance P doping and decreases the O_2 adsorption barrier, (ii) the incorporation of P dopants favors the formation of pyridinic N, and (iii) the coupling effect between adjacent N and P atoms optimizes the adsorption energy of the oxygen molecule. Yang et al. [85] synthesized nitrogen and sulphur co-doped honeycomb-like porous carbon (N, S@C) by pyrolysis followed by an etching method for ORR activity. The porosity of the carbon framework depends on the amount of hard template, i.e. SiO_2, while the doping amount of N and S depends on the temperature of pyrolysis. N, S@CM-1000 displays more positive onset potential of 0.90V vs. RHE, half-wave potential of 0.76V vs. RHE and high diffusion limiting current density of 5.5 mA cm^{-2} because of the mutual effect of nitrogen and sulphur, defect rich carbon, high conductivity, and porous structure of the catalyst. Yang et al. [86] derived a porous carbon framework (PCF) obtained from N-rich hyper-crosslinked polymers (HCPs) via one-step Friedel-Crafts reaction using a pyrrole monomer as shown in Figure 11.10a and investigated the application as an ORR electrocatalyst. The PCF-HCP pyrolyzed at a temperature of 900° C (PCF-HCP-900) exhibits superior electrocatalytic activity toward ORR than that of PCF-HCPs pyrolyzed at other temperatures due to large specific surface area and high porosity. Moreover, the high density of N doping exposes more reactive sites, contributing to the enhanced ORR activity. The PCF-HCP-900 exhibits 10 mV higher half-wave voltage (0.84 V) than that of Pt/C catalyst (0.83 V), higher positive onset voltage (0.95 V vs. RHE), larger limiting current density (4.8 mA cm^{-2}), improved tolerance for methanol, and long-term stability in comparison to that of commercial Pt/C (as displayed in Figure 11.10b). Moreover, oxygen reduction takes place via four-electron pathway at PCF-HCP-900 catalyst with lower yield of H_2O_2.

Direct Methanol Fuel Cells

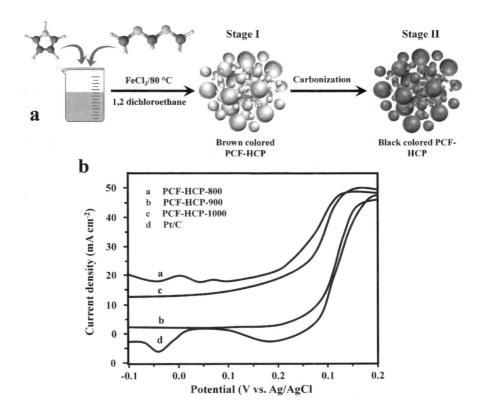

FIGURE 11.10 Synthesis strategies and oxidative stability of porous carbon framework obtained from N-rich hyper-crosslinked polymers (PCF-HCP). (a) Schematic illustration on the synthesis of PCF-HCP-900, and (b) LSV curves of PCF-HCP calcinated at temperatures 800° C, 900° C, and 1000° C and commercial Pt/C catalyst in 0.1 M KOH at 1600 rpm and sweep rate 10 mV s^{-1}. Adapted and reproduced with permission from reference [86]. Copyright 2019 Elsevier.

Based on these properties, the PCF-HCP-900 can be considered as a potential candidate for metal-free ORR catalyst in fuel cells.

11.6 CONCLUSION AND FUTURE OUTLOOK

Conventional energy resources cannot fulfill the increasing global energy demand and are not adequate for mobile electronic and transport systems. Among the various types of fuel cells, DMFC can be considered as promising candidate that can replace the conventional energy resources because it is light weight, cost effective, and environmentally benign. It does not require charging from the alternating current (AC) mains; therefore, it can be used in remote places where there is no supply of electricity. Moreover, the high energy density, easy handling, storage and transportation of methanol are the significant advantages of DMFC over hydrogen fuel cells. However, some serious drawbacks, such as methanol crossover, high cost of Pt, and sluggish ORR kinetics reduce the commercialization of DMFC. Methanol crossover causes polarization loss, resulting in a mixed potential at the cathode. Therefore, tremendous amounts of research has been going on to develop a low-cost, methanol-tolerant cathode catalyst with long-term stability for the successful use in DMFC. This chapter discussed the recent advancements in different kinds of non-Pt-based electrocatalysts for ORR. The working principles, ORR mechanisms related to DMFC, and different synthesis routes of electrocatalysts, such as electrochemical deposition, chemical reduction, hydrothermal, sol-gel, microwave irradiation, and template-directed growth were also discussed. Although, numerous Pt-free catalysts have been developed, including transition metals and their composites with other elements, metal oxides, transition metal-nitrogen macrocycle, and carbon materials, much improvement is still needed to enhance the cell performance and durability for full-scale commercialization of DMFCs that can replace traditional energy conversion devices.

REFERENCES

1. Rayment C, Sherwin S (2003) *Introduction to fuel cell technology.* Department of Aerospace and Mechanical Engineering, University of Notre Dame, Notre Dame, IN 46556:11–12.
2. Kamarudin SK, Achmad F, Daud WRW (2009) Overview on the application of direct methanol fuel cell (DMFC) for portable electronic devices. *International Journal of Hydrogen Energy* 34(16):6902–6916.
3. Cook B (2002) Introduction to fuel cells and hydrogen technology. *Engineering Science & Education Journal* 11(6):205–216.
4. Tiwari JN, Tiwari RN, Singh G, Kim KS (2013) Recent progress in the development of anode and cathode catalysts for direct methanol fuel cells. *Nano Energy* 2(5):553–578.
5. Parsons R, VanderNoot T (1988) The oxidation of small organic molecules: A survey of recent fuel cell related research. *Journal of Electroanalytical Chemistry and Interfacial Electrochemistry* 257(1–2):9–45.
6. Xu Z, Li H, Cao G, Zhang Q, Li K, Zhao X (2011) Electrochemical performance of carbon nanotube-supported cobalt phthalocyanine and its nitrogen-rich derivatives for oxygen reduction. *Journal of Molecular Catalysis A: Chemical* 335(1–2):89–96.
7. Dissanayaka Wijesooriyage W (2011) *Electrochemical deposition and characterization of thermoelectric thin films of (BixSb1-x) 2Te3.* Chalmers University of Technology, Göteborg, Sweden.
8. Kakaei K, Esrafili MD, Ehsani A (2019) Alcohol oxidation and hydrogen evolution. In: *Interface Science and Technology* edited by Kakaei K, Esrafili MD, Ehsani A, vol 27. Elsevier, Amsterdam, Netherlands, pp 253–301.
9. Khan A, Rashid A, Younas R, Chong R (2016) A chemical reduction approach to the synthesis of copper nanoparticles. *International Nano Letters* 6(1):21–26.
10. Suriati G, Mariatti M, Azizan A (2014) Synthesis of silver nanoparticles by chemical reduction method: Effect of reducing agent and surfactant concentration. *International Journal of Automotive and Mechanical Engineering* 10:1920.
11. Feng S-H, Li G-H (2017) Hydrothermal and solvothermal syntheses. In: *Modern inorganic synthetic chemistry* edited by Xu R and Xu Y. Elsevier, Amsterdam, Netherlands, pp 73–104.

12. Li J, Wu Q, Wu J (2015) Synthesis of nanoparticles via solvothermal and hydrothermal methods. *Handbook of Nanoparticles*, edited by Aliofkhazraei M, vol 2. Springer International Publishing Switzerland: 295–328.
13. Rao BG, Mukherjee D, Reddy BM (2017) Novel approaches for preparation of nanoparticles. In: *Nanostructures for novel therapy*, edited by Ficai D and Grumezescu AM. Elsevier, Philadelphia, United States, pp 1–36.
14. Thiagarajan S, Sanmugam A, Vikraman D (2017) Facile methodology of sol-gel synthesis for metal oxide nanostructures. *Recent Applications in Sol-Gel Synthesis* edited by Usha Chandra, InTech, Croatia:1–17.
15. Gerbec JA, Magana D, Washington A, Strouse GF (2005) Microwave-enhanced reaction rates for nanoparticle synthesis. *Journal of the American Chemical Society* 127(45):15791–15800.
16. Brace CL (2009) Microwave ablation technology: What every user should know. *Current Problems in Diagnostic Radiology* 38(2):61–67.
17. Nüchter M, Ondruschka B, Bonrath W, Gum A (2004) Microwave assisted synthesis–a critical technology overview. *Green Chemistry* 6(3):128–141.
18. Bao H, Zhang Z, Hua Q, Huang W (2014) Compositions, structures, and catalytic activities of CeO2@ Cu2O nanocomposites prepared by the template-assisted method. *Langmuir* 30(22):6427–6436.
19. Ozoemena KI (2016) Nanostructured platinum-free electrocatalysts in alkaline direct alcohol fuel cells: Catalyst design, principles and applications. *RSC Advances* 6(92):89523–89550.
20. Nguyen D, Bach L, Bui Q (2019) A high-performance catalyst based on binary CuFe alloyed nanocrystals encapsulated in nitrogen-doped graphene nanosheets towards oxygen reduction reaction. *Journal of Solid State Chemistry* 273:132–140.
21. Gunji T, Wakabayashi RH, Noh SH, Han B, Matsumoto F, DiSalvo FJ, Abruña HD (2018) The effect of alloying of transition metals (M= Fe, Co, Ni) with palladium catalysts on the electrocatalytic activity for the oxygen reduction reaction in alkaline media. *Electrochimica Acta* 283:1045–1052.
22. Nguyen ATN, Shim JH (2018) Facile one-step synthesis of Ir-Pd bimetallic alloy networks as efficient bifunctional catalysts for oxygen reduction and oxygen evolution reactions. *Journal of Electroanalytical Chemistry* 827:120–127.
23. Thi M, Tran T, Anh PH, Nhac-Vu H-T, Bui Q (2019) An innovative catalyst of nickel-palladium alloy nanocrystals embedded nitrogen-doped graphene for efficient oxygen reduction reaction. *Journal of Alloys and Compounds* 797:314–324.
24. Wang D, Liu S, Wang J, Lin R, Kawasaki M, Rus E, Silberstein KE, Lowe MA, Lin F, Nordlund D (2016) Spontaneous incorporation of gold in palladium-based ternary nanoparticles makes durable electrocatalysts for oxygen reduction reaction. *Nature Communications* 7(1):1–9.
25. Jiang L, Hsu A, Chu D, Chen R (2009) Oxygen reduction reaction on carbon supported Pt and Pd in alkaline solutions. *Journal of the Electrochemical Society* 156(3):B370–B376.
26. Mutyala S, Rajaram R, Karuppasamy D, Suresh C, Mathiyarasu J (2018) Tuning the oxygen reduction reactivity of interconnected porous carbon by incorporation of phosphorus and activity enhancement through blending with 2D metal dichalcogenides materials. *International Journal of Hydrogen Energy* 43(9):4738–4745.
27. Masud J, Nath M (2016) Co7Se8 nanostructures as catalysts for oxygen reduction reaction with high methanol tolerance. *ACS Energy Letters* 1(1):27–31.
28. Yu B, Jin J, Wu H, Wang S, Xia Q, Liu H (2017) Iron and nickel doped CoSe2 as efficient non precious metal catalysts for oxygen reduction. *International Journal of Hydrogen Energy* 42(1):236–242.

29. Karim N, Kamarudin SK (2017) Novel heat-treated cobalt phthalocyanine/carbon-tungsten oxide nanowires (CoPc/C-W18O49) cathode catalyst for direct methanol fuel cell. *Journal of Electroanalytical Chemistry* 803:19–29.
30. Jafri RI, Sujatha N, Rajalakshmi N, Ramaprabhu S (2009) Au–MnO2/MWNT and Au–ZnO/MWNT as oxygen reduction reaction electrocatalyst for polymer electrolyte membrane fuel cell. *International Journal of Hydrogen Energy* 34(15):6371–6376.
31. Chen L, Guo X, Zhang G (2017) N, S co-doped carbon spheres with highly dispersed CoO as non-precious metal catalyst for oxygen reduction reaction. *Journal of Power Sources* 360:106–113.
32. Hota I, Soren S, Mohapatra B, Debnath A, Muthe K, Varadwaj K, Parhi P (2019) Mn-doped ceria/reduced graphene oxide nanocomposite as an efficient oxygen reduction reaction catalyst. *Journal of Electroanalytical Chemistry* 851:113480.
33. Shi Y, Zhang Y, Zhang X, Cai J, Lin S (2019) A non-noble metal oxide Ti2O3/rGO composite as efficient and highly stable electrocatalyst for oxygen reduction. *International Journal of Hydrogen Energy* 44(52):28134–28142.
34. Liu S, Chen X, Wang S, Yang Z, Gao J, Zhu P, Zhao X, Wang G (2018) 3D CNTs-threaded N-doped hierarchical porous carbon hybrid with embedded Co/CoOx nanoparticles as efficient bifunctional catalysts for oxygen electrode reactions. *Electrochimica Acta* 292:707–717.
35. Huang W, Zhong H, Li D, Tang P, Feng Y (2015) Reduced graphene oxide supported CoO/MnO2 electrocatalysts from layered double hydroxides for oxygen reduction reaction. *Electrochimica Acta* 173:575–580.
36. Wang Y, Ma X, Lu L, He Y, Qi X, Deng Y (2013) Carbon supported MnOx–Co3O4 as cathode catalyst for oxygen reduction reaction in alkaline media. *International Journal of Hydrogen Energy* 38(31):13611–13616.
37. Huang D, Luo Y, Li S, Zhang B, Shen Y, Wang M (2014) Active catalysts based on cobalt oxide@ cobalt/NC nanocomposites for oxygen reduction reaction in alkaline solutions. *Nano Research* 7(7):1054–1064.
38. Peng W, Zhao L, Zhang C, Yan Y, Xian Y (2016) Controlled growth cerium oxide nanoparticles on reduced graphene oxide for oxygen catalytic reduction. *Electrochimica Acta* 191:669–676.
39. Sadiq MMJ, Mutyala S, Mathiyarasu J, Bhat DK (2017) RGO/ZnWO4/Fe3O4 nanocomposite as an efficient electrocatalyst for oxygen reduction reaction. *Journal of Electroanalytical Chemistry* 799:102–110.
40. Benzigar MR, Joseph S, Saianand G, Gopalan A-I, Sarkar S, Srinivasan S, Park D-H, Kim S, Talapaneni SN, Ramadass K (2019) Highly ordered iron oxide-mesoporous fullerene nanocomposites for oxygen reduction reaction and supercapacitor applications. *Microporous and Mesoporous Materials* 285:21–31.
41. Shahid MM, Rameshkumar P, Basirun WJ, Juan JC, Huang NM (2017) Cobalt oxide nanocubes interleaved reduced graphene oxide as an efficient electrocatalyst for oxygen reduction reaction in alkaline medium. *Electrochimica Acta* 237:61–68.
42. Liu Y, Shu C, Fang Y, Chen Y, Liu Y (2017) Two 3D structured Co-Ni bimetallic oxides as cathode catalysts for high-performance alkaline direct methanol fuel cells. *Journal of Power Sources* 361:160–169.
43. Samanta A, Raj CR (2019) A new approach for the synthesis of electrocatalytically active CoFe2O4 catalyst for oxygen reduction reaction. *Journal of Electroanalytical Chemistry* 847:113183.
44. Si C, Wang Y, Zhang J, Gao H, Lv L, Han L, Zhang Z (2016) Highly electrocatalytic activity and excellent methanol tolerance of hexagonal spinel-type Mn2AlO4 nanosheets towards oxygen reduction reaction: Experiment and density functional theory calculation. *Nano Energy* 23:105–113.

Direct Methanol Fuel Cells

45. Xiao Y, Hu C, Qu L, Hu C, Cao M (2013) Three-dimensional macroporous NiCo2O4 sheets as a non-noble catalyst for efficient oxygen reduction reactions. *Chemistry–A European Journal* 19(42):14271–14278.

46. Wang Y, Wang F, Fang Y, Zhu J, Luo H, Qi J, Wu W (2019) Self-assembled flower-like MnO2 grown on Fe-containing urea-formaldehyde resins based carbon as catalyst for oxygen reduction reaction in alkaline direct methanol fuel cells. *Applied Surface Science* 496:143566.

47. Liew KB, Daud WRW, Ghasemi M, Loh KS, Ismail M, Lim SS, Leong JX (2015) Manganese oxide/functionalised carbon nanotubes nanocomposite as catalyst for oxygen reduction reaction in microbial fuel cell. *International Journal of Hydrogen Energy* 40(35):11625–11632.

48. Zhang J, Guo C, Zhang L, Li CM (2013) Direct growth of flower-like manganese oxide on reduced graphene oxide towards efficient oxygen reduction reaction. *Chemical Communications* 49(56):6334–6336.

49. Lee K, Ahmed MS, Jeon S (2015) Electrochemical deposition of silver on manganese dioxide coated reduced graphene oxide for enhanced oxygen reduction reaction. *Journal of Power Sources* 288:261–269.

50. Chen R, Yan J, Liu Y, Li J (2015) Three-dimensional nitrogen-doped graphene/MnO nanoparticle hybrids as a high-performance catalyst for oxygen reduction reaction. *The Journal of Physical Chemistry C* 119(15):8032–8037.

51. Wei T, Zhang M, Wu P, Tang Y-J, Li S-L, Shen F-C, Wang X-L, Zhou X-P, Lan Y-Q (2017) POM-based metal-organic framework/reduced graphene oxide nanocomposites with hybrid behavior of battery-supercapacitor for superior lithium storage. *Nano Energy* 34:205–214.

52. Papiya F, Pattanayak P, Kumar V, Das S, Kundu PP (2020) Sulfonated graphene oxide and titanium dioxide coated with nanostructured polyaniline nanocomposites as an efficient cathode catalyst in microbial fuel cells. *Materials Science and Engineering: C* 108:110498.

53. Rezanezhad A, Rezaie E, Ghadimi LS, Hajalilou A, Abouzari-Lotf E, Arsalani N (2020) Outstanding supercapacitor performance of Nd–Mn co-doped perovskite LaFeO3@ nitrogen-doped graphene oxide nanocomposites. *Electrochimica Acta* 335:135699.

54. Wang Y, Liu X-y, Xu X, Yang Y, Huang L-h, He Z-y, Xu Y-h, Chen J-j, Feng Z-s (2018) Preparation and characterization of reduced graphene oxide/Fe3O4 nanocomposite by a facile in-situ deposition method for glucose biosensor applications. *Materials Research Bulletin* 101:340–346.

55. Zuo L-X, Jiang L-P, Abdel-Halim E, Zhu J-J (2017) Sonochemical preparation of stable porous MnO2 and its application as an efficient electrocatalyst for oxygen reduction reaction. *Ultrasonics Sonochemistry* 35:219–225.

56. Yu Q, Xu J, Wu C, Zhang J, Guan L (2016) MnO2 nanofilms on nitrogen-doped hollow graphene spheres as a high-performance electrocatalyst for oxygen reduction reaction. *ACS Applied Materials & Interfaces* 8(51):35264–35269.

57. Kumar A, Zhang Y, Liu W, Sun X (2020) The chemistry, recent advancements and activity descriptors for macrocycles based electrocatalysts in oxygen reduction reaction. *Coordination Chemistry Reviews* 402:213047.

58. Swamy S, Pola S (2008) Spectroscopic studies on Co (II), Ni (II), Cu (II) and Zn (II) complexes with a N4-macrocylic ligands. *Spectrochimica Acta Part A: Molecular and Biomolecular Spectroscopy* 70(4):929–933.

59. Linstead R, Lowe A (1934) 216. Phthalocyanines. Part V. The molecular weight of magnesium phthalocyanine. *Journal of the Chemical Society* (Resumed):1031–1033.

60. Tiwari B, Noori MT, Ghangrekar M (2017) Carbon supported nickel-phthalocyanine/MnOx as novel cathode catalyst for microbial fuel cell application. *International Journal of Hydrogen Energy* 42(36):23085–23094.

61. Ghasemi M, Daud WRW, Rahimnejad M, Rezayi M, Fatemi A, Jafari Y, Somalu MR, Manzour A (2013) Copper-phthalocyanine and nickel nanoparticles as novel cathode catalysts in microbial fuel cells. *International Journal of Hydrogen Energy* 38(22):9533–9540.

62. Ahmed J, Yuan Y, Zhou L, Kim S (2012) Carbon supported cobalt oxide nanoparticles–iron phthalocyanine as alternative cathode catalyst for oxygen reduction in microbial fuel cells. *Journal of Power Sources* 208:170–175.

63. Othman R, Dicks AL, Zhu Z (2012) Non precious metal catalysts for the PEM fuel cell cathode. *International Journal of Hydrogen Energy* 37(1):357–372.

64. Mukherjee M, Samanta M, Banerjee P, Chattopadhyay KK, Das GP (2019) Endorsement of manganese phthalocyanine microstructures as electrocatalyst in ORR: Experimental and computational study. *Electrochimica Acta* 296:528–534.

65. Beck F (1977) The redox mechanism of the chelate-catalysed oxygen cathode. *Journal of Applied Electrochemistry* 7(3):239–245.

66. Liu Y, Yue X, Li K, Qiao J, Wilkinson DP, Zhang J (2016) PEM fuel cell electrocatalysts based on transition metal macrocyclic compounds. *Coordination Chemistry Reviews* 315:153–177.

67. Zhang L, Zhang J, Wilkinson DP, Wang H (2006) Progress in preparation of non-noble electrocatalysts for PEM fuel cell reactions. *Journal of Power Sources* 156(2):171–182.

68. Komba N, Zhang G, Wei Q, Yang X, Prakash J, Chenitz R, Rosei F, Sun S (2019) Iron (II) phthalocyanine/N-doped graphene: A highly efficient non-precious metal catalyst for oxygen reduction. *International Journal of Hydrogen Energy* 44(33):18103–18114.

69. Yang L, Jiang S, Zhao Y, Zhu L, Chen S, Wang X, Wu Q, Ma J, Ma Y, Hu Z (2011) Boron-doped carbon nanotubes as metal-free electrocatalysts for the oxygen reduction reaction. *Angewandte Chemie International Edition* 50(31):7132–7135.

70. Tang J, Liu Y, Lv G, Yang C, Yang G (2019) Localized micro-deflagration induced defect-rich N-doped nanocarbon shells for highly efficient oxygen reduction reaction. *Carbon* 145:411–418.

71. Chen S, Bi J, Zhao Y, Yang L, Zhang C, Ma Y, Wu Q, Wang X, Hu Z (2012) Nitrogen-doped carbon nanocages as efficient metal-free electrocatalysts for oxygen reduction reaction. *Advanced Materials* 24(41):5593–5597.

72. Jeon IY, Zhang S, Zhang L, Choi HJ, Seo JM, Xia Z, Dai L, Baek JB (2013) Edge-selectively sulfurized graphene nanoplatelets as efficient metal-free electrocatalysts for oxygen reduction reaction: The electron spin effect. *Advanced Materials* 25(42):6138–6145.

73. Li H, Tian J, Zhu Z, Cui F, Zhu Y-A, Duan X, Wang S (2018) Magnetic nitrogen-doped nanocarbons for enhanced metal-free catalytic oxidation: Integrated experimental and theoretical investigations for mechanism and application. *Chemical Engineering Journal* 354:507–516.

74. Yu D, Zhang Q, Dai L (2010) Highly efficient metal-free growth of nitrogen-doped single-walled carbon nanotubes on plasma-etched substrates for oxygen reduction. *Journal of the American Chemical Society* 132(43):15127–15129.

75. Wang S, Zhang L, Xia Z, Roy A, Chang DW, Baek JB, Dai L (2012) BCN graphene as efficient metal-free electrocatalyst for the oxygen reduction reaction. *Angewandte Chemie International Edition* 51(17):4209–4212.

76. Lee J-S, Jo K, Lee T, Yun T, Cho J, Kim B-S (2013) Facile synthesis of hybrid graphene and carbon nanotubes as a metal-free electrocatalyst with active dual interfaces for efficient oxygen reduction reaction. *Journal of Materials Chemistry A* 1(34):9603–9607.

77. Maouche C, Zhou Y, Li B, Cheng C, Wu Y, Li J, Gao S, Yang J (2019) Thermal treated three-dimensional N-doped graphene as efficient metal free-catalyst for oxygen reduction reaction. *Journal of Electroanalytical Chemistry* 853:113536.

78. Sa YJ, Park C, Jeong HY, Park SH, Lee Z, Kim KT, Park GG, Joo SH (2014) Carbon nanotubes/heteroatom-doped carbon core–sheath nanostructures as highly active, metal-free oxygen reduction electrocatalysts for alkaline fuel cells. *Angewandte Chemie International Edition* 53(16):4102–4106.
79. Zhang J, Qu L, Shi G, Liu J, Chen J, Dai L (2016) N, P-codoped carbon networks as efficient metal-free bifunctional catalysts for oxygen reduction and hydrogen evolution reactions. *Angewandte Chemie International Edition* 55(6):2230–2234.
80. Yang Z, Yao Z, Li G, Fang G, Nie H, Liu Z, Zhou X, Chen Xa, Huang S (2012) Sulfur-doped graphene as an efficient metal-free cathode catalyst for oxygen reduction. *ACS Nano* 6(1):205–211.
81. Lee J, Noh S, Pham ND, Shim JH (2019) Top-down synthesis of S-doped graphene nanosheets by electrochemical exfoliation of graphite: Metal-free bifunctional catalysts for oxygen reduction and evolution reactions. *Electrochimica Acta* 313:1–9.
82. Wang S, Yu D, Dai L (2011) Polyelectrolyte functionalized carbon nanotubes as efficient metal-free electrocatalysts for oxygen reduction. *Journal of the American Chemical Society* 133(14):5182–5185.
83. Wei W, Liang H, Parvez K, Zhuang X, Feng X, Müllen K (2014) Nitrogen-doped carbon nanosheets with size-defined mesopores as highly efficient metal-free catalyst for the oxygen reduction reaction. *Angewandte Chemie International Edition* 53(6):1570–1574.
84. Li J-C, Hou P-X, Cheng M, Liu C, Cheng H-M, Shao M (2018) Carbon nanotube encapsulated in nitrogen and phosphorus co-doped carbon as a bifunctional electrocatalyst for oxygen reduction and evolution reactions. *Carbon* 139:156–163.
85. Yang J, Xiang F, Guo H, Wang L, Niu X (2020) Honeycomb-like porous carbon with N and S dual-doping as metal-free catalyst for oxygen reduction reaction. *Carbon* 156:514–522.
86. Yang Z, Han J, Jiao R, Sun H, Zhu Z, Liang W, Li A (2019) Porous carbon framework derived from N-rich hypercrosslinked polymer as the efficient metal-free electrocatalyst for oxygen reduction reaction. *Journal of Colloid and Interface Science* 557:664–672.

12 Platinum-Free Anode Electrocatalysts for Methanol Oxidation in Direct Methanol Fuel Cells

Bhagyalakhi Baruah and Ashok Kumar

CONTENTS

12.1 Introduction 261
12.2 Methanol Oxidation Reaction (MOR) Mechanism 262
12.3 Pt-Free Anode Electrocatalysts 262
    12.3.1 Palladium-Based Electrocatalyst 263
    12.3.2 Nickel-Based Electrocatalysts 265
    12.3.3 Rhodium-Based Electrocatalysts 269
    12.3.4 Other Metal-Based Electrocatalysts 270
    12.3.5 Conducting Polymer-Based Electrocatalysts 271
    12.3.6 Graphene-Based Nanohybrid (rGO/PEDOT:PSS/MnO_2)
        Electrocatalyst 273
12.4 Conclusion and Future Prospects 279
References 280

12.1 INTRODUCTION

Direct methanol fuel cells (DMFCs) have gained much attention because of their simple structure, environment friendliness, and highly suitable for portable devices, including cellular phones, laptops, notepads, and cameras. DMFCs have been recognized as the future power generation source that can replace the conventional lithium-ion batteries because of their higher energy density (5.04 kWh L^{-1}), easy storage ability, transportability, and low cost [1]. It is the modified form of proton exchange membrane fuel cells (PEMFCs), in which polymer electrolyte membranes are used to separate anode and cathode chambers [2]. Unlike PEMFC, methanol can be directly used in DMFC without using reformer subsystems, and the fuel can be stored under atmospheric pressure [3]. However, commercialization of DMFC is still difficult because of the following reasons: methanol crossover across the membrane, high cost, carbon monoxide (CO) poisoning, and short-term durability of the electro-catalyst. The significant fuel crossover through the electrolyte membrane reduces the efficiency and cell performance [1, 4]. The performance of DMFC largely depends on the selection of proper cost-effective anode catalyst that can increase the methanol oxidation rate and reduce CO poisoning. Usually, the pure platinum (Pt) is known as an effective anode catalyst because of its effective dissociation and adsorption of methanol molecules; however, methanol oxidation produces carbonaceous intermediates, which block the electrode surface, causing poisoning of Pt-based electrodes [5]. Moreover, the high cost of Pt-based catalysts is another limitation for commercialization of DMFC. Therefore, researchers have made continuous efforts to develop a Pt-free anode catalyst using palladium, nickel, transition metal-based compounds, etc.

This chapter discusses the advancement of Pt-free anode catalysts in DMFCs that have been studied so far. A hybrid nanocomposite based on MnO_2 nanorods, PEDOT:PSS and rGO, has been synthesized via the *in situ* polymerization method, and the electrocatalytic activities toward oxidation of methanol have been studied. Additionally, this chapter discusses the methanol oxidation mechanism.

12.2 METHANOL OXIDATION REACTION (MOR) MECHANISM

In 1988, the methanol oxidation reaction (MOR) mechanism was reviewed by Parsons et al. [6]. The mechanism of the reaction can be described briefly as [7, 8]: (i) adsorption of methanol molecules over the electrode, (ii) dissociation of methanol due to activation of C-H bond, (iii) adsorption and activation of water molecules, (iv) CO_2 generation due to addition of O_2 to the surface adsorbed intermediates produced during MOR. Figure 12.1 illustrates the methanol oxidation mechanism at the Pt surface. Figure 12.1 shows that the intermediates, such as HCOOH, HCHO, and CO, formed during MOR are strongly adsorbed onto the Pt surface. Therefore, surface area of the catalyst decreases and thus the activity of DMFC. To date, three reaction mechanisms have been studied for MOR. Of these paths, one is an indirect mechanism in which methanol molecules are initially oxidized into CO and then to CO_2 (Path 1 as shown in Figure 12.1), while the other two paths (Paths 2 and 3 as shown in Figure 12.1) are direct, in which the methanol units are directly oxidized to CO_2 without forming toxic CO gas.

12.3 Pt-FREE ANODE ELECTROCATALYSTS

This section discusses the recent advancement of Pt-free anode catalysts for applications in DMFCs. In DMFC technology, the methanol oxidation is a six-electron process that occurs at an anodic voltage of 0.046 V; however, MOR produces carbonaceous intermediates, which block the electrode surface, causing poisoning of Pt-based electrodes [5]. Moreover, the high cost of Pt-based catalysts is another limitation for commercialization of DMFC; therefore, researchers have made continuous efforts to develop a Pt-free anode catalyst using Pd, Ni, and other transition metal-based compounds.

Pt-Free Anode Electrocatalysts

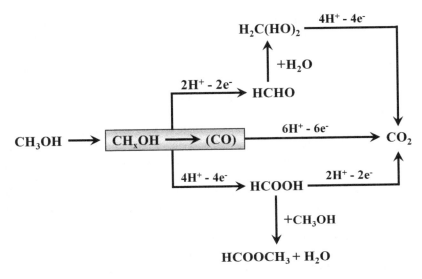

FIGURE 12.1 Schematic illustration of MOR in fuel cell. Adapted and reproduced from reference [7]. Copyright 2013 Elsevier.

12.3.1 Palladium-Based Electrocatalyst

Palladium (Pd) and Pd-based anode catalysts have displayed good electrocatalytic activity because the electrocatalytic properties and CO tolerance of Pd is almost similar to Pt. Moreover, Pd is less expensive and 50 times more abundant in nature than Pt [9, 10]. Although, the activity of Pd is comparatively less than that of Pt, it is active in alkaline medium during methanol electrooxidation [11]. The performance of a Pd electrode toward MOR is improved by incorporating a second metal. The electrocatalytic behavior of Pd in the presence of a second metal (Pd-M) can be explained by ligand or electronic effect and bifunctional mechanism [12]. According to bifunctional mechanism in methanol oxidation, two kinds of reactive sites are present in the catalyst. One type of the active site adsorbs and dissociates methanol unit, whereas the other adsorbs and activates the water molecules [13]. The second metal (M) of the catalyst changes electronic characteristics of Pd, thereby lowering the oxidation potential of adsorbed CO and enhancing the catalytic activity. Yin et al. [14] demonstrated the electrocatalytic performance of Pd-Cu bimetallic nanoparticles toward methanol oxidation by varying the molar ratios of Pd and Cu. They found that the electrocatalytic activity of a Pd-Cu catalyst that contained 15% Cu is comparable to that of commercial Pt/C catalysts. The enhanced catalytic activity of the Pd-Cu system is owing to the presence of Cu, which can accelerate the oxidation of intermediates that generated during oxidation. As a result, the presence of Cu helps in lowering the poisoning effect on Pd sites. Au@Pd core-shell nanoparticles have been synthesized using $HAuCl_4$ and $PdCl_2$ as precursors for use as anode catalysts in DMFCs [15]. The oxidation peak current densities during the MOR in a solution of 1 M KOH and 0.5 M methanol are obtained to be 7.89 mA cm^{-2} and

1.72 mA cm^{-2} for Au@Pd core-shell NPs and Pd NPs, respectively, so the Au@Pd core-shell NPs exhibit the best electrocatalytic activity. These results suggest that enhanced MOR activity is due to the proper electronic tuning of Pd shell by Au core. An increase in the d-band center improves absorption of reactants on metal surface and decreases the activation energy barrier during oxidation of poisonous intermediates and thus leads to the remarkable catalytic activity and stability of Au@Pd core-shell NPs.

Pd-based ternary composites have been extensively used as anode catalysts in DMFC [16, 17]. In these cases, the enhanced electrocatalytic performance and stability of Pd-based composites have been obtained because of incorporation of metals (Ni, Cu, Fe, Au, Ag), carbon-based material (MWCNT, rGO), and metal oxides (CuO, TiO$_2$, MnO$_2$), etc. [18–21]. Enhanced electrocatalytic activity and stability of Pd/PPy-graphene is obtained when Pd/PPy-graphene nanocomposite has been synthesized via *in situ* polymerization reaction, followed by chemical reduction [22]. Pd/PPy-graphene nanocomposite exhibits higher electrocatalytic performance and higher tolerance to CO poisoning compared to commercial Pt. The higher catalytic performance toward MOR can be explained by the following factors: (i) the small size of Pd nanoparticles (small size particles exhibit higher electrocatalytic activity than that of large ones); (ii) uniformly dispersed nanoparticles over the graphene sheets (as shown in scanning electron microscope (SEM), transmission electron microscope (TEM images and histogram representing the size of the particles in Figure 12.2 and Figure 12.3, respectively) with large surface areas and high electrical conductivity; (iii) the maximum utilization of Pd nanoparticles on PPy-graphene nanocomposites that leads to excellent electrocatalytic activity because of the presence of available nucleation centers in the nanocomposite.

Current research also shows that the modification of MWCNTs by MnO$_2$ and supported by Pd nanoparticles (Pd-MnO$_2$/MWCNTs) enhances the oxidation reaction rate and becomes more tolerant to CO poisoning [23]. Figure 12.4 represents the schematic diagram of methanol oxidation activity on the Pd-MnO$_2$/MWCNTs composite. The higher methanol oxidation performance of Pd-MnO$_2$/MWCNTs modified electrode confirms that wrapping the MnO$_2$ layer over MWCNT improves the catalytic activity more than that of Pd/MWCNTs and Pd/Vulcan catalysts. The reason behind the higher electrocatalytic activity of the Pd-MnO$_2$/MWCNT catalyst is the good dispersion of Pd nanoparticles, resulting in a larger electroactive surface area of the catalyst and synergetic contribution from both Pd and MnO$_2$ over the MWCNT surface. MnO$_2$ favors the adsorption of OH$_{ad}$ species formed at lower potential, which can transform poisonous CO species into CO$_2$, inhibiting the blockage of electroactive sites on the electrode surface for further oxidation process.

Different amounts of Pd content result in changes in electrocatalytic activity of Pd-based catalysts. For example, Pd/PdO nanoparticles supported on porous graphene with different weight ratios of Pd/PdO exhibit different methanol oxidation activities in 1 M methanol and 1 M KOH solution [24]. The cyclic voltammogram (CV) results reveal that the Pd-1 (1:19 of Pd/PdO) possesses the highest catalytic activity and stability because of better dispersion of Pd/PdO nanoparticles in porous graphene.

Pt-Free Anode Electrocatalysts 265

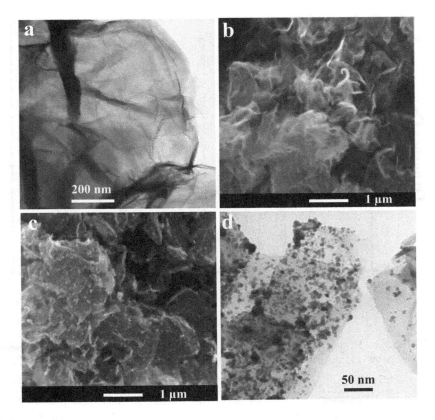

FIGURE 12.2 Morphology of graphene and PPy/graphene nanocomposite. (a) TEM image of graphene (b) SEM image of graphene, (c) SEM image of PPy/graphene (d) TEM image of PPy/graphene. Adapted and reproduced with permission from reference [22]. Copyright 2011 Elsevier.

The Pd-based electrocatalyst with high Pd content can improve the electrochemical activity and oxidation current density and lower the onset potential in DMFCs in an alkaline medium. Moreover, the Pd nanoparticles supported on carbon-based materials or metal oxides have been recognized as promising electrocatalysts because of their uniform distribution and good dispersion of Pd nanoparticles over the support material, which further leads to the enhanced catalytic activity and stability.

12.3.2 Nickel-Based Electrocatalysts

Nickel (Ni) is an extensively used non-noble metal anode catalyst that can replace Pt for alcohol electrooxidation in alkaline media. Ni-based materials, including Ni nanostructures, Ni alloys, Ni oxides, hydroxides, and metallic Ni exhibit excellent electroactivity for the organic molecules oxidation [25, 26]. Ni-based electrodes have attracted much attention because of their high electrochemical activity in energy storage devices [27, 28]. The excellent electrocatalytic property of Ni is due to its

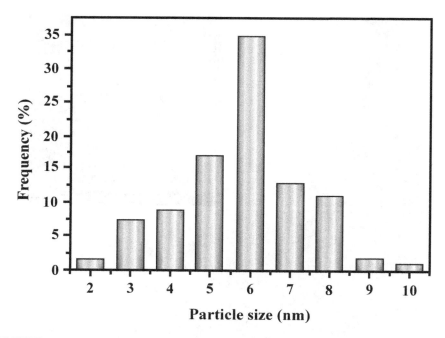

FIGURE 12.3 Histogram of Pd particle-size distribution in Pd/PPy/graphene nanocomposite. Adapted and reproduced with permission from reference [22]. Copyright 2011 Elsevier.

surface oxidation properties. In the 1970s, Fleischmann et al. [29] proposed the electrooxidation mechanism of primary alcohol molecules at Ni-based electrodes in alkaline media.

$$Ni(OH)_2 \rightarrow NiOOH + H^+ + e^- \quad (12.1)$$

$$Ni(OH)_2 + OH^- \rightarrow NiOOH + H_2O + e^- \quad (12.2)$$

$$NiOOH + RCH_3OH \rightarrow RC.HOH + Ni(OH)_2 \quad (12.3)$$

$$RC.HOH + 3OH^- \rightarrow RCOOH + 2H_2O + 3e^- \quad (12.4)$$

Therefore, organic acids are formed in the alkaline solutions due to electrooxidation of alcohol molecules at the Ni-based electrocatalysts. Rahim et al. [30] investigated the electrooxidation of methanol at Ni-modified graphite electrodes in alkaline media. The Ni-modified graphite electrodes exhibit good electrocatalytic activity with current density of 150 mA cm^{-2} and oxidation voltage of 1.25 V. Here, the methanol oxidation is governed by activation-controlled process and chemical reaction with NiOOH to form thin Ni oxides and the charge transfer toward the electrode for

Pt-Free Anode Electrocatalysts

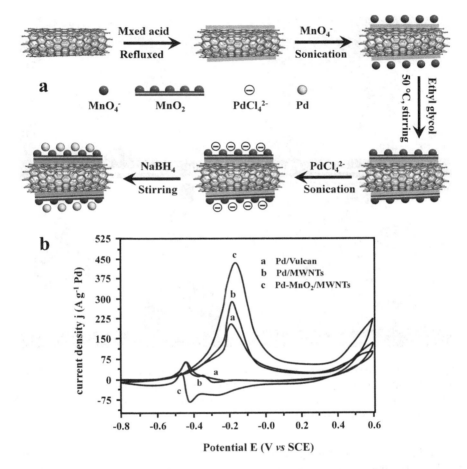

FIGURE 12.4 Synthesis strategy and methanol oxidation activity of Pd composite catalysts. (a) Schematic of synthesis procedure of Pd-MnO$_2$/MWCNTs, and (b) methanol oxidation activity of Pd/Vulcan, Pd/MWCNTs, and Pd-MnO$_2$/MWCNTs nanocomposite catalysts. Adapted and reproduced with permission from reference [23]. Copyright 2010 Elsevier.

thick oxides. Based on these results, Ni-modified graphite electrodes display good electrocatalytic performance toward methanol oxidation. Cheshideh et al. [31] prepared Ni/TiO$_2$ nanotubes modified on a titanium substrate (Ni NPs/TNTs/Ti) and observed the methanol oxidation activity of 0.5 M NaOH and 0.5 M CH$_3$OH solutions and suggested that the redox couple Ni(OH)$_2$β/NiOOHβ favors the transfer of electrons at the interface of electrode material and electrolyte solution during electrooxidation of methanol in basic media. The Ni NPs/TNTs/Ti electrodes exhibit oxidation current density of 2.56 mA cm^{-2} with onset voltage of 0.584 V.

Apart from metallic Ni, the other Ni-based materials, which include different oxides and alloys of Ni, have been investigated toward electrooxidation of methanol in alkaline electrolytes. Eisa et al. [32] observed that Ni/NiO nanorods (NNRs)

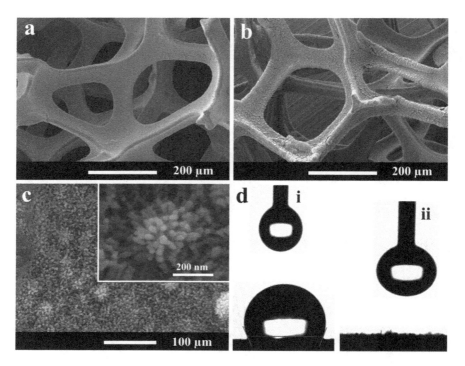

FIGURE 12.5 Surface morphology and hydrophobicity of NNRs coated in Ni foam (NNR/NF). FE-SEM images, (a) and (b) low and (c) high magnification (inset: higher magnified image of (c)), and (d) contact angle of (i) NF, and (ii) NNR/NF. Adapted and reproduced with permission from reference [32]. Copyright 2020 Elsevier.

coated in Ni foam (SEM image in Figure 12.5 (i) and (ii)) that were prepared using the hydrothermal route for electrooxidation of methanol in basic medium exhibit good electrocatalytic performance. This result is due to the superhydrophilic nature (Figure 12.5 (iii)) of the NNR catalyst surface and the high transport of ions between the NNR-modified electrode and electrolytes. The onset voltage of NNR electrodes slightly shift more to the negative side than that of nickel foam (NF) electrodes (from 0.4 V to 0.37 V vs. Hg/HgO), (as shown in Figure 12.5 (iv)), indicating the potential of NNR electrodes as an anode material in DMFC. Moreover, the oxidation current density of NNRs toward methanol oxidation is found to be 392.9 mA cm^{-2}.

Hierarchical Ni oxide nanosheet@nanowire arrays modified in Ni foam (NiO NS@NW/NF) is a promising binder-free anode catalyst in DMFC applications, synthesized by Luo et al. [33] using a hydrothermal method followed by calcinations. This electrocatalyst exhibits high reactivity due to direct formation of NiO on NF electrodes, which ensures strong mechanical adhesion and good electrical contact between the sample and the electrode. Moreover, the hierarchical structure of NiO and three-dimensional (3D) electrodes enhance the number of electroactive sites, and the absence of a binder reduces the series resistance. Therefore, NiO NS@NW/

Pt-Free Anode Electrocatalysts

269

NF can be considered promising alternatives to Pt-based catalysts for the purpose of enhanced MOR.

Besides metallic Ni and Ni oxide, Ni alloys are also widely used anode catalyst material in DMFC. Bimetallic Ni-Ti nanoparticles alloy modified ITO with long-term stability has been prepared by Yu et al. [34]. Ni-Ti nanoparticles alloy modified ITO electrodes prepared via the ion implantation technique exhibit improved electrocatalytic performance and higher stability during methanol oxidation. In ion implantation method, Ti ions of energy at 10 keV and current of 0.6 mA were implanted onto the ITO glasses at an ion dose of 1×10^{17} ions cm^{-2} and thus forming the Ti nanoparticle-implanted ITO electrode (Ti NPs/ITO), followed by implantation of Ni ions over the Ti NPs/ITO electrode under similar conditions. The as-prepared electrode is known as Ni-Ti NPs/ITO electrode. The enhanced catalytic activity of as-modified ITO electrode is due to the presence of Ti, which provides high surface area and the synergistic effects of both Ni and Ti ions. Ni-P and Ni-Cu-P alloys supported on carbon electrodes (Ni-Cu-P/C) have been prepared by the electroless deposition technique [35]. The Ni-Cu-P/C catalysts have shown superior catalytic activity and stability in alkaline media because of the presence of copper hydroxide ($Cu(OH)_2$) and Ni oxyhydroxide (NiOOH) species. Here, $Cu(OH)_2$ prevents the formation of γ-NiOOH phase, which causes swelling of the film and finally stabilizes the β-NiOOH form. The electrocatalytic properties of mesoporous Ni phosphate (Meso NiPO) nanocomposite are influenced by morphology of the nanocomposite [36]. Mesoporous NiPO NT exhibits higher catalytic activity with current density of 40.83 mA cm^{-2} and J_f/J_b ratio of 1.48 and good stability of 91.3% after 24 h, suggesting that Meso NiPO NT can be considered a promising anode catalyst in DMFC. As mentioned previously, Ni-based materials have been examined as Pt-free catalysts because of their remarkable reactivity toward methanol oxidation and high tolerance to the poisonous CO_{ads}.

12.3.3 Rhodium-Based Electrocatalysts

Rhodium (Rh) is a silvery, hard, and durable noble element with high corrosion resistance. Although, Rh has not been recognized as a catalyst for alcohol electrooxidation in a basic medium, numerous studies have investigated electrocatalytic applications of Rh-based materials. Owing to the oxophilic property of Rh, it can help in removal of intermediates, such as CO, by OH$^-$ ion adsorption in alkaline electrolytes [1].

In 2019, Fu et al. [37] prepared ultrathin Rh wavy nanowires of 2–3 nm diameters using an ethylene-glycol-assisted reduction process. The electrocatalytic performance of ultrathin Rh wavy nanowires is much better in comparison to that of commercial Rh black. Rh nanowires possess a larger electroactive surface area (144.2 m^2 g^{-1}) compared to that of commercial Rh black (20 m^2 g^{-1}) because of high surface to volume ratio and presence of surface defects in Rh wavy nanowire. In addition, easy charge transport in the one-dimensional (1D) nanowire helps in maximum utilization of the surface during catalysis [37]. Moreover, this catalyst displays a current peak potential at 0.61 V vs. RHE, which is less in comparison to Pt-based catalysts (0.8–0.9 V vs. RHE). The higher value of I_F/I_R ratio (~2.3) of Rh nanowire catalyst

270   Ceramic and Specialty Electrolytes

compared to that of already reported Pt-based electrocatalysts indicates high oxophilicity because Rh can easily bind with hydroxyl ions and oxygen.

Morphology and structures are the two important factors that control the electrocatalytic activity of the catalysts. There is the atomic-level connection between the active site and catalytic activity in two-dimensional (2D) nanomaterial owing to its interesting characteristics, such as flat and high specific surface area [38]. Recently, Kang et al. [39] developed Rh nanosheets (Rh-NSs)-RGO (Rh-NSs/RGO), a hybrid material, as a Pt-free anode catalyst. There is more negative shifting of anodic peak potential by ca. 120 mV at the Rh-NS and RGO composite catalyst than that of Pt/C catalyst due to MOR. CV results display that the mass performance of MOR at Rh-NS/RGO catalyst (264 Ag^{-1}_{Rh}) is 3.6 times more compared to Pt/C (73 Ag^{-1}_{Pt}) at an oxidation voltage of 0.61 V, suggesting the high electrocatalytic activity of the Rh-NSs/RGO catalyst toward MOR.

Jiang et al. [40] prepared mesoporous Rh nanoparticles with improved catalytic activity for MOR compared to commercial Rh catalysts in an alkaline electrolyte. The mass activity of mesoporous Rh nanoparticles (288 mA mg^{-1}) is 2.6 times higher in comparison to that of commercial Rh catalysts (110 mA mg^{-1}) in 1 M KOH and 1M methanol solution, indicating the maximum utilization of Rh metal in the mesoporous material. Moreover, the mesoporous Rh nanoparticles exhibit a more negative onset and peak voltage than that of Rh/B. The chronoamperometric measurements show that decay of the catalyst is slower because mesoporous structures do not easily aggregate.

12.3.4 OTHER METAL-BASED ELECTROCATALYSTS

Transition metals are the cost effective and abundant in nature compared to noble metals. Transition metals such as Cu, Co, Ti, Mn, Fe, Mo, etc. have been used widely as electrocatalysts for MOR [41–43]. Roy et al. [44] examined the MOR activity in alkaline medium of self-supported CuO grown on Ni foam (CuO/Ni@400) and observed that the self-supported CuO film exhibits methanol oxidation activity in alkaline electrolyte. The detailed study shows that CuO is easily oxidized into CuOOH, which behaves as electroactive media and reacts with methanol molecules to form CO_2 and H_2O.

Abdullah et al. [45] investigated the electrocatalytic performance of $CoCr_7C_3$ nanorods embedded in carbon nanofibers ($CoCr_7C_3$-CNFs) as a novel Pt-free electrocatalyst for MOR in alkaline electrolytes. As shown in Figure 12.6, 25 CV cycles were repeated and scanned, and it was observed that the appearance of redox peaks correspond to the generation of active transition metal oxide/hydroxide layers as shown in Equations 12.5–12.7.

$$Co + 2OH^- \rightarrow Co(OH)_2 + 2e^- \tag{12.5}$$

$$Co(OH)_2 + OH^- \rightarrow CoOOH + H_2O + e^- \tag{12.6}$$

$$CoOOH + OH^- \rightarrow CoO_2 + H_2O + e^- \tag{12.7}$$

Pt-Free Anode Electrocatalysts

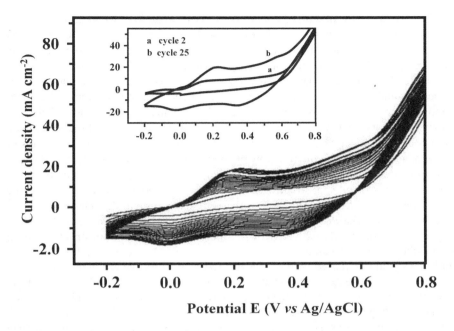

FIGURE 12.6 CVs of CoCr$_7$C$_3$-CNF composite electrode in 1 M KOH electrolyte solution at a scan rate of 100 mV s^{-1} for 25 consecutive cycles. CNF: carbon nanofibers. Adapted and reproduced with permission from Ref. [45]. Copyright 2018 Elsevier.

There is slight shift in anodic and cathodic potentials toward the positive and negative side, respectively, indicating the changes related to the chemical composition of the electroactive species, such as Co(OH)$_2$ and CoOOH, at the surface of the catalyst due to continuous CV cycles. In addition, the increase in anodic and cathodic peak current densities is due to the entry of hydroxyl group into Co(OH)$_2$ active layer, leading to the progressively formed thick CoOOH layer attributing to the Co(OH)$_2$/CoOOH conversion [45].

Zhang et al. [46] synthesized nanospheres, nanorods, and nanotubes of Fe$_2$(MoO$_4$)$_3$ catalysts and investigated the morphology dependent methanol oxidation activity in basic media. The anodic peak current density of methanol oxidation of Fe$_2$(MoO$_4$)$_3$ nanotube-modified GCE electrodes exhibit higher current density (3.27 mA cm^{-2}) than that of a Pt foil electrode (2.8 mA cm^{-2}), indicating that the nanotube Fe$_2$(MoO$_4$)$_3$/GCE can be considered as a promising Pt-free electrocatalyst for methanol oxidation.

12.3.5 Conducting Polymer-Based Electrocatalysts

Conducting polymer and metal composites have received much attention as anode catalyst in DMFC. Individual metal nanostructures, metal composites, and conducting polymers possess remarkable properties; however, the physicochemical properties can be enhanced by making composites of these materials. Conducting-polymer nanostructures have versatile applications, such as energy storage and conversion devices, optoelectronics, tissue engineering, sensors, thermoelectric materials, etc. [47–52]. Examples of different conducting polymers are shown in Figure 12.7.

Conducting polymers have been used as supporting matrices for metal nanostructures and metal-based composites in electrochemical applications. The metal nanostructures supported by a conducting polymer matrix exhibit improved electrocatalytic activity, owing to the large electroactive surface areas and the synergistic effects of both materials [53]. To overcome the aggregation and stability issues of metal nanostructures, conducting polymers have been added to coat the metal nanostructures [53]. There are different synthesis methods through which polymers are used to coat the metal nanostructures without any agglomeration and thus contribute to the electrocatalytic performance of the composite system. Among the different synthesis routes, the *in situ* polymerization is one of the most facile and promising routes for the synthesis of conducting polymer and metal nanostructure-based composites with good catalytic activity. Das et al. [54] developed sulphonated polyaniline (SPAni) supported Ni nanocatalyst (Ni/SPAni) for methanol oxidation. The Ni/SPAni composite exhibits a peak current density of 306 mA cm^{-2} at an oxidation voltage of 0.57 V. Moreover, Ni/SPAni shows a current density of 135 mA cm^{-2}, oxidation voltage of 0.2 V, and the power density of 27 mW cm^{-2} at a temperature of 60° C when the catalyst is used as an anode catalyst in DMFC. The results confirm

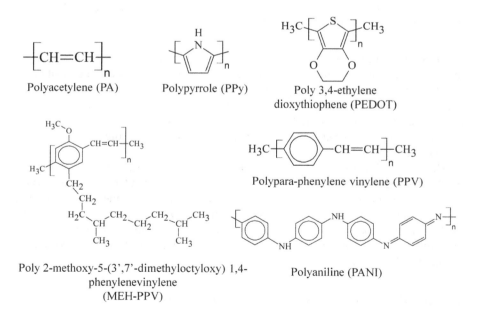

FIGURE 12.7 Typical examples of commonly used electrochemically conducting polymers (chemical structure). Adapted and reproduced with permission from reference [48]. Copyright 2019 Elsevier.

Pt-Free Anode Electrocatalysts

that Ni/SPAni catalyst is far better than that of the commercial Pt-Ru/C, and the sulphonated PAni is the best support system for deposition, distribution, and dispersion of Ni.

12.3.6 GRAPHENE-BASED NANOHYBRID (rGO/ PEDOT:PSS/MnO$_2$) ELECTROCATALYST

The ternary rGO/PEDOT:PSS/MnO$_2$ nanohybrid has been prepared via *in situ* polymerization method, in which the MnO$_2$ nanorods have been synthesized by hydrothermal route [3]. The as-synthesized ternary nanohybrid possesses a large surface area, a higher number of electroactive sites, and high electrical conductivity due to synergistic effects of all three components present in the nanocomposite. PEDOT:PSS/MnO$_2$ binary nanocomposite and MnO$_2$ nanorod fabricated ITO glasses have also been prepared for comparison of electrochemical activities. In this system, the graphite oxide (GO) has been reduced via the chemical reduction method using hydrazine hydrate ($N_2H_4.H_2O$) to produce rGO nanosheets. The MnO$_2$ nanorods have been ultrasonically mixed with rGO nanosheets to assemble over, and, finally, the polymer PEDOT:PSS is polymerized over the MnO$_2$ nanorods.

The rGO/PEDOT:PSS/MnO$_2$ ternary nanohybrid electrode system has been characterized by TEM for morphological characterization and CV and CA for electrochemical characterizations. Figure 12.8 shows the TEM images of rGO nanosheets, MnO$_2$ nanorods, PEDOT:PSS/MnO$_2$ hybrid composites, and PEDOT:PSS/MnO$_2$/ rGO nanohybrids. The TEM image (Figure 12.8a) of an rGO nanosheet shows few layers of a folded and wrinkled-like structure. MnO$_2$ nanorods of diameter in between 10 nm–50 nm and 100 nm–300 nm in length are shown in Figure 12.8b. MnO$_2$ nanorods are wrapped within the thick shell of PEDOT:PSS as revealed in Figure 12.8c. In case of the ternary nanohybrid, the PEDOT:PSS-modified MnO$_2$ nanorods are enclosed inside rGO sheets (Figure 12.8d).

Electrochemical behavior of MnO$_2$ nanorods, binary nanocomposite PEDOT:PSS/ MnO$_2$, and ternary nanohybrid rGO/PEDOT:PSS/MnO$_2$ fabricated ITO glasses has been examined using a solution containing 0.5 M NaOH with a sweep rate of 50 mVs^{-1}, as shown in Figure 12.9a. The as-prepared electrodes display a couple of distinct redox active peaks, which arise because of the charge transfer mechanism through Mn^{3+}/Mn^{4+} redox pairs. The surface-active redox reactions are shown in Equations 12.8 and 12.9:

$$Cathode: MnO_2 + H_2O + e^- \rightarrow MnOOH + OH^- \qquad (12.8)$$

$$Anode: MnOOH + OH^- + e^- \rightarrow MnO_2 + H_2O \qquad (12.9)$$

The rGO/PEDOT:PSS/MnO$_2$ ternary nanocomposite fabricated electrode exhibits higher current density (2.95 mA cm^{-2}), lower peak to peak separation voltage (ΔE_p=170 mV), and larger area under the CV curve than that of the other two electrodes because of homogeneous distribution of the polymer PEDOT:PSS-modified

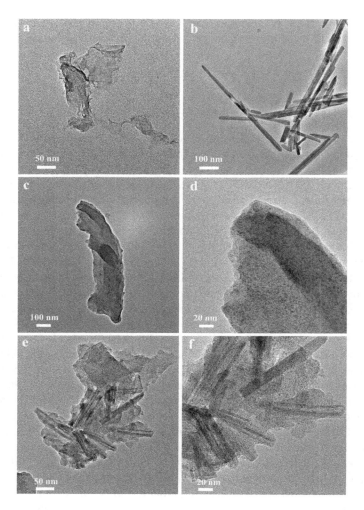

FIGURE 12.8 Morphology (TEM images) of graphene-based nanohybrid electroctalysts. (a) Reduced graphene oxide nanosheets, (b) MnO$_2$ nanorods, (c) and (d) PEDOT:PSS/MnO$_2$ nanocomposite at different magnifications, and (e) and (f) PEDOT:PSS/MnO$_2$/rGO nanohybrid at different magnifications. Adapted and reproduced with permission from reference [3]. Copyright 2018 Elsevier.

MnO$_2$ nanorods within the conductive rGO nanosheets. There is linear proportionality between the peak current densities of anodic and cathodic sweep and the lower value of sweep rates (up to 40 mVs^{-1}). Surface concentration (r^*) of the redox couples Mn^{3+}/Mn^{4+} can be obtained using anodic and cathodic slope of peak current densities vs. sweep rate and Brown-Anson model, as shown in Equation 12.10,

$$Ip = \left(n^2 F^2 r^* A \upsilon\right)/4RT \qquad (12.10)$$

Pt-Free Anode Electrocatalysts

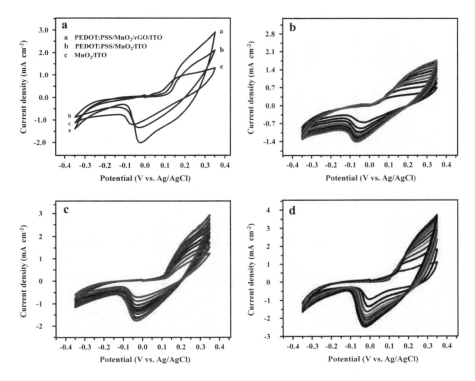

FIGURE 12.9 CV curves of graphene-based nanohybrid electrocatalyst at different sweep rates. (a) Graphene-based nanohybrid electrocatalysts at a sweep rate of 50 mV s^{-1}, (b) MnO$_2$ nanorods, (c) PEDOT:PSS/MnO$_2$, and (d) rGO/PEDOT:PSS/MnO$_2$ nanohybrids at different sweep rates from 10 to100 mV s^{-1} in 0.5 M NaOH electrolyte solution. Adapted and reproduced with permission from reference [3]. Copyright 2018 Elsevier.

where, I_p is the peak current density, n is the number of electrons transferred, ν is sweep rate, A is the area of electrode surface, and other terms have the usual meaning. The surface concentration of MnO$_2$, PEDOT:PSS/MnO$_2$, and rGO/PEDOT:PSS/MnO$_2$ ternary nanohybrid fabricated ITO glasses has been calculated to be 1.38 × 10^{-5}, 1.97 × 10^{-5}, and 3.36 × 10^{-5} mol.cm^{-2}, respectively. The larger surface concentration of rGO/PEDOT:PSS/MnO$_2$ fabricated electrode in comparison to the other two is attributed to the presence of rGO nanosheets having a higher number of redox active sites.

Figure 12.10a depicts the CVs of all the as-prepared electrodes in the presence of 0.5 M methanol solution with a sweep rate 50 mVs^{-1}. The rGO/PEDOT:PSS/MnO$_2$ fabricated ITO exhibits higher anodic peak current of 56.38 mA cm^{-2} with less onset voltage of 0.32 V than that of the other two fabricated electrodes. The porous morphology of the MnO$_2$ nanorods enhances the accessibility of the electrolyte ions to penetrate deep inside the catalyst material. The holes reside in p-type conducting polymer PEDOT:PSS, combine with the electrons obtained from the electrolyte

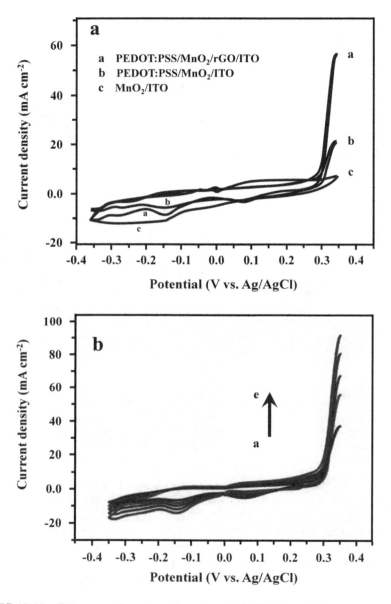

FIGURE 12.10 CV curves of graphene-based nanohybrid electrocatalyst at sweep rate of 50 mV s^{-1}. (a) Graphene-based nanohybrid electrocatalysts with 0.5 M methanol, (b) rGO/PEDOT:PSS/MnO$_2$ nanohybrid electrocatalyst in different molar concentration of methanol (from bottom to top): 0.1 M, 0.5 M, 1 M, 1.5 M, and 2 M, respectively. Adapted and reproduced with permission from reference [3]. Copyright 2018 Elsevier.

Pt-Free Anode Electrocatalysts

during methanol oxidation. The rGO nanosheets wrapped around the polymer coated MnO_2 nanorods in the nanohybrid improve the electron transfer and number of electroactive sites. Figure 12.10b shows CVs of rGO/PEDOT:PSS/MnO_2 fabricated ITO glasses in a solution containing different concentrations of methanol and 0.5 M NaOH solution. The detailed mechanism of methanol oxidation can be summarized in Equations 12.11 and 12.12.

$$Mn(OH)_2 + OH^- \rightarrow MnOOH + H_2O + e^- \tag{12.11}$$

$$MnOOH + CH_3OH + 5/4O_2 \rightarrow Mn(OH)_2 + CO_2 + 3/2H_2O \tag{12.12}$$

Figure 12.10b confirms that MnOOH reduces to $Mn(OH)_2$ because of the appearance of a cathodic peak at 0.06 V. The $Mn(OH)_2$ and MnOOH act as electron mediators in oxidation of methanol [3]. On addition of higher concentrations of methanol, the intensity of cathodic peak decreases because of MnOOH consumption during oxidation process (Equation 12.12), and, finally, the cathodic peak disappears at a methanol concentration of 2 M [3]. The oxidation of methanol causes a decrement in the concentration of electroactive sites over the electrode surface owing to the continuous adsorption of carbonaceous species that were generated as a result of oxidation. Therefore, a backward peak appears at the voltage of -0.14 V due to electrooxidation of carbonaceous intermediates and regeneration of electroactive sites for the continuation of oxidation process. Moreover, the peak becomes significant with continuous increase in methanol concentration as result of electrooxidation of a higher number of carbonaceous species. The oxidation of methanol occurs through two processes [3]: (i) initially, the methanol molecules are adsorbed over the active sites on the surface of electrocatalyst, and then (ii) water molecules split, and oxygen is obtained.

Figure 12.11a represents the chronoamperograms of all the fabricated ITO electrodes in a 0.5 M NaOH and 0.5 M methanol solution for 3600 s at an applied voltage of 0.32 V. Figure 12.11a reveals that rGO/PEDOT:PSS/MnO_2 nanohybrid fabricated electrode exhibits higher current density (50 mA cm^{-2}) than that of PEDOT:PSS/MnO_2 (21 mA cm^{-2}) and MnO_2 (1.6 mA cm^{-2}) electrodes. The drastic decrease in current within a few seconds in all the electrode materials is due to the presence of double layer capacitance and CO poisoning [3]. The tolerance of all the fabricated electrodes toward CO is examined by calculating the rate of deterioration within the duration of 100–3600 s [3].

$$S = \frac{I_{100} - I_{3600}}{I_{100} \times \Delta\tau} \tag{12.13}$$

The rate of deterioration of MnO_2 nanorods, PEDOT:PSS/MnO_2, and rGO/PEDOT:PSS/MnO_2 nanohybrid is obtained to be 1.91×10^{-4}, 5.05×10^{-5}, and 7.73×10^{-6} s^{-1}, respectively. The ternary nanohybrid electrode exhibits higher tolerance than that of the other two because of the incorporation of conductive rGO sheets, which

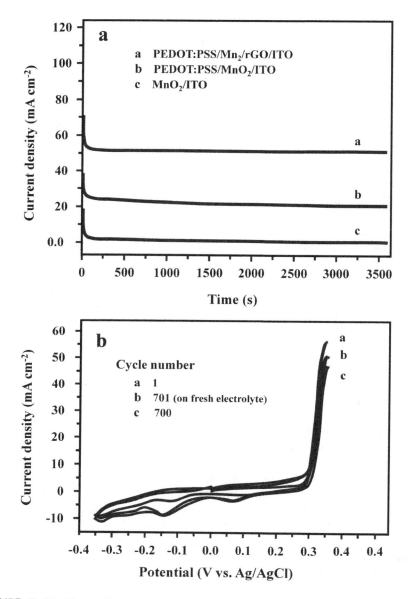

FIGURE 12.11 Electrochemical performance of graphene-based nanohybrid electrocatalyst. (a) Chronoamperograms of MnO$_2$ nanorods, PEDOT:PSS/MnO$_2$ nanocomposite and PEDOT:PSS/MnO$_2$/rGO-coated electrodes at applied potential of 0.32 V, (b) cycling stability of rGO/PEDOT:PSS/MnO$_2$ nanohybrid with a mixture of 0.5 M methanol and NaOH. Adapted and reproduced with permission from reference [3]. Copyright 2018 Elsevier.

Pt-Free Anode Electrocatalysts 279

provide enough electroactive sites for the conversion of CO to CO_2. The cyclic stability test for all the electrodes has been performed by consecutive 700 CV cycles (Figure 12.11b) in the presence of 0.5 M methanol and 0.5 M NaOH solution. The ternary nanohybrid electrode shows retention of current at 83% of the first scan at 700th cycle at the sweep rate of 50 mVs^{-1}. Generation of carbonaceous intermediates and methanol consumption causes a decrease in current density; however, when the new electrolyte is used for the cyclic stability test, then the current retention factor becomes 90% of the initial scan. From the above results, it can be concluded that the rGO/PEDOT:PSS/MnO_2 nanohybrid can be considered a promising alternative to Pt-based electrocatalyst material.

12.4 CONCLUSION AND FUTURE PROSPECTS

DMFCs have drawn researchers' attention because of their high energy density, high conversion efficiency, low operating temperature, easy transportation, easy handling of methanol, and eco-friendly technology. The potential applications of DMFCs are in the field of portable electronics, such as laptop, notepads, cellular phones, and other energy-related devices. Moreover, some reputed automobile companies have already developed vehicles using DMFC. DMFCs have many advantages over other polymer electrolyte membrane fuel cells because there is no hydrogen storage problem and no use of a reformer subsystem. However, the commercialization of DMFC is still difficult because methanol crossover causes a breakdown of cell voltage, sluggish reaction kinetics, use of expensive Pt-catalyst, and CO poisoning of Pt-based catalysts. Therefore, tremendous research taking place to develop a Pt-free anode catalyst with high tolerance to CO poisoning and long-term stability. The recent progress of various Pt-free anode catalysts, such as Pd, Ni, Rh and other transition metal-based materials, have been thoroughly discussed in the present chapter. However, lots of research work is still needed to improve the performance of Pt-free anode catalysts. The use of nanostructured electrode materials, highly porous metal organic frameworks (MOF), 2D materials with high surface areas, including graphene, metal dichalcogenide nanosheets, and MXenes, can improve the electrocatalytic activity. Different electrode materials have already been designed for energy storage and conversion systems, including batteries, supercapacitors, solar cells, etc., using conducting polymer, carbon nanomaterials, metal oxides, and their composite materials [55–59]. However, few studies have been found on the use of conducting polymer, carbon allotropes, and transition metal oxide-based ternary composites as fuel-cell catalysts. The rGO/PEDOT:PSS/MnO_2 nanohybrid fabricated ITO electrode shows oxidation current density of 56.38 mA cm^{-2} at the onset voltage 0.32 V, and the retention of current density at 83% of the initial scan up to 700 cycles. The high electrocatalytic activity of the ternary nanohybrid electrode is attributed to the fast transport of electrons and ions through the 1D MnO_2 nanorods and excellent conductivity of the rGO nanosheets, whereas the long-term stability of the electrode is due to wrapping of PEDOT:PSS over the nanorods, inhibiting the agglomeration and dissolution of the nanorods in the electrolyte solution.

REFERENCES

1. Mansor M, Timmiati SN, Lim KL, Wong WY, Kamarudin SK, Kamarudin NHN (2019) Recent progress of anode catalysts and their support materials for methanol electrooxidation reaction. *International Journal of Hydrogen Energy*.44 (29): 14744–14769.
2. Deluca NW, Elabd YA (2006) Polymer electrolyte membranes for the direct methanol fuel cell: A review. *Journal of Polymer Science Part B: Polymer Physics* 44(16):2201–2225.
3. Baruah B, Kumar A (2018) PEDOT: PSS/MnO2/rGO ternary nanocomposite based anode catalyst for enhanced electrocatalytic activity of methanol oxidation for direct methanol fuel cell. *Synthetic Metals* 245:74–86.
4. Basri S, Kamarudin SK, Daud WRW, Yaakob Z, Kadhum AAH (2014) Novel anode catalyst for direct methanol fuel cells. *The Scientific World Journal* 2014:1–8.
5. Cai Z-x, Liu C-c, Wu G-h, Chen X-m, Chen X (2013) Palladium nanoparticles deposit on multi-walled carbon nanotubes and their catalytic applications for electrooxidation of ethanol and glucose. *Electrochimica Acta* 112:756–762.
6. Parsons R, VanderNoot T (1988) The oxidation of small organic molecules: A survey of recent fuel cell related research. *Journal of Electroanalytical Chemistry and Interfacial Electrochemistry* 257(1–2):9–45.
7. Tiwari JN, Tiwari RN, Singh G, Kim KS (2013) Recent progress in the development of anode and cathode catalysts for direct methanol fuel cells. *Nano Energy* 2(5):553–578.
8. Hamnett A (1997) Mechanism and electrocatalysis in the direct methanol fuel cell. *Catalysis Today* 38(4):445–457.
9. Ha S, Larsen R, Masel R (2005) Performance characterization of Pd/C nanocatalyst for direct formic acid fuel cells. *Journal of Power Sources* 144(1):28–34.
10. Zhou WP, Lewera A, Larsen R, Masel RI, Bagus PS, Wieckowski A (2006) Size effects in electronic and catalytic properties of unsupported palladium nanoparticles in electrooxidation of formic acid. *The Journal of Physical Chemistry B* 110(27):13393–13398.
11. Yin Z, Zhang Y, Chen K, Li J, Li W, Tang P, Zhao H, Zhu Q, Bao X, Ma D (2014) Monodispersed bimetallic PdAg nanoparticles with twinned structures: Formation and enhancement for the methanol oxidation. *Scientific Reports* 4:4288.
12. Wang X, Tang B, Huang X, Ma Y, Zhang Z (2013) High activity of novel nanoporous Pd–Au catalyst for methanol electro-oxidation in alkaline media. *Journal of Alloys and Compounds* 565:120–126.
13. Zhang J, Shuihua T, Longyu L, Weifei Y (2013) Progress in non-platinum catalysts with applications in low temperature fuel cells. *Chinese Journal of Catalysis* 34(6):1051–1065.
14. Yin Z, Zhou W, Gao Y, Ma D, Kiely CJ, Bao X (2012) Supported Pd–Cu bimetallic nanoparticles that have high activity for the electrochemical oxidation of methanol. *Chemistry–A European Journal* 18(16):4887–4893.
15. Tan Q, Du C, Yin G, Zuo P, Cheng X, Chen M (2012) Highly efficient and stable non-platinum anode catalyst with Au@ Pd core–shell nanostructures for methanol electro-oxidation. *Journal of Catalysis* 295:217–222.
16. Wang Y, Sheng ZM, Yang H, Li CM (2010) Electrocatalysis of carbon black-or activated carbon nanotubes-supported Pd–Ag towards methanol oxidation in alkaline media. *International Journal of Hydrogen Energy* 35(19):10087–10093.
17. Wang Y, Wang X, Li CM (2010) Electrocatalysis of Pd–Co supported on carbon black or ball-milled carbon nanotubes towards methanol oxidation in alkaline media. *Applied Catalysis B: Environmental* 99(1–2):229–234.
18. Singh R, Singh A (2009) Electrocatalytic activity of binary and ternary composite films of Pd, MWCNT and Ni, Part II: Methanol electrooxidation in 1 M KOH. *International Journal of Hydrogen Energy* 34(4):2052–2057.

19. Xu W, Zhu S, Li Z, Cui Z, Yang X (2015) Evolution of palladium/copper oxide–titanium dioxide nanostructures by dealloying and their catalytic performance for methanol electro-oxidation. *Journal of Power Sources* 274:1034–1042.
20. Yu B, Wen W, Li W, Yang Y, Hou D, Liu C (2016) Fabrication of high performance carbon-supported ternary Pd-Cu-Fe electrocatalysts for formic acid electrooxidation via partly galvanic sacrifice of tunable binary Cu-Fe alloy templates. *Electrochimica Acta* 196:223–230.
21. Zhang L, Wang H, Li X, Xia F, Liu Y, Xu X, Gao J, Xing F (2015) One-step synthesis of palladium-gold-silver ternary nanoparticles supported on reduced graphene oxide for the electrooxidation of methanol and ethanol. *Electrochimica Acta* 172:42–51.
22. Zhao Y, Zhan L, Tian J, Nie S, Ning Z (2011) Enhanced electrocatalytic oxidation of methanol on Pd/polypyrrole–graphene in alkaline medium. *Electrochimica Acta* 56(5):1967–1972.
23. Zhao Y, Zhan L, Tian J, Nie S, Ning Z (2010) MnO2 modified multi-walled carbon nanotubes supported Pd nanoparticles for methanol electro-oxidation in alkaline media. *International Journal of Hydrogen Energy* 35(19):10522–10526.
24. Yang F, Wang C, Dong S, Chi C, Jia X, Zhang L, Li Y (2016) Plasma synthesis of Pd/PdO supported on porous graphene as electrocatalyst for methanol oxidation. *Materials Letters* 174:192–196.
25. Vyas AN, Saratale GD, Sartale SD (2020) Recent developments in nickel based electrocatalysts for ethanol electrooxidation. *International Journal of Hydrogen Energy* 45(10):5928–5947.
26. Li P, Gu Y, Yu Z, Gao P, An Y, Li J (2019) TiO2-SnO2/SO42– mesoporous solid superacid decorated nickel-based material as efficient electrocatalysts for methanol oxidation reaction. *Electrochimica Acta* 297:864–871.
27. Huang Y-Y, Lin L-Y, Li X (2019) Efficient battery supercapacitor hybrid devices with quaternary metal oxide electrodes based on nickel and cobalt. *Journal of Energy Storage* 25:100826.
28. Hong W-L, Lin L-Y (2019) Studying the substrate effects on energy storage abilities of flexible battery supercapacitor hybrids based on nickel cobalt oxide and nickel cobalt oxide@ nickel molybdenum oxide. *Electrochimica Acta* 308:83–90.
29. Fleischmann M, Korinek K, Pletcher D (1971) The oxidation of organic compounds at a nickel anode in alkaline solution. *Journal of Electroanalytical Chemistry and Interfacial Electrochemistry* 31(1):39–49.
30. Rahim MA, Hameed RA, Khalil M (2004) Nickel as a catalyst for the electro-oxidation of methanol in alkaline medium. *Journal of Power Sources* 134(2):160–169.
31. Cheshideh H, Nasirpouri F (2017) Cyclic voltammetry deposition of nickel nanoparticles on TiO2 nanotubes and their enhanced properties for electro-oxidation of methanol. *Journal of Electroanalytical Chemistry* 797:121–133.
32. Eisa T, Mohamed HO, Choi Y-J, Park S-G, Ali R, Abdelkareem MA, Oh S-E, Chae K-J (2020) Nickel nanorods over nickel foam as standalone anode for direct alkaline methanol and ethanol fuel cell. *International Journal of Hydrogen Energy* 45(10):5948–5959.
33. Luo Q, Peng M, Sun X, Asiri AM (2016) Hierarchical nickel oxide nanosheet@ nanowire arrays on nickel foam: An efficient 3D electrode for methanol electro-oxidation. *Catalysis Science & Technology* 6(4):1157–1161.
34. Yu Y, Yang Q, Li X, Guo M, Hu J (2016) A bimetallic Ni–Ti nanoparticle modified indium tin oxide electrode fabricated by the ion implantation method for studying the direct electrocatalytic oxidation of methanol. *Green Chemistry* 18(9):2827–2833.
35. Hameed RA, El-Khatib K (2010) Ni–P and Ni–Cu–P modified carbon catalysts for methanol electro-oxidation in KOH solution. *International Journal of Hydrogen Energy* 35(6):2517–2529.

36. Song X, Sun Q, Gao L, Chen W, Wu Y, Li Y, Mao L, Yang J-H (2018) Nickel phosphate as advanced promising electrochemical catalyst for the electro-oxidation of methanol. *International Journal of Hydrogen Energy* 43(27):12091–12102.

37. Fu X, Zhao Z, Wan C, Wang Y, Fan Z, Song F, Cao B, Li M, Xue W, Huang Y (2019) Ultrathin wavy Rh nanowires as highly effective electrocatalysts for methanol oxidation reaction with ultrahigh ECSA. *Nano Research* 12(1):211–215.

38. Sun Y, Gao S, Lei F, Xie Y (2015) Atomically-thin two-dimensional sheets for understanding active sites in catalysis. *Chemical Society Reviews* 44(3):623–636.

39. Kang Y, Xue Q, Jin P, Jiang J, Zeng J, Chen Y (2017) Rhodium nanosheets–reduced graphene oxide hybrids: A highly active platinum-alternative electrocatalyst for the methanol oxidation reaction in alkaline media. *ACS Sustainable Chemistry & Engineering* 5(11):10156–10162.

40. Jiang B, Li C, Dag Ö, Abe H, Takei T, Imai T, Hossain MSA, Islam MT, Wood K, Henzie J (2017) Mesoporous metallic rhodium nanoparticles. *Nature Communications* 8(1):1–8.

41. Park JC, Choi CH (2017) Graphene-derived Fe/Co-NC catalyst in direct methanol fuel cells: Effects of the methanol concentration and ionomer content on cell performance. *Journal of Power Sources* 358:76–84.

42. Askari MB, Salarizadeh P, Seifi M, Rozati SM (2019) Electrocatalytic properties of CoS2/MoS2/rGO as a non-noble dual metal electrocatalyst: The investigation of hydrogen evolution and methanol oxidation. *Journal of Physics and Chemistry of Solids* 135:109103.

43. Askari MB, Beheshti-Marnani A, Seifi M, Rozati SM, Salarizadeh P (2019) Fe3O4@MoS2/RGO as an effective nano-electrocatalyst toward electrochemical hydrogen evolution reaction and methanol oxidation in two settings for fuel cell application. *Journal of Colloid and Interface Science* 537:186–196.

44. Roy A, Jadhav HS, Cho M, Seo JG (2019) Electrochemical deposition of self-supported bifunctional copper oxide electrocatalyst for methanol oxidation and oxygen evolution reaction. *Journal of Industrial and Engineering Chemistry* 76:515–523.

45. Al-Enizi AM, Brooks RM, El-Halwany M, Yousef A, Nafady A, Hameed RA (2018) CoCr7C3-like nanorods embedded on carbon nanofibers as effective electrocatalyst for methanol electro-oxidation. *International Journal of Hydrogen Energy* 43(21):9943–9953.

46. Zhang D, Zhang L, Zhang W, Huo M, Yin J, Dang G, Ren Z, Zhang Q, Xie J, Mao SS (2017) Morphology-dependent electrocatalytic performance of Fe2 (MoO4) 3 for electro-oxidation of methanol in alkaline medium. *Journal of Materiomics* 3(2):135–143.

47. Talikowska M, Fu X, Lisak G (2019) Application of conducting polymers to wound care and skin tissue engineering: A review. *Biosensors and Bioelectronics.* 135: 50–63.

48. Dakshayini B, Reddy KR, Mishra A, Shetti NP, Malode SJ, Basu S, Naveen S, Raghu AV (2019) Role of conducting polymer and metal oxide-based hybrids for applications in ampereometric sensors and biosensors. *Microchemical Journal.*147: 7-24

49. Kang T-G, Park J-K, Kim B-H, Lee JJ, Choi HH, Lee H-J, Yook J-G (2019) Microwave characterization of conducting polymer PEDOT: PSS film using a microstrip line for humidity sensor application. *Measurement* 137:272–277.

50. Kausar A (2017) Overview on conducting polymer in energy storage and energy conversion system. *Journal of Macromolecular Science, Part A* 54(9):640–653.

51. Lee BH, Lee JH, Kahng YH, Kim N, Kim YJ, Lee J, Lee T, Lee K (2014) Graphene-conducting polymer hybrid transparent electrodes for efficient organic optoelectronic devices. *Advanced Functional Materials* 24(13):1847–1856.

52. Bharti M, Singh A, Samanta S, Aswal D (2018) Conductive polymers for thermoelectric power generation. *Progress in Materials Science* 93:270–310.

Pt-Free Anode Electrocatalysts

53. Pattanayak P, Pramanik N, Kumar P, Kundu PP (2018) Fabrication of cost-effective non-noble metal supported on conducting polymer composite such as copper/polypyrrole graphene oxide (Cu2O/PPy–GO) as an anode catalyst for methanol oxidation in DMFC. *International Journal of Hydrogen Energy* 43(25):11505–11519.

54. Das S, Dutta K, Kundu PP (2015) Nickel nanocatalysts supported on sulfonated polyaniline: Potential toward methanol oxidation and as anode materials for DMFCs. *Journal of Materials Chemistry A* 3(21):11349–11357.

55. Bach-Toledo L, Hryniewicz BM, Marchesi LF, Dall'Antonia LH, Vidotti M, Wolfart F (2020) Conducting polymers and composites nanowires for energy devices: A brief review. *Materials Science for Energy Technologies* 3:78–90.

56. Abdah MAAM, Azman NHN, Kulandaivalu S, Sulaiman Y (2019) Review of the use of transition-metal-oxide and conducting polymer-based fibres for high-performance supercapacitors. *Materials & Design* 186:108199.

57. Shabzendedar S, Modarresi-Alam AR, Bahrpeyma A, Noroozifar M, Kerman K (2020) Novel conductive multi-walled polymeric nanotubes of poly (diazoaminobenzene) for single-layer polymer solar cell. *Reactive and Functional Polymers* 149:104529.

58. Weng S, Huo T, Liu K, Zhang J, Li W (2020) In-situ polymerization of hydroquinone-formaldehyde resin to construct 3D porous composite LiFePO4/carbon for remarkable performance of lithium-ion batteries. *Journal of Alloys and Compounds* 818:152858.

59. Masouras A, Giannopoulos D, Hasa B, Katsaounis A, Kostopoulos V (2019) Hybrid graphene nanoplatelet/manganese oxide electrodes for solid-state supercapacitors and application to carbon fiber composite multifunctional materials. *Journal of Energy Storage* 23:515–525.

13 Ionic Liquid-Based Electrolytes for Supercapacitor Applications

Bhuvaneshwari Balasubramaniam,
Ankit Tyagi, Raju Kumar Gupta

CONTENTS

13.1 Introduction 285
13.2 Need of Gel- and Ionic-Liquid-Based Electrolytes in SCs.........................286
13.3 Importance of GPEs and Ionic-Liquid-Based Electrolytes in
Commercial Applications 288
13.4 GPEs 288
13.5 Status of Research on Polymer Electrolytes in India 290
    13.5.1 Usage of Ionic-Liquid Electrolytes and GPEs in the
Construction of SC Devices... 291
13.6 Microanalytical Characterization Techniques Used for Interface
Analysis of Electrode and Electrolyte 300
    13.6.1 Morphological and Surface Characterization.....................................300
    13.6.2 Electrochemical Characterization Techniques (Half-Cell Studies).......300
    13.6.3 The Way Forward 300
13.7 Conclusion 301
Acknowledgments.. 301
References... 302

13.1 INTRODUCTION

It is essential to note that global population growth combined with industrial development will lead to the doubling of electricity usage by 2030. Energy storage systems will occupy a larger part in our lives as the power demand increases to twice that of overall energy consumption. This immense need will require an increase in the energy supply in the future, especially electricity generated in an eco-friendly manner. Supercapacitors (SCs) (also called electric double-layer capacitors (EDLCs), electrochemical capacitors, and ultracapacitors) are one of the most promising high-power energy storage systems, in which the capacitance arises from the charge separation at an electrode–electrolyte interface. SCs possess multiple advantages over batteries and fuel cells, as they are eco-friendly and exhibit super high capacitance, lower internal resistance, large energy density in a short period of time, safe operation over a wide range of temperatures (-40° C–70° C), and a longer shelf-life, thus enhancing reliability. Recently, much attention has been given to on solid-state, flexible SCs for fabricating wearable electronics and electronics that have bendable displays. Simple and scalable fabrication processes using unique electrodes and electrolytes in highly flexible SCs are currently needed. Recent research proves that superior performance of SCs is possible through the combination of selected advanced carbon- and graphene-based electrodes and ion-conducting stable gel polymer electrolytes (GPEs). One of the main challenges in constructing/fabricating the novel, highly flexible, and solid-state SCs is developing and choosing highly functional and significant electrolytes, as the overall performance of the constructed cell assembly is directly proportional to the stability of the electrolyte. These requirements show the path for an urgent need to develop unique and suitable multifunctional electrode–electrolyte-based fabrications in highly flexible SCs with outstanding performance. Research on multifunctional GPEs is encouraged because of their solid or quasi-solid-state form and their ability to function as a self-separator (lowers the internal resistivity of the cell). Further, they also overcome difficulties such as lack of physical flexibility, leakage, corrosion, and risk of explosion experienced with SCs containing liquid electrolytes. Therefore, considerable attention needs to be paid to address the many grey and challenging areas by adopting fundamental studies on ionic mobility in bulk materials.

13.2 NEED OF GEL- AND IONIC-LIQUID-BASED ELECTROLYTES IN SCs

The sustainable production of renewable energy, namely solar and wind energy, is mainly dependent on its continuous availability of their sources and environmental conditions, such as time and weather and velocity and direction of the wind. Therefore, the inevitable challenge in expanding these technologies lies in the question of how to store the energy these renewable sources generate. Such concerns have led to the creation of high-performance energy storage devices for storing the generated energy as well for stabilizing the connected electricity grid. Also, the increased demand for energy storage systems has gained great interest in academic research to develop highly energy efficient materials for the energy applications. SCs are one of the great electrochemical energy storage devices that possess high power density ($10,000$ W kg^{-1}) when compared to batteries, which suffer from major drawbacks due to issues related to cycling stability and safety [1, 2]. SCs' many advantages, including device fabrication (efficient shaping, patterning, and integration), safety (non-explosive), stability, and electrochemical properties, are fulfilling the need for energy storage devices that can be used in applications that require timeline, long life, light weight, low maintenance, and eco-friendliness [1]. However, in terms of energy density, SC is still behind batteries, which are usually 3–30 times lower, and the major disadvantage is the operating voltage of the SC cell, which should be kept low to avoid chemical decomposition of electrolytes [3]. There are generally three

IL-Based Electrolytes for SC Applications

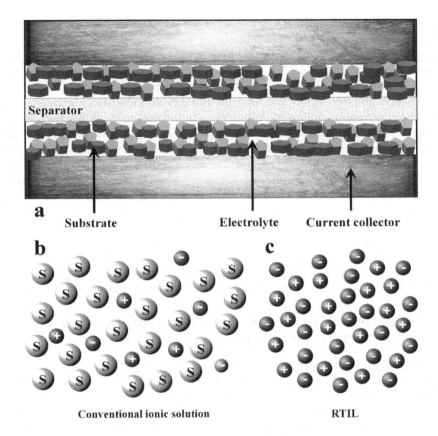

FIGURE 13.1 Schematic illustration of (a) structure of SC, and (b) difference between conventional ionic solution and room temperature ILs. Adapted and reproduced with permission from reference [1]. Copyright 2016 Elsevier.

types of electrolytes used for SC applications: aqueous, organic, and ionic liquid (IL) (Figure 13.1) [1]. Among them, ionic-liquid-based GPEs are gaining commercial importance on solid-state, flexible SCs because of their wide voltage potential, as they are resistant to the reduction and oxidation reactions during operation.

One of the major advantages to note regarding the use of ionic-liquid-based gel electrolytes is the possibility of providing the cell voltage of around 4.5 V, even sometimes up to 6 V, which makes them a unique choice for the construction of solid-state, flexible, stretchable SCs [4]. One of the main challenges in fabricating the novel, highly flexible, and solid-state SCs is developing and choosing highly functional and significant gel electrolytes, as the overall performance of the constructed cell assembly is directly proportional to the stability of electrolyte. As the equivalent series resistance (ESR) of the SC cell depends entirely on the electrolyte conductivity [1], which is also an essential factor for the power devices, it is of utmost importance to design a new electrolyte with multifunctional characteristics. GPEs, also known as plasticized polymer electrolytes, are neither liquid nor solid, but instead they have characteristics of both liquids and solids. The unique characteristics of the gel, such as cohesive properties of solids and diffusive properties of liquids, makes them an outstanding candidate for electrochemical energy storage applications [5]. When selecting suitable electrolytes to synthesize new gel electrolytes the most important properties to take into account include robust mechanical stability, high ionic concentration, low viscosity, high electrochemical stability, wide voltage window, low volatility, low toxicity, and high purity [5, 6]. Further, the use of such electrolytes also overcome the difficulties that SCs containing liquid electrolytes face, such as lack of physical flexibility, leakage, corrosion, and risk of explosion. Most importantly, ample opportunities are thrown open to produce thin, transparent, and uniform films with the polymer- and gel-based electrolytes including heteropolyacids, redox-mediators, polyzwitter-ions with the support of PVA, PVC, PFTA, PVP, PVDF, etc., which add uniqueness to the creation of solid-state, flexible SCs [5, 7–16]. It is clear that the research advances in the design and synthesis of multifunctional gel electrolytes are extremely vital to improve power quality of stored energy, will create a successful breakthrough in flexible and stretchable electronics [17, 18] applications, and opens the possibilities for the creation of hybrid sources [19].

13.3 IMPORTANCE OF GPES AND IONIC-LIQUID-BASED ELECTROLYTES IN COMMERCIAL APPLICATIONS

Developing GPEs accelerates the evolution of solid-state SCs from traditional sandwich-type SCs to flexible, transparent, and planar SCs (micro-SCs), and thus offers power support to flexible and even transparent electronics [19]. Generally, gels are defined as cross-linked network systems that mainly consist of homopolymer or copolymer chains networked by either physical interactions or chemical bonds. Gel materials are one of the promising candidates for energy-related applications because of their inherent chemical, microstructural, and mechanical features and their molecular tailoring makes them responsive to interaction with their environments. One of the main advantages of the ionic gel electrolytes is that it provides higher ionic conductivity to the SC systems, even with lower concentrations, thereby increasing the overall electrochemical performance of SCs [5, 6, 11, 20]. Surface areas between the electrode and the gel electrolyte define the EDLC of the SC systems. Interestingly, the affinity between the electrode and the gel electrolyte is one of the crucial factors. Also, the advantage of using the ideal gel electrolyte, apart from superior electrochemical performance, is that it also serves as a binder with the mechanical strength to hold two electrodes together.

13.4 GPES

The conductivity of GPEs used in flexible SCs are widely reported to range between 10^{-4} and 10^{-3} S cm^{-1} under ambient conditions, and exhibit liquid-like ionic conductivity, which also, simultaneously, maintains the dimensional stability of a solid system. Recently, redox-mediators (potassium iodide (KI), $VOSO_4$, p-phenylenediamine,

NaI/I$_2$, indigo carmine, IL) and polyzwitter-ions have been introduced to improve the gel polymers' ionic conductivity, which also enhanced the pseudo-capacitance of SCs. Based on the type of solvent used, GPEs can be categorized into aqueous or organic GPEs. Among these, aqueous GPEs are attractive because of their high ionic conductivity, low raw material cost, environmental friendliness, and simple preparation process. Also, organic GPEs have wider electrochemical windows. The most commonly used material to prepare aqueous GPE polymers is mainly based on poly(vinyl alcohol) (PVA) because of its excellent chemical stability and durability. Traditional approaches to prepare the PVA-based GPEs have not reached their full potential use, as they are normally prepared with a thickness that eliminates short circuiting during assembling process [21–23]. Many research reports suggest using the electrodeposition (ED) method of preparation for the gel electrolytes by surface deposition on the electrode itself, as it does not need any monomers or organic cross-linker for gelation process, and, additionally, it overcomes the need for separators [24, 25]. Further, the direct ED on electrode surfaces facilitates the preparation of ultrathin GPEs. Also, the main advantages of the ED process are that it shows high efficiency, saving material and energy. The schematic representation of the nanocomposite GPE is shown in Figure 13.2.

It has been reported that inclusion of inorganic fillers, inert ceramic-oxide additives, nanotubes/fibers, etc., are composited with the polymeric and gel electrolyte

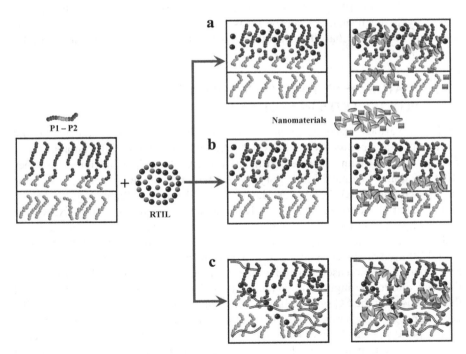

FIGURE 13.2 Schematic illustration of the synthesis strategy of nanocomposite GPE (P1 and P2 denotes the different polymers).

systems to improve the mechanical, thermal, and electrochemical stabilities of the gel electrolytes, which also enhance the ion transport [5, 11, 16]. Further, gel polymers with heteropolyacids [12] and various supramolecule- (polyzwitter-ions) based electrolytes show high ionic conductivity for fuel-cell applications, but their uses in SCs applications have only recently emerged and need further fine tuning before they can be adopted, scaled, and commercialized. Further, their improvement on mechanical stability, interface characteristics, easy and binder-free deposition, and thermal stability are very little reported.

As far as carbon/graphene-based electrode materials in SCs are concerned, understanding ion transport and adsorption phenomena within the pores of nanoscale carbon remains a challenge. It is important to note that, in order to improve the SCs power capabilities, interface resistance should be minimized by enhancing the rate of ion transport within porous carbon and minimizing ion diffusion distance. Xu et al. [16] used the poly (propylsulfonate dimethylammonium propylmethacrylamide)- (PPDP) based zwitterionic gel electrolyte for the construction of graphene-based solid-state SCs and reported a volume capacitance of 300.8 F cm^{-3} at 0.8 A cm^{-3} and a rate capacity of only 14.9% capacitance loss, while the current density increased from 0.8 to 20 A cm^{-3}. The study noted that the value reported is one of the best among the previously reported solid-state SCs based on graphene. In order to confirm the ion migration channel, a impedance spectroscopic study was conducted, and the ESR of the PPDP-solid-state sample was reported as 40.54 Ω, which, comparatively, is much smaller than the PVA-solid-state sample of 122.6 Ω. Therefore, the study concluded that the as-synthesized PPDP gel may be good candidate for solid-state SCs.

13.5 STATUS OF RESEARCH ON POLYMER ELECTROLYTES IN INDIA

In India, various research groups from different institutions, namely Cochin University of Science and Technology (CUSAT), Indian Institute of Technology (IIT), Central Electro Chemical Research Institute (CECRI), Indian Institute of Science (IISc), National Chemical Laboratory (NCL), Indian Institute of Science Education and Research (IISER), Centre for Materials for Electronics Technology (C-MET), and Jawaharlal Nehru Centre For Advanced Scientific Research (JNCASR), are actively involved in the development of cost-effective and energy-efficient electrode and electrolyte materials for the fabrication of solid and flexible SCs [26]. Kalpana et al. [27] used a new class of alkaline gel electrolyte or carbon-aerogel-based SCs and reported an increase in specific energy of the system. The study claimed that this was due to the high ionic conductivity and the lower electronic resistance of the GPE used in the SC system. From cyclic voltammetry (CV) studies, the specific capacitance of 9 F g^{-1} was found and reported. Anothumakkool et al. [28] fabricated a high-performance flexible solid-state SC by adopting an *in situ*-generated GPE strategy to strengthen the interface of electrode/electrolyte. The study claimed that the method adopted for this study was very simple, and a prototype flexible solid-state SC was constructed. The capacitance of 130 F/g was showed a substantially

IL-Based Electrolytes for SC Applications

reduced internal resistance of 0.5 Ω. Further, a high capacitance retention of 84% after 32000 cycles was also noted. A poly (hydroxyethyl methacrylate-co-trimethylolpropane allyl ether) copolymer- (PHEMA-co-TMPA) based gel, which contains phosphoric acid, was used as the electrolyte. From the mechanical property analysis, it was found that the gel material used possessed 0.6 M Pa of compressive strength. Further, the tensile results show 25% stretchability and that it can withstand a tension of 0.04 MPa. The report also emphasized the need for studies on extending the electrode–electrolyte interface into the porous architecture of the electrode materials while dealing with the polymer electrolytes. Kumar et al. [29] used gel electrolytes consisting of lithium trifluoromethanesulfonate (Li-triflate or LiTf)/IL, 1-ethyl-3-methylimidazolium trifluoromethanesulfonate (EMITf)/poly(vinylidene fluoride-co-hexafluoropropylene) (PVdF-co-HFP) for the fabrication of a flexible SC consisting of two different electrodes (multiwalled carbon nanotube- (MWCNT) based and charcoal-based). To enhance the flexibility of the electrolytes, ethylene carbonate and propylene carbonate (PC) is used. In comparison, it was reported that high specific energy is obtained in the case of charcoal-based electrodes and high specific power is attained for the MWCNT electrode. Amrita and Tripathi [30] reported the performance of nanocomposite GPEs with the combinations of PVdF-co-HFP-PC-magnesium perchlorate–nanofumed silica on EDLC-based electrode system. Room-temperature ionic conductivity of the optimized gel electrolyte was reported as 5.4×10^{-3} S cm^{-1}. The maximum capacitance obtained was 324 mF cm^{-2}.

13.5.1 Usage of Ionic-Liquid Electrolytes and GPEs in the Construction of SC Devices

As stated by Kwon et al. [31], by increasing the potential window through the use of ionic-liquid electrolytes, as they possess good electric stability, it is possible to broaden the voltage for SC. The study used 1-ethyl-3-methylimidazolium tetrafluoroborate (EMIBF$_4$) and imide-based co-salt, such as 1-ethyl-3-methylimidazolium bis(trifluoromethylesulfonyl) imide (EMITFSI), as electrolytes owing to their increased ionic conductivity and stability through the inhibition of electrolyte decomposition in the SC fabrication. Results show that the potential window of the SC is improved, and it exhibited increased cycling stability. The noted specific capacitance losses while adding 7 wt% EMIBF$_4$ or EMITFSI to the electrolyte showed the loss of 2.5% and 8.7%, respectively. This was noticed after 10,000 cycles at 3.5 V, with respect to the initial discharge specific capacitance of the constructed SC.

Pilathottathil et al. [32] constructed a symmetric SC using activated porous carbon as the active electrode material and trihexyl (tetradecyl) phosphonium bis (trifluoromethanesulfonyl) imide [PC$_6$C$_6$C$_6$C$_{14}$][Tf$_2$N] as the electrolyte. Many microanalytical characterization techniques were used for examining the surface morphology and related physical properties. The thermal stability of the ionic-liquid-based electrolytes used were studied through differential scanning calorimetry (DSC) and thermogravimetric analysis (TGA). The electrochemical performance of the SC was tested using CV, frequency response analyzer- (FRA) impedance spectroscopy and charge–discharge investigations. Experimental results reported 300 F g^{-1}

specific capacitance, and ultra-high energy density of 110 Wh kg^{-1} with a high rate of scalability (up to 1000 cycles) was achieved. Also, the voltage window of 3.5 V was achieved in the presence of the IL, which shows the potential use of the constructed SC.

Electrochemical investigation of two ILs was conducted to assess the performance of the SC. It was found that an SC with 1-ethyl-3-methylimidazolium acetate (EMIM Ac) electrolyte performed better than the SC with 1-butyl-3-methylimidazolium chloride (BMIM Cl) electrolyte. The results are based on the comprehensive study on the capacitive performance of the SC with respect to high temperature (HT) endurance, focusing on system integration in microelectronics [33].

Sekitani et al. [34] used a dispersion technique using 1-butyl-3-methylimidazolium bis(trifluoromethanesulfonyl)imide based IL for uniform dispersion of single-walled carbon nanotubes (SWCNT). It was then used as stable dopants in a vinylidene fluoride-hexafluoropropylene copolymer matrix, which created a composite film. Also, the mechanical stability and softness of the copolymer was not disturbed while increasing the SWCNT content up to 20 wt%. The first layer-by-layer casting fabrication of a fully plastic actuator was developed using SWCNT with ILs as dispersing agents. A simple three-layered configuration of soft electrodes was quite compatible for the actuator in terms of testing the electrolyte layers, which can be operated when exposed to air even at low voltages [35].

Kang et al. [36] demonstrated a 3-V flexible SC for the first time for alternating current (AC) line filtering, which consists of IL-based GPEs. The electrode used was made up of carbon nanotubes. The device exhibited extremely high areal energy density. Results compared with a previously constructed 1-V flexible SC (0.66 vs 0.03 µWh cm^{-2}) and showed more than 20 times higher efficiency upon the excellent capacitive property maintained at 120 Hz. The constructed SC exhibited a maximum areal power density of 1.5 W cm^{-2} with a time constant of 1 ms. The results noted that SC performance improved in applications related to wearable and/or portable electronics. This was achieved by playing with the cell voltage, which does not also alter the fast-response capability of the device. The surface morphology of the polytetraflouroethylene (PTFE) fiber is shown in Figure 13.3 with a pore size of 100 nm. A schematic of IL-based triblock copolymer along with polystyrene (PS) and poly(ethylene oxide) (PEO) is shown in Figure 13.3.

Reports show the potential application of various ILs with structurally different anions, such as tetrafluoroborate, trifluoromethanesulfonimide, trifluoromethanesulfonate, and cations, such as imidazolium, pyridinium, piperidinium, ammonium, and pyrrolidinium, for SC application. Mousavi et al. [37] demonstrated that the cation size of the IL electrolyte influences the viscosity, conductivity, and capacitance behavior of EDLCs. It was reported that imidazolium- and pyridinium-based ILs provide the highest cell capacitance. Further, ammonium-based ILs impart larger potential windows than imidazolium- and pyridinium-based ILs. It is important to note that the alkyl substituents chain length increment in 1-alkyl-3-methylimidazolium trifluoromethanesulfonimide does not favor widening the ILs' potential window. The best performing IL electrolytes that show the highest specific energies possess small ionic volumes, low viscosity, and electrochemical stability in a

IL-Based Electrolytes for SC Applications 293

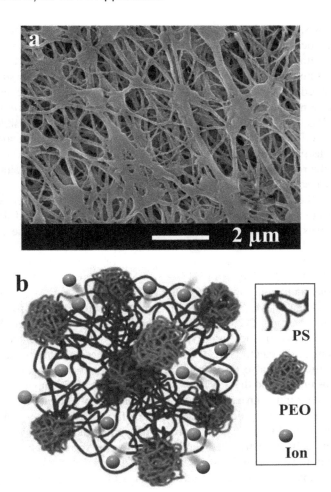

FIGURE 13.3 (a) FE-SEM images on surface morphology of PTFE, and (b) schematic illustration of IL-based poly(styrene-*b*-ethylene oxide-*b*-styrene) (PS-PEO-PS) triblock co-GPE. PS is a hydrophobic and PEO is hydrophilic chain segment in the (PS-PEO-PS) triblock co-polymer. Adapted and reproduced with permission from reference [36]. Copyright 2016 American Chemical Society.

moderate level, thereby achieving high conductivity. The 1-ethyl-3-methylimidazolium bis(trifluoromethylsulfonyl)-imide-based IL was reported as one of the best performing IL electrolytes.

It is known that the electrochemical-reaction kinetics of solids are several orders of magnitude slower compared to their liquid counterparts due to much lower ion diffusivity. However, the density of redox species that were maximized by the solids, and in liquids, were at least two orders of magnitude lower due to solubility limitations. These phenomena lead to limited power in the high-energy batteries, and in high-power SCs, they create an energy deficiency. In order to overcome such effects in electrochemical energy storage devices, the liquid state of the ideal system should be endowed with a density of redox species, which should be closer to the solid state. Based on that knowledge, Mourad et al. [38] used biredox ILs in their study, achieving bulk-like redox density in the liquid-like fast kinetics. Very fast reversible redox reactions were maintained by the cation and anion present in the biredox ILs. By using these ILs in SCs, decoupling charge storage from an ion-accessible electrode surface was noticed, which was achieved mainly by storing a significant charge in the porous electrodes. Also, the self-discharge and leakage current was minimized by keeping the redox species in the pores. In addition, the working voltage window widened because of their wide electrochemical window.

Yu et al.[39] conducted a critical literature review on IL-based electrolytes used in the fabrication of SCs and micro-SCs. The importance and need for IL-based electrolytes was discussed elaborately, and the prospects for the use of IL-based electrolytes in electrochemical energy storage devices were discussed.

Brandt et al. [40] used two concentrations of trimethyl-sulfonium bis[(trifluoromethyl)sulfonyl]imide (Me$_3$STFSI) IL mixtures along with PC as electrolytes and constructed carbon-based EDLCs. The two different mixtures, one with 3.8 mol L^{-1} content of Me$_3$STFSI and another with 1.9 mol L^{-1} of Me$_3$STFSI, were used as electrolytes with PC at room temperature. They have examined the physicochemical and electrochemical properties of the EDLCs in the presence of different concentrations of the electrolyte. Also, conductivity, thermal stability, and viscosity of both mixtures were also investigated before the electrochemical tests were conducted. It was understood that EDLCs with an operative voltage up to 3.0 V is possible by using these innovative electrolytes. Experimental investigations prove that the cycle life of EDLC totally depends on the Me$_3$STFSI concentrations in electrolyte mixture. The main discussion was based on the suppression of anodic oxidation of the Al current collector when ILs were employed while the device was operating at high potential. It was concluded that, at high salt concentration of IL, a high-energy EDLC with a longer cycle life and a broad range of working temperatures can be achieved.

Shahzad [41] discussed the importance and novelty of ILs in the development of sustainable and high-performance electrochemical energy conversion and storage (EES) devices, mainly for electrochemical capacitors (ECs). The study underscored that exploring the use of ILs for high-performance EES devices is one of the fascinating fields of the current era, as these studies attained exponential growth due to the versatile and novel nature of electrolytes. The associated properties, along with physicochemical properties, such as enhanced ionic conductivity, high thermal stability, robustness, and high voltage, as they limit the decomposition were discussed in detail in the report. In conclusion, the report stated that ILs bring potentially upgraded power and energy performance of ECs without any compromise on power density, cyclic stability, or safety.

Designing devices using liquid-like dynamics along with improved specific capacitance is a challenging task. In this regard, Bodin et al. [42] introduced a new approach, which increases the specific capacitance with the help of biredox ILs.

Tethering the redox moieties to the electrolyte ions allows increased redox concentrations as well as pseudo-capacitive storage in a liquid state. Further, anions were functionalized with anthraquinone (AQ), and cations were subjected to functionalization with 2,2,6,6-tetramethylpiperidinyl-1-oxyl (TEMPO) moieties. Different diffusion dynamics-related studies were employed toward understanding the biredox ILs electrochemical responses. Therefore, different carbon structures of electrode materials with respect to its different double layer structures in the presence of biredox ILs can be well understood.

Efforts have been made to design new electrolytes to expand the SCs' electrochemical windows, compared to those of aqueous and/or conventional organic electrolytes, toward increasing energy density. It was reported that tetracyanoborate anions $[B(CN)_4]$ of ILs widen the electrochemical stability compared to conventional electrolytes. The high ionic conductivity, such as $6.9\,mS\,cm^{-1}$, was maintained during the analysis. High maximum operating voltage of $3.7\,V$ was achieved, and high specific capacitances were demonstrated by devices when it was operated relatively at high rates, for example ca. $20\,F\,g^{-1}$ @ $15\,A\,g^{-1}$. It was concluded that the fabricated SC can store more energy in the presence of the tetracyanoborate anions $[B(CN)_4]$ of IL electrolytes that also can be operated at a higher power at all rates [43].

In recent years, interesting research on understanding the redox activity of the electrolytes used in SC is happing at a rapid pace. It was confirmed that such redox activity of the electrolytes can offer an increased charge storage capacity as well as many other associated benefits to SCs. Conventional understanding is that an electrolyte is defined as an electrochemically inert substance that can increase the potential window of the devices. However, with the advanced characterization tools, it is possible to investigate the redox properties of the electrolytes. Still, there is some confusion in understanding the redox electrolyte contributions on the increased storage capacity while comparing the pseudo-capacitance properties and the overall increased charge storage capacity or capacitance. Akinwolemiwa et al. [44] discussed in detail the pros and cons of such types of redox electrolytes applied in new electrochemical energy storage devices.

Although ILs can offer high energy storage capacity to SCs due to their wide operating voltages, currently they cannot satisfy and compete with organic electrolytes as far as power performance is concerned. To explore the full potential of IL-based electrolytes, it is necessary to understand the dynamics of the charge storage of these materials using advanced characterization techniques. In this regard, Forse et al. [45] explored the potential application of nuclear magnetic resonance spectroscopy (NMR) for studying the molecular structure and dynamics of ILs confined in the porous carbon electrodes. It was confirmed through the NMR that ILs spontaneously wet the carbon micropores when the applied potential is off. It was found that the adsorption and desorption of carbon pores was more dominant in anions than in cations. Because the charging mechanism was elucidated, they moved to investigate the factors affecting the rate of ionic diffusion occurring at the micropores of carbon, which explained SC charging dynamics. This study confirmed the effective diffusion rate of ILs as well as in the presence of few additives. On the whole, it was concluded that NMR measurements would rationalize the SCs power performances in different electrolytes.

The template-free polymerization of aniline with an oxidant, namely ammonium persulfate, was employed for the PANI-doped ILs containing carboxyl and different alkyl chains. They have used this composite as an electrode material. A schematic illustration of maize-like PANI-IL synthesis is shown in the Figure 13.4. Microanalytical characterizations were used to understand and elucidate the as-prepared PANI-IL composites. Further, CV and galvanostatic charge–discharge techniques were used for electrochemical performance analysis. From the experimental findings, researchers determined that the alkyl chains of ILs influence the morphology and capacitance performance of the electrode materials. Because of the presence of shorter chain length, 1-vinyl-3-carboxymethyl-imidazolium chloride ([VCMIm]Cl) with PANI electrodes showed the highest specific capacitance. It was demonstrated that 82% capacitance retention was achieved after 1000 cycles in the presence of 0.5 M H_2SO_4 [46].

Lin et al. [47] prepared compact graphene films and used eutectic electrolytes of IL mixture with 1:1 ratio of N-methyl-N-propylpiperidinium bis(fluorosulfonyl)imide and N-butyl-N-methylpyrrolidinium bis(fluorosulfonyl)imide) for the electrochemical testing of SCs at various temperatures. It was found that a wide temperature window (-30° C–80° C) with a large potential window (3.5 V) at room temperature and below could be achieved with the proposed electrode–electrolyte composition. The reported gravimetric capacitance of the SC was 175 F g^{-1} (85 mAh g^{-1}) at 80° C. Further, they were able to achieve gravimetric capacitances of 130 F g^{-1} at -20° C and 100 F g^{-1} at -30° C. The graphene film, with a thickness of 60 μm, shows a volumetric capacitance of 50 F cm^{-3}. Further, based on these properties, the proposed

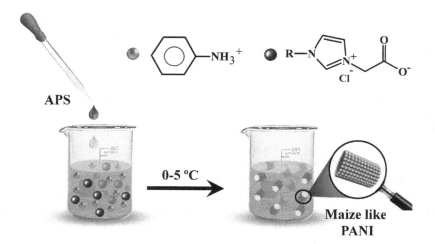

FIGURE 13.4 Schematic illustration of the synthesis strategy of maize-like IL PANI nanomaterial. Adapted and reproduced with permission from reference [46]. Copyright 2019 Song *et al.*, published by De Gruyter.

IL-Based Electrolytes for SC Applications

eutectic IL mixture electrolyte with graphene film composite as an electrode can create a promising alternative to EDLC-based SCs, especially in the HT conditions.

A solvent-free IL was used as an electrolyte to fabricate EDLC SCs, and the role played by carbon porosity, as well as the chemistry of the electrolyte, was discussed with respect to the extended electrochemical stability window. The ILs used for voltammetry performance were N-methyl-N-butyl-pyrrolidinium bis(trifluoromethanesulfonyl)imide (PYR14TFSI), N-methyl-N-butyl-pyrrolidinium tris(pentafluoroethyl)trifluorophosphate (PYR14FAP), and N-trimethyl-N-propylammonium bis(trifluoromethanesulfonyl)imide (N1113TFSI). The IL PYR14TFSI – tetraethyl ammonium bis(trifluoromethanesulfonyl)imide (N2222TFSI) demonstrated that the pore to ion size ratio plays a major role with respect to porous electrode–IL interface. This interfacial property caused a higher impact on the electrical response of the electrode compared to the inherent bulk properties of IL. The capacitance and charge storage capacity of the carbon electrode with respect to its porosity was discussed in relation to the properties of ILs [48].

An all-in-one solid-state device was fabricated using graphene oxide gels mixed in a solution of water-ethanol-IL for assembling graphene-IL EDLC. The graphene oxide-IL composite was subjected to thermal reduction, which resulted in the conversion of graphene oxide to electrically conductive functionalized graphene. It was reported that the electrolyte also served as a spacer for separating graphene sheets, thereby increasing the electrolyte-accessible surface area. The constructed device showed an outstanding energy density with 17.5 Wh kg^{-1} at a gravimetric capacitance of 156 F g^{-1}. The device was tested at 3 V operating voltage [49].

Pohlmann et al. [50] studied for first time the azepanium-based ILs, such as N-methyl, N-butyl-azepanium bis(trifluoromethanesulfonyl)imide (Azp$_{14}$TFSI) and N-methyl, N-hexyl-azepanium bis(trifluoromethanesulfonyl)imide (Azp$_{16}$TFSI) as electrolytes for EDLC device construction. The results were analyzed based on the viscosity, thermal stability, conductivity, and electrochemical behavior in EDLC systems, and comparisons were made to N-butyl, N-methylpyrrolidinium bis(trifluoromethanesulfonyl)imide- (Pyr$_{14}$TFSI) based IL electrolytes. It was confirmed that both electrolytes can be used for EDLC application without compromising the operative voltages up to 3.5 V and also without any degradation of the electrolyte.

Sathyamoorthi et al. [51] studied the performance of SCs constructed with activated charcoal-based electrodes, containing an organic redox shuttle hydroquinone (HQ) and triethylammonium bis(trifluoromethane)sulfonimide (TEATFSI) IL. the pseudocapacitive contribution of HQ was analyzed by CV studies and low charge transfer was found in the presence of HQ through electrochemical impedance spectroscopy. Galvanostatic charge discharge (GCD) analysis showed an enhanced specific capacitance of 72 F g^{-1} and specific energy of 31.22 Wh Kg^{-1}. The redox mediated electrolyte was compared to protic IL to analyze the cyclic stability of the SC.

The overview on flexible solid-state electrochemical SCs was conducted by Yang et al. [52]. They also reviewed various types of electrolyte and electrode materials used to construct flexible solid-state SCs. They summarized that the recent development of the flexible solid-state SC was focused mainly on freestanding, interdigitated, asymmetric, and fiber-based SCs. The scope for future research was also clearly presented. Major scanning electron microscope (SEM) images of SWCNTs and their thin film are shown in Figure 13.5. SWCNTs always took a prominent position, owing to their high surface area, conductivity, flexibility, etc.

A polyurethane-poly (acrylic acid) (PAA) copolymer is prepared by cross-linking the PAA backbone with the water-borne polyurethane (WPU). The prepared polymer was neutralized and soaked in a solution containing 1 M KOH (WPU-PAAK-K). The ionic conductivity of the prepared gel electrolyte was greater than 10^{-2} S cm^{-1}, which was suitable for the flexible all-solid-state EDLC. The amount of carboxyl groups increased in the copolymer matrix due to PAA backbone chains, which promotes the segmental motion and facilitates the water-uptake capacity. Therefore, ion transport was ensured and ionic conductivity was promoted. SCs consisting of acid-treated carbon paper as electrodes with prepared GPEs showed an excellent capacitive behavior. And the areal capacitance calculated was 211.6 mF cm^{-2} at 10 mV s^{-1}. The full cell device displayed a 0.44 Ω low ESR, as calculated from electrochemical impedance spectroscopic measurements. An all-solid-state showed the 94.6 mF cm^{-2} of areal specific capacitance at 1 mA cm^{-2}. The device's flexibility while bending at 180° exhibited a remarkable 90% capacitance retention [53].

Kwon et al. [54] developed an epoxy-based solid polymer electrolyte (SPE) cross-linked with IL/lithium salt electrolyte (ILE), and fast ion-diffusing IL, through a simple one-pot curing process for use in energy storage applications. The comparative analysis was done on epoxy-rich SPE and IL-rich SPE on mechanical and thermal stability-related parameters. It was found that higher Young's modulus and higher glass transition temperatures were obtained using the epoxy-rich SPEs, however higher ionic conductivity was achieved using the IL-rich SPEs.

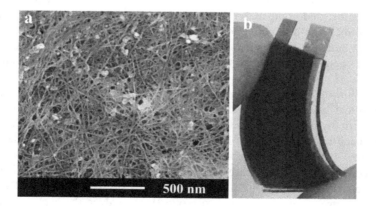

FIGURE 13.5 Images of a SWCNT-based SC with PVA/H$_3$PO$_4$-based GPE. (a) FE-SEM images on surface morphology of as-deposited SWCNTs network, and (b) optical image of thin film SC using sprayed SWCNT films on PET as electrodes and PVA/H$_3$PO$_4$-based GPE. Adapted and reproduced with permission from reference [52]. Copyright 2014 Elsevier.

IL-Based Electrolytes for SC Applications

It was proven that ionogels are promising electrolyte for flexible and shape-conformable all-solid-state energy storage devices. Due to their ion conduciveness, semi-solidness, and mechanically stability, the ionogels were considered suitable electrolytes; however, the challenge lies in identifying easy routes for synthesizing ionogels for energy storage devices with proper compatibility on electrode–electrolyte interfaces. Considering this effect, Yin et al. [55] constructed a novel all-in-gel SC with composite ionogels as the electrolyte. The bucky gel electrodes were prepared via the one-step method. Based on the analyzed mechanical properties and ionic conductivities, further comparisons were made between pure ionogels and composite ionogels. It was found that the composite ionogels help to enhance the self-recovery of the SC, which showed 78% retention of mechanical robustness after 300 cycles at 60% strain and achieved the ionic conductivity of 8.7 mS cm^{-1}, which, comparatively, were quite high. The mechanism for the enhanced ionic conductivity was attributed mainly to the presence of a robust amorphous polymer phase, which helped in ILs' facile permeation. It enabled the effective diffusion of charge carriers. It was concluded that the all-in-gel SC with gel electrodes and electrolytes was able to yield a specific capacitance of 43 mF cm^{-2} at a current density of 1.0 mA cm^{-2}. Also, the interface between electrode–electrolyte developed significant interfacial contact, thereby high capacitance. Additionally, it was proposed that using this all-in-gel design, it would be easy to fabricate SCs possessing capacitance ranging between 22 mF cm^{-2} and 81 mF cm^{-2} with a large operating temperature range from -40° C to 100° C at 0.2 mA cm^{-2} current density [55]. The bucky gel electrode formed in a circular shape and a cross section of the SEM images of Xanthum gum (XG) aerogel are shown in Figure 13.6.

The SPEs were prepared by adding the poly(ethylene glycol) monomethyl ether acrylate (1A9OMe) to the IL, such as 1-ethyl-3-methylimidazolium trifluoromethanesulfonate ([EMIm][OTF]) and 1-ethyl-3-methylimidazolium bis(trifluoromethane sulfonyl) imide ([EMIm][TFSI]), prior to thermal cure. Three ratios of 1:9, 3:7,

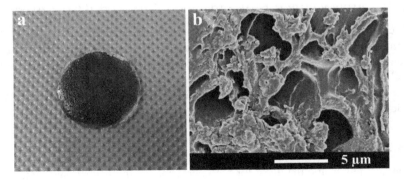

FIGURE 13.6 Structure of the all-in-gel SC consisting of an ionogel electrolyte (PDMAA-PBMAA+Xanthan gum+[BMIM]BF$_4$) layer, sandwiched between two bucky gel electrodes (CNT+[BMIM]BF$_4$+PVdF-*co*-HFP). (a) Optical image of all-in-gel SC (flat state), and (b) FE-SEM image of the cross sectional morphology of the all-in-gel SC. Adapted and reproduced with permission from reference [55]. Copyright 2019 Royal Society of Chemistry.

and 5:5, with respect to 1A9OMe and IL, was prepared. Based on the electrochemical and physicochemical characterizations, it was found that highest ionic conductivity of 4.90×10^{-4} S cm^{-1} was achieved for SPEs with 1A9OMe/[EMIm][OTF] of 3:7. The increase in specific capacitance of SCs with an increase in IL contents were witnessed. Also, the large ion size of ILs lowered the specific capacitance of SCs, and ILs with smaller ion size enhanced it [56]. Fabricating highly electroconductive polymer/carbon-based materials, such as carbon nanotube composite materials, with IL as gelling medium were also discussed, and results showed an enhancement in dynamic hardness of the composites [57]. These types of studies can be explored for SC device construction while using gel-based ILs.

13.6 MICROANALYTICAL CHARACTERIZATION TECHNIQUES USED FOR INTERFACE ANALYSIS OF ELECTRODE AND ELECTROLYTE

13.6.1 MORPHOLOGICAL AND SURFACE CHARACTERIZATION

The morphology of the electrode and electrolyte materials were examined using SEM. Morphology and the lattice structures of the electrode materials and the influence of polymeric electrolytes usually are studied using transmission electron microscopy (TEM). The layer thickness and the number of layers of gel/IL electrolytes are examined using atomic force microscopy (AFM). Thermal stability of GPE is generally tested by TGA and DSC. The electrochemical window stability and ionic conductivity of the GPE are analyzed using CV and complex-impedance measurements, respectively. NMR studies are useful in studying the transport characteristics of the gel electrolytes. Functional groups present in GPEs are analyzed using Fourier transform infrared spectroscopy (FT-IR).

13.6.2 ELECTROCHEMICAL CHARACTERIZATION TECHNIQUES (HALF-CELL STUDIES)

Half-cell studies, such as CV and GCD, are employed to understand the electrochemical interactions of electrode–electrolyte in a standard three-electrode configuration system that consists of working, reference, and counter electrodes, respectively, at 25° C with different potential ranges. Based on the findings, the efficiency of the SC is assessed. Cycling performance of solid-state devices shows the nature and efficiency of the constructed device for area specific applications.

13.6.3 THE WAY FORWARD

In the past few years, the quest for high performance multifunctional materials for electrochemical energy storage and conversion devices has begun. It requires many efforts to prepare thin, flexible, and light-weight solid-state SCs. Finding the combination of efficient and facile synthesis strategies requires further development in this field. Because the energy and power density of the SC systems are affected because of the nature of the electrolytes used, the utmost care is required for choosing electrolytes. According to the literature, exploration of extraordinary electrochemical capacitive performance of SCs with various porous nanocarbon electrode materials with IL electrolytes is urgently required to create the next generation of energy storage devices. Although, considerable improvements in energy density have been witnessed, SC devices with IL electrolytes generally suffer from issues related to low power density as well as large IR drop, which need greater attention. However, various types of electrolytes are currently available, but they have not reached their commercial applications because of their low voltage window, part in electrode corrosion, mechanical weakness, leakage, etc. Development of multifunctional gel electrolytes extend their application to other technological areas such as artificial skins, flexible biosensors, and smart energy devices, such as soft machines and electronics. Nanoionics play a major role in understanding the interfacial characteristics of the electrochemical properties of the cell. Achieving self-assembled multifunctional gel materials into macroscopic three-dimensional architectures is challenging research and requires bottom-up strategies. Further, fine tuning molecular-level modifications and nano-level processing will help researchers gain a deeper knowledge of gel materials, thereby advancing gel materials with outstanding nano/microstructural and mechanical properties for energy conversion and storage applications.

13.7 CONCLUSION

In summary, it is important to mention that efforts to develop a highly compatible multifunctional GPE have been initiated at the international level along with the electrode developments using various nanostructured materials. However, it is understood from the literature that the task of discovering specific or smart gel electrolytes with highly compatible, mechanically stable, and energy efficient properties for the application of solid state and flexible SC systems is still in its infancy. Thus, the versatility of the properties of the multifunctional gel electrolytes needs to be broadly explored with a unified approach, which, ultimately, will offer attractive possibilities and significant opportunities for commercialization.

A new insight has to be adopted for developing ion conducting multifunctional GPEs, which, in turn, will provide opportunities to further improve/develop multifunctional superionic polymers for flexible SCs and will create platforms for advanced energy applications. A novel and multifunctional GPE will be a great replacement for liquid electrolytes in multifunctional energy storage systems, which would significantly improve safety, reduce weight, and increase capacitance, especially for next-generation flexible and solid state SCs. Also, simple, scalable, and inexpensive synthesis and fabrication methodology is currently required.

ACKNOWLEDGMENTS

The authors acknowledge the Indian Institute of Technology Kanpur for their constant encouragement and support. Raju Kumar Gupta acknowledges financial assistance from the Department of Science and Technology (DST), India, through the INSPIRE Faculty Award (Project No. IFA-13 ENG-57) and Grant No. DST/TMD/CERI/C140(G) under Clean Energy Research Initiative. B. Bhuvaneshwari acknowledges DST India for the Women Science Project (Grant No: SR/WOS-A/CS-17/2017).

REFERENCES

1. González A, Goikolea E, Barrena JA, Mysyk R (2016) Review on supercapacitors: Technologies and materials. *Renewable and Sustainable Energy Reviews* 58:1189–1206. doi:10.1016/j.rser.2015.12.249
2. Wu ZS, Parvez K, Feng X, Müllen K (2013) Graphene-based in-plane micro-supercapacitors with high power and energy densities. *Nature Communications* 4:2487, 1–8, I DOI: 10.1038/ncomms3487 I www.nature.com/naturecommunications.
3. Miller JR, Simon P (2008) Electrochemical capacitors for energy management. *Science* 321(5889):651–652. doi:10.1126/science.1158736
4. Galiński M, Lewandowski A, Stępniak I (2006) Ionic liquids as electrolytes. *Electrochimica Acta* 51(26):5567–5580. doi:10.1016/j.electacta.2006.03.016
5. Shi Y, Zhang J, Pan L, Shi Y, Yu G (2016) Energy gels: A bio-inspired material platform for advanced energy applications. *Nano Today* 11(6):738–762. doi:10.1016/j.nantod.2016.10.002
6. Moganty SS, Srivastava S, Lu Y, Schaefer JL, Rizvi SA, Archer LA (2012) Ionic liquid-tethered nanoparticle suspensions: A novel class of ionogels. *Chemistry of Materials* 24(7):1386–1392. doi:10.1021/cm300424v
7. Stephan AM (2006) Review on gel polymer electrolytes for lithium batteries. *European Polymer Journal* 42(1):21–42.
8. Cui M, Lee PS (2016) Solid polymer electrolyte with high ionic conductivity via layer-by-layer deposition. *Chemistry of Materials* 28(9):2934–2940. doi:10.1021/acs.chemmater.5b04739
9. Shi Y, Wang M, Ma C, Wang Y, Li X, Yu G (2015) A conductive self-healing hybrid gel enabled by metal–ligand supramolecule and nanostructured conductive polymer. *Nano Letters* 15(9):6276–6281. doi:10.1021/acs.nanolett.5b03069
10. Borges RS, Reddy ALM, Rodrigues M-TF, Gullapalli H, Balakrishnan K, Silva GG, Ajayan PM (2013) Supercapacitor operating at 200 degrees celsius. *Scientific Reports* 3, 2572, 1–6. https://doi.org/10.1038/srep02572.
11. Ammam M, Fransaer J (2011) Ionic liquid–heteropolyacid: Synthesis, characterization, and supercapacitor study of films deposited by electrophoresis. *Journal of the Electrochemical Society* 158(1):A14–A21.
12. Seok Jang H, Justin Raj C, Lee W-G, Chul Kim B, Hyun Yu K (2016) Enhanced supercapacitive performances of functionalized activated carbon in novel gel polymer electrolytes with ionic liquid redox-mediated poly(vinyl alcohol)/phosphoric acid. *RSC Advances* 6(79):75376–75383. doi:10.1039/C6RA15070E
13. Choudhury N, Sampath S, Shukla A (2009) Hydrogel-polymer electrolytes for electrochemical capacitors: An overview. *Energy & Environmental Science* 2(1):55–67.
14. Ye Y-S, Rick J, Hwang B-J (2013) Ionic liquid polymer electrolytes. *Journal of Materials Chemistry A* 1(8):2719–2743. doi:10.1039/C2TA00126H
15. Liew C-W, Ramesh S, Arof AK (2014) Investigation of ionic liquid-based poly(vinyl alcohol) proton conductor for electrochemical double-layer capacitor. *High Performance Polymers* 26(6):632–636. doi:10.1177/0954008314536212
16. Gao H, Lian K (2014) Proton-conducting polymer electrolytes and their applications in solid supercapacitors: A review. *RSC Advances* 4(62):33091–33113. doi:10.1039/C4RA05151C
17. Peng X, Liu H, Yin Q, Wu J, Chen P, Zhang G, Liu G, Wu C, Xie Y (2016) A zwitterionic gel electrolyte for efficient solid-state supercapacitors. *Nature Communications* 7, 11782, 1–8. https://doi.org/10.1038/ncomms11782.
18. Pu X, Liu M, Chen X, Sun J, Du C, Zhang Y, Zhai J, Hu W, Wang ZL (2017) Ultrastretchable, transparent triboelectric nanogenerator as electronic skin for biomechanical energy harvesting and tactile sensing. *Science Advances* 3(5) e1700015, 1–10. doi:10.1126/sciadv.1700015

19. Wirthl D, Pichler R, Drack M, Kettlguber G, Moser R, Gerstmayr R, Hartmann F, Bradt E, Kaltseis R, Siket CM, Schausberger SE, Hild S, Bauer S, Kaltenbrunner M (2017) Instant tough bonding of hydrogels for soft machines and electronics. *Science Advances* 3(6), e1700053, 1–9. doi:10.1126/sciadv.1700053

20. Wen Z, Yeh M-H, Guo H, Wang J, Zi Y, Xu W, Deng J, Zhu L, Wang X, Hu C, Zhu L, Sun X, Wang ZL (2016) Self-powered textile for wearable electronics by hybridizing fiber-shaped nanogenerators, solar cells, and supercapacitors. *Science Advances* 2(10), e1600097, 1-8 doi:10.1126/sciadv.1600097

21. Lin H-L, Liu Y-F, Yu TL, Liu W-H, Rwei S-P (2005) Light scattering and visco-elasticity study of poly (vinyl alcohol)–borax aqueous solutions and gels. *Polymer* 46(15):5541–5549.

22. Mansur HS, Sadahira CM, Souza AN, Mansur AA (2008) FTIR spectroscopy characterization of poly (vinyl alcohol) hydrogel with different hydrolysis degree and chemically crosslinked with glutaraldehyde. *Materials Science and Engineering: C* 28(4):539–548.

23. Yang C-C, Hsu S-T, Chien W-C (2005) All solid-state electric double-layer capacitors based on alkaline polyvinyl alcohol polymer electrolytes. *Journal of Power Sources* 152:303–310.

24. Jiang M, Zhu J, Chen C, Lu Y, Ge Y, Zhang X (2016) Poly(vinyl alcohol) borate gel polymer electrolytes prepared by electrodeposition and their application in electrochemical supercapacitors. *ACS Applied Materials & Interfaces* 8(5):3473–3481. doi:10.1021/acsami.5b11984

25. Ma G, Li J, Sun K, Peng H, Mu J, Lei Z (2014) High performance solid-state supercapacitor with PVA–KOH–K 3 [Fe (CN) 6] gel polymer as electrolyte and separator. *Journal of Power Sources* 256:281–287.

26. Sampath S, Sarma DD, Shukla AK (2016) Electrochemical energy storage: The Indian scenario. *ACS Energy Letters* 1(6):1162–1164. doi:10.1021/acsenergylett.6b00567

27. Kalpana D, Renganathan N, Pitchumani S (2006) A new class of alkaline gel polymer electrolyte for carbon aerogel supercapacitors. *Journal of Power Sources* 157(1):621–623.

28. Anothumakkool B, Torris A. T A, Veeliyath S, Vijayakumar V, Badiger MV, Kurungot S (2016) High-performance flexible solid-state supercapacitor with an extended nanoregime interface through in situ polymer electrolyte generation. *ACS Applied Materials & Interfaces* 8(2):1233–1241. doi:10.1021/acsami.5b09677

29. Kumar Y, Pandey GP, Hashmi SA (2012) Gel polymer electrolyte based electrical double layer capacitors: Comparative study with multiwalled carbon nanotubes and activated carbon electrodes. *The Journal of Physical Chemistry C* 116(50):26118–26127. doi:10.1021/jp305128z

30. Jain A, Tripathi SK (2013) Experimental studies on high-performance supercapacitor based on nanogel polymer electrolyte with treated activated charcoal. *Ionics* 19(3):549–557. doi:10.1007/s11581-012-0782-0

31. Kwon H-N, Jang S-J, Kang YC, Roh KC (2019) The effect of ILs as co-salts in electrolytes for high voltage supercapacitors. *Scientific Reports* 9(1):1180. doi:10.1038/s41598-018-37322-y

32. Pilathottathil S, Thasneema KK, Shahin Thayyil M, Pillai MP, Niveditha CV (2017) A high voltage supercapacitor based on ionic liquid with an activated carbon electrode. *Materials Research Express* 4(7):075503. doi:10.1088/2053-1591/aa7116

33. Haque M, Li Q, Kuzmenko V, Smith AD, Enoksson P (2017) Ionic liquid electrolyte for supercapacitor with high temperature compatibility. *Journal of Physics: Conference Series* 922:012011. doi:10.1088/1742-6596/922/1/012011

34. Sekitani T, Noguchi Y, Hata K, Fukushima T, Aida T, Someya T (2008) A rubber-like stretchable active matrix using elastic conductors. *Science* 321(5895):1468–1472. doi:10.1126/science.1160309

35. Fukushima T, Asaka K, Kosaka A, Aida T (2005) Fully plastic actuator through layer-by-layer casting with ionic-liquid-based bucky gel. *Angewandte Chemie International Edition* 44(16):2410–2413. doi:10.1002/anie.200462318

36. Kang YJ, Yoo Y, Kim W (2016) 3-V solid-state flexible supercapacitors with ionic-liquid-based gel polymer electrolyte for AC line filtering. *ACS Applied Materials & Interfaces* 8(22):13909–13917. doi:10.1021/acsami.6b02690

37. Mousavi MPS, Wilson BE, Kashefolgheta S, Anderson EL, He S, Bühlmann P, Stein A (2016) Ionic liquids as electrolytes for electrochemical double-layer capacitors: Structures that optimize specific energy. *ACS Applied Materials & Interfaces* 8(5):3396–3406. doi:10.1021/acsami.5b11353

38. Mourad E, Coustan L, Lannelongue P, Zigah D, Mehdi A, Vioux A, Freunberger Stefan A, Favier F, Fontaine O (2016) Biredox ionic liquids with solid-like redox density in the liquid state for high-energy supercapacitors. *Nature Materials* 16:446. doi:10.1038/nmat4808 https://www.nature.com/articles/nmat4808#supplementary-information

39. Yu L, Chen GZ (2019) Ionic liquid-based electrolytes for supercapacitor and supercapattery. *Frontiers in Chemistry* 7(272), 1–15. doi:10.3389/fchem.2019.00272

40. Brandt A, Ramirez-Castro C, Anouti M, Balducci A (2013) An investigation about the use of mixtures of sulfonium-based ionic liquids and propylene carbonate as electrolytes for supercapacitors. *Journal of Materials Chemistry A* 1(40):12669–12678. doi:10.1039/C3TA12737K

41. Shahzad S, Shah A, Kowsari E, Iftikhar FJ, Nawab A, Piro B, Akhter MS, Rana UA, Zou Y (2019) Ionic liquids as environmentally benign electrolytes for high-performance supercapacitors. *Global Challenges* 3(1):1800023. doi:10.1002/gch2.201800023

42. Bodin C, Mourad E, Zigah D, Le Vot S, Freunberger SA, Favier F, Fontaine O (2018) Biredox ionic liquids: New opportunities toward high performance supercapacitors. *Faraday Discussions* 206:393–404. doi:10.1039/C7FD00174F

43. Martins VL, Rennie AJR, Sanchez-Ramirez N, Torresi RM, Hall PJ (2018) Improved performance of ionic liquid supercapacitors by using tetracyanoborate anions. *ChemElectroChem* 5(4):598–604. doi:10.1002/celc.201701164

44. Akinwolemiwa B, Peng C, Chen GZ (2015) Redox electrolytes in supercapacitors. *Journal of the Electrochemical Society* 162(5):A5054–A5059. doi:10.1149/2.0111505jes

45. Forse AC, Griffin JM, Merlet C, Bayley PM, Wang H, Simon P, Grey CP (2015) NMR study of ion dynamics and charge storage in ionic liquid supercapacitors. *Journal of the American Chemical Society* 137(22):7231–7242. doi:10.1021/jacs.5b03958

46. Song H, Zhang J, Song P, Xiong Y (2019) Maize-like ionic liquid@polyaniline nanocomposites for high performance supercapacitor. *e-Polymers* 19, 313–322. doi:10.1515/epoly-2019-0032

47. Lin Z, Taberna P-L, Simon P (2016) Graphene-based supercapacitors using eutectic ionic liquid mixture electrolyte. *Electrochimica Acta* 206:446–451. doi:10.1016/j.electacta.2015.12.097

48. Lazzari M, Mastragostino M, Pandolfo AG, Ruiz V, Soavi F (2011) Role of carbon porosity and ion size in the development of ionic liquid based supercapacitors. *Journal of the Electrochemical Society* 158(1):A22–A25. doi:10.1149/1.3514694

49. Pope MA, Korkut S, Punckt C, Aksay IA (2013) Supercapacitor electrodes produced through evaporative consolidation of graphene oxide-water-ionic liquid gels. *Journal of the Electrochemical Society* 160(10):A1653–A1660. doi:10.1149/2.017310jes

50. Pohlmann S, Olyschläger T, Goodrich P, Alvarez Vicente J, Jacquemin J, Balducci A (2015) Azepanium-based ionic liquids as green electrolytes for high voltage supercapacitors. *Journal of Power Sources* 273:931–936. doi:10.1016/j.jpowsour.2014.09.167

51. Sathyamoorthi S, Suryanarayanan V, Velayutham D (2015) Organo-redox shuttle promoted protic ionic liquid electrolyte for supercapacitor. *Journal of Power Sources* 274:1135–1139. doi:10.1016/j.jpowsour.2014.10.166
52. Yang P, Mai W (2014) Flexible solid-state electrochemical supercapacitors. *Nano Energy* 8:274–290. doi:10.1016/j.nanoen.2014.05.022
53. Wang J-A, Lu Y-T, Lin S-C, Wang Y-S, Ma C-CM, Hu C-C (2018) Designing a novel polymer electrolyte for improving the electrode/electrolyte interface in flexible all-solid-state electrical double-layer capacitors. *ACS Applied Materials & Interfaces* 10(21):17871–17882. doi:10.1021/acsami.8b02046
54. Kwon SJ, Kim T, Jung BM, Lee SB, Choi UH (2018) Multifunctional epoxy-based solid polymer electrolytes for solid-state supercapacitors. *ACS Applied Materials & Interfaces* 10(41):35108–35117. doi:10.1021/acsami.8b11016
55. Yin C, Liu X, Wei J, Tan R, Zhou J, Ouyang M, Wang H, Cooper SJ, Wu B, George C, Wang Q (2019) "All-in-gel" design for supercapacitors towards solid-state energy devices with thermal and mechanical compliance. *Journal of Materials Chemistry A* 7(15):8826–8831. doi:10.1039/C9TA01155B
56. Cho B-S, Choi J, Kim K-Y (2017) Preparation and properties of solid polymer electrolyte based on imidazolium-based ionic liquids for structural capacitors. *Fibers and Polymers* 18(8):1452–1458. doi:10.1007/s12221-017-7266-9
57. Fukushima T, Kosaka A, Ishimura Y, Yamamoto T, Takigawa T, Ishii N, Aida T (2003) Molecular ordering of organic molten salts triggered by single-walled carbon nanotubes. *Science* 300(5628):2072–2074. doi:10.1126/science.1082289

Index

A

Ab initio, 33, 64
    density functional theory (DFT), 29
    molecular dynamics (AIMD), 29, 40, 64
Acrylonitrile (AN), 5, 126
Alkaline fuel cells (AFC), 259
Anthraquinone (AQ), 295

B

Benzyl, 181
    polybenzyl methacrylate (PBMA), 130
Borate, 149
    bis(oxolato)borate (BOB), 143
    butyl triphenyl borates, 179
    lithium bis oxalate borate (LiBOB), 74, 140,
        141, 143, 145, 165
    lithium diflouro oxalate borate (LiODFOB),
        143, 145, 149, 165
    lithium difluoro(sulphato) borate, 143, 145
    lithium polyacrylic acid oxalate borate
        (LiPAAOB), 125
    lithium polyvinyl alcohol oxalate borate
        (LiPVAOB), 125, 150
    lithium tetrafluoroborate (LiBF$_4$), 74, 140
    tetraphenyl borate, 179
    tri(methyl)borate, 5
    triphenyl borate, 179
    tris(hepta-fluorobutyl)borate, 5
    tris(hexa-fluorocumyl)borate, 5
    tris(hexa-fluoroisopropyl)borate, 5
    tris(penta-fluorophenyl) borate, 5
    tris(perfluoro-tert-butyl)borate, 5
    tris(tri-fluoromethyl)borate, 5
    tris(triphenyl)borate, 5
Boron, 123, 252
    hexagonal boron nitride, 74, 92, 152

C

Celgard, 3, 74
Cell capacity, 2, 196
Cellulose, 119, 125, 126, 220, 231, 234
Copper, 248
    chloride, 230
    electrode, 222
    foil, 180, 181
    hydroxide (Cu(OH)$_2$), 269
    oxide (CuO), 124

D

Dendrite, 3, 6, 53, 56, 75, 114, 119, 120, 178, 179,
    187, 210, 223
Dimethyl carbonate (DMC), 2, 21, 52, 74, 140,
    165, 171, 212
Dissolution, 5, 114, 125, 141, 145, 178, 181, 187,
    193, 195, 200, 206, 211, 212, 227, 279

E

Electric vehicles (EVs), 2, 3, 14, 21, 52, 73, 74,
    98, 139, 140, 147, 177, 194, 226
Electrochemical
    double-layer capacitor (EDLC), 220, 288,
        291, 294, 297, 298
    energy storage devices, 1, 286, 294, 295
    stability, 2, 5, 21, 33, 35, 36, 52, 85, 90, 92,
        98, 99, 121, 124, 125, 128, 140, 145,
        151, 152, 166, 179, 180, 186, 196, 198,
        202, 203, 205, 207, 210, 231, 252, 288,
        292, 295, 297
Electrodeposition (ED), 179, 240, 289
Energy density, 1, 3, 4, 14, 52, 85, 129, 140, 161,
    194, 196, 202–204, 209, 210, 212,
    217, 218, 230, 253, 261, 279, 286, 292,
    295, 297
Environmental, 2, 7, 20, 28, 41, 114, 139, 187,
    194, 199, 217, 219, 230, 286, 289
Equivalent series resistance (ESR), 287
Ethylene carbonate (EC), 2, 21, 52, 74, 123, 126,
    140, 148, 165, 212, 291
Ethyl methyl carbonate (EMC), 2, 21, 140

F

Flammability, 2, 52, 114, 129, 150, 195, 205, 209
Fluorine, 27, 145, 149
    fluorine-doped tin oxide (FTO), 240
Formic acid (FA) HCOOH, 220, 232, 262

G

Galvanostatic
    charge–discharge (GCD), 254
    conditions, 107
    cycling, 107
    discharge curves, 268
    measurements, 254
    polarization, 64

308

Gas diffusion layer (GDL), 233
Glass ceramic solid electrolyte, 7
Glass transition temperature, 26, 29, 33, 34, 36, 100, 136, 140, 142
Glassy carbon electrode, 240, 245, 271

H

Hafnium, 54–56
Hollow, 198, 246
Hop, 9, 12, 27
Hot iso-tactic pressing (HIT), 218, 222, 223
Hydroquinone (HQ), 297

I

Impedance, 5, 40–43, 82, 84, 85, 87, 97, 98, 117, 145, 149, 165, 182, 183, 185, 222, 224, 290, 291, 297, 298, 300
Indium tin oxide (ITO), 220, 227, 229, 231, 232, 240, 269, 273, 275, 277, 279
Inorganic solid electrolyte, 21, 30, 195
Ionic liquid (IL), 76–86, 92, 97–100, 102, 103, 129, 152, 169–173, 217, 230, 232, 287, 289, 291–301
Iso-structural, 8, 54

L

Lithium
    aluminum germanium phosphate (LAGP), 43, 56, 74, 76, 129
    aluminum titanium phosphate (LATP), 43, 55, 56, 74, 76
    bis(fluorosulfonyl)imide (LiFSI), 149
    cobalt oxide (LCO), 4, 33, 52, 87, 92, 149, 152, 197, 199
    garnet type solid-state electrolyte, 57
    iron phosphate (LFP), 4, 56, 61, 98, 101, 102, 119, 130, 151, 152, 197, 199, 201, 211, 219, 222, 225, 226
    lanthanum titanate (LLT), 24, 53
    metal polymer battery (LMPB), 3
    nitride, 22, 23
    phosphorous oxy-nitride (LiPON), 57
    solid electrolyte, 22
    super ionic conductors (LISICON), 9, 22, 30–33, 37, 44, 54, 74, 203, 204, 222
    tantalum oxide (LLTaO), 61, 64
    titanate (LTO), 4, 93–97, 152, 153, 170

M

Maleic anhydride (MAH), 219, 223, 224
Mechanical
    robustness, 114, 118, 151, 171, 222, 299

stability, 151, 183, 220, 223, 226, 230, 234, 288, 290, 292
strength, 2, 3, 7, 114, 118, 120, 126, 128, 131, 145, 204, 209, 210, 288
Memory effect, 1
Mesocarbon micro bead, 149

N

Nernst–Einstein equation, 42
Nuclear magnetic resonance (NMR), 9, 34, 38, 42, 60, 64, 65, 84, 295, 296, 300
Nudged elastic band (NEB), 65

O

Organic
    liquid electrolyte (OLE), 2, 3, 21, 22, 34, 52, 178, 209, 218
    solid electrolyte, 21

P

Perovskite, 4, 19, 22–30, 44, 53, 54
Polarization, 5, 32, 42, 61, 80, 86, 91, 94, 95, 102, 117, 183, 184, 201, 222, 223, 226, 248, 254
Polyacrylonitrile (PAN), 4, 5, 7, 8, 24, 43, 90, 113–115, 119, 125–127, 130, 163, 183, 186, 203, 209, 219
Polyethylene oxide (PEO), 4, 5, 7, 8, 11, 24–26, 43, 56, 74, 90, 113–115, 119, 120–126, 128, 130, 151, 163, 183, 185, 186, 203, 218, 221, 222, 233, 234, 292, 293
Polymer solid electrolyte, 43
Polymethyl methacrylate (PMMA), 114, 115, 119, 122, 124–127, 129, 130, 163, 169–172, 203, 204
Polyvinyl acetate (PVAc), 183
Poly vinyl alcohol (PVA), 119, 126, 130, 183, 184, 186, 230, 289, 290, 298
Polyvinyl chloride (PVC), 119, 130, 153, 288
Polyvinylidene difluoride (PVdF), 5, 7, 8, 43, 90, 95, 113–115, 119, 122, 125, 126, 129, 130, 151, 163, 203, 204, 209, 219, 224, 288
Polyvinylidene difluoride-*co*-
    hexaflouropropylene (PVdF-*co*-HFP), 2, 4, 7, 8, 90, 92, 94, 119, 125, 126, 130, 163, 164, 183, 185, 224, 291, 299
Propylene carbonate (PC), 2, 21, 52, 74, 123, 126, 140, 167, 171, 291
Pulsed field gradient (PFG), 42

Q

Quasi-solid electrolyte, 2, 73, 76

Index

309

R

Rate capability, 6, 12, 21, 52, 57, 75, 85, 93, 125, 193–196, 198, 201, 210, 225
Reduction potential, 5, 117
Rhombohedral, 54, 56
Room temperature ionic liquid (RTIL), 21, 76–78, 80–84, 86–88, 90–98, 100, 123, 139, 140, 145, 147, 154, 159, 172, 186, 220, 230–232, 234

S

Self-discharge, 1, 5, 28, 52, 115, 140, 204, 294
Sodium superionic conductor (NASICON), 4, 22, 51, 53–56, 65, 74, 207
Solid electrolytes, 2–4, 22, 23, 25, 52, 53, 74, 75, 119, 121, 151
    glass ceramic solid electrolyte, 7
    inorganic solid electrolyte, 21, 30, 195
    LISICON-type solid electrolyte, 30, 32, 33
    organic solid electrolyte, 21
    polymer solid electrolyte, 43
    quasi solid electrolyte, 2, 73, 76
Solid polymer electrolyte (SPEs), 3–5, 7–13, 21, 22, 24, 50, 52, 53, 56, 57, 114, 163, 177, 183, 220
Sulfide solid electrolyte, 32, 35

T

Thermal stability, 3, 6, 21, 26, 41, 44, 65, 76, 77, 81, 82, 86, 87, 90, 92, 97–100, 114, 118, 120, 123, 142, 144, 149, 151, 152, 195, 203, 205, 232, 290, 291, 294, 297, 298, 300
Thio LISICON, 22, 32–34, 36, 37, 41, 44
Transference number, 2–5, 11, 12, 53, 61, 75, 91, 94, 98, 102, 117, 125, 127, 183, 218, 224

V

Vinylene carbonate (VC), 201
Vogel–Tammann–Fulcher equation (VTF), 11, 84, 91, 94, 98

W

Water contact angle (WCA), 219, 221
William–Landel–Ferry equation (WLF), 11

X

X-ray diffraction (XRD), 13, 33, 42, 186

Z

Zinc ion battery, 114
Zirconium, 54–57, 59

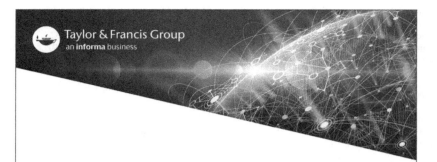

Taylor & Francis eBooks

www.taylorfrancis.com

A single destination for eBooks from Taylor & Francis with increased functionality and an improved user experience to meet the needs of our customers.

90,000+ eBooks of award-winning academic content in Humanities, Social Science, Science, Technology, Engineering, and Medical written by a global network of editors and authors.

TAYLOR & FRANCIS EBOOKS OFFERS:

- A streamlined experience for our library customers
- A single point of discovery for all of our eBook content
- Improved search and discovery of content at both book and chapter level

REQUEST A FREE TRIAL
support@taylorfrancis.com